DOSTOE

CRIME & PU

(For Your Cat)

by

SAM AUSTEN

I

MEOW I

Meow meow meow meow meow meow meow Meow meow meow meow meow meow meow meow meow meow meow meow meow meow Meow. Meow meow meow meow, meow meow meow meow, meow Meow.

Meow meow meow meow meow meow meow meow meow meow. Meow meow meow meow meow meow meow meow meow, meow-meow meow meow meow meow meow meow meow meow meow meow. Meow meow meow meow meow meow meow, meow, meow meow, meow meow meow meow meow, meow meow meow meow meow meow meow meow meow meow meow meow meow, meow meow meow meow meow meow meow. Meow meow meow meow meow, meow meow meow meow meow meow, meow meow, meow meow meow meow meow meow meow. Meow meow meow meow meow meow meow meow, meow meow meow meow meow meow.

Meow meow meow meow meow meow meow meow meow, meow meow meow; meow meow meow meow meow meow meow meow meow meow meow meow, meow meow meow. Meow meow meow meow meow meow meow, meow meow meow meow meow meow meow meow meow, meow meow meow meow, meow meow meow meow. Meow meow meow meow meow, meow meow meow meow meow meow meow meow meow meow meow meow meow meow. Meow meow meow meow meow meow meow meow meow; meow meow meow meow meow meow meow meow. Meow meow meow meow meow meow meow meow meow meow meow meow. Meow meow meow meow meow meow meow, meow meow meow meow meow meow meow meow, meow meow, meow meow meow meow meow, meow meow meow, meow meow meow meow meow meow meow, meow meow, meow meow—meow, meow meow meow, meow meow meow meow meow meow meow meow meow meow meow meow.

"Meow meow meow meow meow meow meow meow meow meow meow meow meow meow," meow meow, meow meow meow meow. "Meow... meow, meow meow meow meow meow'meow meow meow meow meow meow meow meow meow meow, meow'meow meow meow. Meow meow meow meow meow meow meow meow meow meow meow meow meow meow. Meow meow meow meow, meow meow meow meow meow meow meow meow meow.... Meow Meow meow meow meow meow. Meow'meow meow Meow meow meow Meow meow meow. Meow meow meow meow meow Meow meow meow Meow meow meow. Meow'meow meow meow meow meow meow meow, meow meow meow meow meow meow meow meow... meow Meow meow Meow-meow.

Meow meow meow meow meow meow meow: meow meow meow, meow meow meow meow meow, meow, meow, meow meow meow meow meow, meow meow meow Meow meow, meow meow meow meow meow meow meow meow meow meow meow meow meow meow—meow meow meow meow meow meow meow'meow meow meow meow. Meow meow meow meow meow meow-meow, meow meow meow meow meow meow meow

meow meow meow, meow meow meow meow meow meow meow meow, meow meow meow meow meow meow, meow meow meow meow meow meow meow. Meow meow meow meow meow meow meow meow meow meow meow meow meow meow'meow meow meow. Meow meow, meow meow meow, meow meow, meow meow meow meow meow, meow, meow-meow, meow meow meow meow meow meow meow meow. Meow meow meow meow meow meow, meow meow meow meow meow meow meow meow meow meow; meow meow meow meow meow meow meow meow meow meow meow meow meow meow meow. Meow meow meow meow, meow meow meow meow, meow meow meow meow meow meow meow, meow meow meow meow meow meow. Meow meow meow meow meow meow meow meow meow meow meow meow meow meow meow meow meow meow meow meow meow; meow meow meow meow meow meow meow meow.

Meow meow meow meow meow meow meow meow meow meow meow meow meow meow meow meow meow meow meow meow meow meow meow meow meow. Meow meow meow meow meow meow, meow, meow meow meow meow meow meow meow meow meow. Meow meow meow meow meow meow Meow Meow, meow meow meow meow meow meow meow, meow meow meow meow meow meow meow meow meow meow meow meow meow meow meow meow meow meow meow Meow, meow meow meow meow meow meow meow meow meow meow meow meow meow, meow meow, meow meow meow meow. Meow meow meow meow meow meow meow meow meow meow meow'meow meow, meow, meow meow meow meow meow meow meow meow, meow meow meow meow meow meow meow meow meow meow. Meow meow meow meow meow meow meow meow meow meow meow meow meow, meow, meow, meow meow meow meow meow meow. Meow meow meow meow meow meow meow, meow meow meow meow, meow meow meow meow meow meow meow meow meow meow meow meow meow meow, meow meow meow meow meow meow meow meow: "Meow meow, Meow meow" meow meow meow meow meow meow meow meow meow meow meow—meow meow meow meow meow meow meow meow meow meow meow. Meow meow meow meow meow meow meow Meow'meow, meow meow meow meow, meow meow meow, meow meow meow meow, meow meow meow meow meow meow meow meow meow meow meow. Meow meow, meow, meow meow meow meow meow meow meow meow meow meow.

"Meow meow meow," meow meow meow meow, "Meow meow meow! Meow'meow meow meow meow meow! Meow, meow meow meow meow meow, meow meow meow meow meow meow meow meow meow. Meow, meow meow meow meow meow.... Meow meow meow meow meow meow meow meow.... Meow meow meow Meow meow meow meow meow meow, meow meow meow meow meow, meow meow meow meow meow. Meow meow meow meow meow, meow meow meow meow meow meow meow, meow meow meow meow.... Meow meow meow meow meow meow meow meow, meow meow meow meow meow meow meow. Meow meow meow

meow meow meow meow meow meow meow meow.... Meow, meow meow meow meow! Meow, meow'meow meow meow meow meow meow meow meow...."

Meow meow meow meow meow meow; meow meow meow meow meow meow meow meow meow meow meow meow meow meow meow: meow meow meow meow meow. Meow meow meow meow meow meow meow meow meow meow meow meow. Meow meow meow meow meow meow meow meow meow meow meow meow meow meow meow meow meow meow meow meow meow meow meow. Meow, meow meow meow, meow meow meow meow meow meow meow meow, meow, meow meow meow meow meow meow meow meow meow meow meow meow meow meow meow, meow meow meow meow meow meow meow "meow" meow meow meow meow meow meow meow, meow meow meow meow meow meow meow meow. Meow meow meow meow meow meow meow "meow" meow meow meow, meow meow meow meow meow meow meow meow meow meow meow.

Meow meow meow meow meow meow meow meow, meow meow meow meow meow meow meow meow meow meow meow meow meow meow meow meow, meow meow meow meow meow meow meow. Meow meow meow meow meow meow meow meow meow meow meow meow meow meow meow meow meow meow—meow, meow, meow, Meow meow meow, meow meow meow meow meow meow meow meow meow, meow meow, meow. Meow meow meow meow meow meow meow meow meow meow meow meow meow meow meow meow meow meow meow. Meow meow meow meow-meow meow meow meow meow meow. Meow meow meow meow meow meow meow meow meow meow, meow meow meow meow meow meow meow meow meow meow meow, meow meow meow meow. Meow meow meow meow meow, meow meow meow, meow meow meow meow meow meow meow, meow meow meow meow, meow meow meow meow meow meow: meow meow meow meow meow meow meow meow meow meow meow meow meow.

"Meow Meow meow meow meow meow, meow meow meow meow meow meow meow meow meow meow meow Meow meow meow meow meow meow meow?" meow meow meow meow meow meow meow meow meow meow meow meow. Meow meow meow meow meow meow meow meow meow meow meow meow meow meow meow meow meow meow. Meow meow meow meow meow meow meow meow meow meow Meow meow meow meow meow meow, meow meow meow. Meow Meow meow meow meow meow, meow meow meow meow meow meow meow meow meow meow meow meow meow meow meow meow. "Meow'meow meow meow meow meow," meow meow meow meow, meow meow meow meow meow meow meow meow meow'meow meow. Meow meow meow meow meow meow meow meow meow meow meow meow meow meow meow.

Meow meow meow meow meow meow meow meow meow meow meow meow meow. Meow meow meow meow meow meow meow meow, meow meow meow meow meow meow meow meow meow meow meow meow

meow meow meow meow meow meow.... Meow meow, meow meow meow meow meow meow meow. Meow meow meow meow, meow meow meow meow meow meow meow: meow meow meow meow meow meow meow meow meow meow meow meow, meow meow meow meow meow meow meow meow meow, meow meow meow meow. Meow, meow meow meow meow meow meow meow meow, meow meow meow, meow meow meow meow meow. Meow meow meow meow meow meow meow meow, meow meow meow meow meow meow meow meow. Meow meow meow meow meow meow meow meow meow meow meow meow meow.

Meow meow meow meow, meow meow meow meow meow meow, meow meow meow meow meow meow meow meow meow. Meow meow, meow meow meow meow meow meow meow meow, meow meow meow meow meow meow meow. Meow meow meow meow, meow meow meow meow meow'meow meow, meow meow meow meow meow meow meow, meow, meow meow meow meow meow, meow meow meow meow meow meow, meow meow meow meow, meow meow meow. Meow meow meow meow meow meow meow meow meow. Meow meow meow meow meow meow meow meow meow meow meow meow meow, meow meow meow meow meow meow meow meow meow meow.

"Meow, meow meow, Meow meow meow meow meow meow," meow meow meow meow meow meow meow, meow meow meow meow, meow meow meow meow meow meow meow meow.

"Meow meow, meow meow meow, Meow meow meow meow meow meow meow," meow meow meow meow meow, meow meow meow meow meow meow meow meow.

"Meow meow... Meow meow meow meow meow meow meow," Meow meow, meow meow meow meow meow meow meow meow meow'meow meow. "Meow meow meow meow meow meow meow, meow Meow meow meow meow meow meow meow meow," meow meow meow meow meow meow.

Meow meow meow meow, meow meow meow; meow meow meow meow meow, meow meow meow meow meow meow meow meow, meow meow, meow meow meow meow meow meow meow meow:

"Meow meow, meow meow meow."

Meow meow meow meow meow meow meow meow meow, meow meow meow meow meow meow, meow meow meow meow meow meow meow, meow meow meow meow meow meow meow meow meow meow meow.

"Meow meow meow meow meow meow meow meow meow!" meow meow meow meow meow meow meow Meow'meow meow, meow meow meow meow meow meow meow meow meow meow meow, meow meow meow meow meow meow meow meow meow meow meow. Meow meow meow meow meow meow meow meow. Meow meow, meow meow meow meow meow meow meow, meow meow meow meow meow meow meow meow meow meow, meow meow meow meow meow meow meow meow, meow meow-meow meow meow meow-meow meow meow meow meow meow meow, meow meow meow meow meow meow meow meow meow-meow meow meow meow meow, meow Meow meow meow meow

meow meow—meow meow meow. Meow meow meow meow meow meow meow meow meow meow meow. Meow meow meow meow; meow meow meow meow meow meow meow meow; meow meow.

"Meow'meow meow," meow meow meow meow. Meow meow meow meow meow meow meow meow meow meow meow meow meow meow.

"Meow'meow meow meow meow meow meow meow meow meow meow meow meow meow," Meow meow meow, meow meow meow meow meow meow meow meow meow meow meow meow meow meow meow meow meow meow, meow meow meow meow meow meow'meow meow meow meow meow meow meow meow meow meow meow meow meow meow. Meow meow meow meow meow meow meow meow.

"Meow meow meow meow?" meow meow meow meow meow, meow meow meow meow meow, meow meow, meow meow meow meow meow meow meow meow meow meow meow meow meow meow.

"Meow'meow meow meow meow meow meow," meow meow meow meow meow meow meow meow meow-meow meow meow meow, meow meow meow meow meow meow meow meow meow; meow meow meow meow meow.

"Meow meow meow meow meow meow meow meow meow. Meow meow meow meow meow meow meow meow." "Meow meow meow meow meow meow meow meow meow; meow meow meow."

"Meow meow'meow meow meow meow meow meow Meow meow, meow meow meow, meow meow meow meow meow meow meow meow meow." "Meow meow meow meow meow meow meow meow meow, Meow Meow?"

"Meow meow meow meow meow, meow meow meow, meow'meow meow meow meow. Meow meow meow meow meow meow meow meow meow meow meow meow meow meow meow meow meow meow meow meow'meow meow meow meow meow meow meow."

"Meow meow meow meow meow meow, Meow meow meow meow, meow meow meow meow'meow. Meow meow meow meow meow meow meow."

"Meow meow meow meow meow, meow meow meow meow, meow meow meow!" "Meow meow meow meow meow!" meow meow meow meow.

"Meow meow"—meow meow meow meow meow meow meow meow meow. Meow meow meow meow meow, meow meow meow meow meow meow meow meow meow meow meow meow meow; meow meow meow meow meow, meow meow meow meow meow meow meow meow meow, meow meow meow meow meow meow meow meow meow meow.

"Meow meow meow," meow meow meow.

Meow meow meow meow meow meow meow meow meow meow, meow meow meow meow meow meow meow meow meow. Meow meow meow, meow meow meow meow meow meow meow meow meow, meow meow, meow. Meow meow meow meow meow meow meow meow meow.

"Meow meow meow meow meow meow," meow meow. "Meow meow meow meow meow meow meow meow meow meow meow. Meow meow

meow meow meow meow meow meow.... Meow meow'meow meow meow meow, meow meow meow meow meow meow meow meow, meow meow meow; meow meow'meow meow meow meow meow meow meow meow meow... meow meow meow meow meow meow meow meow meow-meow... meow'meow meow meow. Meow-meow meow meow meow meow meow... meow meow meow meow meow meow."

Meow meow meow meow meow.

"Meow, meow: meow meow meow meow meow meow meow meow meow, meow Meow meow meow meow meow meow meow meow meow meow meow meow meow meow meow meow. Meow meow meow meow meow Meow meow meow meow, meow meow meow meow meow meow meow meow meow meow meow meow. Meow meow meow-meow meow meow. Meow Meow meow meow meow meow meow meow meow meow meow meow meow. Meow meow meow."

"Meow! meow meow meow meow meow meow meow!"

"Meow meow."

Meow meow meow meow meow, meow meow meow meow meow meow meow meow, meow meow meow meow meow meow meow meow meow meow meow meow meow, meow meow meow meow meow meow meow meow.

"Meow meow meow meow meow meow meow meow meow meow meow meow, Meow Meow—meow meow meow— meow—meow meow-meow, meow meow meow Meow meow meow meow meow meow meow..." meow meow meow meow meow.

"Meow, meow meow meow meow meow meow, meow."

"Meow-meow—meow meow meow meow meow meow, meow meow meow meow meow meow meow?" Meow meow meow meow meow meow meow meow meow meow meow meow meow meow.

"Meow meow meow meow meow meow, meow meow meow?"

"Meow, meow meow, Meow meow meow. Meow meow meow meow.... Meow-meow, Meow Meow."

Meow meow meow meow meow meow. Meow meow meow meow meow meow meow. Meow meow meow meow meow meow, meow meow meow meow, meow meow meow meow, meow meow meow meow meow meow meow. Meow meow meow meow meow meow meow meow meow, "Meow, Meow, meow meow meow meow meow! meow meow Meow, meow Meow meow.... Meow, meow'meow meow, meow'meow meow!" meow meow meow. "Meow meow meow meow meow meow meow meow meow meow meow? Meow meow meow meow meow meow meow meow. Meow, meow meow meow, meow, meow, meow!—meow meow meow meow meow Meow'meow meow...."

Meow meow meow, meow meow, meow meow meow meow. Meow meow meow meow meow, meow meow meow meow meow meow meow meow meow meow meow meow meow meow meow meow meow meow meow meow, meow meow meow meow meow meow meow meow meow meow meow meow meow meow meow meow meow meow meow meow meow meow meow meow meow meow meow meow meow meow. Meow meow meow

meow meow meow meow meow meow, meow meow meow meow-meow, meow meow meow meow, meow meow meow meow meow meow meow meow meow meow meow meow meow. Meow meow, meow meow meow meow meow meow meow meow meow meow meow meow meow meow meow meow meow meow meow meow meow meow. Meow meow meow meow meow meow meow meow meow meow meow, meow meow meow meow meow meow, meow meow meow meow. Meow meow meow meow, Meow meow meow meow meow meow meow. Meow meow meow meow meow meow meow meow meow meow, meow meow meow meow meow meow meow meow meow meow meow meow. Meow meow meow meow meow meow meow meow, meow meow meow meow meow meow meow meow meow meow. Meow meow meow meow meow meow meow meow meow meow meow meow meow meow; meow meow meow, meow meow meow meow meow meow meow. Meow meow meow meow meow; meow meow meow meow meow.

"Meow meow'meow meow," meow meow meow, "meow meow meow meow meow meow meow meow meow meow! Meow'meow meow meow meow. Meow meow meow meow meow, meow meow meow meow meow—meow meow meow meow meow meow meow meow, meow meow meow meow meow meow meow meow meow! Meow, meow meow meow meow meow meow!"

Meow meow meow meow meow meow meow, meow meow meow meow meow meow meow meow meow meow meow meow meow meow meow meow meow: meow meow meow meow meow meow meow meow meow meow meow meow meow meow. Meow meow meow meow meow meow meow meow meow meow meow meow meow meow meow meow meow meow meow meow.

Meow meow meow meow meow meow meow meow meow meow. Meow meow meow meow meow meow meow meow meow meow meow, meow meow meow meow meow meow meow meow meow meow meow meow meow meow meow meow meow meow meow meow meow. Meow meow meow meow meow meow meow meow meow. Meow meow meow meow meow meow meow meow meow meow meow meow meow meow meow meow, meow, meow meow meow meow, meow meow meow meow meow meow, meow meow meow, meow meow, meow meow meow meow meow meow, meow meow meow meow-meow meow. Meow meow meow meow: meow meow meow meow meow meow meow; meow meow meow meow, meow meow meow meow meow meow meow, meow meow meow, meow meow meow meow meow meow meow meow meow meow meow meow meow meow meow meow meow meow, meow meow meow meow meow meow, meow meow meow meow meow meow meow meow:

"Meow meow meow meow meow meow meow
Meow meow meow—meow meow meow—meow meow."

Meow meow meow meow meow:

"Meow meow meow meow meow Meow meow meow meow meow meow meow meow."

Meow meow meow meow meow meow: meow meow meow meow meow meow meow meow meow meow meow meow meow. Meow meow meow meow meow meow meow meow meow meow meow meow meow meow meow. Meow meow meow meow, meow meow meow meow meow meow meow meow meow meow meow meow meow. Meow, meow, meow meow meow meow meow meow.

MEOW II

Meow meow meow meow meow meow, meow, meow meow meow meow, meow meow meow meow meow meow, meow meow meow meow. Meow meow meow meow meow meow meow meow meow meow meow meow meow meow. Meow meow meow meow meow meow meow meow meow, meow meow meow meow meow meow meow meow meow meow meow. Meow meow meow meow meow meow meow meow meow meow meow meow meow meow meow meow meow meow meow, meow meow meow meow meow, meow meow meow meow, meow meow meow meow; meow, meow meow meow meow meow meow meow meow, meow meow meow meow meow meow meow meow meow.

Meow meow meow meow meow meow meow meow meow, meow meow meow meow meow meow meow meow meow meow meow, meow meow, meow meow meow meow meow-meow meow meow meow meow meow meow meow meow meow meow meow meow. Meow meow meow meow meow meow meow meow meow meow meow meow, meow meow meow, meow meow meow meow meow meow meow meow meow meow meow meow. Meow meow meow meow meow meow meow meow meow, meow meow meow meow meow meow meow meow meow meow meow meow. Meow meow meow meow meow meow meow, meow meow meow meow meow meow, meow meow meow, meow meow meow, meow meow meow meow. Meow meow meow meow, meow meow meow meow meow meow meow meow meow meow meow meow meow meow meow meow meow meow meow meow meow.

Meow meow meow meow meow meow meow meow meow meow meow meow meow, meow meow meow meow meow. Meow meow meow meow meow meow Meow meow meow meow meow meow meow meow meow meow, meow meow meow meow meow meow. Meow meow meow meow meow meow meow meow, meow meow meow meow meow meow. Meow meow meow meow meow meow, meow meow meow meow meow meow meow meow meow meow meow, meow meow meow meow meow meow. Meow meow meow meow meow meow meow, meow meow meow-meow, meow meow meow meow meow meow meow meow meow meow meow, meow meow meow meow, meow meow meow meow meow meow meow meow meow meow meow meow meow meow meow meow meow meow, meow meow meow meow meow meow meow meow meow meow. Meow meow meow meow meow meow, meow meow meow, meow meow meow, meow meow meow. Meow meow, meow meow meow meow, meow meow meow meow, meow meow, meow, meow meow meow meow meow meow meow meow meow meow meow meow meow. Meow meow meow meow meow meow meow meow; meow meow meow meow meow meow meow meow meow meow meow meow—meow meow meow meow meow meow meow, meow meow meow meow meow meow meow meow meow meow meow meow meow. Meow meow meow meow meow meow meow meow meow meow meow, meow meow meow meow meow meow meow, meow meow meow meow meow meow, meow meow meow meow meow meow

meow meow. Meow meow meow meow, meow meow meow meow meow, meow meow meow meow meow. Meow meow meow, meow meow meow meow, meow meow, meow meow meow meow meow meow meow meow meow meow meow meow meow meow meow. Meow meow meow meow meow meow meow meow meow meow meow meow meow. Meow meow meow meow; meow meow meow meow meow meow meow meow meow meow meow meow meow meow meow meow meow meow meow meow meow meow meow meow meow meow meow meow meow. Meow meow meow meow meow meow Meow, meow meow meow meow meow:

“Meow Meow meow, meow meow, meow meow meow meow meow meow? Meow meow, meow meow meow meow meow meow meow, meow meow meow meow meow meow meow meow meow meow meow meow meow meow meow meow. Meow meow meow meow meow meow meow meow meow meow meow, meow Meow meow meow meow meow meow meow meow. Meow—meow meow meow meow; meow meow. Meow meow meow meow meow—meow meow meow meow meow meow?”

“Meow, Meow meow meow,” meow meow meow meow, meow meow meow meow meow meow meow meow meow meow meow meow meow meow meow meow. Meow meow meow meow meow meow meow meow meow meow meow meow meow meow meow meow, meow meow meow meow meow meow meow meow meow meow meow meow meow meow meow meow meow meow meow meow meow meow meow meow meow meow meow meow meow.

“Meow meow meow, meow meow meow meow,” meow meow meow. “Meow meow Meow meow! Meow’meow meow meow meow meow, meow meow, meow,” meow meow meow meow meow meow meow meow meow meow- meow. “Meow’meow meow meow meow meow meow meow meow meow meow!... Meow meow meow....” Meow meow meow, meow, meow meow meow meow meow meow, meow meow meow meow meow meow meow, meow meow meow meow meow. Meow meow meow, meow meow meow meow meow, meow meow meow meow meow meow meow meow meow meow meow meow. Meow meow meow Meow meow meow meow meow meow meow meow meow meow meow meow meow meow meow meow.

“Meow meow,” meow meow meow meow meow, “meow meow meow meow meow, meow’meow meow meow meow. Meow Meow meow meow meow meow meow meow meow meow, meow meow meow’meow meow meow. Meow meow, meow meow, meow meow meow meow. Meow meow meow meow meow meow meow meow meow meow meow, meow meow meow—meow—meow meow. Meow meow meow meow meow meow meow meow meow meow meow meow meow meow, meow meow meow meow meow mcow meow, meow meow meow meow meow meow meow meow meow; meow meow meow, meow, meow meow meow meow Meow meow meow meow meow meow meow meow meow meow. Meow meow meow-meow! Meow meow, meow meow meow Meow. Meow meow meow meow meow meow, meow meow meow meow meow meow meow meow meow meow! Meow meow meow? Meow meow meow meow meow meow meow

meow meow meow meow: meow meow meow meow meow meow meow meow meow meow, meow meow Meow?"

"Meow, Meow meow meow meow meow," meow Meow. "Meow meow meow meow?"

"Meow, Meow'meow meow meow meow meow meow meow'meow meow meow meow Meow'meow meow meow...." Meow meow meow meow, meow meow meow meow. Meow meow meow meow meow meow meow meow meow meow meow meow meow meow meow. Meow meow meow meow meow meow meow meow meow meow meow meow meow meow meow meow. Meow meow, meow, meow meow. Meow meow meow meow meow, meow meow meow.

Meow meow meow meow meow meow meow meow meow meow. Meow meow meow meow meow meow meow meow. Meow meow meow meow meow meow meow, meow meow meow meow meow meow meow "meow meow" meow meow meow meow meow meow meow, meow meow, meow meow meow. Meow Meow meow meow meow meow meow, meow meow meow meow meow meow meow meow meow meow-meow meow meow meow meow meow meow meow meow meow meow meow meow meow meow meow meow meow. Meow meow meow meow meow meow meow meow, meow meow meow meow meow meow meow meow meow meow meow meow meow meow meow. Meow meow meow meow meow meow meow meow meow meow meow meow meow meow meow meow meow meow.

"Meow meow!" meow meow meow. "Meow meow meow'meow meow meow, meow meow'meow meow meow meow meow, meow meow meow meow meow meow?"

"Meow meow Meow meow meow meow meow, meow meow," Meow meow meow, meow meow meow meow Meow, meow meow meow meow meow meow meow meow meow meow meow meow. "Meow meow Meow meow meow meow meow? Meow meow meow meow meow meow meow meow meow meow meow Meow meow? Meow meow meow meow Meow. Meow meow meow meow meow meow meow meow, meow Meow meow meow, meow'meow Meow meow? Meow meow, meow meow, meow meow meow meow meow meow... meow... meow, meow meow meow meow meow meow?"

"Meow, meow meow. Meow meow meow meow meow meow meow?"

"Meow meow meow meow meow, meow meow meow meow meow meow meow meow meow meow meow. Meow meow, meow meow, meow meow meow meow meow meow meow, meow meow meow meow meow meow, meow meow meow meow meow meow meow; meow meow Meow meow meow meow meow meow? Meow meow meow meow meow meow Meow meow'meow meow meow meow. Meow meow? Meow Meow. Meow meow meow meow meow meow meow meow meow meow meow meow meow meow meow meow meow meow meow, meow meow meow'meow meow meow meow meow meow Meow, meow meow meow meow meow. Meow, Meow meow meow, meow meow meow meow meow meow? Meow meow

meow Meow meow meow meow meow meow'meow, Meow meow meow meow meow meow..."

"Meow meow meow meow?" meow meow Meow.

"Meow, meow meow meow meow meow, meow meow meow meow meow! Meow meow meow meow meow meow meow meow. Meow meow meow meow meow meow meow meow meow meow! Meow meow meow meow meow meow meow meow meow meow meow, meow Meow meow meow meow... (meow meow meow meow meow meow meow)," meow meow meow meow, meow meow meow meow meow meow meow meow meow. "Meow meow, meow, meow meow!" meow meow meow meow meow meow meow meow meow meow meow meow meow meow meow meow meow meow meow meow meow—"Meow meow, Meow meow meow meow meow meow meow meow meow meow; meow meow meow meow meow meow meow, meow meow meow meow meow meow meow meow. Meow Meow meow meow meow, meow meow meow, meow meow meow. Meow meow meow! Meow meow meow! 'Meow meow meow!' Meow meow, meow meow, meow meow.... Meow, meow meow meow meow meow meow meow meow; meow meow meow meow meow meow, meow meow meow, meow meow Meow meow meow meow meow?"

Meow meow meow meow meow meow meow meow.

"Meow," meow meow meow meow meow meow meow meow meow meow, meow meow meow meow meow meow meow meow meow meow. "Meow, meow meow meow, Meow meow meow meow, meow meow meow meow meow! Meow meow meow meow meow meow meow, meow Meow Meow, meow meow, meow meow meow meow meow meow meow meow'meow meow. Meow, meow, Meow meow meow meow, meow meow meow meow meow meow meow meow meow, meow meow meow, meow meow meow. Meow meow... meow, meow meow meow meow meow meow! Meow meow, meow meow, meow meow meow meow meow meow meow meow meow meow meow meow meow meow meow meow! Meow Meow Meow, meow meow meow meow, meow meow meow.... Meow meow, meow Meow meow meow meow meow meow meow meow meow meow meow meow meow meow meow—meow Meow meow meow meow meow, meow meow meow meow, meow meow," meow meow meow meow meow, meow meow meow meow—"meow, meow Meow, meow meow meow meow meow.... Meow meow, meow! Meow'meow meow meow meow meow meow'meow meow meow meow! Meow meow meow! Meow meow meow meow, meow meow meow meow meow meow meow meow meow meow meow meow meow meow... meow meow meow meow meow Meow meow meow meow meow meow!"

"Meow!" meow meow meow meow. Meow meow meow meow meow meow meow meow.

"Meow meow meow meow! Meow meow meow, meow, meow meow meow, Meow meow meow meow meow meow meow meow? Meow meow meow—meow meow meow meow meow meow meow meow meow meow meow, meow meow meow, meow meow Meow meow meow meow meow! Meow meow meow Meow meow meow meow, meow meow meow meow

meow meow, meow meow meow, meow meow; meow meow meow meow meow meow meow meow meow meow meow meow meow meow meow meow meow meow meow meow meow. Meow meow meow meow meow meow Meow Meow meow meow meow meow meow meow meow; meow meow meow meow meow meow meow meow meow, meow meow'meow meow meow meow meow meow meow meow. Meow meow meow meow meow meow meow meow meow meow meow meow meow Meow meow meow! Meow meow meow Meow meow'meow meow meow? Meow meow meow Meow meow meow meow Meow meow meow. Meow'meow meow Meow meow meow. Meow meow meow meow meow meow meow meow meow.... Meow meow meow meow Meow meow meow meow meow meow!" Meow meow meow meow meow meow meow meow meow meow meow meow meow.

"Meow meow," meow meow meow, meow meow meow meow, "meow meow meow Meow meow meow meow meow meow meow meow. Meow meow meow meow Meow meow meow, meow meow meow meow Meow meow meow meow meow. Meow meow meow meow meow meow meow meow meow meow, Meow meow meow meow meow meow meow meow meow-meow meow meow meow meow, meow meow meow meow meow meow meow, meow Meow meow meow meow meow meow meow meow meow meow. Meow meow meow meow meow meow meow meow meow meow-meow meow meow meow meow meow meow, meow meow meow meow meow meow meow meow meow meow meow meow meow meow meow meow meow meow meow meow meow meow meow meow meow meow meow meow meow meow. Meow meow... meow, meow meow meow meow meow meow—meow meow, meow... meow meow meow meow meow meow meow. meow meow meow meow meow meow meow meow meow meow meow meow meow.

Meow meow meow meow meow meow meow meow meow meow meow meow, meow meow meow meow meow meow meow meow meow meow meow meow meow meow meow meow meow meow meow meow. Meow meow'meow meow meow meow meow, Meow meow'meow meow meow, meow meow meow meow meow meow meow meow meow meow meow, meow meow meow meow meow meow meow meow. Meow, meow, meow meow meow meow meow meow, meow meow meow. Meow meow meow meow meow meow meow meow meow meow meow meow meow, meow meow'meow meow meow meow meow meow meow meow. Meow'meow meow meow meow meow meow Meow.

Meow'meow meow meow meow, meow meow meow meow meow meow meow meow meow meow, meow meow meow meow meow meow meow meow meow meow meow meow meow meow meow meow. Meow meow meow meow meow Meow meow meow, meow meow meow, meow meow meow meow meow. Meow meow meow meow meow, meow meow meow, meow meow, meow meow meow meow meow meow meow meow'meow meow. Meow meow meow meow meow meow meow; meow meow meow meow meow meow, meow meow meow meow meow meow meow meow. Meow meow meow meow meow meow meow meow: meow meow meow

meow meow meow, meow meow Meow meow meow meow meow, meow meow meow meow meow meow meow meow meow meow meow meow meow meow meow meow; meow Meow meow meow, Meow meow meow meow, meow meow meow meow, meow meow meow meow meow meow meow meow meow meow.... Meow meow meow meow meow meow meow meow meow meow meow meow meow meow meow meow meow Meow meow meow meow meow meow meow; meow meow meow meow meow meow meow meow meow, meow Meow meow meow meow meow meow meow meow meow meow, Meow meow'meow meow meow meow meow meow meow.

Meow meow meow meow meow meow meow. Meow meow meow meow, meow, meow meow.... Meow meow, meow meow, meow meow, Meow, meow meow meow meow meow meow, meow meow meow meow meow meow meow meow meow meow meow, meow meow meow meow, meow Meow meow meow meow meow meow meow meow meow. Meow meow meow meow meow meow meow meow, meow meow, meow meow meow meow meow meow meow meow meow, meow meow meow meow meow meow meow.

Meow meow meow! Meow meow meow meow meow meow meow, meow meow meow! Meow meow meow meow meow meow! Meow meow meow, meow, meow meow meow meow meow meow meow meow meow meow meow meow meow? Meow, meow meow meow'meow meow meow.... Meow meow meow meow meow, Meow meow meow meow meow meow meow, meow meow meow meow meow" (meow meow meow meow meow meow meow), "meow Meow meow meow. Meow meow meow, Meow meow meow meow meow; meow meow Meow meow meow meow meow, meow meow meow meow meow meow meow meow meow meow meow meow meow; meow meow Meow meow meow meow!... Meow meow meow meow meow meow meow meow meow meow meow meow meow meow meow meow meow meow meow meow meow meow meow meow meow meow meow, meow meow meow meow. Meow Meow meow meow meow.... Meow meow meow meow Meow meow meow meow. Meow meow meow? Meow meow meow meow meow meow meow meow Meow meow meow: meow meow meow meow meow meow.... Meow meow meow meow meow meow meow meow Meow Meow Meow'meow; meow meow meow meow meow meow meow meow meow meow meow meow, Meow meow meow meow.

Meow meow meow meow meow meow meow meow meow meow. Meow meow meow, meow meow Meow... meow... meow... Meow meow meow meow meow meow meow meow meow meow meow; meow meow meow meow meow meow meow meow meow meow meow meow meow-meow meow meow meow meow meow, Meow meow'meow meow meow. Meow, meow Meow Meow meow meow meow meow meow, meow meow meow meow meow, meow meow meow-meow.... Meow. Meow meow'meow meow meow meow meow meow! Meow, meow meow meow meow meow, meow meow meow meow. Meow meow meow meow meow meow meow meow meow meow meow meow meow meow meow meow meow, meow meow Meow meow meow meow meow meow meow meow meow meow

meow meow meow meow meow meow, meow meow meow meow meow... meow, meow meow meow meow meow meow meow, meow meow meow meow meow meow meow meow. Meow meow meow Meow meow Meow.

Meow meow meow meow meow meow meow, meow meow meow meow meow meow meow meow meow meow meow meow meow meow meow meow meow meow meow meow meow meow Meow. Meow, Meow' —meow meow meow meow?—meow meow meow meow meow meow meow meow: meow meow'meow meow meow meow meow meow. Meow meow meow Meow meow meow meow meow, meow meow, meow meow meow meow meow meow meow meow. Meow meow meow meow meow meow meow meow meow meow meow meow meow meow? Meow meow meow meow meow meow meow meow, meow meow meow meow meow meow meow meow meow meow meow meow meow meow meow meow meow meow meow meow! Meow meow'meow meow, Meow Meow Meow meow meow meow—meow meow meow meow meow?—meow meow meow meow meow meow meow meow meow meow-meow meow meow meow meow meow meow meow meow meow meow, meow meow meow meow, meow meow meow meow meow meow meow meow meow meow meow meow meow meow meow meow meow meow meow. Meow meow meow meow meow meow meow.... Meow Meow Meow meow meow meow meow meow meow meow meow, meow meow meow meow, meow meow meow meow meow meow meow: 'Meow meow meow meow meow,' meow meow, 'meow meow meow meow meow meow meow meow meow meow meow meow meow meow.' Meow meow meow meow meow meow meow meow meow meow meow meow meow meow meow meow meow meow meow meow meow! Meow meow meow meow meow meow meow... meow, meow meow meow! Meow meow meow meow meow Meow meow meow Meow meow (meow meow meow meow meow meow meow meow meow meow... meow meow meow meow meow meow, meow meow meow). Meow meow: 'Meow Meow, meow Meow meow meow meow meow meow meow meow?' Meow Meow Meow, meow meow meow meow meow meow meow meow meow meow meow meow, meow meow meow meow meow meow meow meow meow meow meow meow meow. 'Meow meow meow?' meow Meow Meow meow meow meow, 'meow meow meow meow meow meow meow meow meow meow!' Meow meow'meow meow meow, meow'meow meow meow, meow meow, meow'meow meow meow! Meow meow meow meow meow meow meow, meow meow meow meow meow meow meow meow meow meow meow meow meow meow; meow meow meow meow meow meow meow meow meow meow meow.... Meow meow'meow Meow Meow'meow meow, meow meow meow meow, meow meow meow, meow meow meow meow meow meow meow.

Meow meow meow'meow Meow meow Meow meow meow, meow meow meow meow meow meow meow, meow meow meow meow meow meow meow meow meow meow'meow meow meow meow. Meow meow meow meow meow Meow Meow meow meow meow meow meow meow meow meow meow meow meow meow. Meow meow meow meow meow meow, meow meow meow meow meow meow meow, meow meow meow meow

meow meow meow meow meow meow meow (meow meow meow meow, meow meow meow meow), meow meow meow meow meow meow meow meow meow meow meow meow meow meow meow meow meow meow meow; meow meow meow meow meow meow meow meow meow.... Meow Meow meow meow meow meow, meow meow meow.... Meow meow Meow meow, meow meow, Meow meow Meow Meow, meow meow meow meow meow meow meow Meow'meow meow meow; meow meow meow meow meow meow meow meow meow Meow'meow meow, meow meow meow meow meow, meow meow meow meow meow meow meow meow meow'meow meow... meow, meow... meow... meow Meow... meow meow."

Meow meow meow, meow meow meow meow meow meow meow. Meow meow meow meow meow meow, meow, meow meow meow meow.

"Meow meow, meow," meow meow meow meow meow meow meow—"Meow meow, meow meow meow meow meow meow meow meow meow meow meow-meow meow—meow meow meow Meow Meow meow meow meow meow meow meow meow meow meow meow meow meow meow meow meow meow— meow meow meow meow Meow Meow meow meow meow meow meow meow meow meow, meow meow meow meow meow meow meow meow meow meow meow meow meow. Meow meow meow, Meow Meow meow meow meow meow meow (meow meow meow meow meow Meow Meow meow) meow Meow. Meow meow... meow.... Meow meow meow meow meow meow Meow Meow meow meow Meow'meow meow. Meow meow meow meow meow meow meow meow Meow meow meow meow meow meow meow meow meow meow meow meow meow: 'meow,' meow meow, 'meow meow meow meow meow meow meow meow meow meow meow meow meow meow meow meow meow?' Meow Meow Meow meow meow meow meow meow, meow meow meow meow meow... meow meow meow'meow meow meow meow. Meow Meow meow meow meow meow, meow meow meow; meow meow Meow Meow meow meow meow meow meow meow.... Meow meow meow meow meow meow Meow' meow meow, meow meow meow meow; Meow meow meow meow meow meow meow meow meow meow meow meow meow meow meow meow meow meow meow. Meow meow meow, meow, meow meow meow meow. Meow meow meow meow meow meow, meow Meow meow meow meow, meow meow.... Meow... meow... meow meow meow meow meow meow meow meow... meow. Meow Meow meow meow meow meow meow, meow meow meow meow meow, meow meow meow meow meow meow meow meow meow meow meow meow Meow Meow. Meow meow Meow Meow, meow meow meow meow? Meow? Meow, meow, meow'meow meow meow meow Meow meow meow'meow meow. Meow meow meow... meow meow meow meow meow meow Meow; meow meow meow meow!... Meow meow meow meow meow meow meow meow meow. 'Meow, meow meow meow meow meow meow meow... Meow'meow meow meow meow meow meow meow meow meow'—meow'meow meow meow meow, 'meow,' meow meow, 'meow meow meow meow meow.' Meow meow meow meow meow meow meow—meow meow meow, meow meow meow meow meow meow meow meow meow meow meow meow, meow meow meow meow meow

meow meow meow meow meow meow meow. Meow meow meow, meow meow Meow meow meow Meow'meow meow meow meow meow meow meow meow meow meow meow meow, meow, meow meow meow-meow meow meow!..."

Meow meow meow meow meow meow. Meow meow meow meow meow meow meow meow meow meow meow meow meow meow meow, meow meow meow meow meow meow meow meow meow meow meow meow meow meow meow meow meow meow "Meow Meow" meow meow meow meow meow. Meow meow meow meow meow meow. Meow meow-meow meow meow meow meow meow meow meow meow-meow. Meow meow meow meow meow meow meow meow meow meow meow. Meow meow meow meow meow meow meow meow, meow meow meow meow meow meow meow meow, meow meow meow meow meow meow. Meow meow meow meow meow meow meow meow meow meow meow meow meow meow, meow meow meow meow meow meow meow meow meow meow meow meow meow. Meow meow meow.

"Meow meow meow meow meow, meow. Meow.... Meow meow meow Meow Meow meow Meow meow meow meow, meow meow meow, meow meow meow meow Meow meow meow meow meow meow Meow. Meow meow meow meow: meow meow meow meow meow meow, meow meow meow. Meow meow meow meow meow meow, meow meow meow. 'Meow Meow meow meow meow meow meow meow meow meow, meow meow meow, meow!' Meow meow meow meow Meow meow meow meow meow meow meow meow meow! Meow meow meow meow meow meow meow, meow meow meow meow? Meow meow meow meow meow meow meow meow meow meow meow meow— meow meow, meow meow, Meow meow'meow meow. Meow, meow meow-meow—meow meow, meow meow, meow meow meow meow meow meow meow, meow meow meow meow meow meow. Meow meow meow Meow meow meow meow meow meow Meow meow Meow Meow meow meow meow meow meow meow— meow meow meow meow meow meow meow—meow meow meow meow meow meow meow meow. Meow meow meow meow meow... meow meow meow, meow meow meow meow meow meow meow meow meow meow meow meow meow; meow meow meow meow'meow meow meow meow meow meow, meow meow meow meow meow meow meow meow, meow'meow meow meow meow meow, meow meow meow meow meow meow meow meow, meow, meow meow meow meow, meow meow meow meow, meow meow meow meow meow meow. Meow, meow meow meow, meow meow meow meow meow 'meow meow meow,' meow meow, 'meow meow'meow meow meow meow meow meow meow meow meow meow meow. Meow meow meow meow meow meow meow meow.' Meow meow meow, meow meow meow? Meow meow meow meow meow meow meow meow meow meow meow meow meow: meow Meow Meow meow meow meow meow meow meow meow meow meow Meow Meow meow meow meow meow, meow meow meow meow meow meow meow meow meow meow. Meow meow meow meow meow meow, meow meow. 'Meow Meow meow meow meow meow meow, meow, meow meow meow meow,'

meow meow, 'meow meow meow meow meow meow meow meow meow meow meow meow meow meow meow, meow meow meow meow meow meow meow Meow Meow meow meow meow meow meow meow meow meow.' Meow meow meow, meow meow meow? 'Meow meow meow,' meow meow, 'Meow Meow, meow meow meow meow,' meow meow, 'meow meow meow meow meow meow meow meow meow meow, meow meow meow meow meow meow meow meow'meow meow meow meow meow meow,' (meow meow meow, meow meow meow;) 'meow meow,' meow meow, 'Meow meow meow meow meow meow meow meow meow.' Meow meow meow, meow meow meow meow, meow meow meow meow meow meow meow, meow meow meow meow meow meow, meow meow meow meow meow; meow, meow meow meow meow meow, meow meow meow meow meow meow meow, meow meow meow meow meow! Meow Meow meow'meow meow meow meow meow, meow, Meow meow'meow meow meow!... Meow meow meow meow Meow meow meow meow meow meow meow meow—meow- meow meow meow meow meow—meow meow meow meow meow: 'meow,' meow meow, 'meow meow meow.' Meow meow meow meow meow meow, meow meow? Meow meow meow meow meow meow meow, meow meow meow meow meow meow meow meow meow meow, meow meow?... Meow, meow meow meow meow, 'meow meow meow,' meow meow."

Meow meow meow, meow meow meow, meow meow meow meow meow meow meow. Meow meow meow meow. Meow meow, meow meow meow meow meow meow, meow meow meow meow meow meow meow, meow meow meow meow meow, meow meow meow meow meow meow meow meow meow meow meow meow meow meow. Meow meow meow meow meow meow meow. Meow meow meow meow meow meow meow meow.

"Meow meow, meow meow," meow Meow meow meow—"Meow, meow, meow meow meow meow meow meow meow meow meow, meow meow meow meow meow, meow meow Meow meow meow meow meow meow meow meow meow meow meow meow meow meow meow meow meow, meow meow meow meow meow meow meow meow meow. Meow Meow meow meow meow meow.... Meow meow meow meow meow meow meow meow meow meow meow meow meow meow meow meow Meow meow meow meow meow meow meow Meow meow meow meow meow, meow meow Meow meow meow meow meow meow, meow meow Meow meow meow meow meow, meow meow Meow meow meow meow meow meow meow meow meow meow meow meow meow meow meow meow meow.... Meow meow meow meow meow.... Meow meow, meow. Meow, meow, meow" (Meow meow meow meow meow meow meow, meow meow meow meow meow meow meow meow meow) "meow, meow meow meow meow meow meow meow meow meow, meow meow meow meow, meow meow meow meow, meow meow meow, meow meow meow meow, meow meow meow meow meow meow, Meow meow meow Meow Meow meow meow meow meow meow, meow meow meow meow meow meow meow meow, meow meow meow meow Meow meow meow, meow meow meow meow meow, meow meow meow! Meow'meow meow meow meow meow Meow

meow meow, meow meow meow meow meow meow meow meow meow'meow meow meow meow meow meow, meow meow meow meow meow meow meow meow meow meow Meow meow. Meow meow meow meow meow meow Meow meow meow... meow meow'meow meow meow meow meow!"

Meow meow meow meow meow meow meow, meow meow meow, meow meow meow meow meow meow meow meow meow meow meow meow. Meow meow meow meow meow meow meow meow meow meow meow meow meow meow meow meow meow meow, meow meow meow Meow, meow meow meow:

"Meow meow Meow meow meow meow Meow, Meow meow meow meow meow meow meow meow-meow-meow! Meow-meow-meow!"

"Meow meow'meow meow meow meow meow meow meow?" meow meow meow meow meow-meow; meow meow meow meow meow meow meow meow meow meow.

"Meow meow meow meow meow meow meow meow," Meow meow, meow meow meow meow Meow. "Meow meow meow meow meow meow meow meow meow, meow meow, meow meow meow, meow Meow meow.... Meow meow meow, meow meow meow meow meow meow meow meow.... Meow meow meow, meow meow meow... meow meow meow meow, meow meow, meow meow meow'meow meow meow, meow meow'meow meow meow! Meow meow meow meow, meow meow meow meow meow meow'meow meow! Meow meow meow! Meow meow meow meow meow meow, meow? Meow meow meow meow, meow meow meow? Meow meow meow'meow meow meow meow meow meow meow. Meow meow meow, meow meow, meow meow meow, meow meow? Meow meow meow? Meow meow'meow meow, meow, meow meow, meow meow meow meow; meow, meow meow, meow, meow, meow meow meow meow meow meow meow meow meow meow meow meow meow meow meow meow. Meow meow meow, meow, meow meow meow meow meow meow meow meow? Meow meow Meow, meow meow meow, meow Meow meow meow meow meow meow meow meow meow meow! Meow Meow meow meow meow! Meow Meow meow meow meow meow! Meow, meow meow meow meow meow meow meow meow meow, meow? Meow meow meow meow meow, meow, meow meow? Meow meow, meow, meow meow meow meow meow? Meow-meow-meow!"

Meow meow meow meow meow meow, meow meow meow meow meow meow. Meow meow meow meow. "Meow meow meow meow meow meow meow?" meow meow meow-meow meow meow meow meow meow.

Meow meow meow meow meow meow meow. Meow meow meow meow meow meow meow meow meow meow meow meow meow meow meow meow meow meow meow meow meow meow meow meow meow meow meow meow meow meow meow.

"Meow meow meow! Meow meow Meow meow meow meow?" Meow meow meow, meow meow meow meow meow meow, meow meow meow meow meow meow meow meow meow meow.

"Meow meow Meow meow meow meow, meow meow? Meow! meow'meow meow meow meow meow meow! Meow meow meow meow meow, meow meow meow meow, meow meow! Meow meow, meow meow, meow meow meow meow meow! Meow meow Meow meow meow meow meow meow meow meow, meow meow'meow meow meow-meow Meow meow meow meow meow meow!... Meow meow meow, meow meow meow, meow meow meow meow meow meow meow meow meow meow? Meow meow meow Meow meow meow meow meow meow meow, meow meow meow, meow meow meow meow, meow Meow meow meow meow; meow Meow meow meow meow Meow meow meow meow meow meow meow, Meow meow meow meow meow meow meow meow, Meow meow meow Meow, Meow meow meow meow meow. Meow meow meow meow meow meow meow Meow meow meow: 'Meow meow meow meow meow meow meow meow meow meow, meow meow-meow meow meow meow meow meow meow meow? Meow meow meow meow meow meow meow meow meow meow meow, meow meow meow, meow meow meow meow?' Meow Meow meow meow, 'Meow meow meow! Meow meow meow meow meow meow.... Meow meow meow meow meow.... Meow meow meow meow meow meow meow meow meow meow meow meow meow....' Meow meow meow meow meow Meow, Meow meow meow, Meow meow meow... Meow meow meow meow meow meow meow Meow meow meow meow meow meow! Meow Meow meow meow meow meow meow meow, meow meow meow meow meow, meow meow meow meow meow.... Meow meow Meow meow meow meow meow meow meow, meow Meow meow meow meow. 'Meow meow meow meow,' Meow meow meow, 'Meow meow meow meow, meow meow, meow meow meow, meow meow, meow meow meow meow!' Meow meow meow meow meow meow, meow meow meow meow meow meow meow. Meow Meow meow meow meow meow, 'Meow meow meow, meow meow meow Meow meow meow Meow meow meow meow meow; meow meow meow meow!' Meow meow meow meow meow meow meow meow meow meow, 'Meow Meow, meow meow Meow meow meow meow?' Meow Meow meow meow, 'Meow meow meow Meow meow meow, meow meow meow, meow meow meow Meow meow meow, meow meow meow meow, meow meow meow meow meow meow meow meow meow meow meow meow.' Meow Meow meow meow meow Meow meow meow meow meow meow meow meow meow meow meow... meow meow meow meow... meow meow meow meow meow meow! Meow meow meow meow meow!... meow meow meow meow, Meow Meow meow... meow meow meow.... Meow, Meow meow meow!" Meow meow meow meow meow meow meow meow, meow meow, meow meow meow meow, meow meow meow meow meow meow meow meow meow meow. Meow meow meow meow meow meow meow; meow meow meow meow meow meow; meow meow meow meow meow meow meow meow.

"Meow'meow meow meow!" "Meow meow meow!" "Meow meow meow meow meow!" Meow meow meow, meow meow meow.

"Meow meow meow, meow," meow Meow meow meow meow, meow meow meow meow meow Meow— "meow meow meow meow...

Meow'meow meow, meow meow meow meow. Meow'meow meow meow Meow Meow—meow Meow meow."

Meow meow meow meow meow meow meow meow meow meow meow meow meow meow meow meow. Meow meow meow meow meow meow meow meow meow meow meow meow meow meow meow meow meow meow. Meow meow meow meow meow meow meow meow meow. Meow meow meow meow meow meow meow meow meow meow meow meow meow meow meow meow meow meow.

"Meow'meow meow Meow Meow Meow meow meow meow meow," meow meow meow meow—"meow meow meow meow meow meow meow meow. Meow meow meow meow meow! Meow meow meow! Meow'meow meow Meow meow! Meow meow meow meow meow meow meow meow meow meow meow, meow'meow meow meow Meow meow meow meow... meow'meow meow meow Meow meow meow meow... meow, meow meow... meow meow meow meow meow, meow, meow meow... meow meow meow meow.... Meow meow meow meow meow meow meow meow meow... meow meow meow meow? Meow meow meow meow meow meow'meow meow, meow.... Meow meow Meow meow meow meow meow meow... Meow meow'meow meow meow'meow meow! Meow meow'meow meow! Meow meow Meow meow meow meow meow.... Meow, meow, meow meow meow meow meow meow meow meow meow, meow meow meow meow. Meow meow Meow meow'meow meow meow meow meow.... Meow'meow meow meow. Meow meow meow meow, meow meow meow meow... meow'meow meow meow... Meow meow meow meow. Meow meow meow Meow, meow meow-meow... meow Meow, meow-meow-meow. Meow meow meow!"

Meow meow meow meow meow meow meow meow meow meow meow meow. Meow meow meow meow meow meow meow meow meow meow. Meow meow meow meow meow'meow meow meow meow meow meow Meow meow meow meow meow meow, meow meow meow meow meow meow meow meow meow meow meow.

Meow meow meow meow meow meow meow meow meow meow meow meow meow. Meow meow meow-meow meow meow meow meow meow meow meow meow meow meow meow-meow; meow meow meow meow meow meow meow meow meow. Meow meow meow meow meow, meow meow meow meow meow meow meow, meow meow'meow meow. Meow meow meow meow meow meow meow meow meow. Meow meow meow meow meow meow. Meow meow meow meow meow meow meow meow meow meow meow meow meow meow meow Meow meow, meow meow meow, meow meow meow meow meow meow meow-meow, meow meow meow. Meow meow meow meow meow meow meow meow meow meow-meow meow meow meow meow. Meow meow meow meow meow meow meow meow meow meow, meow meow meow meow meow, meow meow meow meow meow meow meow. Meow meow meow meow meow meow meow, meow meow meow, meow meow Meow Meow'meow meow meow meow meow meow meow, meow meow meow meow, meow meow meow meow. Meow meow meow meow meow meow meow meow meow meow. Meow meow meow meow meow meow meow meow meow meow meow meow.

Meow meow Meow Meow meow meow. Meow meow meow meow meow, meow meow meow meow, meow meow, meow meow meow meow meow meow meow meow meow meow meow meow meow. Meow meow meow meow meow meow meow meow meow meow, meow meow meow meow meow meow; meow meow meow meow meow meow meow meow meow meow meow. Meow meow meow meow meow meow meow meow meow meow meow meow meow meow. Meow meow meow meow meow meow meow meow meow meow meow meow meow meow-meow meow meow meow meow meow meow meow. Meow meow meow Meow meow meow meow meow meow meow meow meow meow meow meow Meow.... Meow meow meow meow meow meow meow meow meow meow meow. Meow meow meow meow meow meow meow, meow meow meow meow. Meow meow meow meow, meow meow meow meow meow meow meow; meow meow meow meow meow meow, meow meow meow meow meow meow meow meow meow meow. Meow meow meow meow meow meow meow meow meow meow, meow meow meow, meow meow meow meow meow meow. Meow meow meow, meow meow meow meow, meow meow, meow meow meow meow meow meow meow meow meow meow meow meow. Meow meow meow meow meow meow meow meow meow meow meow, meow meow meow meow meow meow meow. Meow meow meow meow meow meow meow meow meow, meow meow meow, meow meow meow meow meow meow meow meow meow meow meow meow meow meow meow meow, meow meow meow meow meow meow meow. Meow meow, meow meow meow meow meow, meow meow meow meow'meow meow. Meow meow meow meow meow meow, meow meow meow meow, meow meow meow meow meow meow meow meow meow meow meow. Meow meow meow meow meow meow meow meow, meow meow meow meow meow meow meow meow meow meow meow meow, meow meow meow meow meow meow. Meow meow meow meow meow meow, meow meow meow meow meow meow meow meow meow, meow Meow meow meow meow meow. Meow meow meow meow meow meow meow meow meow, meow meow meow meow meow meow meow meow meow meow meow meow meow meow meow. Meow meow meow meow meow meow meow meow meow meow meow meow, meow meow meow meow meow meow meow meow meow meow. Meow meow meow meow meow meow, meow meow meow meow meow meow meow meow meow meow meow meow meow meow meow meow meow meow meow meow meow meow meow meow meow meow meow meow.

"Meow!" meow meow meow meow meow meow, "meow meow meow meow! Meow meow! meow meow!... Meow meow meow meow meow? Meow'meow meow meow meow, meow meow! Meow meow meow meow meow meow! Meow meow meow meow? Meow meow meow meow! Meow!"

Meow meow meow meow meow meow. Meow meow meow meow meow meow meow meow meow meow meow meow. Meow meow meow meow meow.

"Meow meow meow meow?" meow meow—"Meow meow meow, meow meow meow meow meow meow? Meow meow meow meow meow meow

meow meow meow!" meow meow meow meow meow meow meow meow meow meow meow meow meow meow meow meow. Meow meow meow meow meow meow meow meow meow meow meow.

"Meow meow meow meow meow meow meow! Meow meow meow meow meow, meow meow meow meow meow-meow-meow-meow, meow-meow-meow meow," meow meow meow, meow meow meow meow meow meow meow meow meow meow meow meow meow meow meow meow. Meow meow meow meow meow meow meow meow, meow meow meow meow. Meow meow meow meow meow meow meow meow meow meow meow meow meow meow meow meow meow meow meow meow, meow meow meow meow. Meow meow meow meow meow meow meow meow.

"Meow'meow meow meow! meow'meow meow meow meow," meow meow meow meow meow meow meow—"meow meow meow meow meow! Meow meow meow meow, meow!"—meow meow meow meow meow meow meow meow meow. "Meow, meow meow! Meow meow, meow meow meow meow?"—meow meow meow meow meow meow Meow—"meow meow meow! Meow meow meow meow meow meow? Meow meow meow meow meow meow, meow! Meow meow!"

Meow meow meow meow meow meow meow meow meow meow. Meow meow meow meow meow meow meow meow meow meow meow meow meow meow meow. Meow meow meow meow meow meow meow meow meow meow meow meow meow meow meow meow meow. Meow meow meow meow meow meow meow meow meow meow meow, meow meow meow meow meow, meow meow meow meow meow meow meow meow. Meow meow meow meow, meow Meow, meow meow meow meow meow, meow meow meow meow meow meow meow meow. Meow meow meow meow meow meow meow meow; meow meow meow meow meow meow meow meow: meow meow meow Meow Meow meow meow meow meow meow meow meow meow meow meow meow meow meow meow meow meow meow meow meow meow meow meow meow meow meow meow meow meow meow meow meow meow meow meow meow meow meow meow meow meow meow. Meow meow meow meow, Meow meow meow meow meow meow meow meow meow meow, meow meow meow meow meow meow meow meow meow meow meow meow meow meow meow meow meow meow meow meow meow meow meow meow meow meow. Meow meow meow meow, meow meow meow meow meow meow meow meow meow.

"Meow meow meow meow Meow'meow meow," meow meow meow meow, "meow meow Meow meow Meow meow meow meow." Meow meow meow meow meow meow meow meow meow meow meow meow meow meow meow meow meow meow meow meow meow meow meow, meow meow meow meow meow meow meow meow meow meow meow meow meow meow meow. "Meow meow meow meow," meow meow meow meow meow meow meow meow, meow meow meow meow—"meow meow meow meow.... Meow! Meow meow Meow meow meow meow meow meow-meow, meow meow meow meow meow meow, meow meow meow... meow meow meow... meow meow meow meow meow meow meow meow meow-meow meow meow meow meow. Meow meow Meow! Meow meow meow

meow'meow meow meow! Meow meow'meow meow meow meow meow meow! Meow, meow meow meow meow meow meow meow! Meow'meow meow meow meow meow meow meow meow meow. Meow meow meow meow meow, meow meow!"

Meow meow meow meow.

"Meow meow meow Meow meow meow," meow meow meow meow meow meow'meow meow. "Meow meow meow meow meow meow meow meow, meow meow meow, Meow meow, meow meow meow meow meow—meow meow meow meow meow meow, meow meow meow meow meow meow meow meow meow meow'meow meow meow meow meow meow."

MEOW III

Meow meow meow meow meow meow meow meow meow meow. Meow meow meow meow meow meow meow; meow meow meow meow, meow, meow-meow, meow meow meow meow meow meow meow. Meow meow meow meow meow meow meow meow meow meow meow meow meow. Meow meow meow meow-meow meow meow meow meow meow meow meow meow meow meow, meow meow meow meow meow-meow meow meow meow meow meow meow meow meow meow meow meow meow meow meow meow meow meow meow meow meow meow meow meow meow meow meow meow meow meow meow. Meow meow meow meow meow meow meow meow: meow meow meow meow meow, meow meow; meow meow meow meow meow meow meow meow meow meow meow meow meow meow; meow meow meow meow meow meow meow meow meow meow meow meow meow meow. Meow meow meow meow meow meow meow meow meow meow meow meow meow meow meow meow meow meow meow; meow meow meow meow meow meow, meow meow meow meow meow meow meow Meow meow meow meow. Meow meow meow meow meow meow meow, meow meow meow, meow meow, meow meow, meow meow meow meow meow'meow meow, meow meow meow meow meow meow meow, meow meow meow meow meow meow meow meow meow meow, meow meow meow, meow meow meow meow meow. Meow meow meow meow meow meow meow meow meow.

Meow meow meow meow meow meow meow meow meow meow meow meow meow, meow meow Meow meow meow meow meow meow meow meow meow meow meow. Meow meow meow meow meow meow meow, meow meow meow meow meow meow, meow meow meow meow meow meow meow meow meow meow meow meow meow meow meow meow meow meow meow meow meow meow meow meow meow meow meow meow meow. Meow meow meow meow meow meow meow meow meow meow meow meow meow meow. Meow meow meow meow meow meow meow meow meow meow meow meow meow, meow meow meow meow meow meow meow meow meow meow, meow meow meow meow meow meow. Meow, meow meow meow meow meow, meow meow meow meow meow meow'meow meow meow meow meow meow meow meow meow meow meow meow, meow meow meow meow meow meow meow meow meow meow meow meow meow meow meow. Meow meow meow meow meow meow.

"Meow meow, meow meow meow meow?" meow meow meow meow. "Meow'meow meow meow, Meow meow meow meow meow meow; meow meow meow meow meow? Meow meow meow meow'meow meow meow?"

Meow meow meow meow, meow meow meow Meow.

"Meow meow meow, meow?" meow meow, meow meow meow meow meow meow meow meow meow meow meow.

"Meow meow meow, meow!"

Meow meow meow meow meow meow meow meow meow meow meow meow meow meow meow meow meow meow meow meow meow meow meow meow meow meow.

"Meow, Meow, meow meow meow," meow meow, meow meow meow meow (meow meow meow meow meow meow meow) meow meow meow meow meow meow meow—"meow meow meow meow meow meow. Meow meow meow meow meow meow, meow meow, meow meow meow-meow'meow."

"Meow meow Meow'meow meow meow meow meow meow, meow meow'meow meow meow meow meow meow meow meow meow meow? Meow'meow meow meow, meow'meow. Meow meow meow meow meow meow, meow meow meow meow meow. Meow'meow meow meow."

Meow meow meow meow meow meow, meow meow meow meow meow meow, Meow meow meow meow meow meow meow meow meow meow meow. Meow meow meow meow meow-meow meow meow meow meow meow.

"Meow Meow meow meow meow meow meow meow meow meow," meow meow. Meow meow.

"Meow meow meow? Meow meow meow meow?"

"Meow meow'meow meow meow meow meow meow meow'meow meow meow meow meow meow. Meow'meow meow meow meow, meow meow meow."

"Meow meow, meow'meow meow meow meow," meow meow, meow meow meow, "meow, meow meow meow meow meow... meow meow. Meow meow meow meow," meow meow meow. "Meow'meow meow meow meow meow meow meow-meow."

"Meow meow meow meow meow meow, meow meow Meow meow. Meow meow, meow meow meow meow meow, meow meow meow meow meow meow meow meow meow meow meow meow meow meow? Meow meow meow meow meow meow meow, meow meow, meow meow meow. Meow meow meow meow meow meow meow meow?"

"Meow meow meow..." Meow meow meow meow meow. "Meow meow meow meow?"

"Meow..."

"Meow meow meow meow?"

"Meow meow meow," meow meow meow meow meow meow.

Meow meow meow meow meow meow meow meow. Meow meow meow meow meow meow meow meow meow meow, meow meow meow, meow meow meow meow meow meow meow meow meow.

"Meow meow meow meow meow meow meow meow meow?" meow meow meow meow meow meow.

"Meow meow'meow meow meow meow meow meow meow meow. Meow Meow'meow meow meow meow."

"Meow'meow meow meow meow meow meow meow."

"Meow meow meow meow meow meow. Meow'meow meow meow meow meow meow meow?" meow meow, meow, meow meow meow meow meow meow meow.

"Meow meow meow meow meow meow meow meow meow meow?"

Meow meow meow meow meow.

"Meow, Meow meow meow meow," meow meow meow, meow meow meow meow.

"Meow'meow meow meow meow meow meow, meow meow meow meow! Meow Meow meow meow meow meow meow meow?"

"Meow meow meow."

"Meow, Meow meow! Meow meow meow meow meow meow meow meow meow meow."

"Meow meow? meow meow! meow meow?"

"Meow meow'meow meow. Meow meow meow meow meow meow meow meow meow meow meow meow. Meow meow meow meow meow?"

"Meow meow meow meow meow, meow Meow'meow meow, meow meow," meow Meow meow meow—"meow Meow!"

Meow meow meow meow meow meow meow meow. Meow meow meow: meow meow meow, meow meow meow meow Meow——. Meow meow meow meow meow meow meow. Meow meow meow meow meow meow meow meow meow meow meow, meow meow meow meow meow meow meow meow.

"Meow, meow meow meow, meow meow' meow; meow meow meow meow meow, meow meow meow' meow, meow meow meow meow!"

Meow meow meow meow meow meow meow; meow meow meow meow meow meow meow meow meow meow; meow meow meow meow meow meow meow meow meow. Meow Meow meow meow meow, meow meow meow meow meow meow meow meow meow meow; meow meow meow meow meow meow meow, meow meow, meow meow, meow meow meow meow, meow meow meow meow meow meow meow meow meow meow meow meow. Meow meow; meow meow meow meow meow meow. Meow meow meow meow meow; meow meow meow meow meow meow, meow meow meow meow, meow meow meow meow meow meow meow meow meow meow meow meow.

"Meow meow Meow," meow meow meow—"meow'meow meow meow meow Meow meow meow meow meow meow meow meow meow meow meow meow meow meow meow meow meow meow meow meow, meow. Meow Meow meow meow meow meow meow meow meow meow meow meow meow. Meow meow meow Meow meow meow; meow meow meow meow meow meow meow meow, Meow meow Meow, meow meow meow meow, meow meow meow, meow meow meow. Meow meow meow meow meow meow meow meow Meow meow meow meow meow meow meow meow meow meow meow meow, meow meow meow meow meow meow meow meow meow meow meow meow meow meow meow meow meow meow! Meow meow Meow meow meow meow meow meow meow meow meow meow meow meow meow? Meow meow meow Meow meow meow meow meow meow Meow meow, meow meow meow, meow meow meow meow meow, meow Meow Meow Meow meow meow meow meow meow. Meow meow meow meow-meow meow meow meow meow meow meow meow meow'meow meow. Meow meow meow meow meow meow meow meow meow meow, Meow meow meow meow meow meow meow meow meow meow meow meow meow meow meow meow, meow meow

Meow'meow meow meow meow meow meow meow meow meow meow. Meow meow, meow Meow, Meow meow Meow meow meow meow meow meow meow meow meow meow meow meow meow meow meow meow meow meow meow meow meow, meow meow Meow meow meow meow meow. Meow meow meow meow, meow meow meow meow, meow Meow, meow meow meow meow meow meow meow meow meow meow meow meow meow meow meow meow meow meow meow meow meow meow. Meow Meow, meow meow meow meow, meow Meow meow meow meow meow meow meow, meow meow meow meow meow meow meow meow meow meow meow meow meow meow meow meow meow meow meow meow. Meow meow meow meow meow meow meow meow meow meow meow meow meow Meow meow meow meow meow meow meow meow meow meow meow meow meow, meow meow meow meow meow meow meow meow meow meow meow meow meow—meow meow Meow meow meow meow meow meow? Meow Meow meow meow meow meow meow meow meow, Meow meow meow meow meow meow meow meow meow meow meow meow meow meow, meow meow meow meow meow meow meow meow meow, meow Meow meow meow meow meow meow meow, meow meow meow meow meow meow meow meow meow. Meow meow meow meow, meow meow meow Meow meow? Meow, meow, Meow meow meow meow meow meow meow meow meow. Meow meow meow meow meow meow meow Meow meow meow meow meow meow meow meow meow meow meow meow meow meow meow meow meow, meow meow meow meow meow meow meow meow meow meow meow, meow meow meow meow meow meow meow meow meow meow meow meow meow meow. Meow meow (meow Meow meow meow meow meow meow meow, meow meow Meow) meow meow meow meow meow meow meow meow meow meow, meow meow meow meow meow meow meow meow meow meow meow meow meow meow. Meow meow meow meow, meow meow meow meow meow meow Meow'meow meow, meow meow meow meow meow, meow meow Meow meow meow meow meow meow, meow, meow Meow, meow meow meow meow meow meow meow, meow meow meow meow meow meow. Meow meow meow meow meow meow meow meow meow. Meow meow meow Meow. meow meow meow meow meow meow meow meow meow meow meow meow meow meow.... Meow Meow meow'meow meow meow meow meow meow meow meow meow, meow meow meow meow meow meow meow meow meow meow meow meow meow meow. Meow meow, meow meow meow meow meow meow meow meow meow Meow Meow, Meow. Meow'meow meow, meow meow meow meow meow meow meow, Meow meow meow meow meow meow, meow meow Meow. Meow, meow meow meow meow meow meow, meow meow meow meow meow Meow. Meow meow meow meow meow meow meow meow meow meow meow? Meow meow meow meow meow meow meow meow meow meow meow meow Meow meow meow meow, meow meow meow meow meow meow meow meow meow meow meow. Meow meow meow meow meow meow meow meow meow meow meow meow, meow meow meow meow meow meow meow meow meow meow meow; meow

meow meow meow meow meow Meow. Meow meow, meow, meow meow meow meow meow meow meow meow meow meow meow meow meow meow. Meow meow meow meow meow meow meow meow meow meow meow meow meow Meow meow meow meow meow meow, meow meow meow meow meow meow meow meow, meow, meow meow meow meow meow meow meow meow meow meow meow meow, meow meow meow. Meow meow meow meow meow meow meow! Meow meow meow meow meow meow meow meow meow meow meow meow meow meow meow meow, meow meow meow meow meow meow meow Meow Meow, meow meow meow meow meow meow: meow meow Meow meow meow meow meow meow meow meow meow meow meow meow. Meow meow meow meow meow meow meow meow meow Meow meow; meow meow meow meow meow. Meow meow meow meow meow meow meow meow Meow meow meow meow meow meow meow meow meow meow meow meow meow meow. Meow meow Meow, meow meow; meow meow meow meow meow meow meow meow meow meow meow meow meow. Meow meow meow meow meow meow meow meow meow meow meow meow meow meow meow meow meow meow meow meow meow meow. Meow meow meow meow meow meow meow meow meow meow meow meow meow, meow meow meow meow meow meow. Meow meow meow meow meow. Meow Meow meow meow meow meow meow Meow meow meow meow, meow, meow meow meow meow meow meow meow meow, meow meow meow meow meow, meow meow meow meow meow meow meow meow meow. Meow meow meow meow meow meow meow meow meow meow meow meow meow; Meow Meow meow meow meow meow meow meow Meow, meow meow meow meow meow meow meow meow meow meow meow meow meow meow meow meow meow meow meow Meow meow meow meow meow meow meow meow meow meow meow meow meow meow′meow meow, meow meow meow meow meow meow meow, meow meow meow meow meow, meow meow-meow, meow meow meow meow meow meow meow. Meow meow meow meow meow meow meow meow, meow, meow Meow, meow meow meow meow meow, meow meow meow meow meow meow meow meow meow meow meow meow meow meow meow meow. Meow meow meow meow meow meow Meow meow meow meow meow meow Meow meow meow meow meow meow meow meow meow meow Meow meow meow? Meow meow meow meow; Meow meow meow meow meow meow meow meow meow meow meow meow meow meow meow, meow meow meow, meow meow meow meow meow meow? Meow meow meow meow meow meow, meow, meow, Meow meow meow meow meow; meow meow meow meow meow meow meow meow meow meow meow meow meow meow meow, Meow meow meow. Meow meow meow meow meow meow meow meow meow meow meow meow meow, meow meow meow meow meow meow meow meow Meow meow Meow meow meow meow meow meow meow meow meow meow meow meow meow meow, meow, meow meow meow meow meow meow meow. Meow meow meow meow meow, meow meow meow meow meow meow meow meow, meow Meow meow meow meow meow meow meow meow meow meow meow meow

meow meow meow meow, meow meow meow meow meow meow meow meow, meow meow meow meow meow meow meow meow meow meow meow. Meow meow meow meow meow meow Meow Meow meow meow meow meow Meow meow meow meow meow meow meow meow meow. Meow meow meow meow meow meow, meow meow meow meow meow meow meow meow meow meow, meow meow meow meow meow meow meow meow meow meow meow meow meow meow meow meow meow meow meow meow meow meow meow meow meow meow meow— meow meow meow meow meow meow—meow meow meow meow meow meow meow meow meow meow meow meow meow meow meow, meow meow meow meow meow meow. Meow meow meow meow, meow Meow meow meow meow meow Meow meow, meow meow meow meow meow meow meow meow meow meow meow meow meow meow meow meow meow meow meow meow meow! Meow meow meow meow! Meow meow Meow'meow meow, meow meow meow meow meow: Meow. Meow meow meow meow meow meow meow meow, meow meow meow meow Meow, meow meow meow Meow Meow meow meow meow meow meow meow Meow'meow meow, meow meow meow meow meow meow Meow meow meow meow meow meow meow meow meow meow, meow Meow Meow meow meow meow meow meow meow. Meow meow, meow meow meow Meow. Meow'meow meow meow meow meow, meow meow meow meow meow meow meow meow meow meow, meow meow meow meow meow meow. Meow meow meow meow meow meow meow meow meow meow meow meow meow meow meow meow meow meow meow meow meow meow Meow Meow, meow meow meow meow meow meow meow meow meow meow meow meow meow meow meow meow meow meow meow meow meow meow meow meow meow meow meow meow meow meow meow, meow meow meow. Meow, meow Meow, meow meow meow meow meow meow meow meow meow Meow meow meow Meow meow meow meow meow meow meow Meow meow meow meow meow meow. Meow, meow meow meow meow meow, meow, meow Meow'meow meow; meow meow meow meow meow meow meow meow meow meow Meow. Meow meow meow meow—meow meow meow meow meow meow meow meow. Meow Meow meow meow meow meow, meow 'meow meow' meow meow meow meow meow meow, meow meow meow meow meow meow Meow'meow meow. Meow meow meow meow, meow Meow, meow meow meow meow meow Meow, meow meow meow meow meow meow meow Meow Meow meow meow meow meow meow meow meow meow meow meow meow meow meow meow. Meow meow meow meow meow meow Meow meow meow, meow meow meow meow meow, meow meow meow, meow meow, meow meow Meow meow meow meow meow meow meow. Meow meow meow meow meow meow, meow meow meow meow meow meow meow meow meow meow meow meow, meow meow, meow meow meow meow meow meow meow Meow'meow meow meow meow meow meow meow meow meow meow meow.

Meow meow meow, meow meow meow meow meow meow meow meow meow Meow'meow meow meow meow Meow. Meow meow meow meow meow meow meow meow meow meow—meow Meow meow meow Meow

meow meow meow. Meow meow meow meow meow meow meow meow meow meow meow meow meow meow meow, meow meow meow meow meow meow meow meow meow meow meow meow meow. Meow meow meow meow meow meow meow, meow meow meow meow meow meow meow meow meow meow meow, meow meow meow meow meow meow meow meow meow meow Meow Meow meow meow meow meow meow meow meow meow meow meow meow meow meow meow meow meow meow meow meow, meow meow meow meow meow meow meow meow meow meow meow meow meow meow meow meow meow meow meow'meow. Meow meow meow meow meow meow, meow meow meow meow meow meow meow meow meow; meow meow'meow Meow Meow'meow meow. Meow meow meow meow meow meow-meow Meow'meow meow meow meow meow meow meow meow meow meow meow meow meow meow meow meow meow, meow meow meow meow meow meow, meow meow Meow meow meow meow meow meow meow; meow meow meow meow meow meow meow meow meow. Meow meow meow meow meow meow meow meow meow meow meow, meow meow meow. Meow meow meow meow meow meow meow meow meow meow meow meow meow meow meow meow meow meow meow meow meow meow meow meow meow meow meow meow meow meow meow meow meow meow meow, meow meow meow, meow meow meow meow meow meow. Meow meow meow, meow Meow, meow Meow meow meow meow meow meow meow meow meow meow meow meow meow. Meow meow meow meow meow meow meow meow meow, meow meow meow meow meow meow meow meow meow meow, Meow meow meow meow meow meow meow meow meow meow meow meow meow meow meow meow, meow meow meow meow meow meow meow meow meow meow meow meow meow meow meow meow meow meow meow meow meow meow meow. Meow meow meow meow meow meow meow meow meow meow meow meow meow meow meow meow. Meow meow meow meow meow. Meow meow meow meow meow meow meow meow meow, Meow Meow Meow, meow meow meow meow meow Meow Meow, meow meow meow meow meow meow meow meow meow meow. Meow meow meow meow meow meow meow meow meow meow meow meow meow. Meow meow meow meow, meow meow meow meow meow meow meow meow meow meow meow meow meow meow meow meow meow meow meow meow meow meow meow meow meow meow meow meow meow meow meow meow. Meow meow meow meow meow meow meow meow meow meow meow meow meow meow meow Meow, meow meow meow meow meow meow meow meow. Meow meow, meow meow, meow meow meow meow, meow meow meow meow meow meow meow meow meow. Meow meow meow meow meow meow meow meow meow. Meow meow meow meow-meow-meow meow, meow meow meow meow, meow meow meow meow meow meow meow meow meow meow meow meow meow. Meow meow meow meow meow meow meow-meow meow meow, meow meow meow meow meow meow meow meow meow meow meow meow meow meow meow meow meow, meow meow meow meow meow meow meow meow meow meow, meow meow meow meow meow meow meow meow meow. Meow meow meow meow meow meow meow meow meow meow meow meow

meow. Meow meow, meow Meow, meow meow meow meow Meow, meow meow meow meow meow, meow meow meow meow meow meow meow meow, meow meow meow meow, meow meow meow meow meow meow meow meow meow meow meow meow meow. Meow meow meow meow meow, meow Meow meow meow meow meow meow meow meow meow meow meow meow. Meow, meow meow meow meow meow meow meow meow meow meow meow meow meow meow meow meow meow meow meow, meow meow meow meow meow meow meow meow meow meow meow. Meow Meow Meow, meow meow meow meow, meow meow meow meow meow. Meow meow meow meow, meow, meow meow meow meow meow meow meow meow meow, meow meow meow meow, meow meow meow meow, meow meow meow meow ‘meow meow meow meow meow’ meow meow meow meow meow meow meow meow. Meow meow meow meow meow meow, meow meow meow meow meow meow meow meow meow meow meow meow, meow meow meow meow meow meow. Meow, meow meow, meow meow meow meow meow, meow Meow meow meow meow meow, meow meow meow meow meow meow meow meow meow, meow meow meow meow meow meow meow meow-meow. Meow meow meow meow’meow meow, Meow. Meow meow meow meow, meow, meow meow meow meow, meow meow meow meow meow meow, meow Meow meow meow meow. Meow meow, meow meow meow meow meow meow meow meow meow, meow meow meow, meow Meow meow meow meow meow meow meow meow meow meow meow meow, meow meow meow meow meow meow meow meow meow meow meow meow meow meow meow meow meow meow meow meow meow meow. Meow meow meow meow meow meow meow meow meow, meow meow meow meow meow meow meow meow meow meow meow meow meow. Meow meow meow meow meow meow meow meow meow meow meow meow meow, meow meow meow, meow meow, meow meow meow meow meow meow meow meow meow, meow meow Meow meow meow meow. Meow meow meow meow meow meow meow, meow meow meow meow meow meow meow meow meow—meow meow meow meow meow meow meow meow meow—Meow meow meow meow, meow meow meow meow, meow meow meow meow, meow meow meow meow meow meow meow meow, meow meow meow meow meow meow meow meow meow meow meow meow, meow meow meow meow meow meow meow meow meow meow meow meow. Meow meow meow, meow meow, meow meow, meow meow meow, meow meow meow meow meow meow meow meow meow meow meow, meow meow meow meow meow meow meow meow. Meow meow, meow meow meow meow, meow meow meow meow Meow’meow meow, meow meow meow meow meow, meow meow meow meow meow Meow’meow meow, meow meow meow meow meow meow meow meow meow meow meow meow meow, meow meow meow, meow meow, meow meow meow meow meow, meow, meow meow meow, meow meow meow meow meow meow meow meow meow meow, meow meow meow meow meow meow meow meow meow meow meow meow meow meow meow meow. Meow meow meow meow meow meow meow meow meow meow meow meow Meow meow meow, meow

Meow meow meow meow meow meow meow meow meow meow meow. Meow, meow, meow meow meow meow meow meow meow, meow meow meow meow meow meow meow meow, meow meow meow meow meow meow meow meow meow meow meow meow, meow meow meow meow meow meow meow meow meow meow meow, meow Meow meow meow meow meow Meow. Meow Meow meow meow, meow meow meow 'meow meow meow meow,' meow meow, meow meow, meow meow meow. Meow meow meow meow meow meow meow meow meow meow meow meow, meow, meow meow Meow meow meow, meow meow meow meow meow meow meow meow meow meow meow meow meow meow meow; meow meow meow meow meow meow meow meow meow meow meow meow meow meow meow meow meow meow meow meow meow meow meow meow.

“Meow meow meow meow meow Meow Meow meow meow meow meow meow Meow, meow meow meow meow meow meow meow meow, meow meow meow meow meow meow meow meow. Meow meow meow meow meow meow meow meow meow meow meow meow meow, meow meow meow meow meow meow meow meow meow meow. Meow meow meow meow meow Meow meow meow meow meow meow meow meow meow Meow. Meow, Meow meow, meow meow meow meow meow meow meow meow meow, meow meow meow meow, meow Meow meow Meow meow meow meow meow meow meow meow meow meow meow meow meow meow meow meow meow meow meow meow meow meow meow meow meow meow meow meow meow. Meow, meow meow meow meow meow meow! Meow meow meow meow meow meow meow meow meow meow meow meow meow meow meow meow meow. Meow meow meow meow meow meow. Meow meow meow meow meow meow meow meow meow meow meow meow meow meow Meow Meow. Meow meow meow meow meow meow, meow meow meow, meow meow, meow meow meow meow meow meow meow meow meow, meow meow meow meow meow meow meow meow meow meow meow meow meow meow meow meow meow, meow meow meow meow meow meow meow meow meow meow (meow meow meow meow meow meow meow meow meow meow!) meow meow meow meow meow meow meow meow meow meow meow meow meow meow meow meow meow meow meow meow meow. Meow meow meow meow meow meow, meow Meow meow meow meow meow meow meow. Meow meow meow meow meow meow meow meow meow meow meow meow meow, meow meow meow meow meow meow meow meow meow meow meow meow meow meow meow meow meow meow meow meow meow Meow Meow'meow meow, meow meow meow meow, meow meow meow meow meow meow meow meow. Meow meow meow meow meow meow meow, Meow, meow meow meow meow meow meow meow, meow meow meow meow meow meow meow meow meow. Meow meow meow meow Meow Meow'meow meow, meow meow meow meow (meow meow meow meow meow meow), Meow meow meow meow meow meow meow meow meow meow meow meow meow meow meow meow meow; meow meow meow meow meow. Meow meow meow meow meow meow meow meow meow meow meow meow meow

meow meow meow meow Meow Meow, meow meow meow meow meow meow. Meow meow meow meow meow meow meow meow meow meow meow, meow meow meow meow meow meow meow meow meow-meow. Meow meow meow Meow meow Meow meow meow meow meow meow meow meow meow meow meow meow meow meow meow meow meow meow meow meow meow meow; meow meow meow meow meow meow meow meow meow meow, meow meow meow meow meow meow meow meow, meow meow, meow meow meow meow meow meow meow meow meow meow meow meow meow meow, (meow meow meow meow meow Meow meow) meow meow meow meow meow meow meow meow meow meow meow meow meow meow meow meow meow, meow meow meow meow meow meow meow meow, meow meow meow meow meow meow meow meow meow. Meow meow meow meow meow meow meow meow meow Meow meow meow meow meow. Meow meow meow meow meow meow meow meow meow meow meow, meow meow, meow Meow meow meow meow meow meow meow meow meow meow meow meow meow meow meow.

Meow Meow meow meow meow meow meow meow meow, meow meow meow meow meow meow meow meow meow meow meow meow meow meow, meow meow, meow meow meow meow meow meow meow meow meow meow meow meow meow meow meow. Meow meow meow, meow meow Meow, Meow meow meow meow meow meow meow (meow meow meow meow Meow Meow meow, meow meow meow meow meow, meow meow-meow, meow) Meow meow meow meow meow meow meow meow meow meow, meow, meow meow meow, meow meow meow. Meow meow meow meow meow meow meow meow meow meow meow meow meow meow meow meow meow meow meow meow meow meow meow meow meow meow, meow meow meow meow meow meow meow meow meow, meow meow meow meow meow meow meow meow meow meow; meow Meow meow meow. Meow meow meow meow meow meow meow meow meow meow meow meow’meow meow meow meow meow meow meow-meow-meow, meow Meow meow’meow meow meow meow meow meow meow meow meow’meow meow, meow meow meow meow meow, meow, meow meow meow meow meow, meow meow meow Meow meow meow meow meow meow meow meow meow, meow meow meow meow meow meow Meow.

Meow meow, Meow meow meow meow meow meow, meow meow meow meow meow meow meow, meow Meow, Meow meow meow meow meow meow meow meow meow: meow meow, meow meow meow, meow meow meow, meow, meow meow meow meow meow meow meow meow meow meow meow meow meow meow meow meow meow meow meow meow meow! Meow meow meow meow meow meow Meow meow Meow meow meow meow meow meow Meow, meow meow Meow meow’meow meow, meow meow, meow meow, meow meow meow meow. Meow meow meow meow Meow Meow meow meow meow meow meow meow meow meow meow meow meow meow meow meow meow Meow. Meow meow meow meow meow meow meow meow meow meow meow meow meow meow

meow meow, meow meow meow meow meow Meow Meow, meow meow meow meow meow, meow meow meow meow meow meow meow meow meow, meow meow. Meow, meow meow meow Meow meow meow meow meow meow meow! Meow meow meow meow meow meow meow meow meow meow meow, meow meow meow meow meow meow meow meow meow meow meow meow meow Meow Meow meow meow meow. Meow meow meow meow! Meow meow meow meow meow meow meow meow, meow meow meow meow meow meow meow meow meow meow meow meow, meow meow meow meow meow meow meow meow meow meow meow meow meow meow meow meow, meow meow meow meow meow meow meow meow, meow meow meow meow meow meow meow; meow meow meow meow meow meow meow meow meow meow. Meow meow meow meow meow meow meow meow, meow Meow meow meow meow meow meow meow meow Meow meow meow meow meow meow meow. Meow meow meow meow meow meow Meow meow meow meow Meow Meow, meow meow meow meow meow meow Meow meow meow Meow Meow meow meow meow meow meow meow meow- meow meow meow meow meow meow meow meow, meow meow meow Meow meow meow meow meow meow meow meow- meow meow meow meow meow. Meow meow meow meow meow, meow Meow meow meow meow meow meow meow; meow meow Meow Meow meow meow meow meow meow meow meow meow meow meow meow meow meow meow, meow meow meow meow, meow meow meow meow meow meow meow meow meow meow meow meow meow (meow meow meow meow meow meow meow meow meow), meow meow meow meow meow meow meow meow meow meow Meow, meow meow meow’meow meow meow meow meow meow, meow meow meow meow meow meow meow. Meow meow meow meow meow meow, Meow meow Meow, meow meow meow meow, meow meow meow meow meow meow meow meow meow meow meow. Meow meow meow meow meow meow meow meow meow meow meow meow meow meow meow meow meow meow meow meow meow meow, meow meow meow meow meow meow; meow meow meow Meow meow Meow meow meow meow meow meow meow. Meow meow Meow meow meow meow meow meow meow meow meow meow meow meow-meow, meow meow meow. Meow meow; Meow meow meow meow meow meow meow meow meow meow meow meow meow meow; meow meow meow, meow meow meow meow meow meow!

Meow meow, meow meow Meow, Meow meow meow meow meow meow meow meow’meow meow meow meow meow. Meow Meow meow meow, Meow; meow meow meow meow meow meow meow meow meow meow meow meow meow, meow meow meow. Meow meow meow meow meow meow, Meow, meow meow meow meow meow—meow meow meow, meow meow meow. Meow meow meow meow meow, meow meow meow meow. Meow meow meow meow meow meow, Meow, meow meow meow meow meow meow meow Meow meow meow Meow? Meow meow meow meow meow meow meow meow meow meow meow meow meow meow meow meow meow meow meow meow meow meow meow-meow; Meow meow

meow meow, Meow meow meow meow. Meow, meow meow, meow meow meow meow, meow meow meow meow meow, meow meow meow meow meow meow meow meow meow, meow meow meow meow meow meow meow meow meow. Meow-meow, meow meow meow meow—Meow meow meow meow, meow, meow meow meow.

"Meow meow meow,

"Meow Meow."

Meow meow meow meow, meow meow meow meow meow, Meow'meow meow meow meow meow meow; meow meow meow meow meow, meow meow meow meow meow meow meow meow meow, meow meow meow meow meow meow meow meow. Meow meow meow meow meow meow meow meow meow meow meow meow, meow meow meow meow. Meow meow meow meow meow, meow meow meow meow meow meow meow. Meow meow meow meow meow meow meow meow meow meow meow meow meow meow meow meow meow meow meow meow. Meow meow meow meow meow meow meow meow. Meow meow meow meow meow meow meow meow, meow meow meow meow meow meow meow; meow meow meow meow meow. Meow meow meow meow meow meow meow Meow Meow, meow meow Meow Meow, meow meow meow meow meow meow, meow meow meow, meow meow meow meow, meow meow meow meow, meow meow meow meow meow meow meow, meow meow meow meow meow meow-meow. Meow meow meow meow meow meow meow meow.

MEOW IV

Meow meow'meow meow meow meow meow meow meow meow, meow meow meow meow meow meow meow meow, meow meow meow meow meow meow'meow meow, meow meow meow meow meow meow meow. Meow meow meow meow meow, meow meow meow, meow meow meow: "Meow meow meow meow meow Meow meow meow meow Meow. Meow meow meow!" "Meow meow meow meow meow," meow meow meow meow, meow meow meow meow meow meow meow meow meow meow. "Meow, meow, meow, Meow, meow meow'meow meow meow! meow meow meow meow meow meow meow meow meow meow meow meow meow meow meow meow! Meow meow meow! Meow meow meow meow meow meow meow meow'meow meow meow meow; meow meow meow meow meow meow meow meow meow! Meow meow meow: 'Meow Meow meow meow meow meow meow meow meow meow meow meow meow meow meow meow-meow, meow meow meow.' Meow, Meow, Meow meow meow meow meow Meow meow meow meow meow meow meow meow meow; meow Meow meow meow meow meow meow meow meow, meow meow meow meow meow meow meow meow, meow meow meow meow meow meow meow meow Meow Meow meow Meow meow meow meow meow'meow meow. Meow meow meow meow meow Meow.... Meow... meow meow meow meow meow; meow meow meow meow meow meow meow meow meow, Meow Meow, meow meow meow meow meow (meow meow meow meow meow, meow meow meow meow meow meow meow meow) meow meow meow meow meow meow meow meow meow meow meow meow meow meow meow meow meow, meow meow meow, meow meow meow meow meow meow, meow Meow meow meow. Meow meow meow meow! Meow meow meow Meow meow meow meow 'meow' meow meow meow! Meow! meow!

"... Meow Meow meow meow meow meow meow meow meow meow meow meow meow 'meow meow meow meow'? Meow meow meow meow meow, meow meow meow meow meow meow meow meow meow meow Meow. Meow? Meow, meow meow meow meow! Meow meow meow meow meow meow meow meow: meow meow meow meow meow meow meow meow meow meow meow meow meow meow meow meow meow?

Meow meow meow meow meow meow, meow meow meow meow meow meow meow meow meow meow meow meow meow meow meow meow, meow meow meow meow meow meow meow meow meow meow meow, meow meow meow meow meow meow meow. Meow meow meow meow meow meow meow, meow meow'meow meow meow'meow meow: meow meow meow meow meow meow meow, meow meow meow meow meow meow meow meow meow Meow. Meow meow meow meow meow meow meow meow 'meow meow meow.' Meow meow meow meow! Meow meow meow meow meow meow meow meow meow meow meow meow meow meow meow meow meow meow meow meow meow meow meow meow meow. Meow meow meow meow meow meow meow, 'meow Meow, Meow, meow meow meow meow meow meow meow'? Meow meow meow

meow meow-meow meow meow meow meow meow meow meow? 'Meow meow meow meow meow, meow meow meow meow meow.' Meow, meow!"

Meow meow meow meow meow meow meow, meow meow meow meow meow meow meow Meow. Meow meow meow meow, meow meow meow meow meow.

"Meow... meow, meow'meow meow," meow meow, meow meow meow meow meow meow meow meow meow meow meow, "meow meow meow meow 'meow meow meow meow meow meow meow meow meow meow meow,' meow meow meow meow meow meow Meow. Meow. Meow meow meow meow meow meow 'meow meow meow meow meow meow meow,' meow meow meow, meow'meow meow, meow meow meow meow meow meow meow meow meow! Meow meow meow, meow meow meow meow! Meow meow meow meow meow meow meow meow meow meow meow meow'meow meow meow meow meow (Meow meow, Meow meow meow meow meow meow). Meow meow! Meow meow meow meow meow meow meow meow meow 'meow meow meow, meow meow,' meow meow meow meow! Meow meow, meow. Meow meow meow meow'meow meow meow meow meow'meow meow, meow meow meow meow, Meow. Meow? Meow meow meow meow.... Meow meow meow meow meow meow meow meow meow meow meow meow meow meow meow meow meow meow. Meow meow meow meow'meow meow meow meow meow, meow meow meow meow meow, meow meow meow meow meow;—meow meow meow meow, meow meow meow meow meow. Meow meow meow meow meow meow meow meow meow, meow. Meow meow meow meow meow meow meow meow meow meow meow meow meow meow. Meow meow meow meow meow meow'meow meow meow meow meow, meow meow meow meow meow meow'meow meow meow meow? Meow meow meow meow, meow!

Meow meow meow meow meow meow meow meow meow meow, meow meow meow meow meow meow meow meow! Meow meow meow meow meow meow meow meow, meow meow meow meow, meow meow meow meow meow meow meow. Meow meow meow meow meow meow meow meow, meow'meow meow meow meow meow. Meow meow meow, meow meow meow meow meow meow? Meow meow meow meow meow meow meow meow meow meow Meow? Meow meow meow meow meow 'meow meow' meow meow meow.... meow meow meow... meow. Meow meow meow meow meow meow meow meow Meow meow? Meow meow meow meow meow meow meow meow meow meow meow meow meow Meow meow meow meow, meow meow meow meow meow meow. Meow meow meow meow meow meow meow meow meow meow meow meow meow, meow meow meow meow meow: 'Meow meow meow,' meow meow. Meow meow meow meow meow meow? Meow meow meow meow meow meow meow meow meow meow meow meow meow meow meow meow Meow Meow'meow meow meow meow? Meow meow meow meow meow meow meow, meow meow meow meow. Meow meow meow meow meow'meow meow meow meow meow meow meow meow meow meow meow meow meow, Meow meow meow. Meow meow meow meow meow meow meow meow meow meow meow Meow. Meow'meow meow; 'meow meow meow

meow meow meow, meow meow meow meow meow meow.’ Meow meow meow meow meow meow meow meow! Meow’meow meow meow meow meow meow meow Meow meow meow; meow meow meow meow meow meow meow meow meow meow meow, meow meow meow meow, meow meow meow meow meow meow meow meow meow meow, meow meow meow meow meow meow meow meow meow meow meow meow meow, meow meow meow’meow meow meow meow meow meow meow meow meow; meow meow meow meow meow meow meow meow; meow meow meow meow meow meow meow meow, meow meow meow meow meow meow meow meow meow meow meow meow’meow meow meow meow meow meow meow meow. Meow meow meow meow meow meow Meow. Meow meow meow meow meow meow; Meow meow meow meow meow Meow meow meow meow meow meow meow meow meow meow meow meow meow meow meow meow meow meow meow. Meow meow meow meow meow meow meow meow meow meow, meow! Meow meow meow, meow meow!

“Meow,... meow Meow meow’meow meow meow, meow’meow meow meow, Meow meow meow, meow meow meow Meow? Meow meow, meow meow Meow meow meow meow meow! Meow meow meow meow meow Meow meow meow meow: Meow meow meow meow. Meow meow meow ‘Meow meow meow meow meow meow meow meow.’ Meow meow meow meow meow. Meow meow meow meow meow meow meow meow meow, meow meow meow meow meow meow meow meow meow Meow meow meow meow meow meow, meow meow meow meow, meow ‘Meow meow meow meow meow meow meow meow.’ Meow meow meow meow meow meow Meow. Meow meow meow meow meow meow meow, meow meow meow meow meow meow meow meow meow. Meow meow meow meow meow meow meow meow meow meow meow meow meow meow meow meow meow Meow. Meow, meow meow meow meow meow meow meow meow meow meow meow meow meow meow meow meow meow meow’meow meow—meow meow meow, meow, meow meow meow meow meow. Meow meow meow ‘meow meow meow,’ meow meow meow meow meow meow, (meow meow meow meow meow meow meow meow meow, meow meow meow meow meow meow meow meow meow meow meow) meow Meow, Meow? Meow meow meow meow, meow meow, meow meow meow meow meow meow meow meow meow. Meow! meow’meow meow meow meow meow meow meow, meow meow meow meow meow meow, meow meow meow meow meow meow meow meow meow; meow meow meow meow meow meow meow Meow-Meow, meow meow Meow. Meow’meow meow. Meow, Meow meow meow meow meow meow Meow meow meow meow... meow meow meow meow meow, meow meow! Meow, meow’meow meow meow, meow Meow meow meow meow meow! Meow’meow meow meow meow meow meow meow’meow meow meow meow meow meow meow meow meow meow meow, meow Meow meow meow meow meow meow meow meow meow meow meow meow meow Meow meow meow Meow meow meow meow meow meow, meow meow meow meow, meow meow meow meow meow meow meow meow meow

meow meow meow meow meow meow meow meow meow meow meow meow—meow meow meow meow. Meow meow Meow. Meow meow meow meow meow meow, meow meow meow meow, meow meow meow meow meow meow meow meow meow meow. Meow meow meow meow meow? Meow'meow meow meow meow meow? Meow'meow meow meow? Meow'meow meow meow: meow meow, meow meow meow, meow meow meow meow meow meow meow meow meow, meow meow meow meow meow meow meow meow! Meow meow meow meow, meow meow meow meow, meow meow meow meow! Meow'meow meow meow meow meow meow; meow meow meow, meow meow meow, meow meow meow meow! Meow meow meow meow! Meow meow meow, 'meow meow meow meow meow meow meow,' meow, meow, meow meow, meow, meow meow meow meow meow meow. Meow meow meow meow, meow meow meow meow meow meow meow meow! Meow meow meow, meow meow meow, meow meow meow meow Meow meow meow meow meow meow meow meow meow meow, meow meow meow meow meow meow meow meow'meow meow meow meow meow meow. Meow'meow meow meow meow, meow'meow meow meow meow meow. Meow'meow meow meow Meow Meow Meow meow meow meow meow meow meow meow, meow meow meow meow. Meow, meow, meow meow meow meow meow, meow meow meow meow meow, meow meow meow meow meow meow meow, meow meow meow meow meow; meow meow meow meow meow meow meow meow meow meow, meow, meow, meow meow meow meow meow meow meow meow meow! Meow meow meow? Meow'meow meow Meow, meow Meow, meow meow meow! Meow meow meow meow meow meow meow meow meow meow meow! Meow, meow, meow-meow meow! Meow, meow meow meow meow meow meow meow meow meow Meow'meow meow. Meow, Meow Meow, meow meow meow meow meow meow meow meow meow. Meow meow meow meow meow meow meow meow, meow meow meow? Meow meow meow? Meow meow meow meow? Meow meow meow meow? Meow meow meow meow meow? Meow meow meow meow meow, Meow, Meow'meow meow meow meow meow meow meow meow Meow. Meow. 'Meow meow meow meow meow meow meow,' meow meow. Meow meow meow meow meow meow meow meow meow, meow meow meow meow meow meow meow, meow, meow, meow meow? Meow meow meow meow meow 'meow meow meow meow,' meow. Meow meow meow meow? Meow meow meow meow meow meow meow? Meow meow meow meow meow Meow meow meow meow meow meow meow meow Meow'meow meow meow meow meow, meow, meow, meow meow meow meow, Meow, meow'meow meow meow meow meow, meow meow, meow meow Meow meow'meow meow meow meow meow meow. Meow meow meow meow meow meow, meow meow meow meow meow meow, Meow, meow meow. Meow meow meow meow'meow meow meow meow meow meow meow, meow meow meow meow? Meow meow, meow meow, meow meow, meow meow meow meow meow meow meow, meow meow meow meow meow Meow Meow. Meow meow meow meow meow meow meow? Meow meow meow meow meow, meow meow meow, meow meow, meow meow meow

meow meow meow? Meow Meow? Meow, meow, meow meow meow meow meow meow? Meow meow'meow meow meow meow, Meow, Meow meow'meow meow meow, meow! Meow meow meow meow, meow meow meow Meow meow meow, meow meow meow, meow meow meow! Meow meow'meow meow meow!"

Meow meow meow meow meow meow meow meow meow.

"Meow meow meow meow? Meow meow meow meow meow meow meow meow meow meow? Meow'meow meow meow? Meow meow meow meow meow? Meow meow meow meow meow meow meow meow meow meow meow meow meow meow? Meow meow meow, meow meow meow, meow meow meow meow meow meow meow meow meow meow meow meow meow meow meow? Meow, meow meow meow meow meow meow, meow meow'meow meow meow, meow meow? Meow meow meow meow meow, meow, meow meow meow meow? Meow meow meow meow meow meow? Meow meow meow meow meow. Meow meow meow meow meow meow meow. Meow meow meow meow. Meow meow meow meow meow meow meow meow meow Meow Meow Meow, meow, meow meow Meow meow meow meow meow meow meow meow? Meow meow meow meow? Meow meow meow meow, meow meow meow meow meow meow meow, meow meow meow meow. Meow meow meow meow meow meow meow meow meow; meow meow meow? Meow meow meow meow meow meow meow meow meow meow meow meow meow meow? Meow meow meow meow meow meow meow meow meow meow? Meow meow meow?"

Meow meow meow meow, meow meow meow meow meow, meow meow meow meow meow meow meow meow. Meow meow meow meow meow meow meow meow meow meow meow meow, meow meow meow meow meow. Meow meow meow meow meow meow meow meow meow meow meow meow meow meow. Meow, meow meow meow meow meow meow meow meow meow; meow meow meow meow meow meow, meow meow meow meow meow, meow meow meow meow meow meow meow meow meow, meow meow meow meow, meow meow meow meow meow meow, meow meow meow meow meow. Meow meow meow'meow meow meow meow meow meow meow meow meow. Meow meow meow meow meow meow meow meow meow meow, meow meow meow meow meow, meow meow meow meow meow meow, meow meow meow meow, meow meow meow meow. Meow meow meow meow meow meow, meow meow...

"Meow meow meow meow meow!" meow meow meow, meow meow meow—"meow meow'meow meow meow meow meow meow, meow meow meow meow meow meow meow meow, meow meow meow meow meow meow, meow meow meow!"

"Meow meow meow, meow, meow meow meow meow meow meow meow meow meow meow meow meow meow?" Meow'meow meow meow meow meow meow meow, "meow meow meow meow meow meow meow meow...."

Meow meow meow meow meow; meow meow, meow meow meow meow meow, meow meow meow meow meow. Meow meow meow meow meow meow meow meow meow meow meow, meow meow meow, meow meow

meow meow, meow meow meow meow meow, meow meow meow meow; meow meow meow meow meow meow’meow meow. Meow meow meow meow meow meow meow, meow meow, meow meow meow meow meow meow: meow meow... meow meow meow meow meow meow meow meow, meow meow meow meow meow meow meow meow meow meow, meow meow meow meow meow meow meow meow.... Meow meow meow meow meow meow meow, meow meow meow meow meow meow meow meow.

Meow meow meow meow, meow meow meow meow meow. Meow meow meow meow meow meow meow meow meow meow meow; meow meow meow meow meow Meow— — Meow. Meow meow meow meow meow meow meow meow meow meow meow meow. Meow meow meow meow meow meow meow meow; meow meow meow meow meow meow meow meow meow meow meow meow meow meow meow. Meow meow meow meow, meow meow meow meow meow meow meow meow meow meow meow meow meow, meow meow meow meow meow meow meow meow meow meow meow meow meow meow meow meow meow meow. Meow meow meow meow meow meow meow meow meow meow meow meow meow meow meow meow meow meow meow, meow meow meow meow meow meow meow meow. Meow meow meow meow meow meow meow meow meow meow meow meow meow meow meow meow meow meow, meow meow meow meow meow meow meow meow meow, meow meow meow meow, meow meow meow, meow, meow meow meow meow meow meow. Meow meow meow meow meow meow meow meow meow meow meow meow meow meow meow meow meow meow. Meow meow meow meow, meow meow meow meow meow meow meow meow, meow meow meow meow meow meow meow meow meow meow meow meow meow meow meow, meow meow meow meow meow meow meow meow. Meow meow meow meow meow meow meow meow meow meow, meow meow meow meow meow meow, meow meow meow meow, meow meow meow meow meow meow meow meow meow meow, meow meow meow meow: meow meow meow meow meow meow meow meow. Meow meow meow meow meow meow meow meow meow, meow meow meow meow meow meow. Meow meow meow meow meow, meow, meow meow meow meow meow meow meow. Meow meow Meow’meow meow meow meow meow. Meow meow meow meow meow meow meow, meow, meow meow meow, meow meow meow meow meow, meow meow meow; meow meow meow meow meow meow meow meow meow meow meow meow meow meow meow, meow meow meow meow. Meow meow meow meow, meow meow meow meow meow meow meow meow meow. Meow meow meow meow meow meow meow. Meow meow meow meow meow meow meow meow meow. Meow meow meow meow meow meow meow meow meow meow, meow-meow meow— meow, meow meow meow meow meow, meow meow, meow meow meow, meow meow meow meow meow meow, meow meow meow, meow. Meow meow meow meow meow meow meow meow meow meow; meow meow meow meow meow meow meow, meow meow meow, meow meow meow meow meow meow meow meow meow meow meow meow meow.

Meow meow meow meow meow, meow meow meow meow meow meow meow, meow meow meow meow meow meow. Meow meow meow meow meow meow; meow meow, meow meow meow'meow, meow meow meow meow, meow meow meow meow. Meow meow meow meow meow meow meow meow meow, meow meow meow meow, meow meow meow meow meow meow meow meow meow meow. Meow, meow, meow meow meow meow meow meow meow meow meow meow meow meow meow meow. Meow, meow, meow meow meow meow meow meow meow meow meow meow meow, meow meow Meow meow meow meow. Meow meow meow meow meow, meow meow meow meow meow meow meow, meow meow meow meow meow meow, meow meow meow meow meow meow meow meow meow meow. Meow meow meow meow. Meow meow meow meow meow, meow-meow meow, meow meow, meow meow, meow meow meow meow, meow meow meow meow. Meow meow meow; meow meow meow meow meow meow meow meow meow meow meow meow meow. Meow meow meow meow meow meow meow meow meow meow meow meow.

"Meow! Meow Meow! Meow meow meow meow meow?" meow meow, meow meow meow meow meow, meow meow meow.

"Meow meow meow meow?" meow meow meow meow, meow meow meow meow. "Meow meow, meow'meow meow Meow meow."

"Meow meow meow, meow meow meow!"

Meow meow meow meow. Meow meow meow meow meow meow meow, meow meow meow meow meow meow meow meow meow meow meow meow meow meow. Meow meow meow meow meow meow meow meow meow, meow meow meow meow meow meow meow.

"Meow'meow meow, meow, meow meow, meow, meow meow meow meow. Meow meow meow meow? Meow meow meow?" meow meow Meow meow, meow meow meow.

Meow meow meow meow meow. Meow meow meow meow-meow, meow, meow meow, meow meow meow meow meow.

"Meow meow meow meow meow Meow meow," Meow meow, meow meow meow meow. "Meow meow meow meow, Meow.... Meow meow meow meow meow meow meow," meow meow, meow meow meow, "meow meow, Meow meow meow meow meow meow."

Meow meow meow meow meow meow meow meow meow meow meow meow meow.

"Meow meow, meow meow, meow meow meow meow meow meow meow meow. Meow meow meow meow meow meow meow meow meow, meow meow meow meow meow meow meow. Meow'meow meow meow meow meow meow meow meow meow meow meow... meow meow meow meow... meow meow? meow meow'meow meow meow meow meow meow meow meow meow. Meow meow meow meow meow meow meow meow, meow meow meow meow meow meow meow meow: meow meow meow meow meow meow, meow meow meow meow meow, meow meow meow meow meow, meow meow meow'meow meow; meow'meow meow. Meow meow meow meow: Meow meow'meow meow meow meow meow meow Meow meow meow meow meow, Meow meow meow meow meow meow

meow, meow meow, meow, meow meow meow meow meow meow, meow meow, meow, meow meow meow meow meow meow, meow meow meow meow meow meow meow meow meow meow meow, meow meow meow meow meow meow meow meow meow meow meow... meow'meow meow, meow meow, Meow meow meow meow. Meow meow meow meow meow meow meow meow meow, meow Meow meow meow, meow meow meow meow meow meow meow meow meow meow. Meow meow meow meow meow meow meow, meow meow meow meow, meow meow meow meow meow.... Meow meow meow meow meow meow meow meow meow meow, meow meow meow meow meow meow meow meow?"

Meow meow meow meow meow meow meow meow. Meow meow meow meow meow meow meow, meow meow meow meow meow meow. Meow meow meow meow meow meow meow meow meow, meow meow meow meow meow meow meow.

"Meow, meow meow meow!" meow meow, meow meow meow—"meow, meow meow meow meow meow! Meow meow meow meow, meow meow meow meow meow meow. Meow, meow," meow meow meow meow, "meow meow meow meow?" Meow meow meow meow meow meow meow-meow meow, meow meow meow meow meow meow meow meow meow.

"Meow," meow Meow meow meow meow meow meow meow meow meow, "meow, meow meow meow meow meow meow meow meow meow meow meow meow. Meow meow meow meow meow meow meow meow!"

"Meow, meow!" meow meow meow meow, meow meow meow. "Meow'meow meow meow meow meow meow meow meow meow meow. Meow meow Meow meow meow, meow? Meow meow meow meow?"

"Meow meow! Meow meow'meow meow meow meow," meow meow meow, meow meow meow meow meow meow.

"Meow, meow, meow meow! Meow'meow meow, meow, meow'meow meow meow!" Meow meow meow meow meow, meow, meow meow meow.

"Meow'meow meow meow meow," meow meow meow meow Meow, meow meow meow meow meow, meow meow meow meow meow meow meow meow meow meow. Meow, meow, meow meow meow meow meow meow meow meow: meow meow meow meow meow meow meow!

"Meow meow meow meow meow meow meow?" meow meow meow.

"Meow meow meow meow meow meow meow meow meow meow, meow, meow meow, meow meow meow. Meow meow meow meow meow meow meow meow meow meow meow."

"Meow, meow meow meow meow meow meow meow meow meow meow, Meow meow meow meow meow! Meow meow meow meow meow, meow meow! Meow meow meow meow, meow'meow meow meow meow. Meow meow meow meow meow meow meow meow.... Meow, meow meow meow meow meow! Meow meow meow meow meow meow meow meow meow meow, meow meow meow.... Meow meow meow meow meow meow. Meow meow meow, meow, meow meow meow meow meow meow," meow meow meow meow meow meow meow.

Meow meow meow meow meow meow meow meow, "meow meow meow meow meow" meow meow meow meow meow meow....

"Meow meow meow meow," Meow meow, "meow meow meow meow meow meow meow'meow meow! Meow meow meow meow meow! Meow'meow meow meow meow meow meow meow meow meow; meow, meow meow, meow meow meow meow meow!"

Meow meow meow meow meow meow meow. Meow meow meow meow, meow meow meow meow meow meow meow meow meow, meow meow meow meow meow, meow meow meow meow meow meow meow. Meow meow meow meow meow meow meow meow meow meow meow.

"Meow meow meow meow meow meow meow meow," meow meow meow meow, "meow meow meow'meow meow meow meow meow meow meow, meow meow meow meow.... Meow, meow, meow!" meow meow meow meow meow meow.

Meow meow meow meow meow meow meow meow meow, meow meow meow meow, meow meow meow meow, meow meow meow meow meow meow meow meow meow meow meow meow meow meow meow meow. "Meow meow meow, meow meow'meow meow meow meow!" meow meow, meow meow meow meow. Meow meow meow, meow meow meow meow. Meow meow meow meow, meow meow meow meow, meow meow meow meow meow.

"Meow'meow meow meow, Meow meow'meow meow meow meow meow," meow meow meow meow, meow meow meow meow meow meow.

"Meow, meow meow meow meow meow!" meow meow meow, meow.

Meow meow meow meow meow meow meow Meow; meow meow meow meow meow meow meow meow meow meow meow.

"Meow, meow!" meow meow meow meow meow. Meow meow meow meow.

"Meow meow meow! Meow meow meow meow meow meow meow? Meow meow meow! Meow meow meow meow." Meow meow meow meow, "Meow meow meow meow meow meow meow?"

Meow meow meow meow, meow meow meow meow meow-meow. Meow meow.

"Meow!" meow meow meow, meow meow meow meow meow, meow meow meow meow meow meow meow meow meow, meow meow Meow meow meow meow meow meow meow meow.

"Meow meow meow meow meow meow meow," Meow meow meow meow meow meow meow meow. "Meow, meow meow meow meow meow meow meow meow meow meow meow meow meow meow meow meow meow meow meow meow meow meow. Meow meow meow Meow meow meow meow? Meow meow meow meow meow meow? Meow Meow meow meow meow meow? Meow meow meow meow meow meow – meow meow meow meow? Meow meow Meow meow meow meow meow meow meow? Meow meow meow?"

Meow meow meow meow meow meow meow meow meow meow. Meow meow meow meow meow meow meow. Meow meow meow meow.... Meow

meow meow meow meow meow meow meow meow meow meow meow meow. Meow

meow meow meow meow meow, meow meow meow, meow meow meow meow meow meow meow meow meow....

"Meow meow!" meow meow, meow meow meow meow meow meow meow meow meow—"Meow meow meow meow meow meow meow, meow meow meow meow meow meow meow.... Meow meow meow meow meow meow, meow meow, meow meow meow meow meow, meow meow meow meow meow.... Meow meow meow meow meow meow, meow Meow Meow meow meow meow meow meow, meow meow meow meow meow meow meow meow meow meow meow meow meow meow. Meow meow meow meow meow meow meow (meow'meow meow meow meow meow meow meow meow meow meow, meow meow meow meow meow meow) meow meow... meow meow meow... meow... meow meow... meow meow meow, meow meow meow meow meow—meow meow, meow meow meow meow meow meow meow meow.... Meow meow Meow meow meow meow meow? Meow meow meow meow meow meow meow meow? Meow, meow'meow meow meow meow meow meow meow. Meow! Meow meow meow meow meow? Meow'meow meow meow meow meow, meow meow meow. Meow meow meow, meow meow meow, meow meow meow meow... meow meow... meow meow meow, Meow meow, meow meow meow meow meow meow meow, meow meow meow meow meow. Meow meow! Meow meow meow meow meow; meow meow meow meow, meow meow.... Meow meow'meow meow 'meow' meow'meow meow meow meow meow meow. Meow meow meow meow meow meow... meow meow meow meow meow meow.... Meow meow meow Meow meow meow meow meow meow! Meow meow meow meow meow meow meow?

"Meow meow meow Meow meow?" meow meow meow. "Meow, Meow meow meow meow meow. Meow meow meow Meow meow meow meow meow Meow meow meow.... Meow meow meow meow Meow Meow, meow Meow. Meow'meow meow meow meow... meow Meow meow. Meow meow, meow? Meow meow meow meow meow meow meow meow Meow meow meow meow meow meow? Meow'meow meow."

Meow meow meow meow. Meow meow meow meow meow meow meow meow meow meow. Meow meow meow meow Meow meow meow meow meow meow meow meow; meow meow meow meow meow, meow meow meow meow meow, meow meow meow meow meow meow meow meow meow meow, meow meow meow meow meow meow meow. Meow meow meow meow meow meow meow' meow, meow meow meow. Meow meow meow meow meow meow meow meow, meow meow meow meow meow meow, meow meow meow meow meow. Meow meow meow meow, meow meow meow meow meow meow meow meow meow meow meow meow, meow meow meow meow meow meow meow meow. Meow meow meow meow meow meow meow meow meow meow meow meow meow meow, meow meow meow meow meow meow meow, meow meow meow, meow meow meow meow meow meow meow meow meow.

Meow Meow meow meow meow meow, meow, meow meow, meow meow meow meow meow meow meow meow. Meow meow meow meow meow meow meow meow meow meow meow Meow. Meow meow meow meow meow-meow meow meow meow, meow-meow meow meow meow meow meow, meow meow meow meow meow meow meow meow meow meow. Meow meow meow meow meow meow meow, meow meow meow meow meow meow. Meow meow meow meow, meow meow meow meow meow meow meow meow meow. Meow meow meow meow meow — meow, meow, meow meow meow meow meow. Meow meow meow meow meow meow meow meow meow meow meow meow meow. Meow meow, meow meow meow meow meow meow, meow meow meow meow meow meow meow meow meow meow meow meow. Meow meow meow meow meow meow meow meow, meow meow meow meow meow meow meow; meow meow meow meow meow meow meow meow; meow meow meow meow meow meow meow. Meow meow meow meow Meow, meow meow meow meow, meow meow meow meow meow meow meow meow meow meow meow. Meow meow meow meow, meow meow meow meow meow meow meow meow. Meow meow meow meow, meow meow meow meow meow meow meow meow meow meow meow meow meow meow meow meow. Meow meow meow meow meow meow meow meow meow meow meow meow. Meow meow meow meow meow meow meow meow meow, meow meow meow meow meow meow meow meow meow, meow meow meow meow meow meow meow meow. Meow meow meow meow, meow, meow meow meow meow meow meow meow meow, meow meow meow meow meow meow meow, meow meow meow meow meow meow meow meow meow meow meow meow meow meow meow meow meow meow. Meow meow

meow meow meow meow meow meow meow meow meow meow, meow Meow meow meow meow meow meow meow. Meow meow meow meow, meow meow meow meow meow meow, meow Meow meow meow meow meow meow meow meow meow meow meow meow meow meow meow meow meow. Meow meow Meow meow meow, meow meow meow meow, meow meow meow meow meow meow meow meow.

MEOW V

"Meow meow, Meow'meow meow meow meow meow meow meow Meow'meow meow meow meow meow, meow meow meow meow meow meow meow meow meow..." Meow meow, "meow meow meow meow meow meow meow meow meow? Meow meow meow meow meow, meow meow meow meow meow meow meow meow, meow meow meow meow meow, meow meow Meow meow meow meow meow meow meow meow meow meow meow meow meow... meow... Meow meow meow meow? Meow meow Meow meow meow meow meow meow Meow meow? Meow'meow meow meow Meow meow meow. Meow'meow meow meow meow meow meow meow meow Meow...."

Meow meow meow meow meow meow meow meow Meow meow meow meow meow meow meow meow meow meow; meow meow meow meow meow meow meow meow meow meow meow meow meow.

"Meow Meow meow meow meow meow meow meow meow meow meow meow meow meow meow meow meow meow Meow meow?" meow meow meow meow meow.

Meow meow meow meow meow meow, meow, meow meow meow, meow meow meow, meow, meow meow meow meow meow meow meow meow, meow meow meow meow meow meow meow.

"Meow... meow Meow'meow," meow meow meow meow meow, meow, meow meow meow meow meow meow meow meow. "Meow meow meow meow Meow'meow meow meow, meow... meow meow. Meow meow meow meow meow... meow meow meow meow meow Meow, meow Meow meow meow meow meow meow meow meow meow...."

Meow meow meow meow meow meow meow meow.

"Meow Meow," meow meow, meow meow meow meow meow, "meow meow Meow meow meow meow meow? Meow meow meow meow meow meow meow?" Meow meow meow meow, meow meow meow meow meow meow meow; meow meow meow meow meow, meow, meow meow meow meow meow meow meow meow meow meow meow meow; meow meow meow, meow meow meow meow meow meow meow, meow meow meow meow meow meow meow meow meow meow meow meow; meow meow meow meow meow meow.

Meow meow meow meow meow meow meow meow meow meow meow meow meow; meow meow meow meow meow meow meow meow. Meow meow meow meow meow meow meow meow meow, meow meow meow meow, meow meow meow meow meow meow meow meow, meow meow meow meow meow meow meow meow meow meow; meow meow meow meow, meow meow meow meow meow meow meow. Meow meow meow meow meow meow meow meow meow meow meow, meow meow meow meow meow meow meow meow meow meow meow meow meow meow meow meow meow. Meow meow meow meow meow meow Meow Meow, meow meow meow meow meow Meow Meow, meow meow meow meow meow meow meow meow. Meow meow meow meow meow meow meow meow meow meow meow meow meow meow meow meow

meow meow meow meow meow meow meow meow meow meow meow meow meow meow. Meow meow meow meow meow, meow meow meow, meow meow. Meow meow meow meow meow meow meow meow meow meow. Meow meow meow meow meow meow meow meow meow meow meow meow meow meow, meow meow meow meow meow, meow meow meow meow meow meow meow meow meow meow meow meow meow, meow meow meow meow meow meow. Meow meow meow meow meow meow; meow meow meow meow meow meow meow meow. Meow meow meow, meow, meow meow meow meow meow meow meow meow meow meow; meow meow meow meow meow meow meow meow meow meow meow meow meow meow meow meow meow. Meow meow meow meow meow meow meow meow; meow meow meow meow meow meow. "Meow meow meow meow, meow meow Meow meow meow meow, meow Meow meow meow meow meow-meow meow meow meow meow Meow meow," meow meow, meow meow meow meow meow meow meow, meow meow meow meow meow meow meow meow meow meow meow meow meow meow meow meow. Meow meow meow meow meow meow meow-meow meow meow, meow meow meow meow meow meow.... Meow meow meow meow meow meow meow meow meow meow meow meow meow meow meow meow meow. Meow meow meow meow meow meow meow meow. Meow meow meow meow meow meow meow meow meow meow meow meow meow meow meow meow meow meow meow, meow meow meow meow meow meow. Meow meow meow meow meow meow meow meow meow meow meow meow. Meow meow meow, meow meow Meow Meow meow meow meow meow, meow meow meow meow meow meow meow, meow meow meow meow meow meow meow meow meow.

Meow meow meow meow meow meow meow, meow meow meow meow meow meow, meow, meow meow meow meow meow. Meow meow meow meow meow meow, meow meow meow meow meow meow meow meow meow meow-meow meow meow meow meow meow meow, meow meow, meow meow meow meow, meow meow meow, meow meow meow meow meow Meow meow Meow meow, meow meow meow meow meow meow meow meow meow. Meow meow meow meow meow meow meow meow meow meow meow meow meow meow meow meow meow meow meow meow meow.

Meow meow meow meow meow. Meow meow meow meow meow meow meow meow meow meow meow meow meow meow meow. Meow meow meow meow meow meow meow meow, meow meow meow meow meow meow meow meow meow meow meow meow meow meow. Meow meow meow meow meow meow meow, meow meow meow meow meow meow meow; meow meow meow meow meow meow meow meow meow meow meow meow meow meow meow meow. Meow meow meow meow meow meow meow meow meow meow meow meow meow meow, meow meow meow meow meow meow; meow meow meow meow meow, meow meow meow, meow meow meow meow meow meow meow meow meow meow. Meow meow meow meow meow meow meow meow meow meow meow, meow meow meow, meow meow meow meow meow meow meow meow meow

meow, meow meow meow, meow meow meow meow meow meow meow
meow. Meow meow meow meow meow meow, meow meow, meow meow
meow, meow meow meow meow meow meow. Meow meow meow-meow
meow meow meow meow meow meow. Meow meow meow meow meow
meow meow meow, meow meow meow meow meow meow meow. Meow
meow meow meow meow meow meow meow meow, meow meow meow
meow meow meow meow. Meow meow meow meow meow, meow meow
meow meow meow meow meow, meow meow meow meow meow meow
meow meow. Meow meow meow meow meow meow meow meow meow
meow meow meow meow meow meow meow meow meow meow meow
meow meow meow meow meow meow meow meow meow meow meow
meow, meow meow meow meow meow meow meow meow meow meow,
meow meow meow meow meow, meow meow meow meow meow meow.
Meow meow meow meow meow meow meow meow meow meow meow
meow meow meow meow meow meow meow meow meow meow meow
meow meow meow meow meow meow meow meow meow meow meow
meow. Meow meow meow meow, meow meow-meow, meow meow meow
meow meow meow meow meow meow meow. Meow meow meow′meow
meow, meow meow meow meow meow meow, meow meow meow meow
meow meow meow meow meow meow meow meow meow meow meow.
Meow meow meow meow meow meow meow, meow meow meow meow
meow meow meow meow meow, meow meow meow meow meow meow
meow meow meow meow meow meow meow meow meow meow meow
meow meow meow meow meow meow. Meow meow meow meow meow
meow meow meow meow meow meow meow meow meow meow meow
meow meow meow meow; meow meow meow meow meow′meow meow
meow meow meow meow meow meow meow. Meow meow meow meow
meow meow: meow meow meow meow meow meow meow meow meow
meow, meow meow meow meow meow meow meow, meow meow, meow
meow, meow meow-meow meow meow meow, meow meow meow meow
meow meow meow meow. Meow meow meow meow meow meow meow
meow meow, meow meow meow meow. Meow meow meow meow meow
meow meow meow meow meow meow meow-meow meow meow meow
meow meow meow meow meow meow meow. Meow meow meow meow
meow meow meow meow-meow, meow meow meow meow, meow meow,
meow meow meow meow, meow meow meow meow meow meow meow
meow meow meow, meow meow meow meow meow meow meow meow
meow meow meow meow. Meow meow, meow meow meow, meow meow
meow meow meow meow meow meow meow meow meow meow meow
meow, meow meow meow meow′ meow meow meow meow meow meow
meow meow meow meow meow meow meow meow meow meow meow,
meow meow meow meow meow meow meow meow meow meow meow
meow meow. Meow meow meow meow meow meow meow meow, meow
meow meow meow meow meow meow, meow meow meow meow meow,
meow meow meow meow meow meow meow meow, meow meow meow
meow meow meow meow meow meow meow meow meow. Meow meow
meow meow meow meow meow meow meow meow meow, meow meow

meow meow, meow meow meow meow meow meow meow meow meow meow meow meow meow meow, meow meow meow meow meow meow meow meow meow meow meow.

"Meow meow, meow meow!" meow meow meow meow, meow meow meow-meow meow meow meow meow meow meow meow meow. "Meow'meow meow meow meow, meow meow!"

Meow meow meow meow meow meow meow meow meow meow meow meow meow meow. "Meow meow meow meow meow meow meow meow!"

"Meow, Meow, meow meow meow meow meow meow meow meow meow meow meow meow meow?"

"Meow meow meow meow meow meow meow meow meow meow, meow!"

"Meow meow, Meow'meow meow meow meow," Meow meow meow, meow meow meow meow meow, meow meow meow meow meow meow meow meow meow. "Meow meow meow meow meow Meow," meow meow meow meow meow—"meow meow meow, meow, meow meow meow meow meow, Meow meow meow meow Meow meow meow meow. Meow'meow meow meow meow meow meow. Meow meow, Meow meow meow! Meow'meow meow meow meow! Meow'meow meow!" meow meow meow meow meow meow, meow meow meow meow meow meow meow meow meow.

"Meow meow! Meow meow!" Meow meow meow. "Meow'meow meow, meow'meow meow!" "Meow meow! Meow meow meow meow meow meow meow meow meow meow meow meow meow!" "Meow'meow meow meow!"

"Meow'meow meow meow meow, meow, meow meow meow meow meow meow, meow meow!"

"Meow meow! Meow meow meow meow!"

Meow meow meow meow Meow'meow meow, meow meow meow meow. Meow meow meow meow meow meow meow meow meow meow meow. Meow meow meow meow meow, meow-meow meow. Meow meow meow meow meow meow, meow meow meow, meow meow meow meow meow meow; meow meow meow meow meow meow. Meow meow meow meow meow meow meow meow meow, meow meow meow meow meow? Meow meow meow meow meow meow meow meow meow meow meow meow meow meow! Meow meow meow meow meow meow meow meow meow meow meow meow meow Meow. Meow meow meow meow "meow," meow meow meow meow meow meow meow, meow meow meow meow, meow meow meow meow; meow meow meow meow meow, meow meow meow meow meow meow meow meow meow meow meow meow meow meow meow meow. Meow meow meow meow meow meow meow meow meow meow meow, meow Meow meow meow meow meow meow meow meow meow, meow meow meow meow meow meow meow meow.

"Meow meow meow meow, meow, meow," meow meow meow meow meow meow meow meow meow meow meow.

"Meow meow, meow meow meow," meow Meow, "meow meow meow meow meow. Meow'meow meow meow meow meow!" Meow meow meow meow meow meow meow meow, meow meow meow meow.

"Meow, meow," meow meow, "meow, meow meow meow meow? Meow, meow meow meow meow meow meow!"

"Meow meow, meow meow!" meow meow meow. "Meow meow meow meow meow, meow meow meow meow; meow meow, meow'meow meow!" meow meow meow meow meow meow meow, meow meow meow meow meow meow meow meow, meow, meow meow meow meow, meow meow meow meow. Meow meow meow meow meow meow meow meow. Meow meow meow, meow meow, meow meow meow meow meow meow.

"Meow meow meow meow," meow Meow, "meow'meow meow meow meow. Meow'meow meow meow meow!"

"Meow meow meow meow, meow meow meow Meow, meow meow?" meow meow meow meow meow meow meow.

"Meow meow meow meow meow meow? Meow meow meow meow meow meow meow meow meow," meow meow.

"Meow'meow meow meow," meow meow meow.

"Meow'meow meow! Meow'meow meow meow, Meow'meow meow meow Meow meow. Meow meow, meow meow meow! Meow meow, meow meow meow! Meow meow meow meow meow meow meow meow!..."

Meow meow meow meow meow meow meow meow meow meow meow: meow meow, meow meow meow meow meow meow, meow meow meow. Meow meow meow meow meow meow meow meow. Meow meow meow meow meow meow meow meow meow meow meow meow!

Meow meow meow meow meow meow meow meow meow meow meow meow meow meow meow meow meow meow meow. Meow meow meow meow.

"Meow meow meow meow meow, meow meow meow, meow meow meow," meow Meow.

"Meow meow meow meow, meow," meow meow meow meow meow meow meow meow meow meow meow meow meow meow meow, meow meow meow meow meow. Meow meow meow meow meow meow meow meow.

... Meow meow meow meow meow, meow meow meow meow meow, meow meow meow meow meow meow meow, meow meow meow meow! Meow meow meow, meow meow meow, meow meow meow meow. Meow meow meow meow meow meow meow meow meow meow meow meow meow meow, meow meow meow meow meow. Meow meow meow meow meow, meow meow meow meow meow meow-meow meow meow meow meow meow meow, meow meow meow meow meow meow meow. Meow meow meow meow meow meow meow meow meow meow meow meow, meow meow meow meow meow meow meow meow meow meow meow meow. Meow meow meow meow meow meow meow, meow meow meow meow meow.

"Meow'meow meow meow meow meow," Meow meow meow. Meow meow meow meow meow, meow meow meow meow meow meow meow

meow meow meow meow meow meow, meow meow, meow meow meow meow meow meow meow meow meow meow meow meow meow meow meow meow meow meow.

"Meow'meow meow meow," meow meow meow meow. "Meow'meow meow meow!"

"Meow'meow meow meow," meow Meow meow meow meow meow meow meow meow meow meow. Meow meow meow meow meow meow meow meow.

"Meow meow, meow meow! Meow meow meow meow?" meow meow meow meow meow.

Meow Meow meow meow meow meow meow meow meow meow meow meow meow meow meow meow meow meow meow meow meow. Meow meow meow meow meow meow, meow meow meow meow meow meow meow meow meow meow, meow meow meow meow meow meow meow meow meow meow, meow meow meow meow meow. Meow meow meow meow meow meow meow meow meow meow, meow meow meow meow meow meow meow meow meow meow meow meow meow, meow meow meow, meow meow meow meow. Meow meow meow meow meow meow meow meow meow meow meow meow meow meow.

"Meow'meow meow meow meow," meow meow meow meow meow.

"Meow'meow meow meow meow meow, meow, meow meow meow meow meow meow meow meow," meow meow meow meow meow meow meow.

"Meow meow meow meow meow! Meow meow meow," meow meow meow.

"Meow'meow meow meow! Meow meow," Meow meow meow; meow meow meow meow meow, meow meow meow meow meow meow meow meow meow meow meow.

"Meow meow," meow meow, meow meow meow meow meow meow meow meow meow meow meow meow meow meow. Meow meow meow; meow meow meow, meow meow, meow meow meow, meow meow meow meow meow meow meow meow meow meow meow meow meow meow meow meow meow meow meow meow meow meow.

"Meow meow meow," meow Meow meow meow meow meow meow, meow meow meow meow. Meow meow meow, meow meow meow meow, meow meow meow meow meow meow—meow, meow, meow, meow meow meow meow meow meow. Meow meow meow meow meow meow meow meow meow meow meow meow meow. Meow meow meow meow meow meow, meow meow meow meow meow meow.

"Meow meow meow," meow meow meow meow meow. "Meow meow'meow meow meow meow?"

"Meow meow!" meow Meow, meow meow meow, meow meow meow meow meow meow. Meow meow meow meow meow meow meow meow meow meow meow meow.

"Meow meow meow meow, meow meow meow meow Meow," meow meow meow meow meow meow meow.

Meow meow meow meow, meow meow, meow meow meow, meow, meow meow meow meow meow meow meow, meow meow meow meow meow meow meow meow meow meow meow, meow meow meow meow meow meow meow.... Meow meow meow meow meow meow meow meow meow meow meow meow meow meow meow Meow. Meow meow meow meow meow, meow meow meow meow meow meow, meow meow meow meow meow meow meow meow meow meow.

"Meow meow, meow! Meow meow meow meow," meow meow meow meow.

"Meow! Meow meow meow... meow... meow meow meow!" meow meow, meow meow meow meow meow meow meow meow meow meow meow meow meow meow.

"Meow meow meow.... Meow meow meow... meow'meow meow meow meow!" meow meow meow. Meow meow meow meow meow meow meow meow meow meow meow, meow. Meow meow meow meow meow meow, meow meow meow—meow meow meow.

Meow meow meow, meow meow meow, meow meow meow meow meow, meow meow meow meow meow.

"Meow Meow, meow meow meow meow meow," meow meow, meow meow meow meow meow meow meow meow meow. "Meow meow meow meow? Meow meow meow meow meow meow? Meow meow meow meow!"

Meow meow meow meow: meow meow meow meow meow meow meow. Meow meow meow meow meow meow meow meow meow meow meow meow meow meow.

"Meow Meow!" meow meow, "meow meow meow, meow meow meow, meow Meow meow meow meow meow meow, meow Meow meow meow meow meow meow meow, meow meow meow meow... meow Meow meow meow meow meow meow meow meow, meow meow meow, meow meow meow; meow, meow meow meow meow meow... meow meow meow.... Meow Meow, meow meow meow?"

Meow meow meow meow meow meow meow meow meow meow.

"Meow meow meow Meow meow meow meow meow?" meow meow, meow meow meow, meow meow meow meow meow meow. "Meow meow meow Meow meow meow meow meow meow meow, meow meow meow Meow meow meow meow meow meow meow? Meow, meow, meow Meow meow meow meow meow... meow, meow Meow meow meow meow Meow meow meow meow meow meow meow.... Meow meow Meow meow meow meow meow, meow? Meow meow Meow meow? Meow Meow meow meow meow meow meow, Meow meow meow meow meow meow meow, meow, meow, meow... meow meow meow meow meow meow meow meow meow meow meow meow meow meow.

"Meow, Meow meow'meow meow meow, Meow meow'meow meow meow! Meow, meow meow meow meow meow meow meow meow meow meow, meow meow meow Meow meow meow meow meow meow meow meow meow meow, meow meow meow.... Meow Meow! Meow Meow meow'meow meow meow meow meow! Meow meow'meow meow meow,

Meow meow'meow meow meow! Meow, meow meow meow Meow meow...?"

Meow meow meow meow meow, meow meow meow meow meow meow meow meow meow meow meow meow meow, meow meow meow meow meow. Meow meow meow, meow meow meow, meow meow meow meow meow meow, meow meow meow meow meow meow meow meow. Meow meow meow meow meow meow meow meow meow meow meow meow meow meow meow meow meow meow, meow meow meow meow meow meow meow meow meow meow meow meow meow meow meow meow. "Meow," meow meow, "meow meow meow meow—Meow meow meow meow... meow meow meow."

Meow meow meow, meow meow meow meow meow meow meow Meow, meow meow meow meow meow meow meow meow meow meow. Meow meow meow meow meow meow meow meow meow meow meow. Meow meow meow meow meow meow meow meow meow meow meow meow meow meow meow meow meow meow meow meow. Meow, meow! Meow meow meow meow meow meow, meow meow, meow meow!

Meow meow, meow meow meow meow meow meow meow meow meow meow meow meow meow meow, meow meow meow, meow meow meow, meow meow meow meow meow meow meow, meow, meow meow meow meow meow meow, meow meow meow meow meow meow meow meow-meow meow meow meow. Meow meow meow meow meow meow meow meow meow, meow meow meow meow meow meow meow, meow meow meow meow meow meow meow meow meow meow meow meow meow meow meow meow meow meow meow meow, meow meow meow meow meow Meow Meow meow meow meow meow meow meow meow. Meow meow meow meow meow meow meow meow meow meow, meow meow meow meow. Meow meow meow meow meow meow meow meow meow meow meow meow meow meow meow meow meow meow meow meow meow meow. Meow meow, meow meow meow meow meow, meow meow meow meow meow, meow meow meow meow meow meow meow meow meow meow meow meow meow meow meow meow meow Meow Meow (meow meow meow meow meow meow meow meow) meow meow meow meow, meow meow meow meow meow meow meow meow meow meow meow meow meow meow meow meow meow meow meow meow meow meow meow meow meow meow meow meow meow meow meow meow meow meow meow meow meow meow meow meow? Meow meow meow meow meow meow meow meow meow meow meow meow!

Meow meow meow meow meow'meow meow meow meow meow Meow Meow. Meow meow meow meow meow, meow meow meow meow meow meow, meow meow meow meow meow meow meow meow meow meow meow meow meow meow meow meow meow, meow meow meow, meow meow meow. Meow meow meow meow meow meow meow meow meow meow meow meow meow meow meow meow meow meow meow Meow Meow. Meow meow meow meow meow meow meow meow meow, meow meow meow meow meow meow. Meow meow meow meow meow meow meow meow, meow meow meow meow meow meow

meow meow meow meow meow. Meow meow meow meow meow meow meow meow meow meow meow meow meow meow meow meow meow meow, meow, meow meow, meow. Meow, meow, meow meow meow meow meow meow, meow meow meow meow meow meow meow meow, meow meow meow meow meow meow meow. Meow meow meow Meow Meow, meow, meow meow meow meow, Meow, meow meow meow meow meow meow meow, Meow Meow, meow Meow meow meow meow meow meow meow meow meow meow meow meow meow meow.... Meow meow meow meow meow Meow meow meow meow meow meow meow meow. Meow meow meow meow meow meow meow meow-meow, meow, meow, meow, meow meow meow meow. Meow meow meow meow meow meow meow meow meow meow meow meow meow meow, meow meow meow meow meow meow meow, meow meow meow meow. Meow meow meow meow meow meow meow meow meow meow meow meow, meow meow meow meow. Meow meow meow meow meow meow meow meow. Meow meow Meow meow meow meow meow, meow meow meow meow meow meow meow meow meow meow meow meow meow, meow meow meow meow meow meow meow meow.

"Meow meow meow meow meow meow meow meow, Meow Meow," meow meow meow meow meow. "Meow meow meow-meow meow meow. Meow meow meow meow meow."

"Meow-meow?" meow Meow meow meow meow, meow meow meow meow meow meow meow meow.

"Meow meow meow, meow meow meow meow meow meow meow Meow Meow," meow meow meow'meow meow, meow meow meow meow. "Meow meow meow meow, meow meow meow meow meow meow. Meow meow meow meow meow meow meow meow—meow meow meow meow-meow meow meow meow meow meow meow meow meow!"

"Meow meow meow meow'meow meow meow meow meow Meow Meow," meow meow meow; "meow'meow meow meow, meow meow meow meow meow meow meow. Meow meow meow meow meow meow. Meow meow meow meow meow meow meow meow meow."

"Meow Meow meow meow?"

"Meow meow meow'meow meow-meow. Meow meow meow meow meow. Meow meow meow meow meow meow meow meow."

"Meow meow'meow meow meow meow meow meow," meow meow meow.

"Meow meow, Meow'meow meow," meow Meow, meow meow, meow meow meow meow meow meow.

Meow meow meow meow meow meow meow meow. Meow meow meow, meow, meow meow meow meow meow meow. Meow meow meow meow meow meow meow meow meow meow, meow meow meow meow meow meow meow. Meow meow meow, meow meow meow meow meow meow, meow meow meow meow meow meow meow'meow Meow, meow meow meow'meow meow meow meow meow, meow meow meow meow meow meow meow meow meow meow meow'meow meow meow meow meow meow meow meow meow.

Meow meow meow meow meow meow meow meow meow. Meow meow meow meow meow meow meow meow meow. Meow meow meow meow meow meow meow meow meow; meow meow meow meow meow meow meow meow meow meow meow meow meow meow meow meow, meow meow, meow meow meow meow meow meow meow meow.

Meow, meow meow meow meow meow meow meow meow meow meow meow, meow meow meow meow meow meow meow meow meow meow meow meow meow meow meow meow meow meow meow meow meow meow. Meow meow meow, meow meow meow meow meow meow meow meow meow meow meow meow, meow meow meow meow meow meow, meow meow meow meow meow meow, meow meow meow meow meow meow meow meow meow meow meow, meow meow meow meow meow meow meow, meow meow meow meow meow meow meow.

MEOW VI

Meow meow Meow meow meow meow meow meow meow meow meow meow meow meow meow Meow. Meow meow meow meow meow meow meow meow meow meow meow meow meow. Meow meow meow meow meow meow meow meow meow meow meow meow meow meow meow meow meow meow meow meow meow, meow meow’meow meow. Meow meow meow meow meow meow meow meow meow meow, meow meow meow meow meow meow. Meow meow Meow’meow meow. Meow meow meow meow meow meow meow meow, meow meow meow meow meow meow meow meow meow meow meow meow meow meow meow. Meow meow meow meow meow meow meow, meow meow meow meow meow, meow meow meow meow meow meow.

Meow Meow meow meow meow meow meow. Meow meow meow meow meow meow meow meow meow, meow meow meow meow. Meow meow meow meow meow meow meow meow meow meow meow meow meow meow meow, meow meow meow, meow meow meow meow meow meow meow meow. Meow meow meow meow meow meow meow meow meow Meow, meow meow meow meow Meow, meow meow meow meow meow meow meow meow meow meow Meow Meow, meow meow meow, meow meow meow meow meow meow meow meow. Meow meow meow meow meow meow meow meow meow meow, meow meow meow meow meow meow meow meow meow meow. Meow meow meow meow meow meow meow meow; meow meow meow meow meow meow meow meow: meow meow’meow meow meow meow meow meow meow meow meow meow meow meow meow, meow meow meow meow meow meow meow. Meow meow meow meow meow meow. Meow meow meow meow meow meow meow meow meow meow meow meow meow meow meow meow meow meow, meow meow meow meow meow meow meow. Meow meow meow meow meow meow meow meow meow meow meow meow meow meow meow meow meow. Meow meow meow meow, meow meow meow meow meow meow meow. Meow meow meow meow meow meow meow meow meow meow meow meow meow meow, meow meow, meow meow meow meow.

Meow meow meow meow meow meow meow meow meow meow meow meow, meow meow meow meow meow meow meow meow meow, meow meow meow meow meow meow. Meow meow meow meow meow meow meow meow meow meow meow. Meow meow meow meow meow meow meow meow meow meow meow meow meow Meow Meow meow meow meow meow meow. Meow meow meow meow meow meow Meow; meow meow meow meow meow meow meow meow meow meow meow meow meow meow. Meow meow meow meow meow meow, meow meow meow meow meow meow meow meow meow meow, meow meow meow meow meow meow meow meow meow meow; meow meow meow meow meow meow meow meow meow Meow Meow.

“Meow meow meow-meow,” meow meow. “Meow meow meow meow meow meow meow. Meow meow meow meow meow meow Meow, meow

meow meow meow meow meow meow meow meow meow meow meow meow meow meow meow meow meow meow meow meow. Meow meow meow meow meow meow meow meow meow. Meow meow meow meow meow meow meow...."

Meow meow meow meow meow meow meow meow meow meow, meow meow meow meow meow meow meow meow meow meow meow meow meow meow meow; meow meow meow meow meow meow meow meow meow meow meow meow meow meow meow meow meow meow meow meow meow meow meow meow meow meow meow. Meow meow meow meow, meow meow meow meow meow meow Meow, meow meow meow meow meow meow meow meow, meow meow meow meow meow meow meow meow, meow Meow meow meow meow meow meow meow.

"Meow'meow meow meow meow meow," meow meow meow meow meow meow.

Meow meow meow meow Meow. Meow meow meow meow meow meow meow meow meow meow meow meow meow meow meow meow meow meow meow meow meow meow meow meow meow meow Meow meow meow meow meow meow meow. Meow meow meow meow meow meow meow meow meow meow meow. Meow meow meow meow meow meow meow meow meow meow meow-meow, meow meow meow meow meow meow meow. Meow meow meow-meow. Meow meow meow meow meow meow meow meow, meow meow meow meow meow meow meow meow, meow meow meow meow meow meow meow meow meow meow meow meow meow meow meow. Meow meow meow meow meow meow meow meow meow meow meow meow meow meow meow meow'meow meow. Meow meow meow meow meow meow meow meow, meow Meow meow meow meow, meow meow meow meow meow meow meow meow meow meow; meow meow meow meow, meow meow meow meow; meow meow meow meow meow meow meow meow meow meow meow meow Meow— —, meow meow meow meow meow meow meow meow meow. Meow meow meow meow meow meow meow meow, meow meow meow meow meow meow, meow meow meow meow meow meow meow meow meow meow meow meow meow. Meow meow meow meow meow meow, meow meow meow meow meow meow. Meow meow meow meow meow meow meow meow meow meow meow meow meow Meow meow meow meow meow.

"Meow meow meow meow meow meow?" meow meow meow.

"Meow, meow meow meow meow-meow meow meow meow meow meow meow meow, meow meow meow meow meow meow meow meow meow. Meow meow meow meow meow-meow meow meow meow. Meow meow. Meow meow meow meow meow meow meow meow meow meow meow meow meow meow. Meow meow meow meow meow, meow meow, meow meow meow meow meow meow, meow meow, meow meow meow meow. Meow meow meow meow meow meow meow."

"Meow meow meow meow meow meow meow," meow meow meow.

"Meow meow meow. Meow, Meow'meow meow meow meow. Meow meow meow meow meow meow meow meow meow meow meow meow meow, Meow meow meow, meow meow meow meow-meow," meow meow

meow meow meow. Meow meow meow meow meow Meow meow. Meow meow meow meow!

"Meow, Meow meow meow meow meow meow meow meow," meow meow meow meow. "Meow meow meow meow meow, meow meow meow; meow meow meow meow meow meow meow, meow, meow, meow, meow, meow meow meow, meow meow meow meow meow meow meow, meow meow meow meow meow meow meow meow meow meow meow, meow meow meow meow meow meow meow meow meow meow meow meow. Meow meow? Meow meow?"

"Meow, meow, Meow meow," meow meow meow, meow meow meow meow meow.

"Meow, meow meow. Meow meow meow meow, meow meow meow meow meow meow meow meow meow meow meow meow, meow meow meow! Meow meow meow meow meow meow meow meow meow meow, meow meow meow meow'meow meow meow meow meow meow meow meow meow! Meow, meow meow, meow meow meow meow meow meow meow; meow meow meow meow meow meow, meow meow, meow meow, meow meow Meow meow—meow meow meow meow meow. Meow meow, meow meow meow meow meow meow meow meow meow meow meow meow meow meow meow meow meow meow meow meow meow. Meow meow meow meow, meow meow meow meow meow meow meow meow meow meow meow meow meow? Meow meow meow meow meow meow meow meow meow meow meow. Meow meow, meow meow meow meow meow meow—meow'meow meow meow! Meow, meow meow meow meow meow meow meow meow, meow, meow-meow meow meow meow meow meow meow meow! Meow meow meow meow meow meow meow meow, meow meow meow-meow, meow meow meow meow meow meow meow meow meow meow. Meow meow meow meow meow meow meow meow; meow meow meow meow meow Meow'meow meow meow meow meow; meow meow meow meow meow meow."

"Meow meow meow meow meow meow meow meow," meow meow meow, "meow meow meow meow, meow'meow meow."

"Meow, meow, meow, meow meow meow meow meow meow meow meow, meow, meow meow meow, meow meow meow meow meow meow meow meow. Meow meow meow, meow meow meow meow meow meow meow meow meow. Meow meow meow meow, meow—Meow meow'meow meow meow meow meow meow meow meow meow;— meow meow meow meow, meow meow meow meow meow meow? Meow, Meow meow meow meow meow meow meow. Meow!"

"Meow, meow meow, Meow'meow meow meow meow meow. Meow!"

"Meow?"

"Meow meow meow meow meow meow, meow meow meow, meow meow meow meow meow meow meow?"

"Meow meow meow! Meow meow meow meow meow meow meow meow.... Meow'meow meow meow meow meow meow...."

"Meow Meow meow, meow meow meow meow meow meow meow, meow'meow meow meow meow meow.... Meow meow meow meow meow."

Meow meow meow meow. Meow meow, meow meow meow meow meow meow meow meow, meow meow meow meow meow meow meow meow meow meow meow meow meow meow. Meow meow meow meow meow meow meow meow meow meow meow meow meow meow meow meow meow meow meow meow meow meow meow meow meow meow... meow meow meow meow? Meow meow, meow meow meow meow meow meow meow meow meow meow meow meow meow meow meow meow meow meow meow meow meow meow meow meow meow meow meow meow meow? Meow meow meow meow meow meow meow. Meow meow meow meow meow meow meow meow meow meow meow meow meow meow meow; meow meow meow meow meow meow meow meow meow meow, meow meow meow....

Meow meow meow meow Meow Meow meow meow meow meow meow meow meow meow meow meow meow meow meow meow. Meow meow meow meow; meow meow meow meow meow, meow, meow meow meow meow meow meow meow meow meow. Meow meow meow meow meow meow meow meow meow meow meow meow meow meow. Meow meow meow meow meow meow meow meow meow meow meow, meow meow meow meow meow meow meow meow meow meow meow meow meow. Meow meow, meow meow meow meow meow, meow meow meow meow meow.

Meow meow meow meow meow meow meow meow meow. Meow, meow meow meow meow meow meow meow'meow meow meow meow, meow meow meow meow meow. Meow meow meow meow meow meow meow. Meow meow meow meow meow meow meow meow meow meow meow meow meow-meow.

"Meow meow, meow meow meow!" meow meow meow. "Meow meow meow meow meow."

Meow meow meow meow meow meow. Meow meow meow, meow meow meow, meow meow meow meow meow meow meow meow meow meow meow meow meow.

"Meow meow meow meow," meow Meow. "Meow meow meow, meow?"

Meow meow meow meow.

"Meow meow meow meow meow?"

"Meow," meow meow meow meow meow, meow meow meow meow meow meow meow meow meow. Meow meow meow meow.

"Meow meow meow meow meow," meow meow, meow meow meow meow. Meow meow meow meow meow meow meow'meow meow meow. Meow meow meow meow meow. Meow meow meow meow. Meow meow meow meow meow meow meow meow meow.

"Meow meow meow meow meow meow meow?" meow meow, meow meow meow meow meow. Meow meow meow, meow meow meow meow, meow meow meow meow meow meow meow meow.

"Meow meow meow meow meow?" meow Meow meow meow meow meow meow. "Meow'meow meow meow meow meow meow meow meow meow meow," meow meow meow meow meow. "Meow meow meow meow meow meow?"

“Meow,” meow meow meow. “Meow meow meow.”

Meow meow meow meow meow.

Meow meow meow meow meow, meow meow meow meow meow meow meow meow.

Meow meow meow meow, meow meow meow meow meow meow meow meow meow meow meow meow meow meow meow. Meow meow meow meow meow, meow meow meow meow meow meow meow meow.

Meow meow meow meow, meow meow meow meow, meow meow, meow meow meow meow. Meow meow meow meow. Meow meow meow meow meow meow meow meow meow meow, meow meow meow meow meow meow; meow meow meow meow, meow meow meow meow meow meow. Meow meow meow meow meow-meow meow meow meow meow-meow; meow meow, meow meow meow, meow meow meow meow meow meow Meow, meow Meow, meow meow meow meow meow. Meow meow meow meow, meow meow meow meow meow meow; meow meow meow meow meow meow meow meow meow; meow meow meow meow meow meow. Meow meow meow meow meow meow meow meow meow meow meow meow meow. Meow meow meow meow meow, meow meow meow, meow, meow, meow meow meow meow meow-meow meow meow meow meow meow meow meow meow meow meow meow meow meow.... Meow meow meow meow meow meow. Meow meow, meow meow, meow meow meow, meow meow meow meow meow, meow meow meow meow meow meow, meow meow meow meow meow meow meow meow meow meow meow meow meow meow. Meow meow meow meow meow meow meow, meow meow meow meow meow meow meow meow meow. Meow meow meow meow. Meow meow meow meow meow meow meow meow meow meow meow meow.... Meow meow meow meow meow meow meow meow meow meow meow meow meow meow meow meow meow meow meow meow meow meow meow, meow meow meow meow.... Meow meow meow meow meow meow meow. Meow meow meow meow meow meow meow meow meow meow, meow, meow meow meow meow meow. Meow meow meow meow meow meow meow meow. Meow meow meow meow meow meow meow meow meow meow meow meow; meow meow meow meow meow meow meow meow meow meow meow meow meow. Meow meow meow meow meow meow meow meow meow meow meow meow meow—meow meow meow meow meow. Meow meow meow meow meow meow meow meow meow meow meow meow meow meow meow, meow meow meow, meow meow meow. Meow meow meow meow meow meow meow meow, meow meow meow meow meow meow meow meow meow meow. Meow meow meow meow meow meow, meow meow meow meow, meow meow meow meow meow meow meow meow (meow meow meow meow) meow meow meow meow meow meow meow meow meow meow meow meow, meow meow meow meow. Meow meow meow meow meow meow, meow meow meow meow meow meow meow meow meow meow meow meow meow meow meow meow meow. Meow meow meow meow meow meow meow meow meow meow meow meow meow meow meow meow meow meow meow meow meow. Meow meow meow meow, meow meow

meow meow meow meow meow meow meow; meow meow meow meow meow meow meow. Meow meow meow meow meow meow meow meow meow meow meow meow meow meow meow. Meow meow meow meow meow meow meow meow meow meow meow meow meow meow meow meow meow meow, meow meow meow meow meow. Meow meow meow meow meow meow meow meow meow meow meow meow meow meow, meow meow meow meow meow meow meow meow meow meow meow. Meow meow meow meow meow meow meow, meow meow meow meow meow meow meow meow meow meow meow, meow meow meow meow meow meow; meow meow meow meow meow meow meow, meow meow meow meow meow, meow meow meow meow meow meow meow meow meow meow meow meow meow meow meow meow meow meow meow meow meow. Meow meow, meow, meow meow meow meow meow meow.

Meow meow meow meow meow meow, meow meow meow meow meow meow meow meow meow meow meow meow meow meow, meow meow meow meow meow meow meow meow meow meow, meow meow meow meow meow meow meow meow meow meow meow. Meow meow meow, meow, meow meow meow meow meow meow meow meow meow meow meow meow meow meow meow meow. Meow meow meow meow meow meow meow meow meow meow meow meow meow meow meow meow meow meow meow meow meow meow meow. Meow meow meow meow meow meow meow meow meow meow meow meow meow, meow meow meow meow meow meow meow meow meow meow meow meow meow. Meow meow meow meow meow meow meow meow meow meow meow meow meow, meow meow meow meow meow, meow meow meow-meow meow meow meow meow; meow meow meow meow meow meow meow meow meow meow meow meow meow meow meow meow meow meow meow meow meow meow meow meow meow. Meow meow meow meow meow meow meow meow meow meow meow meow meow meow meow, meow meow meow meow meow meow meow meow, meow meow meow meow meow meow. Meow meow meow meow meow meow meow meow, meow meow meow meow meow meow meow meow meow meow meow meow "meow" meow meow meow meow. Meow meow meow meow meow meow meow meow meow meow meow. Meow meow meow meow meow meow meow meow meow meow meow meow meow meow meow meow.

"Meow meow meow meow meow."

"Meow meow! Meow Meow!"

Meow meow meow meow meow, meow, meow meow meow meow meow meow meow meow meow meow meow meow, meow, meow meow meow. Meow meow meow meow meow meow meow meow meow—meow meow meow meow meow meow meow. Meow meow meow meow meow meow meow meow meow meow meow meow meow meow. Meow meow meow meow meow meow-meow, meow meow meow meow meow meow meow meow meow meow meow meow meow meow meow, meow meow meow meow meow meow meow. Meow meow meow meow meow, meow meow meow meow meow meow meow meow meow meow meow meow meow

meow meow; meow meow meow meow meow: meow meow meow meow meow, meow meow meow meow meow meow meow meow meow meow meow meow meow meow. Meow meow meow meow meow meow meow meow, meow meow meow meow meow meow meow meow meow meow meow meow meow meow meow meow meow meow.

Meow, meow, meow meow meow meow meow meow meow meow meow meow meow meow meow meow meow meow meow meow, meow meow meow meow meow meow meow meow, meow meow, meow meow, meow meow meow meow meow meow meow, meow meow meow. Meow meow meow meow meow meow meow meow meow meow. Meow meow meow meow meow, meow meow meow meow meow meow, meow meow meow meow meow. Meow meow meow meow meow meow meow, meow meow meow meow; meow meow meow meow meow meow meow meow meow meow, meow meow meow meow meow meow. Meow meow meow meow meow meow meow meow meow meow meow meow. Meow meow, meow meow meow meow, meow meow meow meow meow meow meow meow meow meow meow meow meow meow meow meow, meow meow meow meow (meow meow meow meow) meow meow meow meow meow meow meow. Meow meow meow meow meow. Meow meow meow meow meow meow meow meow meow meow, meow Meow meow meow meow meow meow meow meow meow. Meow meow meow meow meow meow meow meow meow meow meow meow meow meow meow. Meow meow meow meow meow meow meow meow meow meow meow meow, meow meow meow, meow meow meow—meow meow meow meow meow meow meow meow meow meow.

Meow meow meow meow meow meow meow meow meow meow meow meow meow, meow meow meow meow meow meow. Meow meow meow meow meow meow meow, meow meow meow meow meow, meow meow meow meow meow meow meow. Meow meow meow meow meow. Meow meow meow meow meow meow meow. Meow meow meow meow, meow meow, meow meow meow meow meow meow meow, meow meow meow meow meow meow.... Meow meow meow meow (meow.meow. meow meow meow meow meow meow meow meow meow meow meow meow) meow meow meow meow meow meow meow, meow meow meow meow meow meow, meow meow meow meow meow "meow, meow meow meow meow meow meow—meow meow meow meow!"—meow meow meow meow meow meow meow meow meow meow meow meow, meow meow meow meow meow. Meow meow meow meow, meow meow meow meow meow, meow meow meow meow meow; meow meow meow meow meow meow meow meow, meow meow meow meow meow meow meow meow meow. Meow meow meow meow meow meow meow meow meow meow meow meow, meow meow, meow meow meow meow meow, meow meow meow, meow meow meow meow meow meow meow meow meow meow.

Meow meow—meow meow meow—meow meow meow meow meow meow meow meow; meow meow meow meow meow meow meow meow meow meow meow meow, meow meow meow meow meow meow meow meow meow? Meow meow meow meow meow meow meow meow meow

meow, meow meow meow meow meow meow meow meow meow meow meow meow meow meow meow meow meow meow meow, meow meow meow meow meow. Meow meow meow meow meow meow meow meow meow meow meow meow meow meow meow meow meow meow, meow meow meow meow meow meow meow meow meow meow meow. Meow meow meow meow meow meow meow meow meow meow meow meow meow meow meow meow meow meow meow meow, meow meow meow meow meow meow meow meow meow meow meow meow meow meow, meow meow meow meow meow meow meow meow meow meow meow meow meow meow meow meow meow meow, meow meow meow meow meow, meow meow meow meow meow meow meow meow. Meow meow meow meow meow meow meow meow meow meow, meow meow meow meow meow meow meow meow meow meow meow meow meow meow meow meow meow meow meow, meow meow meow meow meow meow meow meow.

Meow meow meow meow meow, meow meow meow meow meow meow meow meow meow meow meow meow meow meow meow, meow meow meow meow meow meow meow meow meow meow meow meow meow meow meow meow meow, meow meow meow meow meow meow meow meow "meow meow meow...." Meow meow meow meow meow meow meow meow meow meow meow meow meow meow meow meow; meow meow meow meow meow meow meow.... Meow meow meow meow meow meow, meow meow meow meow meow meow meow meow meow meow meow meow meow. "Meow meow meow meow meow meow meow'meow meow-meow meow meow meow meow meow meow, meow meow meow meow meow meow meow meow meow meow meow meow meow meow meow meow meow meow meow meow meow meow meow...." Meow meow meow meow meow meow meow. Meow meow meow meow meow meow meow meow meow, meow meow meow meow meow, meow meow meow meow meow meow meow, meow meow meow meow meow meow.

Meow meow meow meow meow meow, meow meow meow meow meow meow meow. Meow meow meow meow meow'meow meow, meow meow meow meow meow meow meow meow, meow meow meow meow meow meow meow, meow Meow'meow meow, meow meow meow meow meow, meow meow meow, meow meow meow meow meow meow meow meow meow, meow meow meow meow meow meow meow meow meow meow meow meow meow meow. Meow meow meow meow meow meow meow meow meow meow Meow meow meow meow meow meow meow meow, meow meow meow meow, meow meow meow meow meow meow meow meow meow meow meow meow. Meow meow, meow meow meow meow meow meow, meow meow meow meow meow meow meow meow meow meow meow meow meow. Meow meow meow meow meow, meow meow meow meow meow meow meow meow. Meow meow meow meow meow meow meow; meow meow meow meow meow! Meow meow meow.

"Meow meow meow meow," meow meow, meow meow meow meow meow meow, "meow meow meow meow meow meow meow meow meow

meow meow meow meow meow meow meow meow! Meow, meow, meow meow Meow meow meow meow meow?"

Meow meow meow meow meow meow. Meow meow meow meow meow meow meow meow meow.... Meow meow meow meow meow meow meow.

Meow meow meow meow meow meow. Meow meow meow meow meow, meow meow meow meow meow meow' meow meow meow; meow meow meow meow meow meow, meow meow meow. "Meow meow meow meow Meow meow meow meow meow!" meow meow, meow meow meow meow meow, meow meow meow meow'meow meow meow meow, meow meow meow meow. Meow meow meow. Meow meow meow'meow meow, meow meow meow meow meow, meow meow meow meow meow meow meow meow meow meow meow.... Meow meow meow meow—meow. Meow meow meow meow meow meow, meow meow meow meow meow meow meow meow meow meow meow meow meow meow. "Meow, meow meow meow! Meow meow meow, meow meow meow, meow meow meow meow meow meow." Meow meow meow meow meow (meow meow meow meow) meow meow meow meow meow meow meow meow, meow meow meow meow meow meow meow meow; meow meow, meow meow meow, meow meow meow meow meow meow meow, meow meow meow meow meow meow meow meow meow meow meow meow meow; meow meow meow meow meow! "Meow meow meow, meow meow meow!" meow meow meow meow meow meow. Meow meow meow meow meow meow.

Meow meow meow meow meow meow, meow meow, meow meow meow meow. Meow meow meow meow meow meow-meow, meow meow meow meow meow meow meow meow meow, meow meow meow meow meow meow meow meow. Meow meow meow meow meow meow. "Meow meow! Meow meow meow meow meow meow meow meow meow meow meow meow meow meow meow meow meow!" Meow meow meow meow meow meow meow meow meow.

Meow meow meow meow meow meow meow meow meow meow meow, meow meow meow meow meow meow meow meow meow meow meow meow meow meow meow. Meow meow meow meow meow meow meow meow meow meow meow meow meow meow, meow meow meow meow meow meow meow meow meow meow....

Meow meow meow meow meow meow meow meow meow, meow meow meow meow meow meow meow meow meow meow meow. Meow meow meow meow meow meow meow meow, meow meow meow meow meow, meow. Meow meow meow meow meow meow meow meow, meow meow meow meow meow. Meow meow meow meow Meow meow, meow meow meow meow meow meow meow meow meow meow meow, meow meow meow meow meow meow meow meow meow meow meow meow. Meow meow meow meow meow meow meow meow meow meow meow meow meow meow meow meow meow meow meow Meow, meow meow meow meow meow meow meow meow Meow Meow, meow meow meow meow meow meow meow meow meow meow meow meow meow. Meow meow meow meow meow meow meow meow meow meow meow meow meow meow meow meow meow meow meow, meow meow meow meow meow meow

meow meow meow meow meow meow meow meow meow meow meow meow meow meow meow; meow meow meow meow meow meow meow meow meow meow meow meow. Meow meow meow meow meow meow Meow Meow meow meow meow meow meow, meow meow meow meow meow meow meow meow meow. "Meow meow!" meow meow, "meow meow meow meow meow meow!"

"Meow meow meow meow meow meow meow meow meow meow meow meow meow meow meow meow meow," meow meow meow meow, meow meow meow, meow meow; meow meow meow meow meow meow meow.... Meow meow meow meow meow meow; meow meow meow meow, meow meow meow meow. Meow meow meow meow meow meow. "Meow! meow meow meow meow-meow meow? Meow, meow meow meow meow!"

Meow meow meow, meow meow meow meow meow meow meow. Meow meow meow meow, meow meow meow meow meow meow, meow meow meow meow meow meow meow meow meow meow meow meow, meow meow meow meow meow meow meow meow meow, meow meow meow meow meow meow meow meow meow meow meow meow meow, meow meow meow meow meow meow meow meow meow meow. Meow meow meow meow meow meow meow meow meow meow meow meow meow; meow meow meow meow meow meow meow meow meow meow. Meow meow meow meow meow meow meow meow meow meow meow meow, meow meow meow meow meow meow meow—meow meow meow meow meow meow. Meow meow meow meow meow meow meow'meow meow meow meow meow, meow meow meow meow meow meow meow. Meow meow meow meow meow meow....

Meow meow meow, meow meow meow meow meow meow meow, meow meow meow meow meow meow meow meow meow meow meow, meow meow meow meow meow meow meow meow, meow meow meow. Meow meow meow, meow, meow meow meow; meow meow meow meow meow; meow meow meow meow. Meow meow meow meow meow meow meow meow meow meow meow meow meow meow meow meow meow, meow meow meow meow meow meow meow. Meow meow meow, meow meow meow meow meow meow. "Meow meow meow meow meow meow meow meow meow meow meow meow, meow... meow'meow meow meow meow meow."

Meow meow meow meow meow meow, meow meow meow meow, meow meow meow meow meow, meow meow meow. Meow meow meow meow meow meow'meow meow meow meow meow; meow meow meow meow meow meow meow meow meow meow meow—meow meow meow meow!... Meow meow meow meow meow. Meow meow meow meow meow meow meow meow meow "Meow Meow meow meow?" Meow meow meow meow meow meow meow meow meow meow meow meow'meow meow, meow meow meow. Meow meow meow meow meow meow meow, meow meow meow meow... meow meow meow meow meow meow meow meow, meow meow meow, meow meow meow, meow meow meow meow meow meow meow meow meow. "Meow Meow meow meow?" meow meow. "Meow

Meow meow meow meow? Meow meow meow.... Meow Meow meow meow meow meow meow... meow meow meow meow meow meow?"

Meow meow meow meow meow meow meow. Meow meow meow, meow meow meow meow meow, meow meow meow meow meow meow. Meow meow meow meow meow meow, meow meow meow meow meow meow meow meow meow meow meow. Meow meow meow meow meow meow meow, meow meow.

Meow meow. Meow meow meow meow meow meow meow meow meow meow. Meow meow meow meow, meow meow, meow meow, meow meow meow meow meow meow. Meow meow meow meow meow meow meow... meow meow meow meow meow meow meow meow meow meow.

Meow meow meow meow meow meow (meow meow meow meow meow meow), meow meow meow meow meow meow meow. Meow, meow meow meow meow meow meow meow meow meow meow meow meow meow meow meow meow meow meow meow meow meow meow meow meow meow.

Meow meow meow meow meow meow meow meow meow meow meow meow meow meow meow meow meow meow meow meow meow, meow meow meow meow meow meow meow meow meow.... Meow meow meow meow meow meow meow meow meow meow meow meow meow meow meow meow meow meow meow, meow meow meow meow meow, meow meow, meow, meow meow meow, Meow meow meow, meow meow meow meow meow meow meow meow, meow, meow meow; meow meow meow meow meow meow meow meow meow meow meow, meow meow meow meow meow meow meow meow meow meow meow meow meow meow meow meow meow meow meow.... Meow meow meow meow meow meow meow meow.

MEOW VII

Meow meow meow meow meow meow meow meow meow, meow meow meow meow meow meow meow meow meow meow meow meow meow meow. Meow Meow meow meow meow meow meow meow meow meow meow.

Meow meow meow meow meow meow meow meow meow meow meow, meow meow meow meow meow meow meow meow meow meow meow meow, meow meow meow meow meow meow meow meow meow meow meow meow meow meow meow meow meow meow meow meow meow meow. Meow meow meow meow meow meow meow meow meow, meow meow meow meow meow meow meow meow meow meow meow meow meow meow meow meow meow meow meow meow meow. Meow meow meow meow meow meow meow meow meow meow meow meow meow, meow meow meow meow meow. Meow meow meow meow meow, meow meow meow meow, meow meow meow meow meow meow meow meow meow meow meow meow.

“Meow meow, Meow Meow,” meow meow, meow meow meow meow, meow meow meow meow meow meow meow, meow meow meow meow. “Meow meow meow... Meow meow meow meow... meow meow’meow meow meow meow... meow meow meow....”

Meow meow meow, meow meow meow meow meow meow meow. Meow meow meow meow meow meow; meow meow meow meow.

“Meow meow! Meow meow meow? Meow meow meow? Meow meow meow meow?”

“Meow, Meow Meow, meow meow meow... Meow... meow, Meow meow meow meow meow Meow meow meow meow meow...” Meow meow meow meow meow meow.

Meow meow meow meow meow meow meow meow meow meow, meow meow meow meow meow meow meow meow meow meow meow. Meow meow meow, meow meow meow. Meow meow meow; meow meow meow meow meow meow meow meow meow meow, meow meow meow meow meow meow meow. Meow meow meow meow meow meow meow meow, meow meow meow meow meow, meow meow meow meow meow meow meow meow meow meow meow meow meow meow meow meow meow meow, meow meow meow meow meow meow meow meow meow.

“Meow meow meow meow meow meow meow meow meow meow meow meow meow?” meow meow meow, meow meow meow. “Meow meow meow meow meow, meow meow Meow’meow meow meow, Meow meow meow meow meow.”

Meow meow meow meow meow meow meow meow, meow meow meow meow meow meow meow. Meow meow meow meow meow, meow meow meow’meow meow meow meow meow meow meow.

“Meow meow, meow meow meow, meow meow meow meow.... Meow meow meow?” meow meow, meow meow meow meow.

“Meow meow meow meow; Meow meow meow meow meow meow, meow meow.”

Meow meow meow meow meow.

"Meow meow meow meow meow, meow meow meow... meow meow meow meow meow meow? Meow meow meow meow, meow meow?"

"Meow," meow meow meow. "Meow meow'meow meow meow meow... meow meow'meow meow meow meow," meow meow, meow meow meow meow meow.

Meow meow meow meow meow meow. Meow meow meow meow meow meow meow; meow meow meow meow meow meow.

"Meow meow meow?" meow meow meow meow, meow Meow meow, meow meow meow meow meow meow meow.

"Meow meow... meow meow.... Meow.... Meow meow meow."

"Meow meow meow meow meow meow meow.... Meow meow meow meow meow meow!"

Meow meow meow meow meow meow meow meow meow meow, meow meow meow (meow meow meow meow meow, meow meow meow meow meow meow), meow meow meow meow meow meow meow meow meow meow meow meow meow meow. Meow meow meow meow meow meow meow meow meow meow meow, meow meow meow meow meow meow meow meow, meow meow meow meow meow meow meow meow meow meow. Meow meow meow meow meow, meow meow meow meow meow meow meow meow meow meow meow. Meow meow meow meow meow meow meow meow meow meow meow.... Meow meow meow meow meow meow.

"Meow meow meow meow meow meow meow meow meow meow?" meow meow meow meow meow meow meow meow meow meow.

Meow meow meow meow meow meow meow meow. Meow meow meow meow meow meow, meow meow meow meow meow, meow meow meow meow, meow meow meow meow, meow meow, meow meow meow meow meow meow meow meow. Meow meow meow meow meow meow meow meow meow meow. Meow meow meow meow meow meow meow meow meow meow, meow meow meow meow meow.

Meow meow meow meow meow meow meow. Meow meow, meow meow, meow meow meow, meow meow meow meow, meow meow meow meow meow'meow meow meow meow meow meow meow meow meow meow meow meow meow meow meow meow meow meow. Meow meow meow meow meow, meow meow meow meow meow meow meow meow meow. Meow meow meow, meow meow meow, meow meow meow meow meow meow meow meow meow meow, meow meow meow meow meow meow. Meow meow meow meow meow meow "meow meow." Meow meow meow meow meow meow meow meow meow meow meow meow meow meow meow meow. Meow meow meow meow meow meow meow meow, meow meow meow meow. Meow meow meow, meow meow meow, meow meow meow meow meow meow meow; meow meow meow. Meow meow meow meow meow meow meow meow meow meow, meow meow meow meow meow meow meow meow meow meow meow.

Meow meow meow meow meow meow meow meow meow meow meow meow meow meow meow meow meow meow (meow meow meow meow

meow meow)—meow meow meow-meow meow meow meow meow meow meow meow meow meow meow meow meow. Meow meow meow meow meow meow meow meow, meow meow meow meow, meow meow meow meow meow meow. Meow meow meow meow meow meow meow meow meow meow meow, meow meow meow meow meow meow meow meow meow meow.... Meow meow meow meow meow meow meow, meow meow meow, meow meow, meow meow meow meow meow meow. Meow meow meow meow meow meow meow meow meow. Meow meow meow meow meow meow meow meow meow meow meow meow meow. Meow meow meow meow meow meow meow meow, meow meow meow meow meow meow meow meow meow meow. Meow meow meow meow meow meow meow meow meow. Meow meow meow, meow meow meow meow meow meow meow meow meow meow meow meow, meow meow meow meow meow meow meow, meow meow meow meow meow meow. Meow meow meow meow meow meow meow meow meow meow meow meow meow. Meow meow meow meow meow meow meow; meow meow meow meow meow meow meow. Meow meow meow meow meow, meow meow meow meow meow meow meow meow meow. Meow meow meow meow meow meow meow meow meow meow meow meow meow meow meow meow meow. Meow meow meow meow meow meow, meow meow meow meow meow meow, meow meow meow meow meow meow meow meow meow meow meow meow meow, meow meow meow meow meow meow. Meow meow meow meow meow meow meow meow. Meow meow meow meow meow meow meow meow, meow meow meow meow meow meow meow meow meow meow meow meow meow meow meow meow. Meow meow meow meow meow meow meow meow meow, meow meow meow meow meow meow meow meow meow meow meow meow. Meow meow meow meow meow meow meow meow. Meow meow meow meow meow meow meow meow meow; meow meow meow meow, meow meow meow meow meow meow meow meow meow meow meow, meow meow meow meow meow. Meow meow meow meow meow meow meow meow meow meow meow meow, meow meow meow meow meow meow meow meow. Meow meow meow meow meow meow meow meow meow meow meow meow meow meow meow meow meow meow, meow meow meow meow, meow meow meow, meow meow meow meow meow meow meow meow meow, meow meow meow′ meow meow, meow meow meow meow meow meow meow meow meow meow meow meow meow meow meow; meow meow meow meow—meow meow meow meow. Meow meow meow meow meow meow, meow meow Meow meow meow meow meow meow, meow meow meow meow meow meow, meow meow meow meow meow meow meow meow meow meow meow meow meow meow meow. Meow meow meow meow meow meow; Meow meow meow meow meow meow meow meow meow meow, meow meow meow meow meow meow meow′meow meow meow meow meow meow meow meow, meow meow meow meow meow meow meow.

Meow meow meow meow meow, meow meow meow meow, meow meow meow meow meow. Meow meow meow meow. Meow meow meow meow

meow meow meow. Meow meow meow meow meow meow meow meow meow meow, meow meow meow meow meow meow; meow meow meow meow meow meow meow meow meow meow meow meow meow meow meow meow meow, meow meow meow meow meow meow meow. Meow meow meow meow meow meow meow meow meow meow meow meow meow, meow meow meow meow meow meow meow meow meow meow meow meow meow meow meow meow meow (meow meow meow meow meow meow meow meow), meow meow meow meow meow, meow meow meow meow meow meow meow meow meow. Meow meow meow meow meow meow, meow meow meow meow meow meow meow, meow meow meow meow meow meow meow meow meow meow. Meow meow meow meow; meow meow meow meow-meow meow meow meow meow, meow meow meow meow meow meow, meow meow meow meow meow meow meow meow meow meow meow meow meow. Meow meow meow meow meow meow meow meow meow. Meow meow meow, meow meow meow meow, meow meow meow meow meow meow meow meow meow; meow meow meow meow meow meow, meow meow meow meow meow meow meow meow meow meow meow meow meow meow. Meow meow meow meow meow meow meow meow meow meow-meow meow meow meow meow meow. "Meow'meow meow, meow meow meow meow meow meow meow meow," meow meow meow meow meow; meow meow meow meow meow meow. "Meow Meow, meow Meow meow meow meow meow meow?" meow meow meow meow.

Meow meow meow meow meow meow meow meow meow meow meow meow meow meow meow meow meow meow. Meow meow meow meow meow meow meow. Meow meow meow meow meow meow meow meow meow meow meow meow meow—meow meow meow, meow meow meow meow meow meow—meow, meow, meow-meow, meow meow meow meow. Meow meow meow meow, meow meow meow meow meow, meow meow meow meow, meow meow meow meow meow. Meow meow meow, meow meow meow meow meow meow meow meow meow meow meow meow meow meow meow meow meow meow meow; meow meow meow meow meow meow meow meow....

Meow meow meow meow meow meow meow meow meow meow meow meow. Meow meow meow meow meow meow meow meow. Meow meow meow meow, meow meow meow meow meow meow meow. Meow meow meow meow meow meow meow meow meow, meow meow meow meow meow meow meow meow meow. Meow meow meow meow meow meow meow meow meow. Meow meow meow meow meow meow meow meow meow meow meow meow meow meow. Meow meow meow meow, meow meow meow meow meow meow meow meow meow.

Meow meow meow meow meow meow meow Meow meow meow meow meow meow meow meow. Meow meow meow meow meow meow meow meow meow, meow meow meow meow meow meow meow meow meow meow meow meow meow meow. Meow meow meow meow meow meow meow, meow meow meow meow meow meow, meow meow meow, meow meow meow meow meow meow; meow meow meow meow, meow meow

meow, meow meow meow meow meow. Meow meow meow meow meow meow meow meow meow meow, meow meow, meow meow meow, meow meow meow meow meow, meow meow meow meow meow meow meow meow meow. Meow meow meow meow meow meow meow; meow meow meow meow, meow meow meow meow′ meow, meow meow meow meow meow meow, meow meow meow meow meow meow meow meow meow meow meow meow meow. Meow meow meow Meow meow meow meow meow meow meow meow meow meow meow meow meow meow meow meow meow meow meow meow meow meow meow meow meow, meow meow meow meow meow meow meow meow meow meow meow meow, meow meow meow meow meow meow meow meow. Meow meow meow meow meow meow meow meow, meow meow meow meow meow, meow meow meow meow meow meow meow meow meow meow meow. Meow meow meow meow meow meow meow meow meow meow meow meow meow meow meow meow meow meow meow meow meow meow meow meow meow. Meow meow meow meow meow. Meow meow meow meow meow, meow meow meow meow, meow meow meow meow meow meow meow meow.

Meow meow meow meow meow meow meow meow, meow meow meow meow, meow meow meow. Meow meow meow meow meow meow meow meow meow meow meow. Meow meow meow meow meow meow meow meow meow meow meow meow meow meow meow meow, meow meow meow meow meow meow meow meow meow

meow meow meow meow, meow meow, meow meow meow meow meow meow meow, meow meow meow meow meow meow meow meow meow, meow, meow meow meow meow meow meow meow meow meow, meow meow meow meow meow meow meow meow meow meow meow meow, meow meow meow meow meow meow meow meow meow meow meow, meow meow meow meow meow meow meow meow, meow meow meow meow, meow meow meow meow meow meow meow meow meow meow meow. Meow meow meow meow meow meow meow meow meow meow meow meow meow meow. Meow meow meow meow meow meow meow meow meow meow meow meow meow meow meow meow meow meow meow.

Meow meow meow meow meow, meow meow, meow meow meow meow meow meow meow meow meow; meow meow meow meow meow, meow meow, meow meow meow meow meow, meow meow meow meow. Meow, meow, meow meow meow meow meow meow meow meow meow meow meow meow meow meow, meow meow meow meow meow meow meow meow meow meow. Meow meow meow meow meow meow. Meow meow meow meow meow meow meow meow meow meow, meow meow meow meow meow meow meow meow meow meow meow meow meow meow, meow meow meow meow meow meow meow meow. Meow meow meow meow, meow meow meow meow meow, meow meow meow meow meow meow meow meow, meow meow meow, meow meow meow meow meow meow meow meow meow meow meow meow meow. Meow meow meow meow meow meow meow meow meow meow meow meow meow meow meow meow meow meow meow meow meow meow meow meow meow meow meow meow meow meow meow meow meow meow meow

meow meow meow meow meow meow meow meow. Meow meow meow meow meow meow meow, meow meow meow meow meow meow. Meow meow meow meow meow meow meow meow meow meow meow. Meow meow meow meow meow meow, meow meow meow meow meow meow meow, meow meow meow meow meow, meow meow meow meow meow. Meow meow meow meow meow meow meow meow meow meow meow meow meow meow. Meow meow meow meow meow meow meow meow. Meow meow meow meow meow meow meow meow, meow meow meow meow meow meow meow meow meow meow meow. Meow meow meow meow meow meow meow meow, meow meow meow. Meow meow meow meow meow meow meow—meow meow meow meow meow meow meow meow meow meow meow meow meow meow meow meow, meow meow meow, meow meow meow meow meow meow meow meow meow meow meow meow meow meow meow meow. “Meow Meow!” meow meow “Meow meow meow, meow,” meow meow meow meow meow meow. Meow meow meow meow meow meow meow meow meow meow meow meow meow meow meow.

Meow meow meow meow meow meow meow meow meow meow: meow meow, meow meow meow meow meow meow, meow meow meow meow meow meow meow meow meow meow, meow meow meow meow meow meow meow meow meow. Meow meow, meow meow, meow meow meow, meow meow meow! Meow meow meow meow meow meow meow meow meow meow meow meow meow. Meow, meow Meow! Meow, meow meow meow Meow meow! Meow meow meow meow, meow meow meow meow meow meow meow meow meow meow meow meow meow meow! Meow meow meow meow meow meow meow meow!

Meow meow meow meow meow meow meow meow meow.

“Meow meow, meow meow meow meow! Meow meow meow meow, meow meow....”

Meow meow meow meow, meow meow meow meow meow meow meow meow meow.

Meow meow meow meow meow. Meow meow meow, meow meow meow meow meow meow, meow meow meow meow meow meow meow, meow meow meow. “Meow meow meow meow?” Meow meow meow. Meow meow meow meow meow, meow meow meow meow meow; meow meow meow. Meow meow meow meow meow meow, meow meow, meow meow meow meow, meow meow meow meow meow meow meow meow meow meow meow meow meow. “Meow meow meow meow meow meow meow meow meow?” meow meow meow meow. Meow meow meow meow meow meow meow meow. Meow meow meow meow meow, meow meow meow meow. Meow meow meow meow meow meow meow meow meow meow meow meow meow meow.

Meow meow meow meow meow meow, meow meow meow meow meow meow meow, meow meow meow meow meow meow meow meow meow meow meow meow meow meow meow meow meow meow meow meow meow meow meow meow meow meow meow, meow meow meow meow, meow meow meow meow. Meow? Meow meow meow meow meow, meow? Meow meow

meow meow, meow meow meow. Meow meow meow meow meow meow meow, meow meow meow meow meow, meow meow meow meow meow meow meow! Meow meow meow meow meow meow. Meow meow meow meow meow meow meow meow. Meow meow! Meow meow meow meow meow meow meow meow meow meow meow meow meow meow, meow meow meow meow meow meow meow meow meow meow meow meow, meow meow meow meow meow meow, meow meow meow meow meow meow meow meow meow meow meow'meow meow.

Meow meow meow meow meow meow meow meow meow meow meow, meow meow meow, meow meow meow meow meow meow meow meow meow meow meow meow meow meow meow meow meow. Meow meow meow meow meow meow meow, meow, meow meow meow meow meow. Meow meow meow. Meow meow meow meow meow, meow meow meow meow meow, meow meow meow. Meow meow meow meow meow meow meow meow meow meow. Meow meow meow meow meow meow meow, meow meow meow meow meow meow meow meow meow meow meow, meow meow meow meow meow meow meow meow meow.

Meow meow meow meow meow. "Meow meow meow meow meow, meow meow," meow Meow, meow meow meow meow meow meow. Meow meow meow meow meow meow. Meow meow meow meow meow meow meow meow meow meow meow.

Meow meow meow meow meow meow meow, Meow meow meow meow meow meow meow meow meow meow meow. Meow meow meow meow meow meow. Meow meow meow meow, meow meow meow meow meow meow meow meow meow meow meow meow meow. Meow meow meow meow meow meow meow meow meow meow meow, meow meow meow meow meow meow meow meow meow meow meow meow meow. Meow meow meow meow meow, meow meow meow meow meow meow. Meow meow meow meow meow meow meow, meow meow meow meow meow meow meow. Meow meow meow meow meow meow. "Meow meow meow meow!" meow meow meow meow, meow meow meow meow meow meow meow meow meow meow meow meow.

"Meow'meow meow? Meow meow meow meow meow? Meow-meow meow!" meow meow meow meow meow meow, "Meow, Meow Meow, meow meow! Meow Meow, meow, meow meow! meow meow meow! Meow, meow meow! Meow meow meow meow meow?"

Meow meow, meow, meow meow meow meow meow meow meow meow meow meow meow meow. Meow meow meow meow meow meow meow meow meow meow meow.

Meow meow meow meow meow meow meow meow meow meow meow, meow meow meow. Meow meow meow meow. Meow meow meow meow meow meow meow.

"Meow meow'meow meow meow'meow meow meow meow meow," meow meow-meow meow meow meow meow, meow meow, meow meow meow meow, meow meow meow meow meow meow meow. "Meow meow, Meow."

"Meow meow meow meow meow meow meow meow," meow Meow.

"Meow meow meow meow meow? Meow'meow meow meow meow meow," meow Meow. "Meow meow meow meow meow meow meow meow?"

"Meow! Meow meow meow meow Meow meow meow meow meow meow meow meow meow Meow'." "Meow!"

"Meow meow meow meow meow meow? Meow'meow meow. Meow'meow meow meow meow. Meow meow meow meow meow meow meow? Meow'meow meow meow meow."

"Meow; meow Meow meow meow meow meow, meow."

"Meow, meow meow meow meow? Meow meow, Meow meow, Meow! Meow Meow meow meow meow meow meow meow!" meow meow meow meow.

"Meow meow meow meow meow, meow meow, meow meow meow meow meow meow meow meow? Meow meow meow meow meow meow meow meow meow meow meow. Meow'meow meow meow meow meow. Meow meow meow meow meow meow meow meow meow, Meow meow'meow meow meow. Meow meow meow meow meow'meow meow meow meow'meow meow, meow meow meow; meow meow meow meow meow meow meow meow meow meow meow meow meow meow meow meow!"

"Meow'meow meow meow meow meow meow?"

"Meow?"

"Meow meow'meow meow meow meow meow'meow meow meow."

"Meow.... Meow meow meow!... Meow meow meow.... Meow meow meow meow meow meow meow meow."

Meow meow meow meow meow meow meow meow-meow.

"Meow meow meow. Meow'meow meow meow meow meow, meow meow meow!"

"Meow!" meow meow meow meow meow. "Meow meow meow meow meow meow meow meow meow meow meow?" "Meow?"

"Meow meow meow'meow meow meow, meow meow meow meow meow! Meow meow meow meow meow meow meow?" "Meow?"

"Meow, meow'meow meow meow? Meow meow meow meow meow meow meow meow meow. Meow meow meow meow meow, meow meow meow meow meow meow meow meow meow meow meow meow meow meow meow meow meow meow meow meow. Meow, meow meow meow meow meow meow meow meow? Meow meow meow meow meow meow meow meow meow meow meow meow, meow'meow meow meow. Meow meow meow meow meow meow meow meow'meow meow meow meow!"

"Meow! Meow meow meow meow meow!" meow Meow, meow. "Meow meow meow meow meow meow?" Meow meow meow meow meow meow meow.

"Meow!" meow meow meow meow meow. "Meow'meow meow meow meow! Meow meow meow meow meow.... Meow, meow'meow meow meow meow meow meow meow meow meow meow meow meow'meow meow! Meow meow meow'meow meow meow meow..."

"Meow?"

"Meow meow meow meow. Meow'meow meow meow meow meow, meow meow meow meow meow."

"Meow meow."

Meow meow meow meow.

"Meow. Meow meow meow meow Meow meow meow meow meow meow."

"Meow meow?"

"Meow, meow'meow meow."

"Meow meow."

"Meow'meow meow meow meow meow meow! Meow'meow meow, meow-meow-meow meow'meow meow meow meow!" meow meow meow meow meow, meow meow meow meow.

Meow meow. Meow meow meow meow meow meow meow meow meow meow meow, meow meow, meow meow meow meow meow meow meow, meow meow meow meow-meow meow meow meow meow meow meow meow meow meow meow meow meow meow meow meow meow meow meow meow. Meow meow meow meow meow meow meow meow meow meow meow meow meow: meow meow meow meow meow meow meow meow meow meow meow meow meow meow meow meow.

Meow meow meow meow meow meow meow meow. Meow meow meow meow meow meow meow. Meow meow meow meow meow meow meow meow meow meow meow meow. Meow meow meow meow meow meow, meow meow meow meow meow meow meow meow meow meow meow meow meow meow meow meow meow meow

meow meow meow. Meow meow meow meow meow meow meow meow meow meow, meow meow meow meow, meow meow meow meow meow meow meow! "Meow meow meow!" meow meow meow meow meow meow meow meow.

"Meow meow meow meow meow meow meow?..." Meow meow meow, meow meow, meow meow—meow meow meow. Meow meow meow meow meow.

"Meow meow meow?" meow meow meow meow meow meow meow meow meow meow, meow, meow, meow meow, meow meow meow meow meow meow meow meow meow meow. Meow meow meow meow.

"Meow meow! Meow meow Meow meow meow?"

Meow meow meow meow, meow meow meow—meow meow meow meow. Meow, meow meow meow meow meow, meow meow meow, meow meow meow meow meow meow meow meow, meow meow meow.

Meow meow meow meow meow meow meow meow meow meow meow meow meow meow—meow meow meow meow! Meow meow meow meow. Meow meow meow meow meow meow meow meow.

"Meow meow! Meow meow meow!"

Meow meow meow meow meow meow meow, meow, meow meow meow meow meow meow meow meow, meow meow meow meow meow meow meow.

"Meow! Meow! Meow! Meow! Meow! Meow meow!"

Meow meow meow meow meow meow; meow meow meow meow meow meow meow; meow meow meow. Meow meow meow meow meow meow meow meow meow meow meow meow meow meow meow meow. Meow meow meow meow meow meow meow. Meow meow meow meow meow meow meow meow meow. “Meow!”

Meow meow meow meow meow meow meow meow meow, meow “meow meow meow!” Meow meow meow meow—meow meow meow; meow meow meow meow meow—meow meow meow meow; meow meow meow meow. Meow meow meow; meow meow meow meow meow meow meow—meow meow meow! Meow meow meow meow meow meow meow meow, meow meow meow meow meow meow meow meow meow meow, meow meow meow meow meow meow meow meow meow meow meow meow meow, meow meow, meow meow meow meow meow, meow meow meow meow. Meow meow meow, meow meow, meow meow meow meow meow, meow. Meow meow meow meow meow meow meow, meow meow meow meow meow meow meow meow meow meow meow meow meow meow meow meow meow. Meow meow meow meow meow meow meow meow meow meow meow meow meow meow meow meow meow meow meow meow meow meow meow; meow meow meow meow meow meow. Meow meow meow meow meow meow meow meow meow meow meow, meow meow. Meow meow, meow meow meow meow meow meow meow meow meow.

Meow meow meow meow meow meow, meow meow meow meow. Meow meow meow meow meow meow meow meow meow meow meow meow meow meow.

Meow meow, meow meow meow meow meow meow meow meow meow meow meow meow meow, meow meow meow meow meow meow meow meow meow, meow meow meow meow meow meow meow, meow meow meow meow meow meow meow meow meow, meow meow meow meow meow meow meow meow meow meow meow meow meow meow meow meow meow meow meow meow, meow meow meow meow meow meow, meow meow meow meow meow. Meow meow meow meow meow meow meow meow meow meow meow meow meow, meow meow meow meow meow. Meow meow meow meow meow meow meow meow meow, meow meow meow meow meow meow meow meow meow meow meow. “Meow meow meow meow meow meow meow meow meow meow meow meow meow? Meow, meow! Meow meow meow meow meow meow? Meow meow meow meow meow? Meow, meow!”

Meow meow meow meow meow meow. Meow meow meow meow meow meow meow meow. Meow meow meow meow meow meow meow, meow meow meow meow; meow meow meow meow meow meow meow meow meow meow meow meow, meow meow meow meow meow meow meow meow meow meow meow. Meow meow meow meow meow meow meow meow meow meow meow meow meow meow. Meow meow meow meow meow meow, meow meow meow meow meow. “Meow meow, meow meow meow meow meow!” meow meow meow meow meow meow meow meow meow meow meow meow.

Meow meow meow meow meow meow meow meow, meow meow meow
meow meow meow meow meow meow. Meow meow meow, meow meow
meow meow meow meow meow meow meow, meow meow meow meow
meow meow meow meow meow meow meow meow meow, meow meow
meow meow meow meow meow. Meow meow meow meow meow meow
meow, meow meow meow meow meow meow meow meow meow meow
meow meow meow meow meow meow.

Meow meow meow meow meow meow meow meow meow meow meow
meow meow meow! Meow meow meow meow meow meow meow meow
meow meow meow. Meow meow meow meow meow meow meow meow
meow meow, meow meow meow meow meow meow meow meow meow
meow meow meow meow meow meow. Meow meow meow meow meow
meow meow meow meow meow meow meow meow meow meow meow
meow meow meow meow meow, meow meow meow meow meow meow
meow meow'meow meow. Meow meow meow meow meow, meow meow
meow meow meow'meow meow meow meow meow meow meow, meow
meow meow meow meow meow meow meow meow meow meow meow meow.

Meow meow meow meow meow meow meow meow meow meow meow
meow meow meow meow meow meow meow meow meow. Meow meow
meow meow meow meow, "Meow meow meow meow?" meow meow meow
meow meow meow meow meow meow. Meow meow meow meow meow
meow meow meow, meow meow meow meow meow meow meow meow
meow meow meow, meow meow meow meow meow meow meow meow
meow meow meow. Meow meow meow meow, meow meow meow, meow
meow meow meow meow meow meow; meow meow'meow meow meow
meow. Meow meow meow meow meow meow, meow meow meow meow
meow meow meow meow meow meow—meow meow meow meow, meow
meow meow meow meow. Meow meow meow meow meow meow meow
meow, meow meow meow meow meow meow meow meow meow. Meow
meow meow meow meow meow meow meow meow meow meow meow, meow
meow meow meow meow meow meow, meow meow meow meow meow
meow, meow meow meow meow meow meow...

II

MEOW I

Meow meow meow meow meow meow meow. Meow meow meow meow meow meow meow meow, meow meow meow meow meow meow meow meow meow meow meow meow meow, meow meow meow meow meow meow meow meow meow meow. Meow meow meow meow meow meow meow meow meow meow meow. Meow meow meow meow meow meow, meow meow meow meow meow meow. Meow, meow meow meow meow meow meow meow, meow meow meow meow meow meow, meow, meow meow meow meow meow meow'meow. Meow meow meow meow meow.

"Meow! meow meow meow meow meow meow meow meow," meow meow, "meow'meow meow meow meow'meow," meow meow meow meow meow meow, meow meow meow meow meow meow meow meow.

"Meow! Meow meow meow'meow!"

Meow meow meow meow meow meow—meow meow meow meow! Meow meow meow, meow meow meow, meow meow meow.

Meow meow meow meow meow meow meow meow meow meow. Meow meow meow meow meow meow; meow meow meow meow meow meow meow meow meow meow meow meow meow meow meow. Meow meow meow meow meow meow meow meow, meow meow meow meow meow meow meow meow meow meow meow. Meow meow meow meow meow meow meow—meow meow meow meow meow meow. Meow meow meow meow meow meow meow meow meow meow meow meow, meow meow meow meow meow meow meow meow meow meow meow meow meow meow, meow meow meow meow meow meow meow meow meow, meow meow meow meow meow meow. Meow meow meow meow meow meow meow meow meow meow meow meow.

"Meow meow meow meow meow, meow meow meow meow meow? Meow Meow'meow meow meow..."

Meow meow meow meow meow. Meow meow meow meow, meow meow meow meow meow meow meow meow meow meow meow meow, meow meow meow; meow meow meow meow? Meow meow meow meow meow meow meow meow; meow meow meow, meow meow meow meow meow meow meow meow meow. Meow meow meow meow meow meow meow meow meow meow, meow meow meow, meow meow meow meow meow meow.

Meow meow meow meow meow meow, meow meow, meow meow meow meow, meow meow meow meow meow meow meow meow meow meow meow meow meow meow meow. Meow meow meow meow meow meow meow meow meow meow meow. Meow meow meow meow meow meow.

Meow meow meow meow meow meow meow meow meow meow meow meow meow meow meow meow meow'meow meow meow meow meow meow! Meow meow meow meow meow meow meow meow meow meow meow meow meow! Meow meow meow meow meow meow meow meow meow meow meow meow meow! Meow meow? Meow meow meow

meow meow meow meow meow meow meow meow meow meow. Meow meow meow meow meow meow, meow meow meow meow meow meow meow meow meow meow meow meow meow, meow meow meow meow meow meow meow meow. Meow meow meow meow meow meow meow meow meow meow meow meow meow meow meow. Meow meow meow meow meow meow meow meow meow meow meow meow: "Meow'meow meow! Meow meow meow meow, meow meow meow meow!" meow meow meow, meow meow meow meow meow meow meow meow meow meow meow meow meow meow. Meow meow meow meow meow meow meow; "Meow Meow!" meow meow meow meow: "meow'meow meow meow meow meow? Meow meow meow? Meow meow meow meow meow meow meow?"

Meow meow meow meow meow meow meow meow meow. Meow meow meow meow meow meow, meow meow meow meow meow meow meow-meow.

"Meow meow, meow, meow meow Meow meow meow?" meow meow, "Meow meow meow meow? Meow meow'meow meow meow—meow!"

Meow meow meow meow meow meow meow meow meow meow meow meow meow meow meow meow meow meow meow. Meow meow meow meow meow meow meow meow meow meow'meow meow meow, meow meow meow meow meow meow meow meow, meow meow meow meow meow meow meow meow meow meow meow meow meow. Meow meow meow.

Meow meow meow meow meow meow meow meow meow meow meow meow meow meow, meow meow meow meow meow meow meow meow meow meow meow.

"Meow meow Meow meow meow meow meow meow meow meow? Meow, meow; Meow meow meow meow meow meow meow meow meow! Meow meow meow, meow meow meow meow meow! Meow meow meow meow meow!"

Meow meow meow meow meow, meow meow meow meow meow meow meow meow meow meow meow meow meow meow meow.

"Meow meow meow meow meow'meow meow meow, meow meow; Meow meow meow, Meow meow meow, meow meow!" meow meow, meow meow meow meow meow meow meow, meow meow meow meow meow meow meow meow meow meow meow, meow meow meow meow meow, meow meow meow meow meow meow meow meow meow. Meow meow meow meow meow meow, meow meow, meow meow meow meow meow meow meow meow meow, meow meow meow meow meow meow.

"Meow meow meow'meow meow meow! Meow meow meow'meow meow meow meow meow meow? Meow meow!"

Meow meow meow meow meow meow meow meow meow meow meow meow meow meow meow meow meow meow meow meow meow, meow meow meow meow meow meow meow!

"Meow meow meow meow meow meow!" meow meow meow, meow meow meow.

Meow meow meow meow meow meow meow; meow, meow, meow meow meow meow meow meow meow, meow, meow, meow meow meow meow meow meow, meow meow meow meow meow meow, meow meow meow meow meow meow meow meow meow meow, meow meow meow meow... meow meow meow meow.... Meow meow meow meow meow meow meow meow meow meow meow. "Meow! Meow meow meow meow meow meow meow meow meow, meow Meow meow meow meow meow meow meow meow!"

Meow meow meow meow meow meow meow meow meow meow meow, meow!—meow meow meow, meow meow meow meow meow meow meow!

"Meow meow meow meow meow meow meow meow, meow Meow meow meow meow meow meow meow, meow Meow meow meow meow meow," meow meow meow, meow meow meow meow meow meow; "meow'meow meow meow meow meow meow, meow meow'meow meow," meow meow meow meow meow meow meow meow meow meow meow meow meow meow. Meow meow meow meow meow meow meow meow meow meow; meow meow meow meow meow meow meow meow meow, meow meow meow meow meow! Meow meow meow meow meow; "meow meow! Meow meow meow meow meow meow meow meow meow;" meow meow meow meow meow meow meow meow.... "Meow meow meow Meow meow meow meow meow meow? Meow meow Meow meow meow meow meow meow meow meow meow?"

Meow meow meow meow meow meow meow meow meow meow meow meow meow meow meow meow.

"Meow meow meow? Meow meow meow meow meow meow meow meow meow. Meow meow? Meow meow meow Meow meow meow meow? Meow meow meow meow meow. Meow, meow meow meow meow meow meow meow meow meow. Meow, meow meow meow meow," meow meow, meow meow meow meow meow meow, "meow meow meow, meow meow, meow meow..."

Meow meow meow meow meow meow meow meow. Meow meow meow meow meow meow meow meow; meow meow meow meow meow meow meow.

Meow meow meow meow meow, meow meow meow, meow meow meow meow meow meow meow "meow meow meow meow meow, meow meow, meow meow meow meow meow, meow meow meow meow meow meow meow meow meow meow meow, meow meow, meow meow!" Meow meow meow meow meow meow meow meow meow, meow meow meow.

Meow meow meow meow meow meow meow meow meow meow meow meow meow meow.

"Meow, meow, meow meow meow meow meow? Meow meow meow meow!" meow Meow, meow meow meow meow meow meow meow. "Meow meow meow meow meow'meow meow meow meow meow meow! Meow meow meow meow meow. Meow Meow meow meow. Meow'meow meow meow."

"Meow meow'meow meow meow meow," meow meow meow'meow meow.

"Meow! meow'meow meow meow'meow meow.... Meow meow meow meow?"

Meow meow meow meow meow meow meow meow. Meow meow meow meow meow meow meow meow meow.

"Meow meow meow meow meow meow meow?" meow Meow. "Meow'meow meow meow meow meow meow! Meow meow meow meow meow meow! Meow, meow meow, meow meow!"

"Meow meow meow meow? Meow meow meow? Meow'meow meow. Meow meow meow? Meow meow meow!..." Meow meow meow, meow meow meow meow meow meow.

Meow meow meow meow meow meow meow meow meow meow meow meow meow meow meow. Meow; meow meow meow Meow meow meow meow.

Meow meow meow meow meow meow meow meow. Meow meow meow meow meow meow meow meow meow meow meow, meow meow meow meow meow meow meow meow meow meow meow meow meow-meow.

"Meow meow meow meow meow," meow meow, meow meow meow meow meow meow. "Meow meow meow?"

"Meow meow meow meow meow meow, meow meow. Meow meow meow meow." "Meow meow meow?... Meow meow?..."

"Meow meow Meow meow? Meow'meow meow meow, meow meow meow."

Meow meow meow meow meow meow, meow meow meow meow meow meow meow meow meow.

"Meow'meow meow meow!" meow Meow, meow meow meow meow meow meow. Meow meow meow meow meow meow meow meow. "Meow'meow meow meow meow meow meow meow," meow meow.

Meow meow meow meow meow meow meow meow meow meow meow, meow meow meow. "Meow'meow meow meow meow meow," Meow meow meow meow, meow meow meow meow meow meow meow meow meow meow meow. "Meow'meow meow, meow meow meow'meow meow; meow'meow meow meow meow. Meow meow meow meow meow?"

Meow meow; meow meow meow meow meow meow meow meow meow meow meow meow meow meow, meow meow, meow meow meow meow meow meow. Meow meow meow meow meow meow meow meow meow meow. Meow meow meow meow, meow meow meow meow meow meow meow meow meow, meow meow meow meow meow meow meow meow meow meow meow meow meow meow meow.

"Meow meow meow meow meow'meow meow meow meow meow meow, meow meow meow meow meow meow meow meow meow..."

Meow Meow meow meow meow meow meow meow.

Meow meow meow meow meow meow meow meow meow meow meow meow meow meow meow meow. Meow meow meow meow meow meow meow meow meow meow meow meow meow, meow meow meow meow meow meow meow meow meow meow meow meow meow meow meow meow meow meow meow. "Meow... meow meow?"

"Meow'meow meow meow meow meow! Meow? Meow'meow meow meow, meow'meow meow meow." "Meow... Meow'meow meow; Meow'meow meow meow meow," meow meow, meow meow meow meow meow. "Meow, meow'meow meow meow meow!"

"Meow, Meow'meow meow."

"Meow meow meow."

Meow meow meow meow meow.

Meow meow meow meow meow meow meow meow meow meow meow meow meow meow.

"Meow meow meow, meow meow meow meow; meow meow meow meow, meow meow meow meow meow. Meow meow meow meow meow meow meow meow. Meow meow meow meow meow meow meow meow, meow Meow!" Meow meow meow meow meow meow meow meow meow meow meow meow meow; meow meow meow meow meow meow, meow meow meow. Meow meow meow meow meow meow meow meow meow-meow meow meow meow meow meow meow-meow meow meow meow meow meow meow meow meow.

"Meow meow meow meow meow meow meow? Meow meow meow meow meow meow meow meow meow! Meow meow meow meow-meow?" meow meow meow meow meow. "Meow Meow, meow meow meow meow meow!"

Meow meow meow meow meow meow meow meow meow, meow meow meow meow—meow meow meow meow meow meow, meow meow meow.

Meow meow, meow meow. "Meow Meow'meow meow, Meow meow meow, Meow meow'meow meow! Meow Meow meow meow meow meow?" meow meow meow, "meow meow meow meow meow meow meow meow meow meow meow."

Meow meow meow meow meow meow meow meow meow meow meow meow meow meow meow meow meow meow. Meow meow meow meow, meow meow meow meow meow meow meow meow, meow meow meow meow meow meow meow meow meow—meow meow meow meow.

"Meow'meow meow meow, meow'meow meow meow, meow meow meow meow meow meow meow," meow meow meow meow meow, meow meow meow meow meow meow meow meow meow, meow meow meow meow meow meow, "meow, Meow'meow meow meow meow! Meow meow meow meow meow meow meow!"

Meow meow meow meow meow meow meow meow.

"Meow, meow'meow meow meow meow meow..." meow meow. Meow meow meow. "Meow meow," meow meow. Meow meow meow meow meow meow meow. "Meow'meow meow meow! Meow meow meow meow meow meow meow meow meow meow," meow meow, meow meow meow meow meow meow meow meow—"meow meow meow meow meow Meow'meow meow meow- meow... Meow meow meow meow meow meow..."

Meow meow meow meow meow meow meow meow meow meow meow meow meow meow meow meow meow meow meow meow meow meow, "meow meow meow, meow'meow meow meow meow meow meow

Meow'meow meow," meow meow, meow meow meow. Meow meow meow meow meow meow meow, meow meow meow meow, meow meow meow meow meow meow, meow meow meow meow meow meow meow meow meow meow. "Meow meow meow meow meow!"

Meow meow meow meow meow meow meow meow; meow meow meow meow meow meow meow meow meow meow. Meow meow, meow meow meow, meow meow meow meow meow meow meow meow-meow, meow meow meow meow, meow Meow meow meow meow-meow-meow meow. Meow meow meow meow meow meow meow, meow meow meow meow meow meow meow meow meow meow, meow meow meow meow meow meow meow—meow meow meow meow meow meow meow meow meow meow meow meow meow meow meow meow meow meow meow meow meow meow meow.

Meow meow meow meow meow meow meow meow, meow meow meow meow meow meow meow meow meow... meow meow meow... meow meow meow meow meow meow.

"Meow meow meow meow, meow Meow'meow meow meow," meow meow, meow meow meow meow meow meow-meow.

Meow meow-meow meow meow meow meow meow meow meow meow. Meow meow meow meow meow meow meow meow meow meow meow meow meow meow meow meow. Meow meow meow meow meow meow meow meow meow meow meow meow meow meow. Meow meow meow meow meow, meow meow meow meow meow meow meow meow meow meow meow meow meow meow meow meow meow meow meow meow meow. "Meow meow-meow, meow meow; meow meow, meow meow meow meow," meow meow meow meow meow meow meow meow meow. Meow meow meow meow meow meow meow meow meow.

"Meow'meow meow meow, meow meow meow meow, meow meow meow..." meow meow, meow meow meow meow meow meow.

Meow meow meow meow, meow meow meow meow meow meow meow. Meow meow meow meow meow meow meow meow meow meow meow meow meow meow meow meow meow. Meow meow meow meow meow meow meow meow. Meow meow meow meow meow meow meow meow meow meow meow meow meow meow meow meow, meow, meow meow meow meow meow meow meow meow. Meow meow meow meow meow, meow, meow meow meow. Meow meow meow meow. Meow, meow, meow meow meow meow meow meow meow meow meow meow meow meow meow meow meow meow meow meow meow meow meow meow.

Meow meow meow meow, meow meow meow meow meow meow meow meow meow. Meow meow meow meow meow meow meow-meow. Meow meow meow meow meow meow meow meow. Meow meow meow meow meow meow. Meow meow meow meow meow meow meow meow, meow meow meow meow meow meow, meow meow meow meow-meow meow. Meow meow meow meow meow meow meow.

"Meow meow meow?"

Meow meow meow meow meow meow meow.

"Meow meow meow meow?" meow meow meow, meow meow meow meow.

"Meow, meow meow meow."

Meow meow meow meow meow, meow meow meow meow meow. Meow meow meow meow meow meow meow meow meow meow meow meow meow meow meow meow.

"Meow meow meow meow meow meow meow meow meow, meow meow meow meow meow meow meow," meow Meow.

"Meow meow meow meow meow meow meow," meow meow meow, meow meow meow meow meow.

Meow meow meow meow meow—meow meow meow meow; meow meow meow meow meow meow meow meow meow meow, meow meow meow meow meow meow meow meow. Meow meow meow meow meow. Meow, meow meow meow meow, meow meow meow meow meow meow meow meow, meow meow meow meow meow. Meow meow, meow meow meow, meow meow meow meow meow-meow, meow meow, meow meow meow meow meow meow meow meow meow meow meow meow meow meow, meow meow meow meow meow, meow meow meow meow. Meow meow meow meow meow meow meow meow. Meow meow meow meow meow, meow: "Meow meow meow," meow meow meow meow meow meow meow meow meow.

Meow meow meow meow. "Meow meow'meow meow meow!"

Meow meow meow meow meow meow meow, meow meow meow meow meow meow meow meow meow meow.

"Meow meow, meow meow meow, meow Meow meow meow meow! Meow... meow'meow meow meow meow'meow meow meow meow," meow meow, "meow'meow meow.... Meow meow meow'meow meow meow meow meow... meow meow'meow meow meow..."

Meow meow meow meow meow meow meow meow. Meow meow meow meow meow meow meow-meow; meow meow meow meow meow meow meow meow meow meow meow meow, meow meow meow, meow meow meow meow meow meow meow meow meow. Meow meow meow meow meow meow meow, meow meow meow meow meow meow meow meow meow meow meow meow meow.

Meow meow meow meow meow meow, meow meow meow meow, meow meow meow meow meow meow meow meow meow meow meow. Meow meow meow meow meow meow, meow meow meow meow meow meow meow, meow meow meow meow, meow meow meow meow meow meow meow meow meow-meow meow meow meow meow meow meow meow meow. Meow meow meow meow meow meow meow Meow meow meow meow meow meow meow meow meow, meow meow meow meow meow.

"Meow Meow, meow meow meow meow," meow meow meow meow meow meow-meow, meow-meow meow, meow meow meow meow meow meow meow meow meow meow meow, meow meow meow meow meow meow meow.

"Meow meow," meow meow meow, meow meow, meow meow meow meow meow meow meow meow meow meow. Meow meow meow meow

meow meow meow meow meow meow meow meow meow meow meow-meow meow meow meow meow meow meow. Meow meow meow meow. Meow meow meow meow meow meow meow meow meow meow meow meow meow meow meow meow; meow meow meow meow meow meow meow meow meow meow, meow meow meow meow.

Meow meow meow meow meow meow meow meow, meow meow meow. Meow meow meow, meow meow meow, meow meow meow meow meow meow, meow meow meow meow meow meow meow meow meow meow. Meow meow meow meow meow meow meow meow meow meow meow meow meow meow-meow. Meow meow meow meow meow meow meow meow meow meow meow, meow meow meow meow meow meow meow meow meow; meow meow meow meow meow meow meow meow meow meow, meow meow meow meow meow meow meow meow meow meow meow. Meow meow meow meow meow. Meow meow meow meow meow meow meow meow meow meow meow meow meow meow meow, meow meow meow meow, meow meow meow meow meow meow meow meow. Meow meow meow meow meow meow meow Meow; meow meow meow meow meow meow, meow meow meow meow meow meow meow, meow meow meow meow meow meow meow meow meow meow meow. Meow meow meow meow meow meow meow meow meow meow meow meow, meow meow meow meow meow meow.

"Meow meow meow meow?" meow meow, meow meow meow meow meow meow meow meow meow meow meow meow meow meow meow meow.

"Meow meow meow... meow meow meow..." Meow meow.

"Meow meow meow meow meow meow, meow meow meow," meow meow meow meow meow, meow meow meow meow meow. "Meow!" meow meow meow Meow meow meow meow meow meow meow meow. "Meow meow!"

"Meow? Meow meow?" meow Meow, "meow... meow... meow'meow meow meow meow."

Meow meow meow meow meow. Meow meow meow meow meow meow. Meow meow meow meow meow

meow meow.

"Meow meow, meow meow meow meow meow meow meow, meow?" meow meow meow meow, meow meow meow meow meow meow meow meow meow. "Meow meow meow meow meow meow meow, meow meow meow'meow meow!"

"Meow meow meow meow meow meow meow meow meow meow meow meow," Meow meow meow meow meow meow. Meow meow meow meow, meow, meow meow meow meow meow meow meow meow meow meow. "Meow meow'meow meow meow Meow meow meow meow meow meow meow."

"Meow meow meow meow!"

"Meow'meow meow meow, Meow'meow meow meow meow, meow'meow meow meow meow meow meow meow. Meow'meow meow meow, meow meow meow meow meow meow meow meow."

Meow meow meow meow meow meow meow meow meow meow meow meow meow meow meow meow. Meow meow meow meow meow meow.

"Meow meow! Meow meow meow meow meow meow. Meow'meow meow meow, meow!"

"Meow'meow meow meow meow meow, meow," meow Meow, "meow meow'meow meow meow meow meow meow meow meow, meow meow meow meow meow meow meow meow meow."

Meow meow meow meow meow meow meow meow meow.

Meow meow meow meow meow meow meow meow meow. Meow meow meow meow meow meow meow.

"Meow'meow meow meow meow!" meow meow meow meow meow meow meow. "Meow meow meow meow meow meow meow. Meow meow. Meow Meow. Meow meow meow meow meow meow! Meow meow'meow meow meow meow! Meow'meow meow meow meow!"

Meow Meow meow meow meow meow; meow meow meow meow meow meow meow, meow meow meow meow meow meow. Meow meow meow meow, meow meow meow meow, meow meow meow meow meow.

"Meow meow meow?" meow meow meow meow meow.

"Meow meow meow meow meow meow meow meow meow Meow Meow Meow, meow meow. Meow meow meow meow meow, meow meow meow, meow meow meow meow, meow meow meow meow meow meow meow meow meow meow, meow meow meow meow meow meow meow meow meow meow meow meow meow meow meow, meow meow meow meow meow meow meow meow. Meow meow meow meow meow meow meow meow meow, meow meow meow meow meow meow meow meow."

"Meow Meow... meow meow meow meow meow meow!"

"Meow'meow meow meow meow. Meow, meow Meow Meow Meow meow meow meow meow meow meow, meow meow, meow meow meow meow, meow meow meow meow meow meow, meow meow meow meow meow meow meow meow meow Meow, meow meow meow, meow meow meow meow meow meow Meow meow meow Meow. Meow. Meow meow meow meow, meow."

"Meow meow meow meow meow!"

"Meow meow meow meow meow meow meow?"

Meow meow meow meow meow meow meow meow meow meow meow meow, meow meow meow meow meow meow meow meow meow, meow meow meow meow meow meow meow meow meow meow—meow meow meow meow meow: "Meow, meow meow meow meow meow?" Meow meow meow meow meow meow meow meow Meow Meow Meow, meow meow meow meow meow! Meow meow meow meow meow meow, meow meow meow meow meow! Meow meow, meow meow, meow meow, meow meow, meow meow meow meow meow, meow meow meow. Meow meow meow meow meow, meow meow meow meow meow, meow meow meow meow meow meow meow meow meow meow meow meow meow meow meow, meow meow, meow meow meow meow, meow meow meow meow meow. Meow meow meow meow meow meow, meow, meow meow meow. Meow meow meow meow meow meow meow meow meow meow meow meow meow

meow. Meow meow meow, meow meow meow Meow’meow meow, meow meow meow meow meow meow meow meow meow meow meow, meow meow meow meow meow meow, meow meow meow meow meow meow meow meow meow meow meow meow meow meow meow meow.

“Meow meow meow!” meow meow meow meow meow meow meow meow. (Meow meow meow meow meow meow meow meow.) “Meow meow meow meow meow meow meow meow meow meow? Meow! Meow meow meow, meow’meow meow meow meow meow meow meow. Meow meow meow meow. Meow meow meow meow meow meow meow? Meow, Meow meow meow meow meow meow meow meow Meow meow meow meow meow meow meow meow! Meow meow meow meow meow, meow, meow… meow…!”

Meow meow meow meow meow Meow’meow meow, meow meow meow meow meow meow meow meow meow meow meow meow meow. Meow meow meow meow meow meow meow, meow meow meow meow meow meow meow meow meow meow meow. Meow meow meow meow, meow meow meow meow meow meow meow meow… meow meow meow meow meow meow.

“Meow Meow!” meow meow meow meow meow meow, meow meow meow, meow meow meow meow meow meow meow meow meow meow meow meow meow meow meow meow.

Meow meow meow meow meow, meow meow meow meow meow meow meow meow. Meow, meow meow meow, meow meow meow meow meow meow meow meow meow meow, meow meow meow meow meow, meow meow meow meow meow meow meow meow meow meow meow meow. Meow meow meow, meow meow meow, meow meow meow meow meow meow meow meow meow meow: meow meow meow meow meow meow.

“Meow meow meow meow meow meow meow meow meow meow meow, Meow. Meow,” meow meow meow meow meow, meow meow meow, meow Meow meow, meow meow meow meow Meow meow, “meow meow meow meow meow, meow meow meow meow meow, meow meow’meow meow meow meow Meow meow meow, Meow. Meow, meow Meow meow meow meow meow…. Meow meow meow meow meow, Meow. Meow, meow meow meow, Meow. Meow, meow Meow meow, meow meow meow meow meow. Meow meow meow meow meow, meow meow meow meow meow meow, meow meow meow meow meow meow meow, meow meow meow meow meow meow meow meow, meow meow meow meow meow meow meow meow meow meow meow, meow meow meow meow meow meow, meow meow meow meow meow meow meow meow Meow meow meow. Meow meow meow meow meow meow meow meow meow meow meow meow. Meow meow Meow meow meow meow, meow Meow meow, meow meow meow Meow meow meow meow meow meow meow; meow meow meow Meow meow meow meow, meow, meow meow meow meow meow meow meow meow. Meow meow meow meow meow meow meow meow meow, Meow. Meow, meow Meow meow. Meow meow meow meow meow meow meow meow, meow meow meow meow meow, meow meow meow meow meow; meow meow meow meow. Meow meow meow meow meow meow

meow meow meow meow meow meow meow meow! Meow meow meow! Meow Meow meow meow meow meow meow meow meow meow meow, meow meow meow meow, Meow. Meow, meow meow meow meow. Meow meow meow meow meow meow meow meow meow meow meow meow. Meow Meow meow meow meow, Meow. Meow, meow meow meow meow meow. Meow meow meow meow meow meow meow meow meow meow meow. 'Meow meow meow meow meow,' meow meow, 'meow Meow meow meow meow meow meow meow meow meow.'"

"Meow meow meow meow meow?"

"Meow, Meow. Meow, meow meow meow meow meow meow meow meow meow...." "Meow meow! Meow! Meow meow meow meow meow..."

"Meow Meow!" meow meow meow meow meow.

Meow meow meow meow meow meow; meow meow meow meow meow meow meow.

"... Meow Meow meow meow meow, meow meow Meow Meow, meow Meow meow meow meow meow meow meow meow," meow meow meow meow. "Meow meow meow meow meow meow meow meow meow meow meow, Meow meow meow meow meow meow meow meow-meow, meow meow meow meow meow meow meow. Meow meow meow? Meow meow meow meow, meow meow meow meow meow meow meow meow-meow meow meow 'meow meow'? Meow meow meow, meow meow!"

Meow meow meow meow meow meow meow Meow. "Meow meow meow meow meow meow meow meow meow meow, meow. Meow meow meow meow meow meow meow meow meow meow; 'Meow'meow meow meow meow meow meow,' meow meow. Meow meow meow meow meow meow meow meow meow meow meow meow meow meow meow meow meow meow meow meow meow meow meow meow, meow meow meow meow. Meow meow meow meow meow meow meow meow meow meow meow'meow meow meow meow meow. Meow meow meow meow, meow, meow meow, meow, meow-meow.... Meow! Meow meow meow! Meow meow meow meow meow meow meow meow meow. Meow meow meow meow meow meow! Meow meow meow?"

Meow meow meow, Meow Meow meow meow meow meow meow meow, meow meow meow meow meow meow meow. Meow meow meow meow, meow meow meow meow meow meow-meow meow meow meow meow, meow meow meow meow meow meow meow. Meow meow meow meow meow meow meow meow, Meow Meow. Meow Meow meow meow meow meow meow meow meow meow, meow meow meow meow meow, meow meow meow meow meow meow.

"Meow meow meow meow—meow meow!" meow Meow Meow meow Meow Meow meow meow meow meow meow meow. "Meow meow meow meow, meow meow meow meow! Meow meow meow meow meow meow!"

"Meow, meow meow!" Meow Meow meow meow meow meow; meow meow meow meow meow meow meow meow meow, meow meow meow meow meow meow meow meow meow meow. "Meow, meow meow meow meow meow: meow meow, meow meow meow, meow meow meow meow meow, meow meow meow meow meow, meow meow meow Meow Meow

Meow, meow'meow meow meow meow meow meow, meow meow meow meow meow meow meow meow, meow meow meow meow meow meow meow meow meow meow meow meow meow meow meow meow! Meow meow meow meow meow meow, meow meow meow meow meow, meow. Meow'meow meow meow, meow meow meow meow meow!"

"Meow meow meow meow meow, meow meow, meow meow meow meow meow meow meow meow, meow meow'meow meow meow meow, Meow meow meow meow meow meow meow meow meow meow meow meow," meow Meow Meow, meow meow meow Meow. "Meow meow meow meow meow; meow meow meow meow meow, Meow meow meow, meow meow, meow! Meow meow meow, meow meow, meow meow, meow meow meow meow! Meow meow meow'meow meow meow! Meow meow meow meow meow'meow meow meow meow meow! Meow meow meow meow meow meow meow Meow Meow...."

"Meow meow meow meow meow meow, meow," meow Meow Meow, meow meow meow meow meow meow, meow meow meow.

Meow meow meow meow meow meow meow meow meow meow meow meow meow. "Meow meow, Meow," meow meow meow, meow meow Meow Meow, "meow meow meow meow meow meow?... Meow meow meow meow meow meow, meow Meow meow meow meow-meow. Meow meow meow meow meow, meow meow meow (meow meow meow meow meow meow) meow meow. Meow meow meow meow, meow Meow meow meow meow meow, meow Meow meow meow meow.... Meow meow meow meow meow meow meow meow meow meow Meow. Meow meow meow meow meow meow, meow Meow meow meow. Meow meow meow meow meow-meow meow, meow meow meow meow meow meow meow meow meow meow meow, meow meow meow meow meow meow meow meow meow, meow meow meow meow meow meow meow meow meow... meow Meow meow'meow meow meow Meow Meow Meow meow meow. Meow meow meow meow meow meow meow meow meow Meow Meow Meow. Meow meow Meow meow meow meow? Meow meow meow!..."

"Meow meow meow meow meow meow, meow meow," meow meow meow meow meow.

"Meow, meow. Meow meow meow meow meow. Meow meow meow meow meow..." Meow meow meow meow, meow meow Meow Meow, meow meow meow meow meow meow Meow Meow meow, meow meow meow meow meow meow meow meow meow meow meow meow meow meow meow meow meow meow. "Meow meow meow meow meow Meow meow meow meow meow meow meow meow meow meow meow meow meow... meow meow... meow meow meow Meow meow meow meow, meow meow meow meow Meow meow meow meow meow meow, meow meow meow meow meow, meow meow... meow meow meow meow... meow, Meow meow meow, meow Meow meow meow meow meow meow meow... meow meow meow meow meow... meow meow, Meow meow meow meow, meow meow meow meow meow meow meow meow meow meow, meow Meow meow meow meow meow... Meow meow meow meow..."

“Meow meow meow meow meow meow meow, meow, meow’meow meow meow meow meow,” Meow Meow meow meow meow meow meow meow meow meow; meow Meow meow meow meow, meow meow meow meow meow meow meow meow meow.

“Meow meow meow, meow meow. Meow meow meow meow meow meow... meow meow meow meow... Meow meow meow... meow Meow meow meow meow... meow meow meow. Meow meow meow meow, meow meow meow meow meow. Meow meow meow meow meow meow, meow meow meow meow meow meow meow meow meow, meow meow meow meow... meow meow meow meow meow... meow meow meow meow meow meow meow, meow meow, meow Meow meow meow meow meow Meow Meow Meow meow meow meow meow meow meow, meow meow meow Meow meow meow. Meow meow meow meow Meow meow meow meow, meow meow meow meow meow, meow meow meow Meow meow, meow meow meow meow meow, meow—meow meow meow meow meow—meow meow meow meow Meow Meow Meow meow Meow meow meow meow meow... meow meow, meow Meow meow meow meow meow meow meow meow meow meow, meow meow meow meow meow. Meow meow Meow meow meow meow meow?”

“Meow meow meow meow meow meow meow meow meow.” Meow Meow meow meow. “Meow meow meow meow meow meow meow meow meow meow meow meow meow meow meow meow meow, meow meow meow meow meow meow meow.”

“Meow meow... meow meow meow,” meow Meow Meow, meow meow meow meow meow meow meow meow meow meow. Meow meow meow meow meow.

“Meow!” meow meow meow meow meow Meow. “Meow meow?” meow meow meow, meow.

“Meow meow meow meow meow.”

Meow meow meow meow meow meow meow meow meow meow meow meow meow meow meow, meow meow meow meow meow meow meow meow meow meow meow’meow meow, meow meow meow meow meow meow meow meow, meow meow meow. Meow meow meow meow meow meow meow meow, meow meow meow meow meow meow meow meow meow meow meow meow meow meow meow meow meow meow, meow meow meow meow meow. Meow meow meow meow meow meow meow? Meow meow meow meow meow meow meow meow, meow meow meow meow, meow meow meow meow meow meow meow meow, meow meow meow meow meow meow meow meow meow meow, meow meow meow meow meow. Meow meow meow meow, meow meow meow meow, meow meow meow meow meow meow. Meow meow meow meow meow meow meow meow meow meow Meow Meow, meow meow meow meow meow meow’meow meow meow meow meow meow meow meow meow meow meow meow meow. Meow, meow meow meow meow meow meow meow meow meow meow, meow meow meow meow meow, meow, Meow meow, meow, meow-meow? Meow meow meow meow meow meow meow meow meow meow meow, meow meow meow meow meow, meow meow

meow meow meow meow meow meow meow. Meow meow meow meow meow meow meow, meow meow meow. Meow meow meow meow meow meow, meow meow meow meow meow meow meow meow meow meow meow meow meow meow meow meow meow meow meow meow meow meow-meow meow meow meow meow meow meow meow, meow meow meow meow; meow meow meow meow meow meow meow meow meow meow meow meow meow meow-meow, meow meow meow meow meow meow meow meow meow meow meow meow meow meow meow meow meow meow. Meow meow meow meow meow meow meow meow meow meow. Meow meow meow meow meow—meow meow meow meow meow meow meow meow meow meow, meow meow meow, meow meow meow meow meow meow meow meow meow meow meow meow meow.

Meow meow meow meow meow meow meow meow meow meow meow meow, meow meow meow meow meow, meow meow meow meow meow meow meow meow meow meow, meow meow meow meow meow meow meow, meow meow meow meow, meow meow meow.

"Meow meow meow'meow meow, meow meow meow meow meow meow," meow meow meow meow, meow meow meow meow Meow. "Meow meow meow?"

"Meow, Meow meow meow. Meow meow!"

"Meow'meow meow. Meow meow."

Meow meow meow meow meow meow, meow meow meow meow meow meow.

Meow meow meow meow meow; meow meow meow meow meow meow meow meow, meow meow meow meow meow meow meow meow meow meow meow meow meow meow meow. Meow meow meow meow meow meow meow meow meow meow meow meow. Meow meow meow meow meow meow, meow meow meow meow meow, meow meow meow meow Meow Meow, meow meow meow meow meow meow meow meow, meow meow meow meow meow meow meow meow meow meow meow meow meow meow meow meow meow meow meow meow meow. Meow meow meow meow meow meow meow meow meow meow meow meow meow meow meow meow meow. "Meow'meow Meow meow meow meow meow?" meow meow meow meow. "Meow, meow meow meow meow meow meow meow." Meow meow meow meow meow meow meow, meow meow meow meow. Meow Meow meow meow meow meow Meow Meow, meow meow meow meow meow:

"Meow'meow meow, meow'meow meow meow meow. Meow meow meow, meow meow meow meow meow. Meow meow meow meow meow meow meow, meow meow meow meow meow meow? Meow meow meow meow? Meow meow meow meow? Meow, meow meow meow meow meow! Meow, Meow, meow meow, meow meow meow meow meow meow meow meow meow meow meow meow meow meow meow meow. Meow meow meow meow meow meow, meow meow meow meow meow meow meow, meow meow meow meow meow meow meow meow, meow meow meow meow meow meow. Meow, meow meow meow meow meow meow meow meow meow meow meow meow meow meow meow? Meow meow Meow,

meow meow meow meow meow meow meow meow'meow meow, meow meow meow meow meow meow meow meow meow meow meow meow meow meow meow meow meow meow. Meow meow meow..."

"Meow meow meow, meow meow meow meow meow meow? Meow meow meow meow meow meow meow meow meow meow meow; meow meow meow meow meow meow meow meow meow meow meow, meow meow meow meow meow meow meow."

"Meow'meow meow meow; meow meow meow meow meow meow meow meow meow meow; meow meow'meow meow meow meow meow meow meow Meow meow meow meow meow meow meow meow meow meow meow meow meow meow. Meow meow meow meow meow meow meow meow meow meow meow meow meow. Meow meow meow meow meow meow: 'Meow Meow meow meow meow, meow meow meow meow meow meow meow meow meow meow meow.' Meow meow meow meow meow meow meow meow—meow, meow!"

"Meow meow meow meow meow meow?"

"Meow meow meow meow meow meow; meow meow meow meow meow Meow'meow Meow," meow meow meow meow, meow meow meow.

"Meow'meow meow, meow meow," Meow Meow meow meow.

"Meow, meow meow meow meow meow," Meow Meow meow.

Meow meow meow meow meow meow meow meow meow meow, meow meow meow meow meow meow....

Meow meow meow meow, meow meow meow meow meow meow meow, meow meow meow meow meow meow meow, meow meow meow meow meow meow meow meow, meow meow meow meow meow meow meow, meow Meow Meow meow meow meow, meow meow meow meow. Meow meow meow meow meow meow.

"Meow'meow meow? Meow meow meow?" Meow Meow meow, meow meow.

"Meow meow meow meow meow meow meow meow meow meow," meow meow meow meow, meow meow meow meow meow, meow meow meow meow meow meow.

"Meow meow meow meow meow?" meow Meow Meow meow meow meow, meow meow, meow, meow meow meow meow. Meow meow, meow meow, meow meow meow meow meow meow meow meow meow meow, meow meow meow meow meow meow meow.

"Meow meow," meow Meow meow meow. "Meow meow meow meow meow?"

"Meow."

"Meow meow meow meow?"

"Meow."

"Meow meow meow?" "Meow meow."

"Meow meow meow meow meow, meow Meow meow?"

"Meow meow meow."

"Meow meow meow."

Meow, meow meow meow meow, meow meow meow, meow, meow meow meow meow meow meow meow Meow Meow'meow meow.

"Meow meow meow meow meow. Meow meow..." Meow Meow meow meow. "Meow meow," Meow Meow meow meow meow.

Meow Meow meow meow meow meow meow meow, meow meow meow meow meow meow meow meow meow meow meow meow meow, meow meow meow meow. Meow meow meow meow meow. Meow meow meow.

"Meow meow, meow," meow Meow Meow, "meow meow meow meow meow."

Meow meow meow. Meow meow meow meow meow meow meow meow meow meow, meow meow meow meow meow meow meow meow meow Meow Meow. Meow meow meow, meow meow meow meow meow.

"Meow meow—meow meow meow meow meow meow meow," meow meow meow meow, meow meow. "Meow meow! meow meow."

Meow meow meow meow meow meow meow.

MEOW II

“Meow meow meow meow meow meow meow meow meow? Meow meow Meow meow meow meow meow meow?”

Meow meow meow meow meow. Meow meow meow meow meow meow. Meow meow meow meow meow. Meow Meow meow meow meow meow. Meow meow! meow meow meow meow meow meow meow meow meow meow meow?

Meow meow meow meow meow, meow meow meow meow meow meow, meow meow meow meow meow meow meow meow meow meow. Meow meow meow meow meow meow: meow meow meow meow meow-meow meow meow meow meow meow, meow meow meow meow meow; meow meow meow meow meow. Meow meow meow meow, meow, meow meow meow meow meow meow meow meow meow, meow meow meow meow meow.... Meow meow meow meow meow meow meow meow meow meow meow, meow meow meow meow meow meow meow, meow meow meow meow meow meow meow meow. Meow meow meow meow, meow. Meow meow meow meow meow meow meow, meow meow meow meow. Meow meow meow meow meow, meow meow meow meow meow, meow meow meow meow meow meow. Meow meow meow meow meow, meow meow meow meow meow meow meow-meow, meow meow meow meow meow meow, meow meow meow meow meow meow meow, meow meow meow meow meow, meow meow meow meow meow meow meow. Meow meow meow meow meow meow meow meow meow meow meow, meow meow meow meow meow.... Meow meow meow meow meow?

Meow meow meow meow meow: “Meow meow meow meow meow, meow meow meow meow meow meow meow, meow meow meow meow meow meow meow.” Meow meow meow meow meow meow meow meow meow meow meow meow meow meow meow meow meow meow meow meow meow meow meow meow meow meow, meow meow meow, meow meow meow meow meow meow. Meow meow meow meow meow meow, meow meow meow meow meow meow meow meow. Meow meow meow meow meow meow meow Meow Meow meow meow meow meow meow meow meow meow meow meow meow meow meow meow meow meow meow meow, meow meow meow meow meow meow meow meow meow meow; meow meow meow meow meow meow meow’ meow, meow meow meow meow meow meow meow, meow meow meow meow meow, meow meow meow meow meow. Meow meow meow meow meow meow meow meow meow meow meow meow meow; meow meow meow meow meow meow meow meow meow meow meow meow, meow, meow meow meow meow meow. Meow meow meow meow meow meow meow meow meow meow meow? Meow meow meow meow meow. Meow meow meow meow, meow meow meow meow meow meow meow meow meow, meow meow meow meow meow meow meow meow meow meow meow. “Meow meow meow, meow meow meow meow meow meow?” meow meow.

Meow meow meow meow meow meow meow meow meow meow meow meow meow meow meow Meow. Meow meow meow meow meow meow

meow, meow meow meow meow meow, meow meow meow meow meow meow meow meow meow, meow meow meow meow meow meow. Meow meow meow meow meow meow meow meow meow meow meow meow-meow, meow meow meow meow meow meow meow meow meow meow meow meow. Meow meow meow-meow meow meow meow meow meow meow meow, meow meow meow meow meow meow meow meow meow! Meow meow meow meow meow meow meow meow meow meow meow meow meow. Meow meow meow meow meow.

Meow meow meow meow Meow meow Meow—— Meow, meow meow meow meow meow meow meow meow. “Meow meow meow Meow? Meow meow meow meow meow meow meow meow meow meow, meow meow Meow meow, meow meow meow meow meow meow meow meow meow, meow meow meow meow meow meow meow, meow meow meow meow meow?” Meow meow meow meow meow meow meow meow, meow meow meow meow meow meow meow meow. Meow meow meow meow meow meow meow meow. Meow meow meow meow Meow—— Meow meow meow meow, meow meow meow meow meow meow meow meow meow meow meow meow meow meow meow. Meow meow meow meow, meow meow meow meow meow meow meow-meow meow meow meow meow meow meow; meow meow meow, meow meow meow meow meow meow meow meow meow meow meow meow, meow meow meow meow meow meow meow. Meow meow meow meow meow-meow meow meow meow meow meow meow meow meow. Meow meow meow meow meow meow, meow meow meow meow meow, meow, meow meow, meow meow meow meow meow, meow meow meow meow meow. Meow meow meow meow meow meow’meow meow meow’meow meow; meow meow meow meow meow meow meow meow meow meow meow. Meow meow meow meow meow meow meow meow, meow meow. Meow meow meow meow meow meow, meow meow meow, meow meow meow meow meow meow meow meow meow, meow meow meow meow meow meow meow meow meow meow meow meow meow meow-meow; meow meow meow meow meow meow meow meow meow meow meow meow- meow meow, “Meow meow meow meow.” Meow meow meow meow meow, meow meow meow meow meow meow meow meow meow meow. “Meow Meow meow meow meow meow meow meow meow meow meow meow!”

Meow meow meow meow, meow meow meow meow meow meow meow, meow meow meow meow meow meow, meow meow meow meow meow meow, meow meow meow meow, meow meow meow meow. Meow meow meow meow meow meow meow meow meow. Meow meow meow meow-meow, meow meow meow meow meow, meow meow meow meow meow meow meow meow meow, meow meow meow meow meow meow meow, meow meow meow meow meow, meow meow meow meow meow meow.

Meow meow meow meow meow meow, meow meow meow meow meow meow meow meow meow, meow meow meow meow meow meow meow meow. Meow meow meow meow meow meow meow meow meow meow, meow meow meow meow meow meow meow meow. Meow meow meow meow meow meow, meow meow meow meow meow meow meow meow.

Meow meow meow meow meow meow meow meow meow meow meow meow meow, meow meow meow meow meow meow meow meow meow, meow meow meow meow meow meow meow. Meow meow meow meow meow meow meow meow meow meow meow meow meow meow meow. Meow meow meow meow.

Meow meow meow meow, meow meow meow meow meow. Meow meow meow, meow meow meow meow meow meow meow meow, meow meow meow meow meow meow-meow. "Meow meow meow meow meow! Meow meow, meow meow meow meow meow meow meow meow? Meow meow meow meow meow meow meow meow meow meow meow meow meow, meow meow meow meow meow meow meow. Meow meow meow meow meow, meow meow meow meow meow? Meow meow meow meow! Meow meow!" Meow meow meow. Meow, meow meow meow meow meow meow meow meow, meow meow meow, meow meow meow meow meow meow meow meow meow meow meow meow. Meow meow meow meow meow Meow—— Meow meow meow meow meow meow meow meow meow meow meow, meow meow meow meow. Meow meow meow meow meow meow. Meow meow meow meow meow meow meow meow meow meow meow meow meow meow meow meow meow meow meow meow meow, meow meow meow meow meow, meow meow meow meow meow meow, meow, meow meow meow meow meow meow meow meow meow meow meow meow meow: "Meow meow!"

Meow meow, meow meow meow meow meow meow. Meow meow meow meow meow meow meow meow meow meow meow meow, meow meow meow meow meow meow meow meow meow meow, meow meow meow, meow, meow meow meow meow meow meow—meow meow meow meow meow, meow, meow meow meow meow meow.

"Meow meow meow!" meow meow meow, meow meow meow meow meow meow. "Meow meow meow meow, meow meow meow meow. Meow meow meow meow! Meow Meow, meow meow meow meow!... Meow meow meow Meow meow meow-meow! Meow meow Meow meow meow meow meow Meow Meow! Meow meow meow meow meow! Meow meow Meow meow meow meow meow, meow meow meow meow meow! Meow meow meow meow meow meow! Meow meow meow meow meow meow!"

Meow meow meow; meow meow meow meow meow meow meow meow meow meow meow meow meow.

"Meow meow meow meow meow meow meow meow meow meow meow, meow Meow meow meow meow meow meow meow meow, meow meow meow Meow meow meow meow meow meow meow meow meow meow'meow meow meow Meow meow meow, meow meow Meow meow meow meow meow, meow meow meow meow meow meow, meow meow meow? Meow meow Meow meow meow meow meow meow meow meow meow meow meow meow meow meow meow meow meow Meow meow meow meow meow... meow'meow meow?"

Meow, meow meow meow, meow meow meow meow. Meow meow meow meow meow meow meow, meow meow meow meow meow meow meow meow meow, meow meow meow meow meow meow meow meow

meow meow meow meow, meow meow meow meow meow meow, meow meow meow meow meow meow meow meow.... Meow, meow meow meow meow meow, meow meow meow meow; meow meow meow meow meow meow meow meow meow meow meow meow meow meow meow meow meow meow meow meow meow meow meow-meow meow meow meow.... Meow, meow meow meow.

"Meow meow meow Meow meow meow meow," meow meow meow meow meow, "Meow meow meow meow meow meow meow, meow Meow meow'meow meow meow Meow meow meow.... Meow meow meow meow meow meow meow meow meow meow Meow meow meow meow meow.... Meow meow meow meow meow Meow meow meow meow.... Meow meow meow Meow meow'meow meow meow meow meow? Meow Meow, meow meow Meow meow meow meow meow!"

Meow meow meow meow meow. Meow meow meow meow meow meow meow meow, meow meow meow meow meow meow meow meow, meow meow meow. Meow meow meow meow meow meow meow meow meow meow meow meow meow meow; meow meow meow meow, meow meow, meow meow meow meow meow, meow meow, meow meow meow meow. Meow meow meow meow meow meow meow meow—meow meow meow meow, meow meow, meow meow. Meow meow meow meow meow, meow meow meow meow meow meow meow meow meow meow meow meow meow....

Meow meow meow, meow meow meow meow meow meow meow meow Meow Meow, meow meow meow meow Meow Meow. "Meow, meow meow meow, meow meow meow," meow meow, "meow, Meow meow meow meow meow Meow meow meow meow meow! Meow meow'meow meow meow meow meow meow.... Meow meow meow meow, meow; meow Meow meow meow meow meow meow Meow meow meow meow meow meow? Meow meow, Meow meow meow meow meow meow meow Meow meow meow meow meow meow meow meow meow; meow, meow meow Meow meow! Meow Meow meow meow meow meow meow."

Meow meow meow meow Meow'meow meow meow meow meow meow.

Meow meow meow meow meow meow meow meow, meow meow meow meow meow, meow meow meow meow meow meow. Meow meow meow meow meow meow meow meow meow meow. Meow meow meow meow meow meow-meow, meow meow meow meow meow meow, meow, meow meow meow. Meow meow meow meow.

"Meow meow meow?" meow meow. Meow meow meow meow meow meow meow; meow meow meow meow meow, meow meow. "Meow meow meow meow meow meow! Meow, meow, meow'meow meow meow meow!" meow meow, meow meow Meow'meow meow. "Meow meow meow, meow meow meow, Meow'meow meow meow."

Meow meow meow meow meow meow meow meow Meow meow meow, meow meow meow meow meow meow meow meow meow, Meow meow meow meow meow meow meow meow meow.

"Meow, meow meow meow meow, meow meow meow meow?" Meow meow meow meow meow. Meow meow meow meow meow.

"Meow meow," meow meow, "Meow meow meow meow meow: Meow meow meow meow.... Meow meow,... meow Meow meow'meow meow meow meow...."

"Meow Meow meow! Meow meow meow, meow meow!" Meow meow, meow meow meow. "Meow, Meow meow meow."

Meow meow meow meow meow meow. Meow meow meow meow meow meow meow Meow'meow, meow meow meow meow meow meow meow meow meow meow meow meow meow meow. Meow, meow meow meow, meow meow, meow meow meow meow meow meow meow meow meow meow meow meow meow meow meow meow meow meow meow meow meow meow meow meow. Meow meow meow meow meow. Meow meow meow meow meow meow meow meow meow meow meow meow Meow'meow meow.

"Meow-meow," meow meow meow, meow meow meow meow meow.

"Meow, meow! Meow meow meow."

"Meow meow'meow meow meow," meow meow meow, meow meow meow meow meow.

"Meow meow meow meow meow meow meow? Meow meow meow, meow meow? Meow, meow meow... meow meow! Meow meow'meow meow meow meow meow meow."

"Meow, meow, Meow meow meow meow meow Meow meow meow meow meow meow meow meow meow... meow meow... meow meow meow meow meow meow—meow, Meow meow, meow meow meow... meow meow Meow meow meow Meow meow meow. Meow meow meow? Meow meow meow... meow meow'meow meow... meow meow'meow meow. Meow meow meow meow... meow. Meow, meow'meow meow. Meow meow meow."

"Meow meow meow, meow meow! Meow meow meow meow meow. Meow meow meow meow meow Meow meow. Meow meow meow meow, meow meow meow, meow Meow meow'meow meow meow meow, meow meow'meow meow meow, Meow—meow meow meow meow meow meow meow meow. Meow meow meow meow meow meow meow meow. Meow'meow meow meow meow meow meow, meow meow meow meow meow meow meow meow meow meow meow! Meow meow meow meow meow meow meow! Meow meow meow meow Meow meow meow meow, meow meow Meow, meow meow, meow meow meow meow meow Meow meow! Meow meow meow meow meow meow meow meow, meow meow meow meow meow meow meow meow, meow, meow meow, Meow meow meow. Meow meow meow meow meow meow Meow meow—meow meow meow, meow meow meow; meow meow meow meow, 'Meow meow meow meow meow?' Meow, meow meow, meow meow meow meow meow. Meow meow meow meow meow meow meow meow meow meow meow meow meow meow meow; Meow meow meow meow; meow meow meow meow meow meow meow meow meow meow, meow meow meow meow meow meow meow meow meow meow meow meow meow meow meow meow meow meow meow meow. Meow meow meow! Meow meow meow meow meow meow meow, meow meow meow meow meow meow meow meow

meow meow, meow Meow′meow meow meow meow meow meow. Meow meow meow meow meow, meow meow meow meow meow meow meow meow meow, meow meow meow meow meow meow meow meow meow meow meow meow meow Meow Meow meow meow meow meow meow; meow meow meow Meow, meow Meow meow meow meow meow Meow. Meow meow meow meow Meow meow′meow meow meow, meow meow! Meow, meow meow meow meow meow meow meow meow meow 'Meow meow meow meow meow?' Meow meow meow, meow meow Meow meow meow meow meow—meow meow meow meow, meow meow meow meow; meow meow Meow meow meow meow meow meow meow meow meow meow meow, meow meow meow meow meow meow meow meow. Meow meow meow meow meow meow meow meow meow meow meow meow meow meow meow. Meow meow meow′meow meow Meow meow meow meow meow meow; meow meow meow, meow meow meow meow meow meow, Meow meow meow meow meow meow meow; meow meow meow, Meow meow meow meow meow, meow meow, Meow meow meow meow meow meow Meow, meow meow Meow meow meow meow meow Meow meow meow meow meow meow meow. Meow meow meow meow, meow meow′meow meow meow meow meow meow meow meow meow. Meow meow meow meow, meow meow′meow meow meow meow meow. Meow meow meow meow?"

Meow meow meow Meow meow meow meow, meow meow meow meow meow meow meow meow meow meow. Meow meow meow meow meow meow. Meow meow Meow meow meow meow meow meow, meow meow meow, meow meow meow meow Meow′meow meow meow meow meow meow meow meow Meow meow meow meow meow meow, meow meow meow, meow meow meow meow meow.

"Meow meow meow, meow meow?" Meow meow, meow meow meow meow meow.

"Meow meow meow meow? Meow′meow meow meow meow meow... meow meow meow meow meow meow meow meow, meow meow?"

"Meow meow′meow meow... meow," meow Meow meow meow meow.

"Meow meow meow meow meow meow meow?" meow Meow meow meow. Meow meow meow meow meow meow meow.

"Meow, meow! Meow meow meow meow?" Meow meow.

"Meow, meow meow meow!"

Meow Meow meow meow meow meow meow meow. Meow meow Meow Meow meow meow meow meow meow meow meow meow meow meow meow. Meow meow, meow meow meow meow meow meow meow meow, meow meow meow meow meow meow meow meow meow meow meow, meow meow meow meow meow meow meow′ meow. Meow meow meow meow meow meow meow meow meow meow meow meow (meow meow meow meow meow meow meow meow meow meow meow meow meow meow meow meow meow meow meow). Meow meow meow meow meow meow meow. Meow meow meow, meow meow.

"Meow meow meow!"

"Meow meow Meow meow meow."

"Meow meow meow meow, meow meow, meow meow meow meow meow meow meow; meow meow meow meow meow meow meow."

"Meow'meow meow meow meow, meow'meow meow meow meow."

Meow meow meow meow meow meow meow, meow meow meow meow meow meow meow meow meow, meow meow meow meow, meow meow meow meow meow meow meow meow meow. Meow meow. Meow meow meow meow meow meow meow meow meow meow meow, meow meow meow, meow meow meow meow meow meow, meow meow meow meow meow.

"Meow meow, meow meow meow, meow Meow'meow meow."

Meow meow meow meow meow meow meow. Meow meow meow meow meow meow. Meow meow meow meow meow meow meow meow meow meow meow meow meow meow meow meow meow meow meow, meow meow meow meow meow meow meow meow meow meow meow meow meow, meow meow meow meow meow meow meow.

Meow meow meow meow meow meow meow meow, meow meow meow meow meow, meow meow meow meow Meow, meow meow meow meow. Meow meow meow meow meow meow meow meow meow meow meow meow meow, meow meow meow meow meow meow Meow. Meow meow meow meow meow, meow meow meow meow meow meow meow meow meow meow meow meow meow meow meow, meow meow meow meow, meow meow meow meow meow meow meow meow meow meow meow meow meow. Meow meow meow meow meow meow meow, meow Meow meow meow meow; meow meow meow meow meow meow meow meow meow meow meow. Meow meow meow, meow meow meow meow meow meow meow meow; meow meow meow meow meow meow meow. Meow meow meow meow meow meow, meow meow meow meow meow— meow meow meow meow meow—meow meow meow meow meow, meow meow meow meow meow meow meow meow meow meow meow meow meow meow meow meow meow meow meow meow. Meow meow meow meow meow; meow meow meow meow meow meow meow meow meow. Meow meow meow meow meow meow meow meow meow meow meow, meow meow, meow meow meow meow meow meow meow. Meow meow meow meow meow meow meow meow, meow meow meow meow meow meow meow meow meow meow meow meow meow meow meow meow. Meow meow meow meow meow meow meow, meow meow meow meow meow meow meow meow meow meow meow, meow meow meow meow meow meow meow meow meow meow meow, meow meow meow meow meow meow meow meow meow meow meow meow... meow meow meow meow meow. Meow meow meow meow meow, meow meow meow meow meow meow. Meow meow, meow meow meow meow meow meow meow meow meow meow meow meow—meow meow meow meow, meow meow meow, meow meow meow meow meow, meow meow meow meow meow meow meow meow meow meow, meow.... Meow meow meow meow meow meow meow meow, meow meow meow meow meow meow meow. Meow meow meow meow meow meow meow, meow meow meow meow meow meow meow meow meow meow meow meow. Meow meow meow meow, meow

meow meow meow, meow meow meow meow meow meow meow meow meow meow meow meow; meow meow meow meow meow meow. Meow meow meow meow, meow meow meow meow meow meow meow meow meow meow meow meow meow.

Meow meow meow meow meow meow meow meow, meow meow meow meow meow meow meow meow meow meow. Meow meow meow meow meow meow meow meow meow meow. Meow, meow meow meow meow meow meow, meow meow meow meow meow meow, meow meow meow meow meow, meow meow meow meow meow meow....

Meow meow meow meow meow meow meow meow meow meow meow meow. Meow Meow, meow meow meow! Meow meow meow, meow meow, meow, meow, meow, meow meow meow meow meow meow meow.

Meow meow meow meow meow meow meow, meow meow. Meow meow meow meow meow meow meow, meow meow meow meow. Meow meow meow, meow meow meow meow meow meow meow. Meow meow meow meow meow meow meow meow meow meow meow meow meow. Meow meow meow, meow meow meow, meow, meow, meow, meow meow meow meow meow meow meow meow meow meow meow meow; meow meow meow, meow meow, meow meow meow meow, meow meow meow meow meow meow meow meow meow. Meow meow meow meow meow meow meow meow meow meow meow meow meow meow meow meow meow; meow meow, meow, meow meow meow, meow meow meow meow meow meow, meow meow meow. Meow meow meow Meow meow; meow meow meow meow—meow meow meow meow meow Meow Meow. Meow Meow meow meow meow meow meow! Meow meow meow meow, meow meow meow meow meow meow—meow'meow meow, meow meow meow meow meow meow meow, meow meow meow meow meow meow. Meow meow meow, meow meow meow meow-meow? Meow meow meow meow meow meow meow meow meow meow meow meow meow meow; meow meow meow, meow, meow, meow meow.

"Meow meow, meow, meow meow meow meow meow?" meow meow, meow meow meow meow meow meow meow. Meow meow, meow meow meow meow! Meow meow meow meow meow meow meow meow, "meow meow meow... meow'meow meow meow meow... meow meow.... Meow Meow!" Meow meow meow meow meow meow meow meow, meow meow meow meow meow meow meow... meow, meow meow meow meow. Meow meow meow meow meow meow, meow meow meow meow meow.... Meow meow meow meow meow meow, meow meow meow meow meow, meow meow meow meow. Meow meow meow meow meow meow; Meow Meow meow meow meow meow meow meow.... Meow meow meow meow, meow, meow meow meow meow, meow meow meow meow meow meow meow. "Meow meow meow meow meow? Meow Meow!" Meow, meow meow meow meow meow meow meow, meow meow meow meow... meow meow meow meow meow.... Meow meow meow meow meow meow meow meow meow meow meow, meow, meow, meow meow meow meow, meow meow meow meow meow meow, meow meow meow meow meow. Meow meow meow meow meow meow meow— meow meow meow meow meow

meow meow. "Meow, meow Meow, meow meow meow meow! Meow meow, meow meow meow meow meow!"

Meow meow meow meow meow meow meow, meow meow meow meow meow meow. Meow meow meow meow meow meow meow meow meow, meow meow meow meow meow meow meow meow meow meow meow meow meow. Meow meow meow meow meow meow meow meow. Meow meow meow meow meow meow meow meow meow meow meow. Meow meow meow meow meow meow meow meow meow meow meow, meow meow meow meow meow meow meow meow meow meow meow meow meow meow meow meow—meow, meow, meow meow, meow meow.

"Meow'meow meow meow meow meow, Meow meow. Meow'meow meow meow meow meow meow, meow meow'meow meow meow meow."

"Meow... meow meow meow meow meow meow meow?"

Meow meow meow meow meow.

"Meow meow meow meow?"

"Meow meow... meow meow meow meow, Meow Meow, meow meow meow, meow meow meow.... Meow meow meow meow-meow meow meow meow, meow... meow meow meow meow?"

Meow meow meow, meow meow meow, meow meow meow meow meow meow meow. Meow meow meow, meow meow meow meow meow meow.

"Meow, meow meow'meow meow meow?" meow meow meow meow meow meow meow meow meow.

"Meow'meow meow meow," meow meow meow meow meow, meow meow meow meow meow. "Meow? Meow meow?" meow meow, meow meow meow meow meow meow meow.

Meow meow meow meow meow meow meow.

"Meow meow meow meow meow meow," meow meow meow meow meow meow meow, meow meow. Meow meow meow meow, meow meow meow meow.

"Meow meow meow meow.... Meow meow meow meow... Meow meow meow meow," meow meow meow meow meow. "Meow meow meow meow meow. Meow meow meow meow.... Meow meow meow meow meow meow meow meow meow meow meow."

"Meow meow meow meow meow. Meow'meow meow meow meow meow meow meow. Meow meow'meow meow meow meow meow meow meow meow meow, meow meow meow meow.... Meow meow meow meow?"

Meow meow meow meow. Meow meow meow meow meow, meow meow. "Meow meow meow meow meow... Meow."

Meow meow meow meow meow meow meow meow meow meow meow meow. Meow meow meow meow meow meow meow meow meow meow meow meow meow meow meow meow. Meow meow meow.

MEOW III

Meow meow meow meow meow, meow, meow meow meow meow meow meow; meow meow meow meow meow meow, meow meow, meow meow meow. Meow meow meow meow meow meow. Meow meow meow meow meow meow meow meow meow meow meow meow meow; meow meow meow meow meow meow meow, meow meow meow meow meow meow meow meow meow meow meow. Meow meow meow meow meow meow meow meow; meow meow meow meow meow meow meow meow, meow meow meow meow meow meow meow meow meow meow meow meow meow meow; meow meow meow, meow meow meow, meow, meow meow meow meow. Meow meow Meow meow meow meow meow; meow meow meow meow, meow, meow meow meow meow meow meow meow, meow meow meow meow meow meow meow meow, meow meow meow meow, meow meow meow meow. Meow meow meow meow meow meow meow meow meow meow; meow meow meow meow meow meow meow meow meow meow meow. Meow meow meow—meow meow meow meow meow meow, meow meow meow meow meow meow meow meow meow meow meow meow meow meow meow. Meow meow meow meow meow meow meow meow, meow, meow meow meow meow, meow meow meow meow, meow meow. Meow meow meow meow meow meow, meow meow meow meow, meow meow meow meow meow meow meow, meow meow meow meow meow meow meow meow. Meow meow meow meow meow meow.

Meow meow meow meow meow'meow meow meow meow. Meow meow meow meow meow meow meow meow meow meow meow meow, meow meow meow meow meow meow meow meow meow meow meow meow meow meow meow. Meow meow meow meow meow meow meow meow, meow meow meow, meow meow meow meow meow meow meow. Meow meow meow meow meow meow meow meow, meow meow meow, meow-meow meow, meow meow meow meow meow. Meow meow meow meow meow meow meow meow-meow meow. Meow meow meow.

"Meow meow meow, Meow?" meow meow, meow meow meow meow meow. "Meow meow, meow'meow meow meow!" meow meow.

"Meow meow meow," meow meow meow.

Meow meow meow meow meow meow meow meow, meow meow meow meow meow meow meow. Meow meow meow meow meow meow meow meow meow. Meow meow meow meow meow meow, meow meow meow meow-meow, meow meow meow, meow meow meow meow meow, meow-meow meow meow meow meow, meow meow meow.

"Meow... meow meow?" meow meow meow, meow meow meow. Meow meow meow meow meow meow meow meow meow, meow, meow meow meow, meow meow meow meow meow, Meow meow meow.

"Meow meow meow meow meow!" meow meow. "Meow meow meow meow meow meow. Meow meow meow meow meow! Meow meow meow meow, meow? Meow'meow meow meow meow meow meow Meow."

"Meow meow meow meow meow," meow Meow.

"Meow meow meow," meow meow meow meow, meow meow meow.

"Meow meow meow meow?" Meow meow, meow meow meow. "Meow meow meow Meow, meow meow meow; meow Meow, meow Meow meow meow meow, meow Meow, meow meow meow meow; meow meow meow meow meow. Meow meow meow meow?"

"Meow meow meow meow meow meow meow, meow meow meow Meow, meow Meow'meow meow meow meow."

"Meow meow meow." Meow meow meow meow meow meow meow meow meow meow. "Meow'meow meow meow meow meow'meow meow meow, meow," meow meow meow meow Meow. "Meow meow meow meow meow meow meow meow meow meow meow meow. Meow meow meow meow meow meow meow meow. Meow meow Meow meow meow meow meow. Meow meow Meow? Meow meow meow meow meow meow meow meow meow meow meow meow—meow meow meow meow meow meow meow meow. Meow meow meow, meow meow meow meow meow, meow meow meow meow meow meow meow meow meow meow, meow meow'meow meow meow, meow meow meow meow meow meow meow meow meow. Meow meow meow meow-meow meow! Meow meow meow meow meow meow. Meow, Meow meow'meow meow meow," meow meow, meow meow meow meow. "Meow meow meow meow meow meow? Meow meow meow, Meow, meow meow meow meow meow meow meow meow meow meow meow; meow meow meow meow meow meow meow, meow Meow meow meow meow. Meow meow meow meow meow?"

"Meow meow meow meow meow meow, Meow meow meow meow, meow meow meow, meow. Meow meow Meow Meow; meow meow meow meow meow, meow."

"Meow meow meow meow meow meow, meow'meow meow meow meow?" "Meow, meow, meow, meow meow meow meow meow meow Meow meow." "Meow meow; meow meow."

"Meow meow meow'meow meow, meow Meow Meow Meow, meow meow Meow meow meow meow meow meow meow meow, meow meow meow meow meow meow meow meow meow," meow meow meow, meow Meow. "Meow meow meow meow meow meow meow, Meow'meow meow-meow meow meow meow meow meow, meow Meow Meow meow meow meow Meow Meow meow meow meow'meow meow meow meow meow meow, meow meow meow meow. Meow meow meow meow, meow?"

"Meow, Meow meow... Meow," Meow meow meow.

"Meow meow, meow meow Meow," meow Meow. "Meow meow meow 'meow meow meow'! Meow Meow meow meow meow meow meow meow meow. Meow, meow'meow meow meow meow meow meow meow meow."

"Meow'meow meow meow, Meow, Meow Meow. Meow meow meow meow meow meow meow, meow meow meow meow meow meow meow meow meow meow meow meow meow meow, meow meow meow meow meow meow meow, meow meow meow meow Meow Meow meow meow meow meow meow meow meow-meow meow meow meow meow meow meow meow meow."

"Meow 'meow meow meow meow meow' meow meow meow meow meow'meow meow, meow 'meow meow' meow meow meow meow. Meow meow, meow meow meow meow? Meow meow meow meow, meow?"

"Meow'meow meow meow. Meow meow meow meow meow meow meow meow."

"Meow meow meow meow meow. Meow meow meow meow meow?"

"Meow, meow'meow meow meow."

"Meow meow meow meow. Meow, Meow, meow meow. Meow'meow meow meow. Meow meow meow meow meow 'Meow' meow meow. Meow meow meow, meow, meow meow meow meow meow meow meow."

"Meow meow'meow meow meow," meow Meow, meow meow meow meow. "Meow meow meow?"

"Meow meow'meow meow meow."

"Meow meow meow meow meow meow meow meow meow?"

"Meow meow'meow meow... meow meow."

"Meow'meow meow meow meow! Meow, meow, meow'meow meow, Meow meow meow. Meow'meow meow, meow, meow'meow meow meow meow meow meow meow meow meow. Meow meow'meow meow meow meow meow meow meow meow meow.... Meow meow meow meow meow meow meow meow meow meow meow meow meow, meow meow, meow meow, meow meow meow meow meow meow meow meow. Meow."

"Meow Meow meow meow meow meow."

"Meow, meow. Meow meow meow meow meow? Meow meow meow meow meow meow.... Meow, Meow, meow'meow meow meow meow, meow meow meow meow meow," meow meow meow meow meow meow Meow'meow meow meow meow.

"Meow, Meow'meow meow meow meow," meow meow meow, meow meow meow meow meow meow meow. Meow meow meow meow meow meow meow meow meow.

"Meow! Meow meow, meow, meow meow meow?"

"Meow," meow Meow.

"Meow meow meow meow?"

"Meow meow meow'meow," meow Meow, meow meow meow meow meow. "Meow meow meow meow meow meow?"

"Meow."

"Meow meow meow meow meow. Meow meow meow meow meow meow meow."

"Meow meow."

Meow meow meow meow meow meow meow meow meow meow meow, meow meow. Meow meow meow meow meow meow meow meow meow meow meow meow meow. "Meow meow Meow meow meow meow. Meow meow meow'meow meow," meow meow.

Meow meow meow meow meow Meow meow meow meow meow, meow meow meow meow meow meow meow meow meow. Meow meow meow meow meow meow meow, meow meow, meow, meow, meow meow meow meow, meow meow meow. Meow meow meow meow meow meow meow meow meow meow meow meow meow. Meow meow meow meow.

"Meow meow meow meow meow, Meow, meow Meow Meow meow meow meow meow meow meow meow meow meow meow meow. Meow meow meow meow."

"Meow, meow meow meow meow meow," meow Meow, meow meow meow meow meow meow meow meow.

Meow meow meow meow meow meow meow. Meow Meow meow meow meow meow meow meow meow, meow meow meow meow meow meow meow meow meow meow Meow'meow meow, meow meow meow meow meow meow meow, meow meow meow meow meow meow meow meow meow meow meow, meow meow meow meow meow meow meow meow meow. Meow meow meow meow meow meow meow. Meow meow meow meow meow, meow meow meow, meow meow meow. Meow meow meow meow meow meow meow meow meow meow, Meow meow meow, meow meow meow meow meow meow Meow meow meow meow meow meow meow.

Meow meow meow meow meow meow meow meow. "Meow meow meow meow meow?"

"Meow."

"Meow meow, Meow, meow meow meow meow, meow meow meow meow meow meow meow meow meow. Meow meow meow meow meow!" Meow meow meow meow meow meow, meow meow meow meow meow meow meow meow meow, meow meow meow meow meow meow meow meow meow meow meow meow meow.

"Meow meow meow meow, Meow, Meow meow meow meow meow meow meow meow," meow meow meow meow meow meow meow meow, "meow meow'meow meow Meow, meow meow meow meow, meow meow meow meow; meow meow meow meow meow meow meow. Meow meow'meow meow meow meow, meow, meow meow, Meow meow'meow meow. Meow meow'meow Meow meow meow meow. Meow meow meow meow meow. Meow, meow meow, meow'meow meow meow meow meow?"

"Meow meow meow meow meow!"

"Meow meow meow meow, meow?"

"Meow meow meow meow, meow."

"Meow meow meow. Meow, Meow'meow meow meow meow meow. Meow meow."

Meow meow meow meow meow, meow meow meow, meow meow meow meow meow meow. Meow meow, meow meow meow meow meow meow meow meow meow'meow meow, meow meow meow meow meow meow meow meow meow, meow meow meow meow meow meow meow, meow meow meow meow meow meow meow meow meow meow meow meow meow meow'meow meow. Meow meow meow meow meow meow meow, meow meow meow meow meow meow meow meow meow meow meow meow meow meow meow meow meow meow meow meow meow meow meow meow meow, meow meow meow meow meow meow meow. Meow meow meow meow, meow meow, meow meow meow meow meow meow meow meow meow meow meow meow meow meow meow, meow meow meow meow meow meow meow meow meow meow meow meow meow,

meow meow meow meow meow meow meow meow meow meow. Meow meow meow meow meow meow meow meow meow. Meow meow meow meow meow meow meow, meow meow meow meow meow, meow meow meow meow meow, meow meow meow meow meow meow. Meow meow meow meow meow meow meow meow meow, meow meow meow meow meow, meow meow meow, meow, meow meow meow meow meow.

"Meow meow meow meow meow meow meow meow-meow meow meow meow meow meow meow," meow Meow, meow meow meow meow meow meow meow meow meow meow meow meow.

"Meow meow meow meow meow meow meow meow meow?" meow Meow, meow meow meow meow meow meow meow meow meow meow meow meow meow meow meow.

"Meow'meow meow meow meow meow meow, meow meow. Meow meow, Meow, meow meow meow meow meow meow meow meow meow meow meow meow meow. Meow meow meow meow meow meow meow meow meow meow, Meow meow meow meow meow Meow meow meow meow meow meow meow meow meow. Meow meow meow meow meow meow meow. Meow Meow meow meow meow meow meow meow! Meow meow meow meow Meow meow meow, meow Meow meow meow meow, meow, meow Meow meow meow meow meow; meow meow meow meow meow meow, Meow meow meow meow meow meow meow Meow Meow, Meow'meow meow. Meow meow meow meow meow meow Meow'meow meow, meow meow meow meow meow meow meow meow Meow'meow, meow Meow'meow. Meow meow meow meow meow meow! Meow Meow meow meow meow, meow Meow meow meow meow meow meow meow meow meow meow meow, meow meow meow, meow meow meow meow meow meow meow! Meow meow meow meow meow."

"Meow meow!"

"Meow meow meow meow; meow meow meow Meow Meow meow meow meow meow meow Meow meow meow. Meow, meow'meow meow meow meow. Meow meow meow meow Meow meow meow meow meow meow, Meow meow meow meow meow meow meow meow—meow, meow, meow, Meow meow meow; Meow meow meow meow meow. Meow meow meow meow meow Meow Meow meow Meow Meow, meow meow meow-meow meow Meow. Meow, Meow Meow, meow meow meow meow meow meow meow, meow, meow, meow meow meow, meow Meow; Meow meow meow...."

"Meow'meow meow meow meow," Meow meow, meow meow.

"Meow meow'meow meow meow meow meow meow meow meow, Meow Meow?"

"Meow meow meow meow!" Meow meow meow, meow meow meow meow meow. "Meow meow meow Meow, meow Meow," meow meow meow, meow meow meow meow.

"Meow'meow meow meow meow meow meow. Meow, meow, meow meow meow meow meow meow, Meow meow meow meow meow meow meow meow meow meow meow meow meow meow meow meow meow,

meow Meow meow meow meow. Meow meow meow meow, meow, meow meow meow meow... meow. Meow, meow meow meow meow?”

Meow meow meow meow, meow meow meow meow meow meow meow meow meow, meow meow meow.

“Meow meow meow meow meow meow, meow, meow meow meow,” Meow meow meow, meow meow meow meow meow meow meow.

“Meow, meow meow meow!” Meow meow meow. Meow meow meow meow meow meow.

“Meow’meow meow meow, meow, meow meow meow meow meow meow meow meow meow meow meow meow meow. Meow meow meow meow meow meow meow. Meow meow, meow meow meow, meow meow meow meow. Meow meow meow meow meow meow meow meow.... Meow meow meow meow meow meow meow meow meow meow meow meow meow meow meow meow meow meow? Meow meow Meow Meow Meow? Meow meow meow meow meow meow meow meow Meow Meow Meow. Meow meow meow meow meow meow meow meow, Meow Meow, meow meow?... Meow meow meow meow meow! Meow Meow meow meow’meow meow meow meow meow Meow meow meow meow; meow meow. Meow, meow meow meow, meow meow meow Meow Meow meow meow meow meow meow meow meow meow meow meow meow meow?”

“Meow,” meow Meow, meow meow, meow meow meow meow meow meow meow meow meow meow meow.

“Meow meow’meow, meow meow?” meow Meow, meow meow meow meow meow meow meow meow. “Meow meow meow meow meow meow meow, meow? Meow meow meow, meow meow meow meow! Meow meow meow meow meow meow meow, Meow meow meow.... Meow meow meow meow; meow meow meow meow meow-meow, meow meow meow meow meow meow meow meow meow meow. Meow Meow meow Meow meow meow meow, meow meow meow meow meow meow meow; meow meow meow meow meow meow meow meow meow meow, meow meow meow meow meow meow meow! Meow meow’meow meow meow! Meow, meow’meow meow meow. Meow, meow meow meow meow meow meow meow meow meow meow meow meow meow meow meow meow, meow meow meow meow meow meow’meow meow meow meow meow meow meow meow meow meow meow meow, meow meow meow meow; meow meow meow meow meow meow meow meow meow meow meow meow meow meow meow, meow meow meow meow meow meow meow. Meow meow’meow meow meow meow meow meow meow meow, meow meow meow meow meow meow Meow Meow Meow, meow meow meow meow meow meow meow meow meow meow.”

“Meow meow meow meow meow meow meow meow.... Meow meow meow meow meow meow meow... meow Meow meow meow meow meow meow meow meow... meow meow meow,” Meow meow meow meow meow.

“Meow, meow meow meow meow. Meow meow meow meow meow meow meow meow meow meow Meow. Meow meow meow, meow meow meow. Meow meow meow meow meow meow meow meow meow meow meow meow, meow meow meow meow; meow meow meow meow meow

meow meow meow meow, meow meow meow meow meow meow meow, 'Meow meow meow meow meow meow meow Meow Meow Meow?' Meow: meow meow, meow meow meow meow meow meow meow meow meow Meow meow meow meow meow meow-meow meow meow, meow meow meow meow meow meow; meow meow meow, meow, meow meow meow meow meow meow meow meow. Meow'meow meow meow meow meow meow.... Meow meow meow meow? Meow meow meow meow meow meow meow meow meow meow meow, meow meow meow—meow'meow meow meow meow meow meow meow meow meow meow Meow meow meow meow meow meow meow-meow-meow, meow Meow meow meow meow meow meow meow.... Meow Meow meow meow meow meow meow; meow meow meow meow meow meow meow; meow meow meow meow 'meow meow meow meow meow' meow meow. Meow, meow meow meow meow Meow Meow Meow meow meow meow meow meow meow Meow, meow meow meow meow meow meow meow meow meow meow. Meow Meow meow meow meow meow Meow meow meow meow meow meow, meow, meow meow meow meow, meow meow meow meow meow meow meow meow meow Meow, meow Meow meow meow meow meow meow meow, meow meow meow meow meow. Meow meow meow meow meow, meow. Meow meow meow? Meow meow Meow, meow meow meow meow meow meow meow Meow Meow Meow meow meow meow, meow meow Meow meow meow meow meow meow meow meow meow. Meow meow meow meow meow. Meow, meow meow, meow meow Meow meow meow meow."

Meow meow meow meow meow meow meow. Meow meow meow meow meow meow meow meow meow meow meow meow meow. Meow Meow meow meow meow.

"Meow meow, meow," meow meow meow meow meow, "meow Meow meow meow meow meow meow meow. Meow meow Meow meow meow meow meow meow meow, meow Meow meow Meow meow meow meow meow meow."

"Meow meow meow Meow meow meow meow meow Meow meow meow?" Meow meow, meow meow meow'meow meow meow meow meow meow.

"Meow, meow meow meow meow meow meow meow meow, meow meow Meow meow Meow meow meow."

"Meow? Meow meow meow? Meow meow?" Meow meow meow meow meow meow meow meow meow Meow.

"Meow'meow meow meow meow meow?... Meow meow meow meow meow? Meow meow meow meow meow meow meow Meow meow meow meow meow meow meow meow.... Meow meow Meow meow meow meow meow meow meow meow meow? Meow meow meow meow meow, meow, meow-meow... meow meow meow meow, meow meow. Meow meow meow meow—meow meow meow meow meow meow. Meow meow meow meow meow meow, meow meow. Meow meow meow meow meow. Meow'meow meow meow meow meow Meow Meow meow meow meow.... Meow meow meow Meow, Meow Meow?

"Meow Meow meow meow meow meow?"

"Meow meow meow meow! Meow meow meow meow."

"Meow meow Meow meow meow?"

"Meow meow? Meow meow meow meow meow? Meow meow meow meow meow.... Meow, meow, meow Meow meow meow meow meow. Meow meow." Meow meow meow meow meow meow meow meow meow meow meow.

"Meow meow Meow meow meow?"

"Meow meow meow meow! Meow meow meow meow meow meow meow meow meow? Meow'meow meow meow; meow meow meow meow meow meow. Meow meow meow meow meow meow meow meow, meow meow meow-meow meow meow, meow meow Meow Meow, meow meow meow, meow Meow Meow meow Meow Meow, meow meow meow. Meow meow meow meow meow meow meow meow meow meow meow meow meow meow. Meow meow, 'Meow meow meow meow.' Meow meow meow meow meow meow meow meow meow, meow meow meow meow meow, meow-meow meow meow meow meow meow meow. Meow meow meow meow meow meow, meow meow meow meow meow-meow meow meow meow meow meow meow meow meow meow; meow meow meow meow meow meow meow. Meow meow meow meow meow meow meow meow meow meow meow. Meow meow meow meow meow meow meow meow meow meow meow. Meow meow meow meow meow meow meow meow meow, meow meow meow meow meow meow meow. Meow meow meow! Meow meow meow-meow meow; Meow meow meow meow meow, meow meow meow meow meow meow meow meow meow meow meow meow meow. Meow meow meow Meow meow meow meow meow meow, meow meow meow meow meow meow meow meow meow, meow meow meow meow meow. Meow meow, Meow, meow meow meow meow meow Meow meow meow, meow meow meow meow meow meow meow meow meow meow. Meow Meow meow meow Meow meow meow meow meow. Meow-meow!"

"Meow meow meow Meow! Meow, meow'meow meow meow meow!" meow Meow meow meow meow meow; meow meow meow meow meow meow meow meow, meow meow meow meow meow meow meow meow. Meow meow meow meow meow meow meow meow meow meow meow meow meow. Meow meow meow meow meow meow Meow.

Meow meow meow meow meow meow meow meow meow meow meow meow meow meow meow meow meow meow meow meow meow meow meow. Meow meow, meow meow meow meow meow meow meow meow meow meow meow meow meow meow meow meow meow. Meow meow meow meow? Meow, meow meow meow meow meow, meow meow meow.

"Meow Meow, meow meow meow meow meow: meow meow meow meow meow meow meow meow? Meow meow meow meow meow meow meow meow, meow meow meow Meow meow meow meow, meow meow meow meow meow meow meow meow meow meow meow'meow meow meow meow meow meow meow meow meow meow... Meow meow Meow meow meow meow? Meow'meow meow Meow'meow meow, meow

meow meow meow; meow meow meow meow meow, Meow meow meow meow meow."

Meow meow meow meow meow meow meow meow meow meow meow meow meow meow meow; meow meow meow meow meow, meow meow, meow; meow meow meow meow meow meow meow. Meow, meow meow meow meow, meow meow meow meow meow meow meow meow meow meow meow meow meow, meow meow meow, meow meow meow meow meow meow, meow—meow meow meow meow meow. Meow meow meow meow meow, meow meow meow meow meow meow meow meow; meow meow meow meow meow meow meow meow meow meow meow meow meow meow meow meow meow meow meow meow meow meow meow. Meow meow meow meow, meow! Meow meow meow meow meow meow meow Meow meow meow meow meow meow. Meow, meow meow meow meow meow meow meow meow meow, meow meow meow meow meow meow meow meow meow meow Meow meow meow meow meow meow meow meow.

"Meow, Meow! Meow meow meow! Meow meow meow Meow meow meow meow meow meow meow? Meow'meow meow meow? Meow! Meow meow meow meow meow; meow meow meow. Meow meow meow meow meow meow, meow, meow meow... meow Meow meow meow meow. Meow meow meow Meow meow meow? Meow meow Meow meow meow?" meow meow, meow meow meow meow meow meow. "Meow meow meow meow? Meow Meow meow meow meow, meow meow meow meow? Meow meow meow meow meow.... Meow, Meow meow; Meow meow meow! Meow meow meow meow. Meow, Meow meow, Meow meow meow! Meow... meow meow? Meow meow meow meow meow? Meow'meow meow meow. Meow'meow meow meow meow! Meow'meow meow meow! Meow meow! Meow, meow meow meow meow—meow meow meow meow! Meow meow meow meow meow meow meow, meow Meow! Meow meow'meow meow Meow Meow Meow... Meow'meow meow meow meow meow meow meow meow meow meow. Meow meow'meow meow meow!... Meow, meow meow meow meow? Meow'meow meow meow, Meow meow meow meow. Meow meow meow... meow meow... meow Meow, meow meow meow meow meow meow! Meow meow meow Meow Meow Meow... meow meow meow meow meow meow.... Meow meow meow Meow meow? Meow meow Meow meow meow! Meow meow'meow meow meow Meow meow meow, meow-meow-meow! Meow meow meow meow meow meow meow meow meow meow meow meow! Meow meow Meow meow meow meow! Meow meow meow meow meow meow meow meow meow— meow! Meow'meow meow meow? Meow, meow meow meow meow meow, meow meow meow, meow!"

Meow meow meow meow meow, meow meow meow meow meow meow meow, meow meow meow meow meow, meow meow meow meow meow meow meow meow. Meow meow meow meow meow meow meow meow meow meow meow, meow meow meow meow meow meow meow meow meow meow meow. Meow meow meow meow meow meow meow meow meow. Meow meow meow meow meow meow meow meow meow meow, meow meow meow meow, meow meow meow meow meow. Meow

meow meow meow meow meow meow meow meow meow meow meow, meow meow meow meow meow meow meow, meow meow meow meow meow meow meow, meow meow, meow meow meow meow meow meow meow, meow, meow meow.

Meow meow meow, meow meow meow meow. Meow meow meow meow meow meow Meow meow meow meow meow, meow meow meow meow meow meow meow. Meow meow meow meow meow meow meow meow meow meow meow, meow meow meow meow meow meow.

"Meow, meow meow meow meow! Meow Meow meow! Meow, meow meow meow meow!" Meow meow meow meow meow. "Meow meow meow meow meow meow."

"Meow meow meow meow?" meow Meow, meow meow meow.

"Meow, meow meow meow meow meow, meow, meow'meow meow meow, meow meow meow meow meow'meow meow. Meow meow meow meow meow meow meow."

"Meow meow! Meow Meow?"

"Meow meow meow? Meow meow meow meow meow. Meow'meow meow meow? Meow meow, meow meow? Meow'meow meow meow meow meow. Meow'meow meow meow meow meow meow meow meow meow; Meow'meow meow meow meow meow meow meow meow. Meow'meow meow meow Meow meow; meow meow meow, meow meow! Meow meow meow, meow meow meow meow. Meow Meow'meow meow meow meow meow meow meow, meow. Meow meow Meow'meow meow meow meow-meow, meow meow meow meow. Meow meow meow meow meow meow meow meow. Meow meow'meow meow meow, meow meow. Meow meow meow meow, Meow. Meow meow meow meow meow. Meow meow meow meow meow meow, meow?"

"Meow meow meow meow, Meow meow meow meow. Meow, meow meow meow meow meow?" "Meow meow meow Meow'meow meow meow meow meow meow meow meow."

"Meow, meow."

"Meow meow meow meow?"

"Meow meow meow meow meow meow meow?"

"Meow Meow meow meow meow meow meow meow meow. Meow'meow meow meow?"

Meow meow. Meow meow meow meow meow meow meow meow. Meow meow meow meow meow, meow meow meow meow Meow.

"Meow!" meow meow meow, "meow meow meow. Meow meow meow meow meow meow meow meow meow. Meow meow meow meow meow meow meow.... Meow meow meow meow meow. Meow-meow! Meow, meow meow. Meow meow, meow meow meow."

Meow meow meow meow meow, meow meow meow meow.

"Meow meow, meow, meow meow meow meow meow meow meow. Meow meow meow meow meow meow meow meow. Meow'meow meow meow meow meow. Meow meow meow meow meow?" meow meow, meow meow meow meow meow meow meow meow meow meow meow meow. "Meow meow meow meow meow."

"Meow, meow," meow Meow, meow meow meow meow.

"Meow, Meow, meow meow, meow'meow meow meow, meow meow meow meow meow; meow Meow meow'meow meow meow meow, meow Meow meow meow meow meow, meow meow. Meow meow!" meow meow meow, meow meow meow, "meow meow meow! Meow meow meow-meow meow meow meow meow meow meow meow meow meow meow meow meow meow. Meow, meow meow meow meow, meow meow meow meow meow meow meow meow meow meow meow meow meow meow meow meow meow meow meow meow meow meow meow meow meow. Meow meow meow meow meow meow meow meow, meow meow'meow meow meow meow meow meow meow meow meow'meow meow; meow meow meow meow meow meow! Meow, Meow, meow meow meow meow meow meow: meow Meow"—meow meow meow meow meow Meow'meow meow, meow meow, meow meow meow meow meow, meow meow meow Meow—"meow meow meow! Meow meow meow, Meow, meow meow meow meow Meow meow meow meow, Meow!" meow meow, meow meow meow, meow meow Meow meow meow meow.

"Meow meow, meow meow, Meow meow meow," meow Meow.

"Meow meow, meow!" meow meow, meow. "Meow, meow meow meow meow meow meow meow—meow meow! Meow meow meow meow meow meow meow meow. Meow meow'meow meow meow meow meow meow'meow meow'meow meow meow, meow meow meow meow meow meow meow. Meow, meow meow meow! Meow, meow meow meow meow meow meow Meow Meow meow Meow, meow meow meow meow meow meow. Meow meow meow Meow meow meow meow meow meow," meow meow meow meow Meow meow meow meow meow, meow meow meow meow meow meow. "Meow meow, meow meow, meow meow meow, meow meow meow meow; meow meow meow meow meow, meow meow meow meow. Meow meow meow meow meow meow meow meow, meow'meow meow, meow.... Meow meow, Meow, meow meow meow, meow meow meow meow meow meow meow meow meow meow meow meow meow meow meow meow; meow meow meow'meow meow meow meow meow meow Meow, meow meow meow meow meow meow meow; meow meow'meow meow meow meow meow meow. Meow'meow meow meow, meow Meow'meow meow meow meow meow—meow meow meow meow meow meow meow, meow meow meow meow meow meow meow meow meow meow meow... meow meow meow meow meow meow meow meow meow meow meow meow meow meow meow meow meow meow meow meow meow meow meow. Meow, meow meow! Meow meow meow meow? Meow meow meow-meow meow! Meow meow meow meow: meow meow meow meow meow, meow meow meow meow meow meow meow! Meow meow meow meow meow meow meow meow Meow'meow; meow meow'meow meow meow meow meow, meow meow meow meow meow, meow meow meow meow meow meow meow meow meow meow meow meow. Meow meow meow meow. Meow meow meow meow? Meow meow meow meow meow meow meow meow, meow meow'meow meow meow meow meow meow, meow meow'meow meow meow meow meow meow; meow meow

meow meow Meow Meow meow meow meow meow—meow meow meow meow meow meow meow, meow meow meow meow meow meow meow. Meow—meow meow meow meow meow. Meow meow?"

"Meow meow meow meow'meow meow," meow Meow.

"Meow meow? Meow meow!" meow meow meow meow meow meow meow Meow'meow meow, meow meow, meow meow meow meow meow. "Meow meow meow meow meow-meow—meow meow meow meow meow meow meow. Meow meow meow meow meow. Meow meow meow meow meow, meow meow meow meow meow meow. Meow, meow meow meow meow meow meow, meow meow meow meow meow meow.... Meow meow meow, meow meow meow meow, meow meow meow-meow meow meow meow—meow meow meow meow meow—meow meow meow meow meow meow meow meow—meow, meow meow, meow meow meow meow—meow meow meow meow meow meow-meow meow; meow meow meow meow meow—meow meow meow meow meow meow—meow meow meow meow meow meow-meow meow. Meow-meow meow meow meow meow. Meow meow meow meow? Meow meow, Meow, meow meow meow meow meow meow meow meow meow-meow, meow meow meow meow meow, meow meow meow meow meow meow meow meow. Meow meow meow meow meow'meow meow meow Meow'meow! Meow meow meow meow meow meow meow, Meow meow meow meow meow; meow'meow meow-meow meow meow. Meow meow meow Meow meow meow meow meow meow, meow'meow meow meow. Meow meow meow meow'meow meow meow meow meow. Meow meow, meow, meow meow meow meow meow, meow Meow meow meow meow meow meow meow meow meow meow meow."

"Meow meow meow! Meow meow'meow meow meow!" Meow meow meow meow. Meow meow meow meow meow meow Meow'meow meow meow meow meow meow meow meow.

"Meow, meow, meow'meow meow meow Meow'meow meow meow meow meow meow," Meow meow. "Meow, meow'meow meow meow, meow meow meow—meow'meow meow," meow meow meow meow Meow'meow meow meow meow meow meow. Meow meow meow meow meow meow meow meow meow meow meow meow meow meow meow.

"Meow meow meow meow meow Meow meow meow meow meow," meow meow. "Meow meow meow meow meow meow meow?" meow meow meow meow, meow meow meow meow.

"Meow? Meow, meow meow, meow meow meow meow meow Meow, meow meow meow meow. Meow meow meow meow, meow?"

"Meow meow meow," meow Meow meow meow meow, meow meow. Meow meow meow meow, meow meow meow.

Meow meow meow meow meow meow, meow meow meow meow meow meow meow Meow meow meow.

MEOW IV

Meow meow meow meow, meow meow meow meow meow, meow, meow-meow meow meow meow meow meow. Meow meow meow, meow meow meow meow meow meow meow meow meow. Meow meow meow-meow. Meow meow meow meow meow meow meow meow meow, meow meow meow, meow meow meow meow meow, meow meow meow meow meow; meow meow meow meow, meow meow-meow meow meow. Meow meow meow meow meow meow, meow meow meow, meow, meow meow meow meow meow meow meow meow meow; meow meow meow meow meow meow meow-meow, meow meow meow meow meow meow meow. Meow meow meow meow meow meow, meow meow meow meow meow meow meow meow.

"Meow'meow meow meow meow meow meow-meow, meow. Meow meow, meow'meow meow meow meow," meow Meow.

"Meow meow, Meow meow; meow meow meow meow meow meow, meow?" meow Meow meow Meow, meow meow meow meow, meow meow meow meow meow meow meow meow, meow meow meow meow meow meow meow meow.

"Meow meow meow meow," Meow meow meow. "Meow'meow meow meow meow meow meow meow meow meow."

"Meow'meow meow meow; meow meow meow meow meow meow meow meow meow meow meow meow.... Meow meow meow meow-meow. Meow meow meow meow meow, meow?"

"Meow meow meow, Meow meow meow meow!" Meow meow meow meow meow. Meow meow meow meow meow meow meow meow meow meow meow meow meow, meow meow meow meow meow meow meow meow meow meow meow meow meow meow. Meow meow meow meow.

"Meow meow.... Meow meow meow meow," meow meow meow. "Meow meow meow meow?" Meow meow meow, meow meow meow meow meow meow.

"Meow meow meow meow... meow, meow... meow meow meow, meow meow, meow meow meow meow meow; meow'meow meow meow meow meow meow, meow... meow meow meow meow meow meow meow!" Meow meow meow meow meow meow meow. "Meow meow meow meow meow. Meow'meow meow meow meow meow meow-meow. Meow, meow-meow meow... meow meow meow..."

"Meow-meow meow Meow meow meow meow meow meow meow," meow Meow. "Meow meow meow meow meow Meow meow meow meow meow meow Meow meow Meow."

"Meow meow meow meow meow meow-meow meow meow, meow Meow meow'meow meow... meow meow, meow... meow meow'meow meow."

"Meow, meow meow meow! Meow'meow meow meow meow-meow meow meow-meow; meow'meow meow meow meow meow meow. Meow'meow meow meow? Meow meow meow meow meow meow. Meow meow meow?" Meow meow meow Meow.

"Meow'meow meow, meow meow."

"Meow meow, meow meow meow. Meow meow meow meow meow meow?"

"Meow, meow—meow, meow, meow. Meow meow meow meow meow… meow meow meow." "Meow meow?"

"Meow meow meow, meow meow meow meow, meow meow meow meow, meow meow meow meow meow—meow meow meow meow Meow meow meow meow meow meow meow meow meow. Meow meow meow meow meow meow."

"Meow meow meow?"

"Meow'meow meow meow meow meow meow meow meow meow meow; meow meow meow meow. Meow meow meow- meow—meow meow meow meow.... Meow Meow meow meow meow meow. Meow Meow, meow meow meow meow Meow Meow meow... Meow meow meow meow."

"Meow meow meow meow meow meow, meow?"

"Meow meow meow meow. Meow meow meow meow meow? Meow meow meow meow, meow'meow meow meow meow?"

"Meow meow'meow meow meow meow meow meow."

"Meow meow meow meow. Meow, meow meow meow meow meow, meow meow, meow meow meow, meow meow, meow meow meow Meow."

"Meow meow meow, meow, meow meow meow meow"—Meow meow meow Meow—"meow meow meow meow meow meow Meow?"

"Meow, meow meow meow! Meow! Meow meow meow meow meow, meow meow meow meow meow; meow meow'meow meow meow meow meow meow meow meow meow. Meow meow meow meow meow meow meow, meow'meow meow meow meow Meow meow meow. Meow meow meow meow meow."

"Meow meow meow meow meow."

"Meow, meow meow! meow meow meow meow? Meow meow'meow meow meow meow meow meow meow," Meow meow meow meow meow. "Meow meow'meow meow meow meow meow meow. Meow meow meow meow meow meow meow meow meow meow meow meow! Meow meow meow meow meow meow meow meow meow—meow meow meow meow meow meow? Meow, Meow meow meow Meow meow'meow meow meow meow meow meow meow... meow meow meow meow meow."

"Meow'meow meow meow; Meow'meow meow meow meow meow."

"Meow Meow meow'meow meow meow meow meow meow meow. Meow meow meow meow meow! Meow meow meow meow meow meow meow. Meow meow meow meow meow meow meow meow meow meow meow meow meow. Meow'meow meow meow meow meow meow meow, meow meow meow. Meow meow meow meow meow meow meow meow meow meow. Meow, meow meow meow! Meow meow'meow meow. Meow meow meow meow meow meow meow.... Meow meow meow meow meow meow, meow meow meow meow meow meow."

"Meow meow meow meow meow meow."

"Meow, meow'meow meow meow meow meow-meow.... Meow meow meow meow meow meow meow meow! Meow meow meow'meow meow

meow meow meow. Meow meow meow meow meow-meow. Meow meow meow meow meow."

"Meow meow?"

"Meow, meow'meow Meow meow meow meow meow? Meow meow meow meow meow meow meow meow meow meow meow meow meow meow-meow. Meow, meow meow meow meow meow meow meow..."

"Meow, Meow meow meow meow meow meow meow meow meow meow meow meow... meow... meow meow meow.... Meow meow meow meow meow meow meow, meow...."

"Meow meow meow, meow," Meow meow meow, meow meow Meow. Meow meow meow meow meow meow meow meow, meow meow meow meow meow.

"Meow," meow Meow meow meow.

"Meow, meow meow meow meow. Meow'meow meow meow meow? Meow meow meow meow meow. Meow meow meow meow meow meow, meow."

Meow meow meow meow meow meow meow meow meow, meow meow meow meow meow meow meow, meow meow meow meow meow meow meow meow meow meow meow meow meow meow meow meow meow meow, meow meow meow meow meow meow meow meow meow meow meow meow. Meow meow meow meow meow meow meow meow meow meow meow meow meow meow meow. Meow meow meow meow meow meow, meow meow meow meow meow meow.

"Meow meow meow meow meow?" Meow meow Meow'meow meow meow meow meow. Meow meow meow meow meow.

"Meow, meow meow meow meow meow meow," Meow meow meow meow. "Meow meow meow meow meow meow?"

"Meow, meow! Meow meow meow meow meow, meow meow'meow meow meow meow meow meow. Meow meow meow meow meow meow meow meow meow, Meow meow Meow, meow meow. Meow! meow meow meow'meow meow meow, meow meow meow meow, meow meow'meow meow meow'meow meow! Meow meow meow meow meow-meow.... Meow meow meow, Meow, meow'meow meow meow meow meow meow; meow meow meow meow meow meow, meow meow meow meow meow meow meow meow meow meow meow meow meow meow meow."

Meow meow meow meow Meow. Meow meow meow meow.

"Meow Meow meow, Meow, Meow meow meow meow. Meow meow meow meow meow!" Meow meow.

"Meow Meow meow, meow meow meow meow meow meow meow," meow Meow, meow meow meow meow meow meow meow. "Meow'meow meow meow meow meow meow meow meow—meow meow meow meow meow—meow meow meow meow meow, meow meow meow meow meow—meow meow meow meow meow meow meow meow meow meow meow meow.... Meow meow Meow, meow... Meow meow meow meow meow meow? Meow meow meow meow, meow meow meow meow meow meow meow meow meow meow meow. Meow meow meow meow Meow meow Meow meow meow meow—meow meow meow meow!"

"Meow meow'meow meow meow; meow meow meow meow, meow meow meow meow meow.... Meow, meow meow meow, Meow'meow meow meow meow Meow. Meow meow meow meow meow meow meow meow meow? Meow?"

"Meow, meow meow meow meow. Meow meow meow meow meow, meow. Meow meow meow meow meow meow. Meow meow meow meow! Meow meow meow meow meow meow meow? Meow'meow meow meow meow, meow meow.... Meow meow meow meow meow meow meow meow meow meow meow meow. Meow meow meow meow meow meow meow meow meow meow meow meow meow meow meow meow meow meow. 'Meow meow meow,' meow meow. Meow meow meow meow meow—meow meow meow meow meow meow meow meow meow meow meow!"

"Meow meow meow meow, meow?"

"Meow, meow meow'meow meow meow'meow meow meow meow meow meow meow, meow meow meow, meow meow meow meow meow meow meow meow.... Meow! Meow meow meow meow meow meow meow meow?"

"Meow meow meow meow meow meow meow meow."

"Meow, meow! Meow, meow'meow meow meow. Meow meow meow meow meow meow meow meow, meow meow meow meow meow Meow meow Meow—meow meow meow meow meow meow meow meow meow meow meow meow meow meow meow meow—meow meow meow meow meow. Meow meow meow Meow, meow meow meow meow-meow meow meow meow, meow meow meow meow meow meow meow'meow meow meow meow meow meow-meow, meow meow meow meow meow. 'Meow meow meow meow, meow meow meow meow'meow'—meow meow meow meow meow meow!—'meow meow meow-meow, Meow, meow meow meow meow meow meow meow meow meow meow, meow meow meow meow meow meow meow-meow meow meow, meow meow meow meow meow meow meow meow meow meow. Meow Meow meow meow meow meow meow meow, meow meow meow meow meow meow meow meow meow meow. Meow meow meow meow meow meow meow.' Meow meow meow meow Meow'meow meow. 'Meow meow meow meow meow'—meow meow meow meow—'meow Meow meow meow meow meow meow meow meow meow meow meow meow meow meow. Meow meow meow meow meow meow meow meow—meow'meow meow meow meow meow, meow meow meow meow meow meow meow meow. Meow meow meow meow meow meow meow meow meow meow meow, meow meow meow meow meow, meow Meow meow meow meow, Meow'meow meow meow meow meow meow.' Meow meow, meow'meow meow meow; meow meow meow meow meow, meow Meow meow meow Meow, meow meow meow meow meow meow meow meow meow meow, meow meow meow meow meow Meow meow meow meow meow-meow meow meow meow meow meow meow meow meow meow. Meow meow meow meow. Meow meow meow, meow meow meow Meow'meow meow. 'Meow'meow meow meow meow, Meow Meow, meow meow meow; meow meow meow meow meow meow meow meow meow Meow, meow meow meow Meow meow. Meow meow Meow

meow meow meow meow, meow meow, meow Meow meow meow meow meow meow meow meow meow, meow meow meow Meow, meow meow meow meow meow meow, meow. Meow meow meow meow meow meow meow meow meow meow, meow meow meow meow meow, meow meow meow meow meow meow. Meow Meow meow meow meow Meow meow meow meow. Meow meow meow meow Meow meow meow meow meow meow Meow Meow meow meow meow, Meow Meow, meow meow meow. Meow meow meow, meow Meow meow meow meow meow meow-meow meow meow, meow Meow meow meow meow meow meow meow meow. Meow meow meow meow meow, meow meow meow meow meow meow meow meow meow meow meow meow. Meow meow meow Meow meow, “Meow Meow meow?” Meow meow meow meow Meow meow meow meow meow meow meow; meow meow meow meow meow meow meow, meow meow meow meow meow meow meow, meow meow meow meow. Meow meow’meow meow meow meow meow meow meow meow meow meow. Meow meow meow meow meow meow meow meow meow meow meow, meow meow meow meow. Meow Meow meow meow meow Meow meow meow meow meow meow meow meow’—meow’meow Meow’meow meow—’meow Meow meow meow meow Meow meow meow meow meow, meow meow meow meow meow meow meow meow. Meow meow meow meow’meow meow meow’—meow meow meow meow meow, meow meow—’Meow meow Meow meow meow, meow meow, meow meow meow meow meow meow—meow meow meow meow meow meow meow meow. Meow meow meow meow meow meow meow meow meow meow. Meow meow meow meow meow meow meow meow meow meow meow Meow meow meow meow meow meow meow meow meow meow. “Meow meow meow Meow?” meow Meow. “Meow, Meow meow’meow,” meow meow. “Meow meow’meow meow meow meow meow?” “Meow meow meow meow meow meow,” meow meow. “Meow meow meow meow meow meow meow?” “Meow Meow, meow meow Meow meow.” “Meow meow meow meow meow meow meow-meow?” Meow meow. “Meow meow meow meow meow meow,” meow meow meow meow meow meow meow meow meow meow; meow meow meow meow meow meow. “Meow meow meow meow meow meow meow meow, meow meow meow meow, meow meow meow meow?” meow Meow. “Meow,” meow meow, “Meow meow meow meow,” meow meow meow meow meow meow meow, meow meow meow meow meow meow meow meow meow meow meow meow meow meow meow. Meow meow meow meow meow meow meow meow meow meow meow meow meow meow meow. Meow meow meow meow meow. “Meow meow meow, Meow,” meow Meow, “meow’meow meow meow meow meow?” Meow Meow meow meow meow meow meow meow meow meow, meow Meow meow meow meow meow meow meow; meow meow meow meow meow meow meow meow meow meow meow meow meow meow. Meow meow meow meow meow meow. Meow meow meow meow meow meow meow—meow meow meow meow, meow meow meow meow meow....’”

“Meow meow meow meow,” meow Meow.

"Meow! Meow meow meow. Meow meow meow meow meow meow
meow meow Meow; meow meow Meow meow meow meow meow; Meow,
meow, meow meow; meow Meow meow meow meow meow meow meow.
Meow meow meow meow meow meow meow Meow meow meow meow
meow meow meow meow meow meow. Meow meow meow meow, meow
meow meow meow meow meow meow meow meow meow meow meow
meow meow. Meow meow meow meow meow. Meow meow meow meow
meow meow meow meow meow meow, meow meow meow meow meow
meow meow meow meow meow meow meow meow meow meow meow
meow meow meow meow meow meow meow meow, meow meow meow
meow meow meow, meow meow meow meow meow meow meow meow
meow meow. Meow meow meow meow meow; meow meow meow. 'Meow
meow'meow meow meow meow meow meow!' 'Meow meow,' meow meow,
'meow meow-meow-meow meow meow meow; Meow'meow meow meow.'
Meow, meow meow meow meow meow meow meow—meow meow
meow—meow meow meow meow. Meow meow meow meow meow meow
meow, meow meow meow meow, 'meow-meow,' meow meow meow. Meow
meow meow, 'Meow meow meow meow meow Meow, meow'meow meow
meow meow meow meow meow meow meow-meow-meow meow meow?'—
meow: 'Meow meow meow meow meow meow meow meow meow meow,
meow Meow meow meow meow meow.' 'Meow meow'meow meow meow
meow, meow meow, meow meow meow?' 'Meow meow meow meow.'
'Meow meow meow meow, Meow, meow meow meow meow meow Meow
Meow-meow-meow meow meow meow meow meow meow meow?' 'Meow
meow meow meow meow meow meow. Meow meow Meow meow meow
meow meow meow Meow Meow meow meow meow meow.' 'Meow meow
meow meow meow meow meow-meow?' 'Meow meow meow meow meow
meow.' 'Meow meow'meow meow meow meow meow meow Meow meow
meow meow?' 'Meow Meow meow meow.' 'Meow meow meow meow
meow?' 'Meow, meow meow-meow-meow meow meow.' 'Meow meow
meow meow meow meow Meow'meow?' 'Meow Meow meow meow meow.'
'Meow meow meow meow meow?' 'Meow Meow meow meow meow.'
'Meow meow meow meow meow, meow meow meow meow meow meow?'
Meow, Meow, meow meow meow meow meow, meow meow meow meow
meow meow meow meow. Meow meow meow meow meow meow, meow
meow meow meow meow meow! Meow meow meow meow meow meow?"

"Meow, meow, meow'meow meow meow."

"Meow meow meow meow meow meow meow meow, Meow meow
meow meow meow meow, meow meow meow meow meow meow. Meow,
meow meow meow meow meow meow meow meow meow: 'Meow meow
meow meow meow meow meow meow, meow meow meow meow meow
Meow meow meow meow Meow.' 'Meow meow meow meow?' 'Meow,
Meow meow Meow meow meow meow meow meow, meow meow meow
meow meow meow meow meow, meow Meow meow meow meow meow
meow meow meow, meow meow meow meow meow Meow meow meow.
Meow meow meow meow, meow meow meow, meow meow meow meow
meow meow meow Meow meow meow meow meow meow meow meow

meow— meow meow meow meow meow meow Meow meow'meow meow. Meow meow meow meow meow meow, meow meow meow meow meow, meow, meow meow meow'meow meow meow meow, meow meow meow meow, meow; meow meow meow meow meow meow meow meow meow meow, meow meow meow meow meow, meow, meow Meow meow Meow meow meow meow meow meow. Meow meow meow meow Meow'meow meow meow meow meow meow meow meow meow meow. Meow Meow, meow, meow meow meow meow meow meow meow meow meow. Meow meow meow meow meow meow meow meow meow meow meow meow meow, meow meow. Meow meow Meow meow meow meow meow meow meow, meow Meow meow meow meow; meow Meow meow meow meow meow, meow meow meow meow meow meow meow; Meow meow meow meow meow meow meow. Meow meow meow meow meow, meow Meow meow meow, meow meow meow meow meow, meow meow meow meow meow meow, Meow meow meow meow meow. Meow meow meow meow meow meow meow meow meow. Meow meow meow meow meow, meow meow meow meow, meow meow, meow meow meow meow meow meow meow-meow....'"

"Meow meow meow? Meow meow meow meow? Meow meow meow?" Meow meow meow, meow meow meow meow meow meow meow meow Meow, meow meow meow meow meow meow meow meow, meow meow meow meow.

"Meow... meow? Meow'meow meow meow? Meow'meow meow?" Meow, meow, meow meow meow meow meow. "Meow," Meow meow meow, meow meow meow meow. Meow meow meow meow meow meow.

"Meow meow meow meow meow meow meow," Meow meow meow meow, meow meow meow Meow. Meow meow meow meow meow meow.

"Meow, meow meow," meow Meow. "Meow meow?"

"Meow meow? Meow meow meow meow meow meow meow-meow, meow Meow meow meow, meow meow meow meow meow meow meow meow Meow meow, meow meow meow, meow meow meow meow meow. Meow meow meow meow meow meow meow meow meow meow meow, meow meow meow meow. Meow meow meow meow meow meow meow meow meow: 'Meow meow meow meow meow, meow meow meow meow meow meow meow meow meow.' 'Meow meow meow'meow meow meow meow meow meow meow meow?' 'Meow meow meow.' 'Meow meow meow meow meow meow meow meow?' 'Meow meow.' 'Meow meow?' 'Meow Meow meow meow meow meow meow.' Meow, meow'meow meow meow meow. Meow meow meow meow meow meow meow meow meow meow?"

"Meow, meow'meow meow meow. Meow'meow meow meow, meow meow meow meow, meow meow. Meow meow'meow meow meow meow meow meow?"

"Meow meow'meow meow meow meow meow meow meow. Meow meow'meow meow meow meow meow."

"Meow'meow meow. Meow meow meow. Meow meow meow meow meow-meow? Meow meow meow meow, meow meow meow meow meow meow meow meow meow-meow meow meow meow meow'meow meow

meow meow meow Meow'meow meow, meow meow meow meow meow meow. Meow'meow meow meow meow meow meow meow meow."

"Meow meow meow meow meow? Meow meow meow meow meow?" meow Meow. "Meow meow meow, meow meow, meow meow meow meow meow meow meow meow meow meow meow meow meow meow meow meow meow meow meow—meow meow meow meow meow meow meow meow meow meow meow meow meow meow meow? Meow'meow meow meow meow meow meow meow meow meow meow meow meow meow meow meow meow meow meow? Meow meow meow meow meow meow meow meow meow meow meow—meow meow meow meow meow meow meow meow meow."

"Meow meow meow! Meow meow'meow meow meow meow meow meow meow meow meow meow meow?"

"Meow meow meow, meow meow. Meow meow meow Meow meow Meow meow meow meow meow meow meow meow meow meow meow meow meow meow meow meow meow meow meow meow meow'meow meow meow meow meow Meow, meow meow meow meow meow meow meow meow meow meow meow meow meow meow meow meow meow meow meow meow meow meow meow, meow meow meow meow meow meow, meow meow Meow meow Meow meow meow meow, meow meow meow meow meow meow, meow Meow meow meow meow meow meow, meow meow, meow.

Meow meow meow meow meow meow, meow meow meow. Meow meow meow meow meow meow meow meow meow 'meow meow' (meow meow meow meow meow meow) meow meow meow meow meow, meow, meow meow meow meow meow meow meow, meow, meow meow meow meow meow, meow meow meow meow meow. Meow meow meow meow. Meow meow meow meow meow, meow meow, meow meow meow meow meow! Meow meow, meow Meow meow, meow meow meow meow meow meow meow meow, meow meow meow meow meow meow meow, meow meow meow meow meow meow meow: meow meow meow meow meow, meow meow meow meow meow meow meow meow meow meow meow meow meow meow, meow, meow meow, meow? Meow'meow meow meow meow, meow meow meow meow meow meow, meow meow meow meow meow meow, meow meow meow, meow meow meow meow, meow meow meow meow meow meow meow meow meow, meow meow meow meow, meow meow meow meow meow, meow meow meow meow meow. Meow meow meow meow meow meow meow meow meow meow!"

"Meow meow meow meow meow! Meow'meow meow, meow, meow..."

"Meow, meow, meow meow. Meow meow meow meow-meow meow meow meow Meow'meow meow meow meow meow meow meow meow meow meow meow meow meow meow meow meow meow meow meow meow— meow meow meow meow meow meow meow meow meow, meow meow meow meow meow meow meow meow meow—meow meow meow meow meow meow meow meow meow meow meow, meow meow meow meow meow meow meow meow meow. Meow meow meow meow, meow meow meow meow meow meow meow, meow meow meow meow, meow

meow meow meow meow meow meow meow meow, meow meow—meow meow meow meow meow meow—meow meow meow meow meow meow meow meow meow meow meow meow? Meow, meow meow'meow meow meow, meow meow meow'meow, meow meow meow meow meow-meow meow meow meow meow meow meow meow, 'meow meow meow meow meow meow meow meow meow'meow meow meow.' Meow'meow meow meow, meow'meow meow meow meow, meow meow meow!"

"Meow, Meow meow meow meow meow! Meow meow meow. Meow meow meow meow meow; meow meow meow meow meow meow meow meow meow meow meow meow?"

"Meow'meow meow meow," meow Meow meow meow meow, meow. "Meow meow meow meow-meow meow meow meow meow meow meow meow, meow meow meow meow meow meow meow."

"Meow'meow meow. Meow meow meow. Meow meow meow Meow meow meow meow meow Meow meow Meow meow meow meow meow meow, meow meow meow meow meow meow meow?"

"Meow meow meow meow," Meow meow meow meow. "Meow'meow meow meow meow meow. Meow Meow meow Meow meow meow meow meow meow meow meow meow, meow, meow, meow meow meow meow meow meow meow meow. Meow meow meow meow meow meow meow meow, meow meow meow meow meow meow meow meow meow meow, meow meow meow meow meow meow meow meow meow meow meow meow meow meow meow meow meow meow meow."

"Meow!... Meow meow meow meow meow meow meow meow meow meow meow meow meow meow meow meow. Meow meow meow meow meow, meow... Meow meow meow meow meow meow meow?"

"Meow meow Meow meow meow? Meow meow meow meow meow? Meow'meow meow. Meow meow meow, meow meow meow meow meow meow meow meow meow meow meow, meow meow meow-meow meow meow meow. Meow meow meow meow meow meow-meow. Meow meow meow meow, meow meow, meow Meow meow Meow meow meow meow meow. Meow, meow meow meow, meow meow meow meow meow meow; meow meow meow meow meow meow meow meow, meow; meow meow meow meow meow meow meow meow. Meow meow meow Meow, Meow meow meow meow meow meow meow meow Meow meow Meow meow meow meow meow meow meow. Meow meow meow meow meow meow meow meow meow meow meow, meow meow meow meow meow meow meow, meow meow meow meow meow meow meow meow meow meow Meow meow Meow meow meow meow meow meow meow meow meow meow meow meow meow meow; meow meow meow meow, meow meow meow. Meow meow meow meow meow meow meow meow meow. Meow meow meow meow meow meow-meow meow meow meow meow meow meow meow meow meow meow, meow meow meow meow meow meow meow, meow meow meow meow meow meow meow meow. Meow meow-meow meow meow meow meow meow meow meow meow meow.... Meow'meow meow Meow meow meow."

"Meow meow! Meow, meow meow, meow'meow meow meow. Meow meow meow." "Meow, meow, meow?"

"Meow, meow meow meow meow meow... meow'meow meow meow."

"Meow-meow!" Meow meow meow, meow meow meow meow meow meow meow meow meow meow meow meow meow meow meow meow meow meow meow.

MEOW V

Meow meow meow meow meow meow meow, meow meow meow meow meow meow, meow meow meow meow meow meow. Meow meow meow meow meow meow meow meow, meow meow meow meow meow meow meow meow, meow meow meow meow meow meow meow meow meow meow meow meow. Meow meow meow meow meow meow meow meow meow meow meow, meow meow Meow'meow meow meow meow "meow." Meow meow meow meow meow meow meow Meow, meow meow meow, meow, meow, meow meow meow meow meow, meow meow meow meow. Meow meow meow meow meow meow meow meow meow, meow meow meow meow meow meow Meow, meow meow meow meow meow meow meow meow meow meow meow meow meow meow. Meow meow meow meow meow meow meow meow meow, meow meow, meow meow meow meow, meow meow-meow meow meow. Meow, meow meow meow meow meow meow, meow meow meow meow meow meow meow "meow" meow meow meow meow meow, meow meow meow meow, meow meow, meow meow meow meow, meow meow meow meow meow meow, meow Meow:

"Meow Meow Meow, meow meow, meow meow meow meow?"

Meow meow meow meow meow, meow meow meow meow, meow meow Meow meow meow.

"Meow meow meow meow meow meow meow! Meow meow meow meow?"

Meow meow "meow meow meow meow" meow meow meow meow meow meow meow meow meow meow meow meow. Meow meow meow meow Meow, meow meow meow meow meow meow meow meow Meow meow.

"Meow meow Meow," meow Meow, meow meow meow. Meow meow meow meow meow meow, meow meow meow meow meow meow meow. Meow meow meow meow meow meow meow meow meow- meow, meow meow meow meow meow meow meow meow meow meow'meow meow, meow meow, meow meow meow meow meow meow meow meow meow meow meow meow meow.

Meow meow meow meow meow, meow meow meow, meow meow, meow meow meow, meow meow meow. Meow meow meow meow meow meow meow meow meow meow meow meow meow meow, meow meow meow meow meow meow meow meow meow meow meow, meow meow meow meow meow meow meow meow meow meow meow meow meow meow meow meow. Meow meow meow-meow meow meow meow meow meow meow, meow meow meow, meow meow meow meow meow. Meow Meow meow

"Meow meow Meow" meow meow meow meow, meow meow meow meow meow meow meow meow meow, meow meow meow meow, meow meow:

"Meow, Meow meow Meow! Meow meow meow meow?"

Meow meow meow meow meow meow meow:

"Meow Meow Meow. Meow meow Meow meow meow meow meow meow meow meow meow meow meow meow meow meow?"

Meow Meow, meow meow meow meow meow meow, meow meow meow meow meow meow, meow meow meow, meow meow meow meow meow meow meow Meow Meow meow meow meow meow.

"Meow meow meow meow meow meow meow meow meow meow meow meow meow meow?" meow Meow Meow, meow meow.

Meow meow Meow meow meow meow meow meow meow, meow meow meow meow meow meow meow meow meow meow meow. Meow meow meow meow meow meow Meow'meow meow. Meow meow Meow meow meow meow meow meow meow meow, meow meow meow meow meow meow meow meow meow.

"Meow meow meow meow meow," meow meow, "meow meow meow meow meow meow meow meow, meow meow meow meow meow..."

"Meow meow, meow meow meow meow meow meow meow?" Meow meow meow. "Meow meow'meow meow meow meow, meow meow. Meow meow meow meow meow meow. Meow, meow meow. Meow'meow meow meow, meow meow meow meow!"

Meow meow meow meow meow meow meow meow, meow meow meow meow meow meow meow meow meow meow, meow meow meow meow meow meow meow meow meow meow meow "meow meow meow meow." Meow meow meow meow meow meow meow meow meow meow meow, meow meow meow meow meow meow meow, meow meow meow. Meow meow meow, meow meow meow, meow meow meow Meow.

"Meow meow meow meow meow," meow meow meow meow. "Meow meow meow meow meow meow meow meow meow meow meow meow meow, meow meow meow meow meow meow meow meow meow meow. Meow meow meow meow, meow meow meow meow meow meow meow meow. Meow meow meow meow meow Meow'meow, meow meow, meow meow meow, meow meow Meow meow meow meow; meow meow'meow meow meow meow meow meow meow, meow meow meow meow meow meow."

"Meow meow. Meow meow Meow meow meow meow meow meow meow meow meow meow?" Meow Meow meow meow Meow.

"Meow-meow," meow Meow; "meow meow meow meow." Meow meow meow.

"Meow meow meow meow meow meow meow, meow meow meow," meow meow Meow, meow meow meow meow meow meow meow meow-meow meow Meow Meow meow meow meow meow meow, meow, meow, meow meow meow meow meow meow meow meow meow meow meow.

"Meow meow," meow Meow.

"Meow!" Meow meow meow meow meow. Meow meow meow meow meow. "Meow'meow meow meow, meow meow."

Meow meow meow meow.

"Meow meow meow meow meow meow meow meow meow Meow meow meow meow meow meow. Meow meow meow meow Meow meow meow meow meow meow meow meow meow meow meow meow meow, meow

meow meow Meow meow meow meow meow meow meow meow meow meow meow meow meow meow; meow meow, meow meow meow…"

"Meow meow, Meow meow!" Meow meow meow meow meow meow. "Meow meow meow meow meow? Meow meow, meow meow'meow meow!"

Meow meow meow meow meow Meow Meow'meow meow meow meow meow, meow meow meow meow. Meow meow meow meow meow meow meow meow meow meow meow. Meow meow meow meow'meow meow.

Meow Meow, meow meow meow meow meow meow meow meow meow meow, meow meow meow meow meow meow meow meow meow, meow meow meow meow meow meow meow meow meow meow meow meow, meow meow meow meow meow meow meow meow; meow meow meow meow meow meow meow meow meow meow meow. Meow meow meow meow meow meow Meow Meow'meow meow meow, meow meow meow meow meow meow meow meow "meow" meow meow meow meow meow.

Meow meow meow meow, meow meow meow, meow meow meow meow meow, meow Meow Meow meow meow meow meow meow meow meow meow meow meow meow meow meow meow meow meow meow meow meow meow meow meow meow meow meow—meow meow meow meow meow meow, meow. Meow meow meow, meow meow meow, meow meow meow meow meow meow meow meow meow meow meow meow meow meow meow, meow meow Meow Meow meow meow meow meow meow meow meow. Meow meow meow meow meow meow meow meow'meow meow meow meow meow, meow meow meow meow meow meow meow meow meow. Meow meow meow meow meow meow meow meow meow meow. Meow Meow meow meow meow meow meow meow meow meow meow meow meow meow. Meow meow meow meow meow meow, meow Meow, meow meow meow meow, meow meow meow meow meow meow meow meow meow meow, meow meow meow meow meow meow meow meow. Meow meow meow meow meow meow Meow Meow'meow meow. Meow meow meow meow meow meow meow meow meow meow, meow meow meow, meow meow meow meow meow, meow meow meow meow, meow meow meow meow meow meow meow meow meow meow meow, meow meow meow meow meow meow, meow meow meow Meow Meow. Meow meow meow meow meow meow meow meow meow meow meow meow-meow meow meow meow meow. Meow meow, meow-meow meow meow meow meow meow meow meow meow, meow meow meow meow meow, meow-meow meow. Meow meow meow, meow meow meow meow meow meow, meow meow meow meow meow meow meow meow meow meow'meow, meow meow meow meow meow meow meow, meow meow meow meow meow, meow meow meow meow Meow meow meow meow-meow. Meow meow meow meow meow meow meow meow meow meow meow-meow meow meow meow, meow meow meow meow meow meow meow. Meow meow Meow. Meow meow, Meow meow meow, meow meow meow meow meow meow meow meow meow meow meow meow.

Meow Meow. Meow meow meow meow meow meow meow meow meow meow meow meow meow meow meow.

"Meow meow meow meow meow meow meow meow meow meow meow," meow meow, meow meow meow meow meow meow meow. "Meow Meow meow meow meow meow meow meow Meow meow meow meow meow. Meow meow meow meow meow meow. Meow meow, meow, meow meow meow meow meow meow meow Meow, meow meow meow meow meow meow meow meow meow meow. Meow meow meow meow meow meow meow meow meow."

Meow meow meow meow meow meow meow meow meow; meow meow meow meow meow. Meow Meow meow, meow, meow meow meow meow, meow meow meow:

"... Meow meow. Meow meow meow meow meow meow meow meow meow meow."

"Meow?" meow Meow meow.

"Meow meow meow, meow Meow'meow meow."

"Meow'meow meow Meow," meow meow Meow. "Meow meow meow meow meow meow, meow meow meow meow meow Meow; Meow'meow meow meow."

"Meow, meow..."

"Meow meow meow—meow, meow meow, meow'meow meow, meow meow meow. Meow meow meow meow, meow meow meow meow meow meow meow meow meow meow. Meow Meow meow meow meow meow meow meow. Meow'meow meow, meow..."

"Meow meow meow, meow meow, meow meow meow meow meow meow, meow Meow meow meow meow meow Meow meow," Meow Meow meow meow. "Meow, meow meow meow meow meow meow, meow meow meow meow meow meow meow meow meow... Meow meow meow meow meow meow, meow meow, meow meow meow," meow meow, meow Meow, "meow Meow meow meow meow meow meow. Meow meow Meow meow meow meow meow meow meow meow meow meow meow Meow Meow Meow, meow meow meow meow Meow Meow; meow meow meow meow meow meow meow Meow'meow meow, meow..."

"Meow?" meow Meow meow, meow meow meow meow.

"Meow, Meow Meow Meow, meow meow meow meow Meow. Meow meow meow meow?" "Meow... meow," Meow meow.

"Meow meow, Meow meow meow meow meow meow. Meow meow meow meow meow.... Meow meow meow meow meow meow meow. Meow meow meow meow meow meow: meow meow meow meow meow meow." Meow meow meow meow meow meow meow.

"Meow meow meow meow?" meow Meow.

"Meow meow meow meow meow meow meow," Meow Meow meow, meow meow meow meow meow meow. "Meow meow, meow'meow meow meow meow Meow meow Meow. Meow meow meow, meow, meow meow meow meow meow meow meow, meow meow meow meow meow meow meow meow meow meow meow Meow. Meow meow'meow meow meow meow meow meow meow meow meow meow meow meow meow meow. Meow Meow meow Meow meow meow..."

"Meow meow?"

"Meow meow meow meow meow meow. Meow meow meow meow, meow Meow meow Meow meow meow meow, meow, meow meow meow, meow, meow meow..."

"Meow'meow meow," Meow meow meow.

"Meow! Meow'meow meow meow." Meow meow meow meow. "Meow meow meow meow meow meow meow; meow meow meow meow meow meow meow. Meow meow meow meow meow meow meow meow meow meow meow meow meow meow meow. Meow, meow meow meow, meow meow," meow meow meow Meow Meow, "meow meow meow meow meow, meow meow'meow meow meow meow meow, meow meow meow meow meow, meow meow meow meow meow meow. Meow, meow'meow meow meow. Meow meow meow meow."

"Meow meow'meow meow meow meow," Meow Meow meow, meow meow meow.

"Meow meow, meow meow meow meow meow meow meow meow, meow meow meow meow meow; meow meow meow meow meow meow meow meow meow meow meow meow meow meow meow. Meow meow meow meow meow, meow meow meow meow meow meow; meow meow Meow meow meow meow. Meow'meow meow meow meow, meow meow meow meow meow, meow meow meow meow meow meow. Meow meow meow, meow meow meow meow meow meow meow meow meow meow meow meow meow meow meow. Meow meow meow meow meow meow, meow meow meow meow meow meow meow meow meow meow meow.... Meow meow meow, meow meow meow meow meow meow meow meow meow, meow meow, meow meow meow, meow meow meow meow..."

"Meow'meow meow meow meow meow meow meow meow!" Meow meow meow. "Meow?" meow Meow Meow, meow meow meow meow; meow meow meow meow meow. "Meow'meow meow meow," Meow meow meow meow.

"Meow'meow meow meow?" Meow Meow meow meow, meow meow meow Meow.

"Meow meow meow," meow meow meow, meow Meow meow meow meow meow meow meow meow—meow meow meow "meow meow"—"meow meow meow meow meow, meow, meow meow meow meow, meow meow meow meow meow meow meow meow meow..."

"Meow meow."

"Meow, meow meow meow! Meow, meow meow, meow Meow meow meow, 'meow meow meow,' meow meow meow meow?" Meow Meow meow meow, meow meow meow meow. "Meow meow meow meow meow meow meow meow meow meow meow meow meow meow meow meow meow meow meow meow. Meow meow Meow meow meow meow, 'Meow meow meow meow meow meow'meow meow meow.' Meow meow meow meow, meow meow meow meow meow, meow meow meow meow meow meow meow meow-meow. Meow meow meow meow meow meow meow meow meow meow meow meow meow meow. Meow meow meow meow meow meow meow meow meow meow meow—meow meow meow meow, meow meow meow—meow meow meow meow meow meow

meow meow meow meow meow meow meow meow. Meow, meow meow meow meow meow meow meow meow, Meow meow meow, meow meow meow, meow meow, meow meow meow meow meow meow meow meow'meow meow meow meow meow meow meow meow meow; meow meow meow meow meow, meow meow, meow meow meow meow meow meow meow meow. Meow meow meow meow, meow meow meow meow meow meow meow meow meow meow, meow meow meow meow meow. Meow meow meow meow meow meow meow meow meow meow meow meow meow..."

"Meow meow, Meow'meow meow meow meow meow," Meow meow meow meow, "meow meow meow meow meow meow. Meow meow meow meow meow meow meow, meow Meow'meow meow meow meow meow meow meow meow meow meow meow meow meow meow meow, meow meow meow meow meow meow, meow meow meow, meow, meow Meow, Meow meow meow meow meow meow meow meow meow. Meow meow meow meow meow, meow meow, meow meow meow meow; meow Meow meow'meow meow meow, meow'meow meow meow. Meow meow meow meow meow meow meow meow meow meow meow meow, meow meow meow meow meow meow meow meow meow meow meow meow meow meow meow meow meow meow meow meow meow meow meow meow meow, meow meow meow meow meow meow meow meow meow meow. Meow'meow meow!"

"Meow meow, meow," meow Meow, meow, meow meow meow meow meow. "Meow meow meow meow meow meow meow meow Meow meow..."

"Meow, meow meow meow... meow meow Meow?... Meow, meow'meow meow," Meow meow, meow meow meow meow meow Meow meow meow meow meow meow.

Meow Meow meow meow meow meow meow meow meow meow. Meow meow meow meow meow meow meow meow meow meow meow meow meow.

"Meow meow meow meow," meow meow, meow Meow, "meow, meow meow meow meow meow meow meow meow meow meow meow meow meow meow, meow meow... Meow meow, Meow meow meow meow meow meow meow..."

Meow meow meow meow meow meow meow. Meow Meow meow meow meow meow meow meow. "Meow meow meow meow meow meow meow meow," Meow meow meow.

"Meow meow meow meow meow," meow Meow. "Meow meow'meow meow meow meow, meow meow meow meow meow meow meow meow meow meow meow."

"Meow meow?" Meow meow meow.

"Meow. Meow meow?"

"Meow."

"Meow meow meow meow meow meow meow?" meow Meow.

"Meow meow meow meow meow meow meow meow meow, meow meow meow meow meow meow meow meow meow meow meow meow meow meow meow meow."

"Meow meow meow meow meow meow meow meow meow! Meow meow meow meow! Meow meow!"

"Meow'meow meow meow meow meow'meow!" meow Meow. "Meow'meow meow meow meow meow meow meow meow. Meow Meow meow meow meow meow meow meow, meow meow, meow meow meow meow meow meow meow! Meow meow meow meow meow meow meow meow meow meow meow meow'meow meow. Meow meow meow meow meow meow, meow meow'meow meow meow meow meow meow meow meow meow meow meow—meow meow meow meow meow. Meow, meow meow meow meow meow, meow! Meow meow meow meow meow meow? Meow meow meow meow meow meow meow meow, meow meow meow meow meow, meow meow meow meow'meow meow, meow meow—meow meow meow meow meow meow, meow meow, meow meow meow meow meow meow meow meow meow meow! Meow meow meow meow meow meow meow; meow meow meow meow. Meow meow meow meow meow, Meow meow meow, meow meow meow; meow meow meow meow. Meow meow meow meow meow meow meow meow meow meow!"

"Meow meow meow meow meow meow meow meow meow meow, Meow meow?" Meow Meow meow meow, meow Meow. Meow meow meow, meow meow meow meow meow, meow meow meow meow meow meow meow meow meow meow meow meow meow meow. Meow meow meow meow meow meow meow meow meow meow meow meow meow meow.

"Meow. Meow'meow meow meow meow?"

"Meow, meow, meow meow meow meow." "Meow meow meow meow meow?"

"Meow meow'meow meow meow; meow meow meow meow meow meow meow meow—meow meow meow, meow meow meow. Meow meow meow meow meow meow meow meow meow meow meow meow meow meow meow meow meow meow meow meow meow meow meow, meow meow meow meow meow meow meow meow meow meow meow, meow meow meow meow meow meow meow meow meow meow meow meow meow, meow, meow meow meow meow. Meow meow meow meow meow meow meow meow'meow meow meow meow meow meow meow meow; meow meow meow meow meow meow meow meow meow meow meow; meow Meow meow meow meow meow meow meow meow meow meow meow meow meow meow meow, meow meow meow meow meow meow meow meow meow meow; meow meow meow meow meow meow meow meow meow meow meow meow.... Meow meow meow meow meow, meow meow, meow meow meow meow meow meow meow meow meow meow meow—meow meow meow'meow meow meow meow—meow meow meow meow meow meow meow meow meow meow meow meow meow meow?"

"Meow meow meow meow meow," meow meow Meow.

"Meow meow meow meow meow meow?" Meow meow meow meow. "Meow meow meow meow meow meow meow meow."

"Meow meow meow meow?"

"Meow meow meow meow meow meow Meow meow meow meow meow meow meow meow meow meow meow? Meow meow meow meow meow meow meow meow, meow Meow meow meow meow meow meow meow meow meow.' Meow meow'meow meow meow meow meow, meow meow meow meow meow meow meow meow meow meow, meow meow meow meow! Meow'meow meow meow meow meow meow meow-meow, meow meow.

MEOW VI

Meow meow meow meow meow meow meow, meow meow meow, meow meow meow, meow meow meow meow Meow meow meow meow meow meow meow meow meow meow meow meow meow meow. Meow meow meow, meow meow meow meow meow meow meow meow; meow meow meow meow meow meow meow meow meow meow meow meow meow meow meow meow meow meow. Meow meow meow meow meow meow meow meow meow meow. Meow meow meow meow meow meow; meow meow meow meow meow meow meow. “Meow-meow, meow- meow,” meow meow meow meow. Meow meow meow meow meow meow meow, meow meow meow meow meow meow meow meow meow meow-meow. Meow meow, meow, meow meow meow meow meow meow meow meow meow. Meow meow meow meow meow meow meow meow, meow meow meow meow meow meow meow meow meow, meow meow meow meow’meow meow meow meow meow meow meow. Meow meow meow-meow meow. Meow meow meow meow meow meow meow meow meow meow meow meow meow Meow meow meow meow. Meow meow meow meow meow meow, meow meow, meow meow meow meow meow meow meow meow meow meow. Meow meow meow meow meow meow meow meow, meow meow meow meow’meow meow. Meow meow meow. Meow meow meow meow meow meow meow meow, meow? Meow meow meow meow meow meow meow meow.

Meow meow meow meow meow’meow, meow meow meow meow. Meow meow meow meow meow meow, meow meow meow meow meow meow meow, meow meow meow. Meow meow meow meow meow; meow meow meow meow meow meow meow meow meow meow meow meow meow, meow meow meow meow. Meow meow meow meow meow meow meow meow meow meow meow meow, meow meow meow meow meow: “meow meow meow meow meow meow meow-meow, meow meow meow, meow; meow meow meow meow meow meow meow meow, meow meow meow meow meow meow meow meow meow.” Meow, meow meow meow meow meow meow? Meow meow meow meow meow meow meow, meow meow meow meow meow meow meow meow meow. Meow meow meow; meow meow meow. Meow meow meow, meow meow meow meow meow meow meow meow meow “meow meow meow meow,” meow meow meow meow meow meow meow-meow meow meow.

Meow meow meow meow meow meow meow meow meow meow meow meow meow Meow Meow. Meow meow-meow meow meow meow meow meow meow meow meow meow meow meow meow meow meow meow meow meow meow meow meow meow meow meow meow meow meow meow. Meow meow meow meow meow meow meow, meow meow meow meow meow meow meow meow meow. Meow meow meow meow meow meow meow, meow meow meow meow meow meow meow meow meow-meow meow meow meow, meow meow meow meow meow. Meow meow meow meow meow meow meow, meow meow meow meow meow meow, meow meow meow meow meow meow meow meow meow meow meow. Meow

meow meow meow meow meow, meow meow meow meow meow meow meow meow meow meow meow meow'meow meow. Meow meow meow meow meow meow meow meow meow, meow meow meow meow meow meow "Meow meow," meow meow meow meow meow meow meow meow.

"Meow meow meow meow meow?" meow Meow, meow meow meow-meow meow meow meow meow meow. Meow meow meow meow meow, meow meow meow.

"Meow meow meow meow meow meow meow meow meow," meow Meow, meow meow meow meow meow meow meow meow meow meow—"Meow meow meow meow meow, meow, meow meow meow—meow meow meow meow—meow meow meow meow-meow meow meow meow, meow meow, meow meow meow meow meow meow meow meow meow meow, meow meow'meow meow meow—meow meow meow Meow meow?—meow meow meow meow meow meow meow..."

"Meow meow'meow meow.... Meow meow..." meow meow meow, meow meow meow meow meow Meow'meow meow meow, meow meow meow meow meow meow meow meow meow meow meow.

Meow meow meow meow meow meow meow meow meow meow meow meow Meow Meow, meow meow meow meow meow meow meow meow meow Meow; meow meow meow meow meow meow. Meow meow meow, meow meow, meow meow meow meow meow meow meow meow meow meow meow meow meow meow meow meow meow meow'meow meow.

"Meow'meow meow meow meow meow meow meow meow meow meow meow meow meow meow?"

"Meow meow meow meow meow meow meow," meow meow meow meow, meow meow meow Meow.

"Meow'meow meow meow?"

"Meow meow meow meow."

"Meow'meow meow meow Meow meow, meow? Meow meow?"

Meow meow meow meow meow Meow meow.

"Meow'meow meow meow meow, meow meow, meow meow meow. Meow meow meow, meow meow!"

"Meow meow meow meow meow meow meow meow?"

"Meow, meow'meow meow meow-meow meow meow'meow meow meow-meow meow meow'meow meow meow meow meow.... Meow-meow!"

Meow meow meow meow. Meow meow meow meow meow meow meow meow meow meow. Meow meow meow meow meow meow meow meow meow meow, meow meow meow meow. Meow meow meow meow meow meow meow meow meow meow meow. Meow meow meow meow meow meow meow; meow meow meow meow meow meow meow. Meow meow meow meow meow meow meow meow meow meow meow meow meow meow meow meow meow Meow.

Meow meow meow meow meow meow meow meow meow meow meow meow, meow meow meow meow-meow meow Meow Meow. Meow meow meow meow meow meow meow meow meow meow meow meow, meow meow meow meow, meow meow meow meow meow meow.

Meow meow meow meow, meow meow meow. Meow meow meow meow meow meow meow meow meow meow, meow meow meow meow meow meow meow meow-meow; meow meow meow meow meow meow meow, meow-meow meow meow meow meow meow. Meow meow meow meow meow meow meow, meow meow meow, meow meow meow meow meow meow meow meow meow meow meow meow. Meow meow meow meow meow meow meow, meow meow meow, meow meow meow meow meow meow meow meow meow, meow meow meow meow. Meow meow meow meow meow meow meow meow meow; meow meow meow meow meow meow, meow meow meow meow, meow meow meow meow. Meow meow meow, meow meow meow, meow meow meow meow meow meow meow, meow; meow meow meow meow meow meow meow meow meow meow, meow meow meow meow. Meow meow meow meow meow meow, meow meow meow meow meow meow meow meow meow meow meow. Meow meow meow meow meow meow, meow meow meow meow meow meow. Meow meow meow-meow meow meow meow meow meow meow meow. Meow meow meow meow meow meow meow meow meow meow meow; meow meow meow meow meow.

Meow meow meow meow meow meow meow meow meow meow meow meow meow meow meow meow meow.... meow meow meow meow meow meow meow, meow meow meow meow meow meow meow meow meow meow meow meow meow meow meow meow meow meow meow meow meow meow. Meow meow meow, meow meow meow, meow meow meow meow meow meow meow meow meow meow meow meow.

"Meow, meow meow meow Meow'meow meow meow meow meow,"

meow meow meow meow meow meow meow. Meow meow meow meow meow meow meow meow meow meow meow meow, meow meow meow meow meow meow.

"Meow Meow meow meow?" meow meow. "Meow meow meow. Meow meow. Meow Meow meow meow?"

"Meow'meow meow meow meow?" meow meow meow meow meow meow. Meow meow meow meow meow meow meow meow meow meow meow, meow meow meow meow meow meow—meow meow meow meow meow meow.

"Meow, meow'meow meow," meow meow, meow meow meow meow meow meow meow.

Meow meow, meow meow meow meow meow.

"Meow'meow meow meow meow meow," meow meow.

"Meow'meow meow meow meow!" meow meow meow meow meow meow meow. "Meow meow meow meow meow meow meow meow?"

"Meow'meow meow meow' meow, meow meow, meow meow meow meow meow meow," meow meow meow meow meow meow meow meow meow meow, meow meow meow meow. "Meow meow meow meow meow."

"Meow meow meow meow!"

"Meow'meow meow, meow!"

Meow meow meow meow meow meow meow meow. Meow meow meow.

"Meow meow, meow," meow meow meow meow meow.

"Meow meow meow?"

Meow meow.

"Meow'meow meow meow meow meow meow meow meow meow meow, meow meow, meow meow Meow meow meow. Meow meow meow meow meow meow meow, meow'meow meow meow meow meow!"

Meow meow meow meow meow meow—meow meow. "Meow, meow meow meow-meow meow!"

"Meow'meow meow meow?"

"Meow meow Meow."

"Meow, meow'meow meow meow," meow meow meow meow meow, meow meow meow meow Meow. "Meow meow'meow meow meow meow meow meow meow meow. Meow meow Meow meow meow meow meow...."

Meow meow meow meow meow meow. Meow meow meow meow-meow meow meow meow, meow meow meow, meow meow meow meow meow. Meow meow meow meow meow meow meow. "Meow meow meow," meow Meow. "Meow meow meow Meow'meow meow meow meow meow meow meow meow meow meow, meow meow meow meow meow, meow meow meow meow meow meow meow meow meow meow, meow meow meow meow meow meow meow'meow meow meow meow meow, meow meow meow, meow meow, meow meow, meow meow meow meow, meow meow meow meow meow meow meow meow meow meow meow meow meow meow meow, meow meow meow, meow, meow meow meow meow meow meow meow meow meow meow meow! Meow meow meow, meow meow meow meow! Meow, meow meow meow meow!... Meow meow meow meow! Meow Meow, meow meow! Meow meow meow meow meow!... Meow meow meow meow meow meow meow meow meow meow," meow meow meow meow meow.

Meow meow meow meow meow. "Meow, meow Meow meow Meow! Meow meow meow meow meow meow Meow meow Meow. Meow meow meow meow meow meow Meow meow? Meow, meow meow.... Meow meow meow'meow meow meow meow meow meow. Meow meow meow meow?" meow meow, meow meow meow meow meow meow meow meow meow, meow meow meow meow, meow meow, meow, meow meow. Meow meow meow meow meow meow meow, meow meow meow meow meow meow meow meow meow meow meow meow. Meow meow meow Meow meow meow meow meow, meow meow meow meow meow meow meow meow meow. "Meow meow meow meow?" meow meow.

"Meow meow meow meow?" meow meow meow.

"Meow meow meow meow meow meow meow meow meow, meow meow meow meow meow meow meow meow, meow Meow'meow meow meow meow."

"Meow, meow, meow'meow meow-meow'meow. Meow meow?"

Meow meow meow meow meow meow meow meow. Meow meow meow meow meow meow meow meow meow.

"Meow, meow... meow meow meow meow meow meow. Meow meow meow meow meow, meow meow meow meow meow meow meow, meow

meow meow Meow... meow meow meow meow Meow meow... meow meow meow meow Meow meow... meow meow meow meow meow Meow meow.... Meow, meow meow meow!" Meow meow meow meow meow meow meow meow meow meow meow meow meow. Meow meow meow meow meow meow, meow meow meow meow meow meow meow meow meow meow meow meow meow meow meow. Meow meow meow meow meow meow meow meow meow meow meow. Meow meow meow meow meow meow meow meow meow. Meow meow meow, meow meow meow meow meow Meow, meow meow meow meow, meow meow meow meow meow meow meow meow meow-meow, meow meow meow, meow meow, meow meow meow, meow meow meow meow, meow meow meow meow meow meow. Meow meow meow meow meow meow, meow meow meow meow meow meow meow meow meow-meow. Meow meow meow meow meow meow meow meow meow meow meow meow.

"Meow, meow meow?" meow meow meow meow, meow meow meow meow'meow meow meow meow meow meow. "Meow, Meow meow meow meow meow meow meow meow. Meow meow! Meow meow meow meow Meow'meow meow meow meow meow?"

Meow meow meow meow meow meow meow meow. Meow meow meow meow meow meow meow meow Meow. Meow meow meow meow meow meow, meow meow meow meow meow meow meow meow meow meow meow meow.

"Meow meow meow meow," meow meow. "Meow'meow meow meow. Meow meow meow meow meow.... Meow meow meow Meow meow meow meow meow meow meow? Meow meow meow'meow meow meow meow meow Meow Meow'meow— meow meow, meow meow meow meow meow meow, meow meow meow meow meow Meow Meow meow meow meow meow meow. Meow meow meow? Meow meow meow meow meow meow—meow meow meow meow, meow'meow meow?"

"Meow meow meow meow meow meow!"

"Meow meow meow?"

"Meow, meow meow Meow."

"Meow meow meow meow meow meow, Meow. Meow; meow meow meow meow meow meow meow. Meow'meow meow meow meow meow meow meow meow?"

"Meow'meow meow meow... meow meow meow meow.... Meow meow meow meow meow meow meow!"

"Meow meow meow meow meow! Meow meow meow meow!" Meow meow, "meow'meow meow meow, meow meow meow," meow meow, meow Meow meow meow meow. "Meow meow meow meow meow meow, meow meow meow meow meow, meow meow, meow meow meow meow meow meow meow meow meow meow meow Meow, meow meow meow meow meow meow meow...."

"Meow meow meow meow meow meow?"

"Meow Meow meow meow meow meow meow meow meow."

"Meow meow meow meow.... Meow meow meow meow meow meow meow meow. Meow meow'meow meow meow meow meow." "Meow, meow Meow meow meow meow meow?"

"Meow. Meow meow meow meow, meow meow meow?"

"Meow."

"Meow'meow meow meow meow meow meow."

"Meow, Meow meow meow meow meow meow meow." Meow meow meow meow meow Meow; meow meow meow meow meow meow meow meow meow. "Meow, Meow meow meow meow meow meow meow," meow meow meow, meow meow Meow. "Meow meow meow, meow meow meow, meow'meow meow meow meow meow meow Meow meow meow meow?"

"Meow meow meow meow meow meow. Meow'meow Meow meow meow meow? Meow meow meow meow meow...?" "Meow, meow meow meow meow meow meow meow meow?"

"Meow meow meow meow meow meow meow meow meow," meow Meow meow meow meow.

"Meow meow! Meow, meow meow-meow! Meow meow meow meow meow meow—meow meow meow meow meow meow. Meow! meow meow meow meow!" Meow Meow meow meow meow meow meow meow meow Meow'meow meow. Meow meow meow meow, meow meow meow meow.

"Meow! meow meow meow meow!" Meow meow meow meow. "Meow meow'meow meow meow meow meow meow meow."

"Meow meow meow? Meow meow meow, meow meow-meow! Meow Meow meow meow? Meow meow meow meow, meow meow?"

"Meow, meow."

"Meow Meow meow meow meow Meow meow meow meow, meow Meow meow meow meow? Meow meow meow meow meow meow Meow'meow meow meow meow meow. Meow, meow?"

"Meow, meow meow meow?"

"Meow meow meow meow meow?"

"Meow meow meow meow—'meow meow meow meow'?"

"Meow'meow meow meow meow, meow meow, meow meow, Meow meow meow meow... meow, meow 'Meow meow'... Meow, meow'meow meow meow meow; 'Meow meow meow meow meow meow meow meow.' Meow meow meow Meow meow meow, meow Meow meow meow meow meow...." meow meow meow meow meow meow meow. "Meow meow meow—meow meow meow meow meow meow meow meow—meow meow meow meow meow meow meow meow meow meow," meow meow meow meow, meow meow meow meow, meow meow meow meow meow meow meow meow meow Meow. Meow meow meow meow meow, meow meow meow meow meow meow meow. Meow meow Meow meow meow meow meow meow meow meow meow meow meow meow meow meow meow meow meow, meow meow meow meow meow meow meow meow meow meow.

"Meow meow meow meow meow meow meow meow?" meow meow meow meow, meow meow meow. "Meow'meow meow meow meow meow! Meow meow meow?"

"Meow meow meow meow," Meow meow meow meow meow meow meow, meow meow Meow'meow meow, "meow meow meow meow meow meow meow meow-meow, meow meow, meow Meow meow. Meow, meow meow meow meow?"

"Meow meow meow meow? Meow... meow?" Meow meow meow, meow meow.

Meow'meow meow meow meow meow meow meow meow, meow meow meow meow meow meow meow meow meow meow meow meow, meow meow meow meow meow meow meow. Meow meow meow meow meow meow meow meow meow meow meow meow meow meow meow meow meow, meow meow meow meow meow meow meow meow meow meow meow, meow meow meow meow meow meow meow meow meow meow meow meow, meow meow meow meow meow meow meow meow meow meow, meow meow meow meow, meow meow meow meow meow meow meow, meow meow meow, meow meow, meow meow, meow meow!

"Meow meow meow meow, meow..." meow Meow, meow meow meow meow, meow meow meow meow meow meow meow meow meow meow meow meow meow.

"Meow? Meow meow? Meow? Meow, meow meow!"

"Meow," meow Meow, meow meow, "meow'meow meow meow!"

Meow meow meow. Meow meow meow meow meow meow Meow meow meow meow meow meow. Meow meow meow meow meow meow meow meow meow meow meow meow meow meow. Meow meow meow meow meow meow Meow. Meow meow meow meow meow meow.

"Meow meow'meow meow meow meow meow? Meow'meow meow meow," meow Meow.

"Meow! Meow? Meow, meow...." Meow meow meow meow, meow meow meow meow meow meow meow meow meow, meow meow meow Meow, meow meow meow meow meow meow meow meow. Meow meow meow meow meow meow meow meow meow meow meow. Meow meow meow meow meow.

"Meow meow meow meow meow meow meow meow meow meow," meow Meow.

"Meow meow meow meow Meow meow meow meow Meow Meow meow meow meow meow meow meow meow meow meow meow meow Meow. Meow meow meow meow meow. Meow meow meow meow meow!"

"Meow, meow meow meow meow meow meow meow! Meow meow meow meow meow meow meow," Meow meow meow. "Meow meow meow meow meow?" meow meow, meow.

"Meow meow meow meow meow."

"Meow? Meow meow meow, meow, meow meow! Meow, meow meow meow meow meow meow meow meow meow—meow meow meow! Meow meow meow meow meow, meow meow meow meow meow meow meow meow meow meow meow meow meow meow! Meow meow meow meow meow meow meow meow meow meow meow meow. Meow! Meow meow meow meow meow meow meow meow—meow meow meow meow meow meow meow meow meow! Meow, meow meow meow meow meow meow

meow meow meow meow meow meow, meow meow meow meow meow meow meow meow meow? Meow meow meow meow meow meow meow meow meow meow meow meow! Meow meow meow meow meow! Meow meow meow meow meow meow meow meow meow meow meow; meow meow meow meow meow meow meow meow meow meow, meow meow meow meow. Meow meow meow meow meow meow, meow meow meow meow meow meow meow—meow meow meow meow meow meow meow meow meow meow meow meow meow meow meow meow. Meow meow meow meow meow. Meow meow meow meow meow meow meow meow meow meow meow! Meow meow meow?"

"Meow meow meow meow?" meow Meow, "meow, meow'meow meow meow. Meow, Meow meow meow meow, meow meow. Meow meow meow'meow meow meow."

"Meow'meow meow meow?"

"Meow, meow meow meow meow meow? Meow, Meow meow'meow. Meow meow meow meow meow meow meow meow meow meow meow meow meow? Meow meow meow meow meow meow meow meow meow meow'meow meow meow meow meow meow meow meow meow! Meow, Meow meow meow meow meow meow meow meow meow. Meow meow?"

Meow meow meow meow meow meow "meow meow meow meow meow." Meow meow meow meow meow meow.

"Meow meow meow meow meow meow," Meow meow. "Meow meow meow Meow meow meow meow meow: Meow'meow meow meow meow meow meow meow meow meow meow meow meow, meow meow meow meow meow meow Meow'meow meow meow meow meow meow; Meow'meow meow meow meow-meow meow meow meow meow meow meow-meow meow meow meow meow, meow meow meow, meow meow meow meow meow meow meow—meow meow meow meow meow meow meow meow. 'Meow meow meow,' Meow meow meow, 'meow meow meow meow meow meow-meow meow meow meow meow meow meow meow meow,' meow meow Meow'meow meow meow meow meow meow. Meow meow Meow meow meow meow meow, 'Meow, meow meow,' Meow meow meow, 'Meow meow Meow meow meow meow meow meow meow meow meow meow meow meow, Meow meow meow meow.' Meow meow Meow meow meow meow meow meow meow meow meow meow meow meow meow meow meow meow meow meow meow. Meow meow Meow meow meow, Meow'meow meow meow meow meow meow meow meow meow meow meow meow meow meow meow meow meow meow meow meow meow meow meow meow, 'Meow meow, meow,' meow meow meow meow meow meow meow meow meow meow meow meow meow meow meow meow meow meow meow. Meow Meow'meow meow meow meow meow meow, Meow'meow meow meow, 'Meow, meow meow,' meow meow meow meow meow. Meow'meow meow Meow'meow meow meow."

"Meow! meow meow meow meow meow!" meow Meow, meow. "Meow meow meow meow meow meow. Meow meow meow meow meow meow meow meow meow'meow meow meow meow. Meow meow meow meow meow meow, meow meow meow meow meow meow meow, meow meow

meow meow Meow. Meow meow meow meow meow meow—meow meow meow meow meow meow meow. Meow meow meow meow meow meow meow meow meow, meow meow meow meow meow meow, meow meow meow meow meow—meow meow meow meow, meow. Meow meow meow meow meow meow meow meow, meow meow'meow meow meow. Meow meow meow meow meow..."

Meow meow meow.

"Meow? Meow meow'meow meow meow meow meow?" meow meow, meow meow meow Meow. "Meow, meow meow meow meow."

"Meow? Meow? Meow meow meow meow meow meow meow? Meow'meow meow meow meow! Meow meow meow meow meow meow meow meow meow meow meow meow meow meow. Meow meow meow meow meow meow meow meow meow, meow meow meow meow meow. Meow meow meow meow meow meow meow."

"Meow meow meow meow meow meow meow, meow," meow Meow. "Meow meow meow meow meow meow meow meow meow meow meow meow meow meow meow meow meow meow meow meow meow meow meow. Meow meow meow meow meow, meow meow meow meow meow meow meow meow meow. Meow meow'meow meow meow meow meow, meow meow?"

Meow meow meow meow meow meow Meow.

"Meow meow meow meow meow meow meow meow meow meow meow meow Meow meow meow meow meow meow, meow?" meow meow meow meow.

"Meow meow meow meow," Meow meow meow meow meow. Meow meow meow meow meow meow meow meow meow meow meow meow meow.

"Meow meow?" "Meow meow!"

"Meow meow meow. Meow meow meow Meow meow meow," Meow meow, meow meow meow meow meow meow Meow'meow, meow meow meow meow meow meow meow meow meow, meow meow meow meow meow meow. "Meow meow meow Meow meow meow meow. Meow meow meow meow meow meow meow meow, Meow meow meow meow meow meow meow meow meow meow meow meow meow meow meow meow meow meow meow meow meow meow meow meow meow meow meow meow, meow meow meow meow meow meow meow meow. Meow meow meow meow meow meow meow meow meow meow meow meow meow meow meow meow meow meow meow meow meow meow meow meow meow meow meow meow meow meow. Meow meow meow meow meow—meow meow meow meow meow meow meow meow meow, meow Meow meow meow meow meow meow meow meow meow meow. Meow Meow'meow meow meow meow meow meow meow meow meow meow meow meow, meow meow meow meow meow meow meow meow meow meow. Meow meow meow meow meow meow, meow meow, Meow meow meow meow meow. Meow, meow, meow meow meow! Meow'meow meow meow meow."

"Meow meow meow meow," meow Meow, meow meow meow meow meow meow meow meow meow meow, meow meow meow meow Meow, meow meow meow meow. Meow meow meow meow meow meow meow

meow meow meow meow meow meow. Meow meow meow meow meow meow meow meow Meow, meow meow meow meow meow meow meow meow meow meow. Meow meow meow meow meow meow; meow meow meow meow meow meow, meow meow meow meow meow. Meow meow meow meow meow meow meow, meow meow meow meow meow meow; meow meow meow meow meow meow meow, meow meow meow meow meow meow meow meow, meow meow meow meow.

"Meow meow meow meow meow Meow meow meow meow meow meow meow Meow?" meow meow meow meow— meow meow meow meow meow.

Meow meow meow meow meow meow meow meow meow meow meow. Meow meow meow meow meow meow.

"Meow meow meow meow?" meow meow meow meow. Meow meow meow meow meow.

"Meow meow meow meow meow meow, meow, meow meow?"

"Meow meow meow meow meow, Meow meow meow meow meow meow meow," Meow meow meow.

"Meow'meow meow meow meow-meow! Meow meow meow meow meow meow, meow meow meow meow meow meow meow?"

"Meow meow meow," meow Meow, meow meow. "Meow meow meow meow meow meow meow meow meow meow meow meow?"

"Meow meow'meow meow meow meow? Meow meow meow meow meow meow meow meow meow Meow meow meow meow meow meow-meow? Meow meow meow meow meow meow meow meow meow Meow meow? Meow, meow," meow meow meow meow meow, meow meow meow meow meow meow, "meow meow?"

"Meow meow," meow meow meow, meow meow.

"Meow meow meow meow meow meow meow. Meow meow meow meow meow meow!" meow meow meow meow meow meow meow Meow meow meow meow meow. "Meow meow meow meow, meow-meow meow. Meow meow Meow meow meow? Meow meow meow meow meow meow meow meow? Meow meow Meow meow meow meow meow. Meow'meow meow-meow meow meow, Meow'meow meow meow.... Meow, meow'meow meow! Meow meow! Meow meow meow meow!"

Meow meow meow, meow meow meow meow meow meow meow meow meow meow, meow meow meow meow meow meow meow meow. Meow meow meow meow meow meow meow. Meow meow meow meow meow meow meow meow. Meow meow meow meow. Meow meow, meow meow meow meow meow meow meow meow meow meow, meow meow meow meow meow meow meow meow meow meow.

Meow, meow meow, meow meow meow meow meow meow meow meow meow, meow meow meow. Meow meow meow meow meow meow meow meow meow meow meow meow meow meow meow meow meow meow meow meow meow meow meow.

"Meow Meow meow meow meow," meow meow.

Meow meow meow meow meow meow meow meow meow meow meow meow meow Meow meow meow meow. Meow meow meow meow meow

meow meow meow meow meow meow meow meow. Meow meow meow meow meow meow meow meow meow meow meow. Meow meow meow meow, meow meow, meow meow meow meow meow meow meow.

"Meow meow meow meow!" meow meow meow meow meow meow meow meow—"meow meow meow meow meow meow! Meow meow Meow'meow meow meow meow meow meow meow meow! Meow meow meow meow meow meow. Meow meow meow Meow meow meow meow. Meow meow meow meow meow meow. Meow! Meow meow meow meow meow meow? Meow meow meow meow meow! Meow! Meow meow meow?"

"Meow meow meow Meow'meow meow meow meow meow meow meow meow Meow meow meow meow meow," Meow meow meow.

"Meow? Meow meow meow meow meow meow meow, meow meow meow meow meow meow meow meow meow meow meow meow meow meow meow! Meow!... Meow meow meow meow meow meow meow Meow meow Meow? Meow meow meow meow!"

"Meow meow meow!" meow Meow meow meow meow meow meow. Meow meow meow meow meow Meow; meow meow meow meow meow meow meow.

"Meow meow meow? Meow meow meow meow meow meow meow meow? Meow meow meow meow Meow'meow meow meow meow meow? Meow'meow meow meow meow, meow meow meow meow meow meow, meow meow meow meow meow meow meow meow meow meow!"

"Meow, Meow," Meow meow meow, meow meow—"meow'meow meow meow meow Meow meow'meow meow meow meow? Meow meow meow meow meow meow meow meow meow meow meow meow... meow meow, meow meow meow meow meow meow meow! Meow meow meow meow meow meow meow meow meow meow meow meow? Meow Meow meow meow meow meow meow. Meow'meow Meow meow meow meow meow meow-meow meow meow meow meow meow, meow Meow meow... meow meow meow! Meow meow meow meow meow meow meow! Meow meow meow meow meow meow meow meow meow meow meow, meow meow'meow meow meow meow. Meow meow Meow meow meow meow meow meow meow meow meow. Meow meow meow meow meow, meow meow' meow! Meow meow meow meow, meow, meow meow meow meow meow? Meow'meow meow meow meow Meow meow meow meow meow meow meow meow meow? Meow, meow meow Meow meow meow meow meow meow meow meow meow meow? Meow meow meow meow, Meow meow meow meow, meow meow meow meow, meow Meow'meow meow, meow meow meow! Meow meow meow, meow meow meow!"

Meow meow meow, meow meow meow meow meow meow meow meow meow meow meow, meow meow, meow meow meow, meow meow meow, meow meow meow meow meow Meow.

Meow meow meow meow, meow meow meow meow meow meow.

"Meow, meow meow meow meow," meow meow meow meow meow. "Meow," meow meow, meow Meow meow meow meow meow. "Meow meow meow. Meow meow meow meow, meow meow meow meow meow

meow meow meow, meow meow! Meow meow'meow meow meow meow meow meow meow meow meow meow meow meow meow meow. Meow meow meow meow meow meow meow! Meow meow'meow meow meow meow meow meow meow meow! Meow meow meow meow meow meow meow meow'meow meow meow meow meow meow meow meow. Meow meow'meow meow meow meow meow meow! Meow meow meow meow meow meow meow meow meow meow meow meow meow meow meow meow meow! Meow!" meow meow meow meow meow, meow meow Meow meow meow meow meow meow—"meow meow meow! Meow meow Meow'meow meow meow meow-meow meow meow, Meow meow meow meow'meow meow meow meow, meow Meow meow meow meow meow—Meow meow meow meow—meow meow meow meow. Meow meow meow meow'meow meow meow, meow meow meow, meow meow meow, meow meow meow meow meow meow meow meow meow... meow meow, Meow, Meow meow meow'meow meow meow meow, meow meow'meow meow meow!—meow meow meow meow'meow meow meow meow'meow meow meow meow meow meow meow meow meow meow meow meow meow meow meow meow! Meow meow meow meow meow, meow'meow meow meow meow meow! Meow'meow meow meow meow meow meow meow, meow meow meow meow... meow meow meow meow, meow.... Meow meow meow meow meow meow meow—meow meow meow meow meow meow meow.... Meow meow meow meow meow. Meow meow meow?"

"Meow."

"Meow-meow!" Meow meow, meow meow meow. "Meow meow meow meow? Meow meow'meow meow meow meow! Meow meow'meow meow meow meow meow.... Meow meow meow Meow'meow meow meow meow meow meow meow meow meow meow meow meow meow.... Meow meow meow meow meow meow meow meow meow!

Meow meow, Meow'meow meow meow meow meow meow...."

"Meow, Meow. Meow, Meow meow meow meow'meow meow meow meow meow meow meow meow."

"Meow? Meow? Meow? Meow'meow meow meow meow meow meow meow meow meow! Meow'meow meow, 47, Meow'meow meow...."

"Meow meow meow meow, Meow." Meow meow meow meow meow.

"Meow meow meow meow," Meow meow meow meow. "Meow meow meow meow meow meow meow meow'meow! Meow, meow, meow Meow meow meow?"

"Meow."

"Meow meow meow meow?"

"Meow."

"Meow meow meow?"

"Meow."

"Meow meow? Meow meow, meow'meow meow meow meow. Meow'meow meow, Meow'meow meow, meow!"

Meow meow meow meow meow meow meow meow Meow Meow. Meow meow meow meow meow. Meow meow meow meow meow meow meow meow meow meow meow meow meow meow meow meow meow meow.

“Meow meow,” meow meow meow meow meow. “Meow meow meow meow meow... Meow meow meow meow! Meow meow meow meow'meow meow meow! Meow meow meow meow meow Meow meow meow meow.” Meow meow meow meow meow meow meow. “Meow meow... meow meow Meow meow meow meow meow meow? Meow meow meow meow.... Meow, meow meow meow! Meow meow'meow.” Meow meow meow meow meow meow Meow, meow meow meow meow meow meow meow. Meow meow meow meow meow meow meow meow meow meow Meow meow Meow meow meow Meow.

Meow meow meow meow Meow—Meow, meow meow meow meow, meow meow meow meow meow meow meow meow meow meow meow. Meow meow meow Meow, meow meow meow meow meow meow meow meow meow meow meow meow. Meow meow meow meow meow meow meow meow meow meow meow. Meow meow meow meow, meow meow meow meow meow meow meow meow meow meow meow, meow meow meow meow meow meow meow meow meow meow meow, meow meow meow meow meow meow meow meow meow, meow meow meow meow meow meow meow meow meow meow meow meow meow, meow meow meow meow meow meow meow, meow meow meow meow meow meow meow meow. Meow meow meow meow meow meow meow meow, meow meow meow meow, meow meow-meow, meow meow meow, meow meow, meow meow meow meow meow. Meow meow meow, meow meow meow meow meow meow meow meow meow meow meow. Meow meow meow meow meow meow meow meow meow meow meow meow; meow meow meow meow meow meow meow meow meow meow meow meow meow, meow meow meow, meow, meow meow meow meow meow meow. Meow meow meow meow meow meow, meow meow meow meow meow meow meow meow meow. Meow meow meow meow meow meow meow meow meow, meow meow meow meow meow meow meow, meow meow meow meow meow meow meow meow meow. Meow meow meow meow meow meow meow meow meow meow meow meow, meow meow meow meow meow meow meow meow meow meow meow, meow meow meow meow meow, meow meow meow meow meow meow meow, meow meow meow meow meow meow meow meow meow.

“Meow meow meow! Meow meow meow!” meow meow meow meow; meow meow meow, meow meow meow meow meow meow, meow meow meow meow meow meow Meow, meow meow meow meow.

“Meow meow meow! meow'meow meow Meow!” meow meow meow meow meow meow. “Meow! meow meow! meow meow, meow meow meow!”

“Meow meow, meow meow” meow meow meow meow meow. Meow meow meow meow meow meow meow meow; meow meow meow meow meow meow meow meow meow, meow meow meow meow meow meow meow meow meow meow meow meow meow. Meow meow meow meow meow meow: meow meow meow meow meow meow meow meow meow meow, meow meow meow meow meow meow meow meow meow meow meow meow meow meow meow meow meow meow meow meow meow

meow meow meow; meow meow meow meow meow meow meow meow. Meow meow meow meow meow meow meow meow meow meow. Meow meow meow meow, meow meow meow, meow meow meow meow meow meow meow, meow meow meow meow meow meow meow meow. Meow meow meow.

"Meow'meow meow meow meow meow meow meow," meow meow meow'meow meow meow meow meow meow. "Meow meow meow meow. Meow meow meow meow meow meow meow meow, meow meow meow meow. Meow meow meow meow meow meow meow meow, meow meow meow meow meow meow meow meow—meow meow meow'meow meow meow meow! Meow meow, meow, meow meow, meow meow meow meow, meow meow meow meow meow meow, meow meow...."

Meow meow meow meow. Meow meow meow meow meow meow meow, meow meow meow meow meow.... Meow meow meow meow meow meow meow meow meow meow meow. Meow meow meow. "Meow, meow'meow meow... meow... meow'meow meow meow meow," meow meow meow meow. "Meow meow meow meow meow," meow meow, "meow meow meow meow. Meow meow meow meow meow...? Meow meow meow'meow Meow meow meow meow meow? Meow meow meow meow meow meow meow meow'meow...." Meow meow meow meow meow meow meow meow meow meow meow.

"Meow meow meow!" meow meow meow; meow meow meow meow meow meow meow meow meow meow meow meow meow meow. Meow meow meow meow meow meow. Meow meow meow meow meow meow. Meow meow meow meow meow, meow meow meow meow meow meow meow meow meow meow meow meow meow meow meow "meow meow meow meow meow meow meow." Meow meow meow meow meow meow.

"Meow, meow'meow meow meow meow meow meow," meow meow, meow meow meow meow meow meow meow meow. "Meow Meow'meow meow meow meow, meow Meow meow meow.... Meow meow meow meow meow meow? Meow meow meow meow! Meow'meow meow meow meow meow meow meow—meow! Meow meow meow meow! Meow meow meow meow meow? Meow Meow meow meow meow meow? Meow... meow! Meow meow Meow meow! Meow Meow meow meow meow meow meow meow meow meow meow! Meow Meow meow meow meow meow meow meow meow meow meow. Meow Meow meow'meow meow meow meow meow! Meow meow meow meow meow meow'meow meow."

Meow meow meow meow meow meow meow meow meow meow meow meow meow meow meow meow meow meow meow. Meow meow meow meow meow meow meow. Meow meow meow meow meow meow meow meow, meow meow meow'meow meow, meow meow meow meow meow meow meow meow meow meow meow meow meow, meow meow meow meow, meow meow meow meow meow meow meow meow meow. Meow meow, meow meow meow meow; meow meow meow meow meow meow meow meow; meow meow meow meow meow meow meow meow meow meow meow meow meow meow meow meow. Meow meow meow meow meow, meow meow meow meow meow meow meow meow meow.

Meow meow, meow meow meow meow meow. Meow meow meow meow meow, meow meow meow meow, meow meow meow meow meow meow meow meow, meow meow meow meow meow meow meow meow meow meow. Meow meow, meow meow meow meow meow. Meow meow meow meow meow meow meow meow meow meow meow; meow meow meow meow meow meow meow meow meow meow meow meow meow. "Meow meow'meow meow meow," meow meow. Meow meow meow meow meow meow meow meow meow Meow meow Meow meow meow meow. "Meow'meow meow meow meow meow meow meow meow. Meow meow'meow meow meow." Meow meow meow meow meow meow meow. "Meow!" Meow meow meow meow meow meow meow meow meow meow meow meow. Meow meow meow meow, meow meow meow meow; meow meow meow meow meow. Meow meow meow meow meow meow meow meow meow meow meow meow meow. Meow, meow, meow meow meow meow; meow meow meow meow meow. Meow meow meow meow meow; meow meow meow meow meow meow meow meow meow meow meow meow, meow meow meow meow meow meow meow meow meow meow. Meow meow, meow meow, meow meow; meow meow meow. Meow meow meow meow meow meow meow meow meow meow meow-meow. Meow meow meow meow, meow meow meow, meow meow meow meow meow meow meow. Meow meow meow meow meow meow meow meow meow meow meow meow meow meow, meow meow meow meow, meow, meow meow. Meow meow meow meow meow meow meow meow meow. Meow meow meow meow meow meow meow meow, meow meow meow meow meow meow meow meow meow meow meow. Meow meow meow meow meow meow meow meow meow meow meow meow meow meow meow meow meow meow meow meow meow meow meow meow meow meow. Meow meow meow meow meow Meow'meow meow meow; meow meow meow. Meow meow meow meow meow meow.

"Meow meow meow meow meow meow meow," meow meow meow meow meow meow, "meow meow, meow meow meow. 'Meow meow meow meow meow meow?' meow Meow. 'Meow meow meow meow meow meow meow meow meow, Meow Meow!' Meow'meow meow meow meow meow meow! Meow meow meow meow meow meow meow meow meow!"

"Meow meow meow meow meow meow?" meow meow meow meow. Meow meow meow meow meow meow meow meow.

"Meow meow meow meow meow meow meow meow, meow, meow meow meow meow meow meow meow meow Meow, meow meow meow meow, meow meow meow meow meow meow, meow meow meow meow meow meow meow meow. Meow'meow meow. Meow meow meow meow meow meow meow meow meow meow meow' meow, meow'meow meow meow meow meow meow."

"Meow'meow meow meow meow'meow meow meow Meow," meow meow meow meow, "meow meow meow meow, meow'meow meow!"

"Meow meow, meow'meow meow meow meow meow, meow meow," meow meow meow meow.

Meow meow meow meow meow meow meow meow meow meow meow meow meow, meow meow, meow meow meow meow meow meow meow; meow meow meow meow meow meow meow meow meow meow meow. Meow meow meow meow meow; meow meow meow meow meow meow meow meow meow meow meow meow meow. Meow meow meow meow meow meow meow meow meow. Meow meow meow meow meow meow meow.

"Meow meow meow meow?" meow meow meow.

Meow meow meow Meow meow meow meow meow meow meow meow meow. Meow meow meow, meow meow meow meow. Meow meow meow meow meow meow meow meow meow; meow meow meow meow. Meow meow meow meow meow meow meow meow meow meow meow meow meow meow meow meow meow meow. Meow meow meow meow meow meow meow meow meow meow meow meow meow.

"Meow, meow meow meow meow? Meow meow meow?" meow meow meow, meow meow meow meow. Meow meow meow meow.

"Meow meow meow meow meow meow," meow meow. "Meow meow meow meow."

"Meow'meow meow meow meow meow meow meow meow meow meow! meow meow meow meow meow meow meow meow meow."

"Meow meow meow meow meow, meow meow meow meow?" Meow meow meow. "Meow meow meow meow?"

"Meow meow?"

"Meow, meow meow meow meow meow meow meow meow meow. Meow meow meow meow meow meow."

"Meow meow meow meow?" meow meow meow, meow.

"Meow meow Meow?"

"Meow."

"Meow meow meow meow? Meow meow meow meow meow, Meow'meow meow meow."

Meow meow meow meow meow meow meow.

"Meow'meow meow meow meow meow meow, meow meow meow. Meow meow, Meow. Meow meow meow meow," meow meow meow meow.

"Meow meow, meow meow," meow Meow meow, meow meow meow meow, meow meow meow meow. "Meow, meow," meow meow meow meow meow.

Meow meow meow meow meow meow meow, meow meow meow meow-meow; meow meow meow, meow meow meow, meow meow meow meow meow meow meow meow meow meow. Meow meow meow meow meow.

"Meow meow meow meow?" meow meow meow meow meow.

"Meow meow meow meow meow meow meow?"

"Meow'meow meow meow meow. Meow meow meow meow?"

"Meow meow meow?"

"Meow meow."

"Meow meow meow meow?"

"Meow meow meow meow meow meow. Meow meow meow meow?"

Meow meow meow meow, meow meow meow meow meow meow meow. "Meow'meow meow meow meow meow meow meow," meow meow meow meow, meow meow. "Meow meow?"

"Meow meow meow meow meow. 'Meow meow meow meow meow meow meow?' meow meow. 'Meow meow meow meow meow meow,' meow meow, 'meow Meow'meow meow meow meow meow.' Meow meow meow meow meow meow meow, meow meow meow meow. 'Meow meow meow meow meow,' meow meow. 'Meow'meow meow meow meow meow.' Meow meow'meow meow meow."

Meow meow meow meow Meow, meow meow meow. "Meow meow meow?" meow meow meow meow meow meow meow.

"Meow meow Meow Meow Meow, meow meow meow, Meow meow meow Meow'meow meow, meow meow meow meow, meow Meow 14, meow meow meow, meow meow meow." Meow meow meow meow meow meow meow, meow meow, meow meow meow, meow meow meow meow meow meow meow.

"Meow meow meow meow meow meow meow?"

"Meow meow meow meow."

"Meow meow meow meow meow meow?"

"Meow meow meow meow meow meow meow," meow meow meow meow meow meow meow meow meow. Meow meow meow meow meow meow meow meow meow meow meow meow meow meow, meow meow: "Meow meow."

"Meow, meow meow," meow meow meow meow meow meow. "Meow meow meow meow meow meow, meow'meow meow meow meow, meow?"

"Meow'meow meow meow, meow Meow meow meow'meow meow meow meow meow," meow meow meow.

"Meow meow meow meow meow?" meow meow meow meow, meow meow meow meow meow meow—"Meow meow meow meow meow?"

"Meow meow meow meow meow meow?" meow Meow meow.

"Meow meow meow? Meow meow meow meow meow?"

"Meow'meow meow meow!" meow meow meow meow.

"Meow meow meow meow meow meow?" meow meow meow meow, meow meow meow meow meow meow meow meow meow meow meow meow meow meow. "Meow meow! Meow meow meow meow meow meow meow. Meow meow!"

Meow meow Meow meow meow meow meow meow meow meow meow meow. Meow meow meow, meow meow meow meow, meow meow meow meow meow meow meow meow meow.

"Meow meow!" meow meow meow.

"Meow meow meow meow meow meow," meow meow meow.

"Meow meow meow meow meow meow meow meow meow meow meow meow," meow meow meow meow meow meow meow.

"Meow meow meow meow meow meow meow," meow meow meow meow. "Meow meow meow! Meow meow meow meow, meow meow meow meow, meow meow meow meow meow, meow meow'meow meow meow meow meow.... Meow meow meow meow!"

"Meow Meow meow meow meow meow?" meow Meow, meow meow meow meow meow meow meow meow meow meow-meow, meow meow meow meow meow, meow meow meow meow meow meow meow meow. Meow meow meow meow, meow meow meow meow meow meow meow meow meow meow meow meow, meow meow meow, meow meow meow.... Meow meow meow meow meow meow meow meow meow, meow meow meow meow, meow meow meow meow meow meow meow meow meow meow meow meow meow. Meow meow meow meow meow meow meow meow meow.... Meow meow meow meow meow meow meow meow meow. "Meow meow meow?" Meow meow meow meow meow meow meow meow meow meow meow. Meow meow meow meow meow meow meow meow meow meow meow meow meow, meow meow meow meow meow meow meow meow meow meow meow meow meow meow meow meow meow meow meow meow meow meow meow meow meow meow.

MEOW VII

Meow meow meow meow meow meow meow meow meow meow meow meow meow meow meow meow meow; meow meow meow meow meow meow, meow meow meow meow meow meow meow meow meow meow meow; meow meow meow meow meow meow meow meow.... Meow meow meow meow meow meow meow, meow meow meow meow meow. Meow meow meow meow meow meow meow meow meow meow meow meow meow meow meow meow meow meow. Meow meow meow, meow, meow; meow meow meow meow meow meow meow meow meow:

"Meow meow meow! Meow Meow, meow meow meow!"

Meow meow meow meow meow meow meow meow meow meow, meow meow meow meow meow meow meow meow meow meow meow meow meow. Meow meow meow meow meow meow meow meow meow meow meow meow, meow meow meow meow; meow meow meow meow meow, meow meow meow meow meow. Meow meow meow meow meow meow meow; meow meow meow meow, meow meow meow. Meow meow meow meow meow.

"Meow meow!" meow meow meow, "meow meow meow Meow meow? Meow Meow'meow meow meow meow meow meow meow meow meow meow, meow Meow meow meow meow, meow meow meow meow. Meow meow meow Meow meow meow meow meow meow meow. Meow meow meow meow'meow meow meow, meow meow meow.... Meow meow meow meow meow meow, meow meow meow meow. Meow meow meow meow meow meow meow meow meow, meow Meow meow meow meow meow, meow meow meow meow meow meow meow! Meow meow meow meow meow meow meow meow meow meow meow.... Meow meow meow meow meow meow meow meow meow... meow meow, meow meow... meow meow meow meow. Meow'meow meow meow meow!"

"Meow'meow meow meow meow meow," meow meow meow meow meow meow.

"Meow meow, meow'meow meow, meow meow meow meow," meow meow meow. "Meow meow meow meow, meow meow meow meow," meow meow meow.

Meow meow meow meow meow meow meow meow meow meow. Meow meow meow meow meow meow meow meow meow meow meow meow meow meow meow meow meow meow meow; meow meow, meow meow, meow meow meow meow meow meow meow meow meow meow. Meow meow meow meow meow meow meow meow meow meow meow meow meow meow meow meow meow meow meow. Meow meow meow meow meow.

Meow Meow meow meow meow meow meow meow meow meow. Meow meow meow meow meow meow meow meow'meow meow. Meow meow meow.

"Meow meow meow! Meow meow meow!" meow meow, meow meow meow meow.

"Meow'meow meow meow meow meow meow meow meow, Meow. Meow meow meow meow meow Meow'meow meow.... Meow meow meow

meow meow! Meow meow meow, meow?" Meow meow meow meow meow meow meow meow meow meow meow meow meow. Meow meow meow meow meow.

Meow meow meow meow meow meow meow meow meow meow meow meow meow. Meow meow meow meow meow meow meow, meow, meow meow meow meow meow meow meow meow meow, meow meow meow meow meow meow meow meow Meow meow meow meow meow meow.

"Meow meow, meow meow meow," meow meow meow, "meow meow meow meow Meow, meow meow Meow. Meow meow meow meow, meow meow meow. Meow meow meow, meow meow meow meow. Meow meow meow meow meow, meow meow, meow, meow meow meow meow.... Meow meow meow meow meow meow meow meow meow meow, meow meow meow meow meow meow meow meow meow meow meow. Meow'meow meow, Meow'meow meow! Meow meow meow meow meow meow meow meow meow... meow meow meow meow meow meow. Meow meow'meow meow meow meow meow meow meow meow meow." Meow meow meow meow meow meow meow meow meow'meow meow. Meow meow meow meow meow meow meow, meow meow meow meow meow meow meow meow. Meow meow meow meow meow; meow meow meow meow.

Meow'meow meow meow meow meow meow. Meow meow meow, meow meow Meow'meow meow meow meow meow meow.

"Meow meow, meow meow! Meow meow meow meow meow meow meow. Meow meow! Meow'meow meow, Meow'meow meow meow meow meow meow," meow meow.

Meow Meow meow meow meow, meow meow meow meow meow meow meow meow, meow meow meow meow meow meow meow meow meow meow meow meow meow meow meow, meow meow meow meow meow meow meow, meow meow meow meow meow. Meow meow meow meow meow meow meow meow meow meow meow meow meow meow, Meow, meow meow meow meow, meow, meow meow meow meow meow meow meow meow, meow meow meow meow meow meow meow meow, meow meow meow meow meow meow meow meow meow meow meow meow meow meow meow meow meow meow. Meow meow Meow meow meow meow meow meow, meow meow meow meow meow meow meow meow meow meow meow. Meow meow meow meow meow meow meow meow meow meow meow, meow meow meow meow meow meow meow. Meow meow meow meow meow meow meow meow meow, meow meow meow, meow meow, meow meow meow meow meow meow meow meow—meow meow meow meow meow meow.

Meow meow meow meow meow meow meow meow meow meow meow meow, meow meow meow meow meow meow meow meow-meow meow, meow meow meow meow meow meow meow meow meow meow meow meow meow meow meow meow meow. Meow meow meow, meow meow, meow meow meow meow, meow meow meow meow, meow meow meow meow. Meow meow meow meow meow meow meow meow meow meow meow meow meow meow meow meow meow meow meow meow meow meow meow meow meow meow meow meow meow meow meow meow meow

meow meow meow meow meow, meow meow. Meow Meow meow meow meow meow meow meow meow meow meow meow meow meow meow meow meow meow meow meow meow meow.

"Meow meow'meow meow, meow meow'meow meow, Meow," meow meow, meow meow meow meow, "meow meow meow meow meow meow meow meow meow meow'meow meow meow meow meow meow meow meow meow, meow meow meow meow meow, meow meow! Meow meow meow meow meow meow meow meow meow meow meow meow meow; meow meow meow meow meow meow meow meow meow, 'Meow meow meow meow, Meow Meow, meow meow meow!' Meow Meow... meow..." meow meow meow, "meow, meow meow," meow meow, meow meow meow meow meow meow meow meow meow meow, "meow Meow... meow meow meow meow meow... meow meow meow'meow... Meow Meow meow meow—meow meow meow meow meow meow meow meow meow Meow meow meow, Meow—meow meow meow meow 'Meow'meow meow meow meow meow meow meow meow meow meow meow meow meow-meow?' (Meow meow meow meow meow, meow meow meow meow meow meow meow meow meow Meow meow meow, meow meow-meow—meow, meow, meow—meow meow meow meow meow meow," meow meow meow meow.) "Meow Meow, meow meow, meow meow meow meow Meow meow... meow meow meow meow meow meow meow meow meow meow meow meow meow meow meow; meow Meow meow meow meow meow meow meow meow meow meow meow meow meow meow meow meow'meow. Meow meow meow meow meow, Meow; meow meow meow meow.... Meow meow meow meow? Meow meow meow meow, meow meow meow! Meow," meow meow meow meow meow meow, "meow meow meow meow meow meow meow-meow... meow meow meow meow meow meow meow... Meow'meow meow meow meow.... Meow meow meow meow meow meow meow'meow meow meow? Meow meow meow meow meow meow meow meow meow meow meow-meow, meow meow meow meow meow meow! Meow'meow meow meow meow meow, meow meow meow meow meow meow meow meow meow meow! Meow, meow! (Meow, meow, meow, meow!) Meow! Meow'meow meow?" meow meow, meow meow meow meow meow meow meow meow meow, meow meow meow meow meow meow, meow meow meow. "Meow meow meow? Meow meow meow meow? Meow meow meow!"

"Meow meow meow meow meow meow?" meow meow meow, meow meow meow

Meow, meow meow meow meow meow, meow meow meow meow.

"Meow meow meow! Meow meow meow meow meow, meow meow meow meow meow," Meow meow meow.

"Meow meow meow meow meow! Meow!" meow meow meow meow meow.

Meow Meow meow, meow meow meow meow meow meow. Meow meow meow meow. Meow Meow meow, meow meow Meow meow meow meow meow, meow meow meow.

Meow meow Meow meow, Meow meow meow Meow Meow.

"Meow Meow'meow meow meow meow, meow'meow meow meow!" meow meow, meow meow, "meow meow meow meow meow meow meow meow meow meow meow meow, meow'meow meow meow, meow meow meow meow, Meow meow meow meow meow meow... Meow'meow meow meow meow, meow meow? Meow meow meow meow; Meow'meow meow!"

"Meow'meow meow meow meow meow!" Meow Meow meow meow meow meow meow meow meow meow.

Meow meow meow meow meow meow meow meow meow meow meow meow meow meow meow. Meow meow meow meow meow meow meow'meow meow meow meow, meow meow meow meow meow meow meow meow meow meow meow meow. Meow meow meow meow, meow meow, meow meow meow meow meow meow meow meow meow meow meow meow meow meow meow.

Meow meow meow meow meow meow meow meow meow. Meow meow meow meow, meow meow, meow meow meow meow.

"Meow'meow meow meow meow meow," meow meow meow Meow Meow, "meow'meow meow meow, Meow'meow meow. Meow'meow meow meow?... meow meow meow meow meow meow meow meow, meow, meow meow meow meow meow.... Meow meow meow, meow meow meow, meow meow.... Meow meow meow meow meow meow meow!"

Meow Meow meow meow meow meow; meow, meow meow meow meow meow meow meow, meow meow meow meow meow meow meow meow meow meow, meow meow meow meow meow meow'meow meow meow'meow meow meow meow. Meow meow meow meow meow Meow Meow meow meow meow meow meow meow meow, meow meow meow. Meow meow meow meow meow meow meow meow meow meow meow meow meow meow meow meow meow, meow Meow Meow meow meow meow meow meow, meow meow meow meow meow meow meow, meow meow meow meow meow meow meow meow, meow meow meow meow meow meow meow meow meow, meow meow meow meow meow meow meow meow meow meow meow meow meow meow meow. Meow meow meow meow meow meow meow meow Meow'meow meow, meow meow meow meow meow meow meow. Meow meow meow meow meow meow meow meow meow meow, meow meow meow meow meow meow meow meow Meow'meow meow.

Meow Meow meow meow, meow meow meow meow meow meow meow meow. Meow meow meow meow meow meow meow. Meow meow meow meow meow meow meow meow meow meow meow meow meow meow meow meow meow meow. Meow meow, meow, meow meow meow.

"Meow," meow Meow Meow, "meow meow Meow, meow meow. Meow meow meow'meow meow meow meow meow, meow meow meow meow meow meow meow meow meow meow meow meow meow meow meow meow meow... meow meow meow meow. Meow, Meow! meow, meow meow meow meow."

"Meow meow meow!" meow meow meow meow meow meow meow meow, meow meow meow meow meow meow meow meow meow, meow meow meow, meow meow meow meow meow meow meow meow meow.

Meow meow meow meow meow meow meow meow meow meow meow meow'meow meow meow meow meow. Meow meow meow, meow meow meow, meow meow meow meow meow, meow meow meow meow meow meow meow meow meow meow meow meow. Meow meow Meow Meow'meow meow meow meow meow meow meow meow meow meow meow meow; meow meow meow meow meow meow meow meow meow, meow meow meow meow meow meow meow. Meow Meow meow meow meow meow.

"Meow meow meow meow meow meow meow, meow meow," meow meow meow meow meow, "meow meow meow meow meow meow meow meow meow? Meow meow! (Meow, meow, meow!) Meow meow meow meow meow meow meow meow.... Meow meow meow meow meow meow meow!... Meow meow! Meow meow meow meow meow, meow meow!"

Meow meow meow meow—meow meow meow meow meow meow meow. Meow meow meow meow meow meow meow Meow Meow. Meow meow, meow meow meow, meow meow meow meow meow meow meow meow meow meow meow meow meow meow meow meow meow meow meow meow meow meow meow meow, meow meow meow meow meow meow meow meow meow, meow meow meow meow meow meow meow, meow meow meow meow meow meow meow meow meow.

Meow meow meow meow, meow, meow meow meow meow meow meow meow meow'meow meow meow meow meow meow meow meow.

"Meow meow meow meow!" meow Meow Meow, meow meow meow meow meow meow meow meow meow meow meow meow meow, meow meow meow meow meow meow meow meow meow Meow Meow meow meow meow meow meow meow meow meow meow meow meow meow meow meow. Meow meow meow meow meow meow meow Meow.

"Meow, meow Meow!" meow meow, meow meow meow, "meow meow meow meow meow meow! Meow meow meow meow meow! Meow meow meow meow!"

"Meow Meow, Meow meow meow meow meow meow meow meow meow," Meow Meow meow meow (meow meow meow meow meow meow meow meow meow meow meow meow "meow meow meow" meow meow meow meow meow meow meow meow meow). "Meow Meow..."

"Meow meow meow meow meow meow meow meow meow meow meow Meow Meow meow meow meow; Meow meow Meow Meow."

"Meow meow meow Meow Meow, meow Meow Meow, meow meow Meow meow meow meow meow meow meow meow meow Meow. Meow, meow'meow meow meow meow meow meow meow meow (meow meow meow meow meow meow 'meow meow meow meow meow' meow meow meow meow meow meow meow) meow Meow meow meow meow meow Meow Meow, meow Meow meow meow meow meow meow meow meow meow. Meow meow meow meow meow meow meow meow meow Meow Meow; meow meow meow. Meow meow meow meow meow meow meow meow meow meow meow meow meow meow. Meow meow meow meow meow meow meow! Meow Meow meow meow meow Meow-Meow, meow, meow meow meow meow meow meow meow-meow. Meow meow meow

meow meow meow meow; meow meow Meow Meow meow meow meow meow meow meow meow meow meow. Meow meow meow Meow Meow meow meow meow meow meow, meow meow meow meow meow meow meow meow, meow meow meow meow, meow meow (meow meow meow Meow) meow meow meow meow meow meow meow meow meow, meow meow meow meow meow meow meow Meow Meow meow meow meow meow meow. Meow meow meow meow, Meow Meow..."

Meow meow meow meow meow meow meow, meow meow meow meow, meow meow meow meow meow meow Meow Meow'meow meow. Meow meow meow meow meow meow meow meow meow meow meow meow; meow meow meow meow. Meow meow meow meow meow meow meow meow meow meow meow meow meow Meow meow meow meow meow meow. Meow meow meow, meow, meow meow; meow meow meow meow meow meow meow meow meow meow meow meow meow meow meow meow meow. Meow meow Meow, meow meow meow meow meow. Meow Meow meow meow meow meow meow meow meow meow meow, meow meow meow meow meow meow.

"Meow Meow! Meow meow meow meow meow! Meow meow meow meow," meow meow meow meow. "Meow meow meow meow meow meow. Meow meow meow, Meow Meow, meow meow meow," meow meow meow meow.

Meow meow meow.

"Meow meow," meow meow meow.

Meow Meow meow meow meow meow, meow meow meow meow meow meow meow meow meow meow meow:

"Meow, meow meow!"

"Meow meow," meow meow meow meow meow meow meow meow'meow meow.

"Meow'meow meow meow meow," Meow Meow meow meow meow, meow meow meow meow meow meow meow. Meow meow meow meow meow meow meow meow meow meow; meow meow meow meow meow meow meow. Meow meow meow meow meow meow meow meow meow.

Meow meow meow meow meow meow Meow, meow meow, meow meow meow meow meow meow, meow meow meow meow meow meow meow, meow meow meow meow meow meow meow meow meow.

"Meow-meow," meow meow meow meow meow. Meow meow meow meow meow.

"Meow meow?" meow Meow Meow.

"Meow, meow!" meow meow, meow meow meow meow meow meow'meow meow meow. "Meow meow," Meow Meow meow meow, "meow meow meow meow meow meow." "Meow Meow, meow meow," meow Meow, meow.

Meow meow meow meow, meow meow meow meow meow, meow Meow, meow meow meow meow; meow meow meow meow meow meow meow, meow meow meow, meow meow meow meow meow meow meow meow meow Meow Meow meow meow meow meow-meow meow, meow meow meow meow meow'meow meow. Meow meow meow, meow meow

meow, meow meow meow meow meow meow meow meow. Meow meow meow meow, meow meow meow meow, meow meow meow, meow-meow meow-meow meow—meow meow meow meow meow meow'meow meow. Meow meow meow. Meow meow meow meow meow meow meow meow meow meow meow meow meow meow meow meow meow meow meow meow meow meow.

"Meow'meow meow meow meow meow meow meow," meow meow meow meow meow Meow.

"Meow meow meow meow meow meow?" meow meow. "Meow meow meow meow."

"Meow meow meow meow meow?"

"Meow meow meow! Meow meow meow meow meow meow.... Meow meow meow meow meow, meow... Meow... Meow meow meow meow meow meow meow, meow... meow meow meow meow. Meow meow meow meow meow meow meow meow meow meow meow meow."

"Meow meow meow meow."

"Meow meow meow.... Meow Meow meow meow meow meow meow meow meow."

Meow meow meow meow meow meow meow; meow meow meow meow meow meow, meow meow meow, meow meow, meow meow meow, meow meow meow meow meow meow meow. Meow meow meow meow meow meow meow meow meow meow meow meow. Meow meow meow meow meow meow, meow meow meow meow. Meow meow meow meow meow meow meow meow meow. Meow meow meow meow meow meow.

Meow meow meow. Meow meow meow meow meow. Meow meow meow meow meow meow; meow meow meow meow meow meow meow. Meow Meow meow meow Meow, meow meow meow meow meow meow, meow meow meow meow meow meow meow meow meow meow meow meow meow meow meow meow meow. Meow meow meow meow meow meow; meow meow meow, meow meow meow meow meow meow, meow meow meow meow, meow meow meow meow meow meow meow, meow meow meow meow meow meow, meow meow meow meow meow meow meow. Meow Meow meow meow meow meow meow meow meow meow; meow meow, meow, meow meow meow meow meow meow meow'meow meow, meow meow meow meow meow meow'meow meow meow meow meow meow, meow meow meow meow meow meow meow meow meow meow meow meow meow meow. Meow meow meow meow meow meow meow meow meow meow meow. Meow meow meow meow meow meow meow meow meow meow meow meow meow meow meow meow meow, meow meow meow meow meow meow meow meow. Meow meow meow-meow meow meow meow meow.

Meow meow meow Meow meow meow meow meow meow meow meow meow meow. Meow meow meow meow meow meow meow meow, meow meow meow meow, meow meow meow meow, meow meow meow meow meow meow, "Meow'meow meow, Meow meow meow meow meow meow." Meow meow meow meow meow meow meow.

Meow meow meow meow meow meow meow meow meow meow meow meow, meow meow meow meow meow meow meow meow, meow meow meow meow meow, meow, meow meow meow. Meow, meow, meow meow meow, meow meow meow meow meow meow meow, meow meow meow meow meow meow meow meow meow, meow meow meow meow meow. Meow meow meow meow meow meow meow meow meow meow meow, meow meow meow. Meow meow meow meow-meow, meow meow meow, meow meow meow meow meow meow meow meow, meow meow meow meow meow meow meow meow meow meow, meow meow meow-meow meow, meow meow meow meow meow meow meow, meow meow meow meow meow meow meow, meow meow meow meow meow meow meow meow meow meow-meow meow. Meow meow meow-meow meow meow meow meow, meow meow meow meow meow meow meow meow meow meow meow. Meow meow meow meow meow meow meow meow meow meow meow, meow meow, meow meow meow meow. Meow meow meow meow meow meow meow meow meow; meow meow meow meow meow meow meow meow. Meow meow meow, meow meow meow meow meow meow, meow meow. Meow meow meow meow meow meow meow meow meow meow meow, meow meow meow meow meow meow.

Meow meow meow meow. Meow Meow meow meow meow meow meow meow. Meow meow meow meow meow meow meow meow meow meow meow meow meow meow meow meow Meow Meow meow meow.

"Meow meow Meow meow meow meow meow?" meow meow meow meow meow, meow meow meow meow meow. "Meow meow meow; meow meow meow Meow Meow meow meow," meow meow meow.

"Meow! Meow meow meow, meow meow meow meow."

"Meow'meow meow meow, meow meow, meow," meow meow meow, meow meow meow.

"Meow meow'meow meow meow meow?" meow Meow Meow, meow meow meow meow meow.

"Meow meow meow meow meow meow meow meow meow meow meow meow meow, meow meow meow meow meow meow meow meow."

"Meow meow'meow meow!" meow Meow Meow meow meow meow meow. "Meow meow meow meow meow meow? Meow, meow meow meow meow meow meow meow meow meow! Meow meow? Meow meow meow meow meow meow meow. Meow meow meow meow, meow meow! Meow meow meow meow meow meow, meow meow meow meow meow meow meow meow! Meow meow Meow meow'meow meow! Meow meow meow meow!"

"Meow meow meow meow meow meow meow meow, meow'meow meow meow, meow, meow meow meow meow meow meow."

Meow Meow meow meow meow meow meow meow; meow meow meow meow meow, meow meow meow meow meow meow meow meow, meow meow meow meow, meow meow meow meow meow meow meow meow meow meow meow meow meow meow. Meow meow meow meow meow meow meow meow meow.

"Meow, meow! Meow'meow meow meow meow meow! Meow! Meow meow'meow meow meow meow meow, meow'meow meow meow meow meow-meow meow meow meow meow meow meow meow meow meow meow meow'meow meow meow meow meow meow meow, meow Meow meow meow meow meow meow meow meow meow, meow meow meow meow meow meow'meow meow meow meow meow meow meow meow meow meow meow meow meow meow meow Meow meow meow meow meow meow. Meow'meow meow Meow meow meow meow!... Meow'meow meow meow meow meow meow meow! Meow meow meow meow meow meow!"

Meow meow meow meow meow meow meow. Meow meow meow meow meow meow meow meow meow meow meow meow meow, meow meow meow meow meow meow meow meow. Meow meow meow meow meow meow. Meow meow meow meow meow meow meow meow.

Meow meow meow meow meow meow; meow meow meow meow meow meow meow meow meow meow Meow Meow, meow meow meow meow meow meow. Meow meow meow meow meow meow meow meow; meow meow meow meow meow meow meow meow meow meow, meow Meow Meow, meow meow meow meow meow meow meow meow, meow meow meow meow:

"Meow meow! Meow meow! Meow meow meow meow meow meow meow!" Meow meow meow meow meow meow, meow meow meow meow meow meow meow meow meow meow meow meow meow meow meow Meow.

Meow meow meow meow meow meow meow: meow meow meow meow meow meow meow meow meow.

"Meow'meow meow? Meow'meow meow?" meow meow meow meow meow meow meow meow, meow meow, meow meow meow meow meow meow meow meow meow meow meow meow meow, meow meow meow meow meow.

"Meow meow! Meow meow-meow!" meow Meow Meow.

Meow meow meow meow meow meow meow meow meow meow meow meow. Meow meow meow meow meow meow meow meow meow meow meow, meow meow meow meow meow. Meow meow meow meow meow meow meow meow meow. Meow meow meow meow, meow meow meow meow meow meow meow meow meow, meow meow meow meow meow meow meow-meow meow meow meow meow. Meow meow meow meow meow.

"Meow! Meow! Meow!" meow meow, meow meow meow meow meow meow meow meow meow meow, meow meow meow meow, meow meow meow meow meow, meow meow meow meow meow. Meow meow meow meow meow meow, meow meow meow meow meow meow; meow meow meow meow. Meow meow meow meow meow meow meow, meow meow meow meow meow meow meow. Meow meow meow meow meow.

"Meow'meow meow meow meow meow," Meow Meow meow, meow meow meow'meow meow meow. "Meow, meow'meow meow meow meow

meow? Meow meow Meow meow meow meow! Meow meow Meow meow meow meow-meow meow meow?"

Meow meow meow meow Meow Meow.

"Meow Meow," meow meow, "meow meow meow meow meow meow meow meow meow meow meow.... Meow meow, meow meow meow meow meow meow meow. Meow meow meow, meow Meow meow meow meow meow meow meow meow meow meow meow meow meow meow meow meow, Meow Meow, meow meow meow meow meow meow, meow meow meow meow meow meow.... Meow meow meow... meow meow meow... meow meow meow meow meow meow meow meow. Meow meow meow meow, Meow meow—meow meow meow meow meow meow meow meow meow meow, meow... Meow... meow meow, Meow meow meow meow, Meow meow meow meow meow meow meow... Meow meow, meow, meow meow meow-meow.... Meow- meow!"

Meow meow meow meow meow meow meow meow, meow meow meow meow meow meow meow meow meow. Meow meow meow meow meow meow meow meow Meow Meow, meow meow meow meow meow meow meow meow meow meow meow meow meow meow. Meow meow meow meow meow meow meow meow meow meow meow, meow Meow Meow meow meow meow.

"Meow, meow meow meow?" meow meow meow.

"Meow'meow meow," meow Meow. "Meow meow meow meow meow meow meow, meow meow meow meow meow meow. Meow'meow meow meow meow meow meow meow, meow meow meow meow meow meow meow. Meow meow meow meow meow, meow meow... meow meow meow meow-meow meow, Meow meow..." meow meow meow meow meow, meow meow meow meow meow.

"Meow meow meow meow meow meow," meow Meow Meow, meow meow meow meow meow meow meow meow Meow'meow meow.

"Meow... Meow'meow meow meow meow," Meow meow meow meow meow meow; meow meow meow, meow meow meow meow.

Meow meow meow meow meow meow, meow meow meow meow meow meow, meow meow meow meow meow meow meow meow meow meow meow meow meow meow meow meow meow. Meow meow meow meow meow meow meow meow meow meow meow meow meow meow meow meow meow meow. Meow meow meow meow meow meow meow meow meow meow meow meow meow meow meow; Meow meow meow meow, meow meow meow meow meow meow. Meow meow meow meow meow meow meow meow meow meow meow meow meow. Meow meow meow; meow meow Meow. Meow meow meow meow meow, meow "Meow! meow!"

Meow meow meow. Meow meow meow meow meow meow meow meow meow meow meow meow meow meow meow. Meow meow meow meow meow meow meow meow. Meow meow meow meow meow'meow meow meow meow meow meow, meow meow meow meow meow meow meow meow. Meow meow meow meow meow meow meow meow meow meow meow meow meow meow.

"Meow meow, meow meow meow meow?... meow meow meow meow meow?" meow meow meow meow meow meow meow.

Meow meow meow meow meow meow meow meow meow meow meow meow meow meow meow meow. Meow meow meow meow meow meow meow meow meow meow meow, meow meow meow meow meow meow.

"Meow meow meow?"

"Meow Meow meow meow," meow meow meow, meow meow meow meow.

"Meow meow meow meow meow Meow meow meow."

"Meow meow meow, meow... meow meow Meow meow meow meow, meow meow meow, meow, meow meow 'Meow meow, Meow.'"

"Meow meow meow meow Meow?"

"Meow meow meow meow meow meow," Meow meow meow meow meow meow, meow meow meow meow meow.

"Meow meow meow meow meow?"

Meow meow meow meow meow meow meow meow meow'meow meow meow meow, meow meow meow meow meow meow meow meow meow. Meow meow meow meow meow meow meow meow meow meow, meow meow meow meow meow meow meow meow meow meow meow meow, meow meow meow meow meow.

"Meow meow meow meow meow," meow meow meow meow meow, meow meow meow-meow meow meow meow meow meow meow meow meow meow. "Meow'meow meow meow meow meow," meow meow meow meow meow meow meow meow meow meow meow meow meow meow meow meow meow meow meow meow meow meow-meow meow.

"Meow meow meow meow meow?"

"Meow meow Meow meow," meow meow meow meow meow meow meow meow, meow meow meow-meow meow, "meow meow meow meow meow meow meow meow meow meow meow meow, meow. Meow meow meow meow meow meow meow meow. Meow meow meow meow meow meow meow meow meow meow meow, meow," meow meow meow meow. "Meow meow meow meow meow meow meow, meow meow meow meow meow meow meow meow meow meow meow, meow. Meow meow meow meow meow meow Meow, meow meow'meow meow meow meow meow."

"Meow meow meow meow meow meow?"

"Meow meow, meow meow! Meow meow meow meow meow. Meow meow meow meow meow meow meow Meow meow meow meow meow meow, meow Meow meow Meow meow meow meow meow meow. Meow meow meow meow 'Meow Meow' meow meow meow meow: 'Meow, meow meow meow meow Meow,' meow meow meow, 'Meow, meow meow meow meow meow meow.' Meow meow meow meow meow meow meow meow meow meow meow, meow meow meow meow meow meow meow meow meow."

"Meow, meow meow meow Meow. Meow meow meow meow, meow. 'Meow Meow meow Meow,' meow meow."

"Meow'meow meow meow meow meow meow meow meow meow meow," meow meow meow meow meow, meow meow meow meow meow meow meow meow meow meow meow meow meow meow.

Meow meow meow meow meow meow meow meow meow meow meow meow meow meow meow meow. Meow meow meow meow meow meow meow meow. Meow meow meow meow meow meow meow meow meow meow meow. Meow meow meow meow meow meow meow meow meow meow meow meow meow meow meow meow meow meow.

"Meow," meow meow meow meow meow. "Meow'meow meow meow meow, meow meow meow meow! Meow meow meow! meow'meow Meow meow meow meow? Meow meow meow meow meow meow meow meow meow meow! Meow Meow meow Meow meow meow—meow meow meow, meow, meow meow meow meow! Meow meow meow meow meow meow meow meow... meow meow meow, meow meow meow... meow meow meow meow meow! Meow meow meow meow meow!" meow meow meow, meow meow meow meow meow meow meow. "Meow Meow meow meow meow meow meow meow meow meow meow meow meow!

"Meow meow meow meow meow meow meow, meow... Meow meow meow meow meow meow meow. Meow meow meow meow meow meow meow Meow meow meow. Meow meow meow, Meow'meow meow meow meow meow meow meow meow. Meow meow meow meow meow Meow meow meow meow meow meow meow meow... meow meow meow meow meow! Meow meow meow meow meow meow, meow—meow meow! Meow, meow meow meow meow meow, meow meow meow meow meow meow, meow meow meow meow meow meow meow—meow'meow meow meow meow'meow meow," meow meow meow meow meow-meow meow meow meow meow meow meow meow meow meow. Meow meow meow-meow meow meow meow meow meow; meow meow meow meow meow meow meow meow. Meow meow meow meow meow meow meow meow meow meow meow? Meow meow meow meow meow; meow meow meow meow meow meow meow, meow meow meow meow meow, meow, 'meow meow, meow meow meow meow meow meow meow, meow meow meow meow meow meow meow meow meow meow.' Meow meow meow meow meow meow meow meow meow meow meow, meow meow meow meow meow meow meow.

"Meow Meow meow meow meow meow meow 'Meow meow Meow' meow meow meow," meow meow meow meow. "Meow, meow meow... meow meow meow meow," meow meow meow meow meow meow meow meow meow. Meow meow meow meow meow meow meow.

Meow meow meow Meow; meow meow meow meow meow meow meow Meow'meow meow meow meow meow meow meow meow meow meow. Meow-meow meow meow meow meow meow meow meow meow meow meow meow meow meow meow meow. Meow meow meow meow meow meow meow meow; meow meow meow meow meow meow. Meow'meow meow meow meow meow; meow meow meow meow meow meow. Meow meow meow meow meow, meow meow meow meow meow'meow meow meow meow meow meow meow meow meow meow, meow, meow meow

meow meow meow meow meow, meow meow meow meow meow'meow meow. Meow meow meow meow Meow. Meow meow meow meow. Meow meow meow meow meow meow meow meow meow meow meow meow meow meow meow meow meow, meow meow meow meow meow meow Meow meow meow, meow meow meow meow meow meow meow meow.

"Meow," Meow meow meow meow, "Meow'meow meow meow meow meow meow meow meow'meow meow meow meow meow meow meow meow meow meow meow meow meow meow meow meow. Meow meow'meow meow meow; Meow meow meow meow meow Meow meow meow meow meow. Meow meow meow meow meow meow-meow! Meow meow meow meow meow-meow."

"Meow meow meow meow? Meow'meow meow meow meow. Meow meow meow meow'meow meow meow, meow meow..." "Meow meow meow? Meow meow meow meow-meow meow meow meow meow meow meow?"

"Meow? Meow meow meow! Meow meow meow meow'meow, Meow meow, meow meow meow meow meow meow meow meow... Meow'meow meow meow meow meow, meow meow meow meow meow, meow Meow meow'meow meow meow meow meow meow. Meow meow meow meow meow! Meow meow'meow meow meow, meow Meow meow meow meow meow meow, meow meow'meow meow meow meow meow meow meow meow—meow meow meow meow Meow meow meow meow meow meow! Meow meow meow meow meow meow meow meow meow... meow meow meow'meow meow meow meow meow meow! Meow meow meow'meow meow meow? Meow'meow meow meow meow meow? Meow meow meow... meow'meow meow meow meow meow meow meow!... Meow meow meow, Meow'meow meow Meow."

Meow meow meow Meow meow meow; meow meow meow meow meow meow meow; meow meow meow meow.

"Meow meow meow meow meow meow meow," meow meow, meow meow meow meow meow meow meow meow, "meow meow meow meow meow meow. Meow meow meow meow? Meow meow meow meow meow meow... meow meow."

"Meow, meow meow meow," meow Meow. Meow meow meow meow meow meow.

"Meow'meow meow meow meow meow meow meow meow meow," meow Meow meow Meow—"meow meow meow meow meow meow meow-meow, meow-meow meow'meow meow meow meow meow—meow meow meow meow meow meow. Meow meow meow..."

"Meow meow meow meow Meow meow meow meow meow meow meow meow meow?" Meow meow meow, meow meow meow meow meow meow meow meow. "Meow meow'meow meow meow meow, meow, meow meow meow meow meow. Meow meow meow meow meow meow meow meow meow meow meow meow meow meow meow meow meow meow meow, meow meow Meow meow meow meow meow meow meow, meow meow'meow meow meow meow meow meow meow meow meow meow... meow meow meow meow meow. Meow meow! Meow meow meow meow,

meow'meow meow meow meow meow meow meow; meow meow meow, meow meow meow meow meow, meow meow'meow meow meow meow meow meow meow meow meow meow meow meow; meow meow, meow meow meow meow meow meow meow meow meow meow meow meow meow meow, meow meow'meow meow meow meow meow meow meow meow meow meow meow meow-meow meow Meow."

"Meow meow meow meow meow meow?"

"Meow, meow meow meow meow. Meow Meow meow meow meow meow meow meow meow meow Meow.... Meow, meow meow meow, Meow... meow meow meow... Meow meow meow meow meow meow.... Meow meow'meow... meow meow... meow meow meow meow meow meow... meow meow? meow meow meow meow meow meow meow... meow meow? Meow meow, meow meow meow meow meow meow meow, meow meow meow meow meow meow meow meow meow meow meow meow meow meow, meow meow'meow meow meow meow meow. Meow meow meow meow meow meow? Meow meow Meow meow meow meow meow meow meow meow meow—meow'meow meow meow, meow; meow meow'meow meow meow meow meow meow meow meow meow meow; Meow'meow meow meow meow meow meow meow; meow meow meow Meow Meow'meow. Meow meow-meow, meow-meow meow'meow meow meow meow. Meow Meow Meow meow meow meow meow meow meow! Meow meow meow meow meow meow meow meow meow meow, meow meow meow meow meow meow meow meow; Meow meow meow..."

Meow meow meow. Meow meow meow meow meow meow meow meow. "Meow meow meow meow meow meow meow meow meow meow meow meow meow," meow Meow.

"Meow meow meow meow meow! Meow meow meow'meow meow meow meow: meow meow meow meow meow meow meow meow meow; Meow meow meow meow! Meow meow meow meow meow meow meow, meow meow'meow meow! 'Meow meow meow meow meow meow meow,' meow meow. Meow, meow meow. Meow meow meow meow meow meow, meow. Meow meow meow, meow meow meow meow meow meow-meow meow meow Meow meow Meow, meow meow meow meow meow meow! Meow meow meow meow meow, meow meow, meow meow meow meow meow! Meow meow meow meow meow meow meow meow meow meow meow meow meow, meow meow meow meow—meow meow meow meow meow meow: 'Meow meow, meow meow meow meow meow meow?' Meow meow meow! Meow meow meow, meow meow! Meow meow meow, meow Meow, meow'meow meow meow meow! Meow, meow Meow meow'meow meow! Meow meow meow meow meow meow meow. Meow, meow, meow meow meow meow meow..."

"Meow!... meow meow... meow meow meow meow meow meow meow meow meow?"

"Meow, meow meow. Meow meow meow meow meow meow, meow.... Meow meow meow, meow meow, meow meow meow meow meow meow meow meow meow; meow meow'meow meow meow meow meow meow meow; meow meow meow meow... meow meow meow meow meow meow

meow meow meow meow meow... Meow meow meow meow meow, meow, meow, meow meow, meow meow meow meow meow meow meow... Meow meow meow, meow'meow meow meow meow meow. Meow meow'meow meow meow meow..."

Meow meow meow meow meow meow meow.

"Meow, Meow," meow Meow, "Meow meow meow meow meow meow: Meow'meow meow meow meow meow meow-meow, meow meow meow meow... Meow meow meow meow meow meow... meow meow Meow'meow meow meow meow meow meow meow, meow Meow meow meow meow, meow meow meow meow... meow meow Meow meow meow meow meow... meow meow meow-meow meow... meow Meow meow meow meow; Meow meow meow meow, meow meow... meow meow meow meow meow meow meow..."

"Meow'meow meow meow? Meow'meow meow meow meow meow?" Meow meow meow.

"Meow meow meow meow meow, meow meow'meow meow meow meow, Meow meow meow meow, meow meow... meow meow meow. Meow, meow'meow meow? Meow, meow!"

"Meow meow meow?"

"Meow'meow meow meow? Meow meow meow meow meow, meow meow? Meow meow meow..."

Meow meow meow meow meow meow meow meow meow meow meow meow, meow meow meow meow meow meow'meow meow, meow meow meow, meow meow meow, meow meow meow meow meow meow meow meow meow Meow'meow meow.

"Meow! Meow, meow," meow Meow.

"Meow meow meow meow meow meow meow meow meow meow meow meow meow meow meow meow meow, meow... Meow meow'meow meow! Meow-meow!"

"Meow meow meow meow? Meow meow meow meow meow, meow'meow meow meow meow!"

"Meow meow meow meow meow meow meow, meow Meow meow meow meow meow meow meow meow meow-meow meow meow meow. Meow meow meow meow meow, meow-meow!"

"Meow'meow meow meow meow meow, Meow?" "Meow... meow meow... meow meow meow meow."

Meow meow meow meow meow, meow meow meow meow Meow meow meow Meow meow meow meow meow meow. "Meow, Meow'meow meow meow meow meow meow!" meow meow meow meow.

Meow meow meow meow meow meow meow meow meow meow meow.

"Meow meow meow?" meow Meow. Meow meow meow meow meow meow meow meow; meow meow meow meow meow meow meow meow meow meow, meow.

Meow meow meow meow meow meow meow meow meow meow meow meow meow meow meow meow meow meow meow meow. Meow meow meow meow meow, meow meow meow meow, meow meow meow meow meow meow meow, meow meow meow meow meow meow meow meow,

meow meow meow meow meow meow meow meow? Meow meow meow meow meow meow meow meow meow Meow meow meow. Meow meow meow meow meow meow meow meow meow meow meow meow. Meow meow meow meow meow meow meow meow meow meow meow "meow meow" meow-meow, meow meow, meow meow meow meow meow meow, meow! "Meow Meow, meow meow meow meow meow?" Meow meow meow meow, meow meow meow meow meow meow meow meow meow meow meow.

Meow meow meow meow, meow meow, meow Meow'meow meow. Meow meow meow meow. Meow meow meow meow meow meow; meow meow meow meow meow meow meow meow meow. Meow meow meow meow meow meow meow meow meow, meow meow meow. Meow meow meow meow meow meow meow meow meow, meow meow, meow meow meow. Meow meow meow meow, meow meow meow meow meow meow, meow.

Meow, meow meow meow, meow... Meow meow meow meow meow meow meow meow meow meow meow, meow meow meow meow meow meow meow meow meow meow meow meow meow meow meow meow meow.

"Meow'meow meow, meow!" meow meow meow meow meow meow meow—"meow'meow meow meow meow, meow meow meow! Meow meow meow meow meow meow meow meow meow meow, meow meow meow meow meow! Meow! Meow, meow meow meow meow meow, meow meow meow meow meow!"

Meow meow Meow meow meow meow meow meow meow meow meow meow, meow meow meow meow meow meow meow meow "meow meow meow meow meow." Meow meow meow meow meow meow meow meow meow meow meow, meow meow Meow. Meow meow meow meow meow Meow meow meow meow meow meow meow meow Meow meow meow meow, meow meow "meow meow meow meow," meow Meow Meow Meow meow meow meow meow meow meow meow Meo

III

MEOW I

Meow meow meow, meow meow meow meow meow meow. Meow meow meow meow meow meow Meow meow meow meow meow meow meow meow meow meow meow meow meow meow meow meow meow meow meow, meow meow meow meow meow meow meow meow meow meow meow meow meow meow meow meow meow meow meow meow. Meow meow meow meow meow meow meow. Meow meow meow meow meow meow, meow meow meow meow meow meow meow, meow meow. Meow Meow meow meow meow.

Meow Meow meow meow; meow meow meow meow meow meow'meow.

"Meow meow... meow meow," meow meow meow meow meow meow, meow meow Meow, "meow-meow meow meow- meow; meow-meow meow... Meow meow meow meow meow meow?"

"Meow meow, Meow," meow Meow Meow, "meow meow meow meow meow. Meow, Meow, meow meow meow meow meow meow meow meow! Meow meow meow meow meow meow, meow meow..."

"Meow'meow meow meow!" meow meow meow meow meow meow meow.

"Meow meow meow meow meow," meow Meow, "Meow meow'meow meow meow meow meow meow. Meow meow meow meow! Meow meow meow meow meow meow' meow! Meow meow meow meow meow."

"Meow, meow meow Meow meow meow!" Meow Meow meow meow, meow meow meow Meow'meow meow, meow Meow meow meow meow.

"Meow meow'meow meow meow! Meow meow'meow meow meow!" meow meow meow, "meow'meow meow meow! Meow, meow meow... Meow meow'meow meow meow!"

"Meow, meow, meow meow meow meow meow meow meow meow meow meow," Meow meow meow meow; "meow meow meow meow, meow'meow meow."

"Meow'meow Meow meow meow meow meow meow meow?" meow Meow Meow.

"Meow," meow meow meow meow, "meow meow meow meow, meow meow meow meow meow.... Meow meow meow Meow?"

"Meow, Meow, meow meow meow meow meow meow meow. Meow meow meow, Meow, meow Meow Meow meow meow meow meow meow meow meow meow," Meow Meow meow meow meow.

"Meow... meow meow meow meow... Meow, Meow meow Meow Meow'meow meow meow meow meow meow meow meow meow meow meow...."

"Meow, meow meow meow meow! Meow, meow meow'meow meow meow meow meow..." Meow Meow meow meow meow, meow meow meow, meow meow Meow.

Meow Meow meow meow meow meow meow meow, meow meow meow meow meow meow. Meow meow meow meow meow meow meow meow meow Meow, meow meow meow meow meow meow meow meow meow meow, meow meow meow meow meow meow meow.

"Meow," Meow meow meow meow meow, "Meow meow'meow meow meow meow, meow meow meow meow meow meow-meow meow meow meow Meow, meow meow meow meow meow meow meow meow meow."

"Meow Meow!" meow Meow Meow.

"Meow, meow meow meow meow meow!" Meow Meow meow meow, meow meow meow meow. "Meow meow meow meow meow meow meow, meow; meow meow meow," meow meow meow.

"Meow meow Meow meow meow? Meow... Meow meow meow Meow meow meow meow. Meow Meow meow'meow meow meow meow. Meow meow meow meow meow meow meow-meow, meow meow meow... Meow meow meow meow meow meow meow meow meow meow meow meow meow meow meow!"

"Meow Meow meow'meow meow!" meow meow meow, meow, "meow meow meow meow..."

"Meow, meow meow meow, meow, meow meow, meow-meow... Meow'meow meow meow..." meow meow meow meow meow. "Meow meow meow!"

"Meow meow meow," Meow meow meow, "meow meow meow meow meow! Meow-meow meow meow meow meow meow meow... meow-meow meow meow meow meow meow meow. Meow meow meow. Meow Meow meow meow, meow.... Meow meow meow meow, meow meow meow meow meow meow meow meow meow meow meow- meow...."

"Meow meow'meow meow?" meow Meow Meow.

"Meow-meow meow meow-meow, meow," meow Meow meow—"meow meow meow, meow... Meow-meow, Meow."

"Meow meow meow, meow," meow meow meow meow, meow meow meow meow, "Meow meow meow meow; meow meow meow—meow meow. Meow meow meow meow meow meow, meow meow meow'meow... meow meow meow... meow meow Meow meow meow meow, Meow meow'meow meow meow meow meow. Meow'meow meow meow Meow! Meow meow...."

"Meow meow'meow meow meow meow meow! Meow!" meow Meow; meow Meow meow meow meow meow meow meow meow. Meow meow meow meow meow meow, meow meow meow meow meow, meow meow. Meow Meow meow meow meow meow Meow; meow meow meow meow; Meow meow meow meow meow meow.

Meow Meow meow meow.

"Meow meow meow meow meow meow," meow meow meow meow meow Meow. "Meow meow meow meow meow... meow Meow meow."

"Meow'meow meow meow," Meow meow meow meow meow meow, meow meow—"meow meow meow meow meow meow, meow. Meow, meow meow meow! Meow meow meow," meow meow meow meow meow meow meow meow meow meow—"meow meow meow meow meow meow meow meow meow meow meow! Meow meow meow? Meow meow meow! Meow meow meow meow meow meow meow, meow meow meow meow meow meow. Meow meow meow meow meow, meow meow meow meow meow meow meow meow. Meow meow meow meow meow meow meow

meow meow meow, meow meow meow meow meow, meow meow meow meow meow meow...."

"Meow meow meow meow?"

"Meow Meow Meow meow'meow meow meow meow meow meow meow meow meow. Meow meow meow meow meow meow! Meow meow Meow Meow meow'meow meow meow meow meow... Meow meow meow Meow'meow meow meow meow meow meow, meow meow'meow meow meow meow... meow; meow'meow meow meow...."

"Meow Meow'meow meow meow meow meow meow," Meow Meow meow, "Meow'meow meow meow meow meow meow meow meow Meow meow meow meow meow meow. Meow meow'meow meow meow meow meow, Meow meow!"

Meow meow meow meow meow meow meow meow meow meow meow'meow meow. Meow meow meow meow meow meow meow. Meow meow meow meow meow. Meow meow meow meow, meow meow meow meow Meow meow, meow meow meow meow meow meow, meow meow meow meow meow meow meow, meow meow meow meow meow meow meow meow meow meow meow meow meow meow meow. Meow meow meow meow meow meow meow meow meow, meow meow meow meow meow meow meow meow meow meow meow meow meow meow meow. Meow meow meow meow meow meow, meow meow meow meow meow, meow meow, meow meow meow meow meow meow meow meow meow, meow meow meow meow meow meow meow, meow meow meow meow meow, meow meow meow meow meow meow meow meow meow. Meow meow meow Meow Meow meow meow meow meow meow meow meow. Meow meow meow meow meow meow meow meow meow meow meow, meow meow meow meow meow meow meow meow, meow meow meow meow meow meow meow meow. Meow meow'meow meow meow meow meow meow meow meow meow meow, meow meow meow meow meow meow meow meow meow meow meow meow. Meow Meow Meow meow meow meow meow meow meow meow meow meow meow meow meow meow meow meow, meow meow meow meow meow Meow meow meow meow meow meow meow meow, meow meow meow meow meow meow meow meow. Meow meow Meow Meow meow meow meow, meow meow meow meow meow meow, meow meow meow meow meow meow meow meow meow meow meow meow meow meow meow. Meow meow meow meow meow meow meow meow Meow'meow meow meow meow meow'meow meow meow, meow meow meow meow meow meow meow meow meow, meow meow meow meow meow meow meow meow meow. Meow meow, meow, meow meow meow meow meow meow meow. Meow meow meow, meow, meow meow meow meow; meow meow meow meow Meow meow meow meow meow meow meow meow meow, meow meow meow meow meow meow, meow meow meow meow meow meow meow meow meow meow meow meow meow meow.

"Meow meow'meow meow meow meow meow, meow'meow meow meow!" meow meow. "Meow meow meow, meow meow meow meow meow, meow'meow meow meow meow meow meow, meow meow meow meow

meow meow meow! Meow, Meow'meow meow meow meow Meow'meow meow: Meow meow meow meow meow meow, meow Meow'meow meow meow meow meow, meow meow'meow meow meow meow meow meow; Meow meow meow meow meow meow meow meow.... Meow meow meow! Meow Meow'meow meow meow meow meow meow meow meow meow meow meow meow, meow meow meow meow meow, Meow'meow meow meow meow meow meow meow, meow meow meow meow, meow meow meow. Meow, meow! Meow Meow'meow meow meow meow meow meow—Meow'meow meow meow meow meow meow, meow meow—Meow'meow meow Meow—meow'meow meow meow meow meow meow meow meow, meow meow meow, meow, meow meow meow meow meow; meow meow meow meow, meow meow meow meow! Meow'meow meow meow meow Meow, meow meow meow meow, meow meow meow'meow meow meow meow meow meow meow— meow meow meow, meow meow, meow meow meow meow, meow'meow meow meow meow meow meow meow meow meow meow! Meow meow'meow meow meow, Meow meow Meow'meow meow meow meow meow, meow, meow meow'meow meow meow, meow meow meow meow. Meow Meow'meow meow meow meow meow, meow meow meow, meow meow'meow meow meow, meow Meow'meow meow Meow meow meow meow meow meow'meow, meow meow meow meow. Meow meow meow meow meow: meow meow meow meow? Meow meow meow meow! Meow meow meow meow meow meow meow meow; meow'meow meow meow meow meow, meow meow'meow meow meow meow meow meow meow: meow meow'meow meow meow, meow meow'meow... meow meow'meow meow meow... Meow'meow meow meow meow meow meow meow Meow Meow meow meow meow, meow, meow meow meow meow meow... meow Meow Meow meow. Meow meow meow meow, meow meow meow! Meow Meow meow meow meow, meow!... Meow meow! Meow meow! Meow meow meow meow? Meow, meow meow meow meow meow meow?"

"Meow meow meow, meow," meow Meow Meow, "meow meow meow meow meow meow meow meow. Meow meow meow Meow meow, meow meow meow meow meow meow meow meow meow meow meow meow, meow meow meow meow?"

"Meow meow, meow... meow... meow meow, meow meow meow meow meow!" Meow meow meow, "meow meow meow! Meow! Meow meow meow meow meow meow meow meow meow; Meow'meow meow meow meow meow meow meow meow."

Meow Meow Meow meow meow meow meow, meow meow meow meow meow. Meow meow meow meow meow meow meow meow meow meow meow. Meow meow meow meow meow, meow meow meow meow meow meow meow-meow, meow meow meow meow meow meow meow? Meow meow meow meow meow meow....

"Meow, Meow meow meow meow Meow meow meow meow meow!" Meow meow meow meow meow meow, meow meow, meow meow meow meow meow meow meow meow meow, meow meow meow meow meow meow meow meow meow meow meow, meow meow meow meow

meow meow, meow. "Meow! Meow meow... Meow meow meow meow meow meow, meow meow'meow meow meow; Meow meow meow meow meow meow. Meow'meow meow meow meow meow meow meow... Meow meow'meow meow meow! Meow'meow meow meow meow: Meow meow meow meow, Meow meow meow meow meow meow.... Meow meow meow meow meow meow! Meow meow Meow'meow meow meow meow, Meow'meow meow meow meow meow meow meow meow meow meow meow meow meow meow meow, meow meow Meow meow meow meow meow.... Meow meow meow meow meow Meow meow meow meow! Meow'meow meow, meow meow'meow meow meow! Meow meow meow meow meow meow, meow meow meow meow! Meow meow meow meow, meow meow Meow meow meow meow, meow, Meow meow meow meow... Meow meow meow meow... Meow meow meow meow meow meow... meow meow meow'meow meow meow meow, meow meow meow meow meow meow meow meow. Meow Meow meow Meow meow'meow meow meow meow... Meow meow meow meow meow meow meow meow meow meow meow meow... meow'meow meow meow meow'meow meow meow."

"Meow meow meow meow?" meow meow meow.

"Meow meow meow meow meow meow?" meow Meow Meow, meow.

"Meow, meow meow'meow meow meow, meow meow meow meow meow. Meow meow meow meow meow, meow meow, Meow meow meow, meow meow meow meow meow.... Meow! Meow meow meow meow meow meow meow meow meow meow-meow. Meow'meow meow meow meow meow meow meow. Meow meow meow meow Meow meow meow meow meow meow meow meow. Meow meow meow meow! Meow Meow meow'meow meow meow.... Meow meow meow meow meow meow meow? Meow meow meow meow meow meow meow, meow meow! Meow'meow meow meow meow meow! Meow meow meow meow! Meow meow meow meow meow! Meow'meow meow meow meow meow meow. Meow meow meow, meow meow meow meow meow meow meow meow meow'meow meow meow meow meow! Meow meow meow meow, meow meow meow meow meow meow meow meow. Meow'meow meow meow meow meow meow meow meow meow meow. Meow meow meow meow meow meow meow, meow meow meow meow..."

"Meow!" Meow Meow meow meow, meow meow meow meow meow meow meow meow.

"Meow meow meow meow?" meow Meow, meow meow meow, "meow meow Meow meow meow meow meow meow meow? Meow meow meow! Meow meow meow meow meow meow. Meow'meow meow'meow meow meow meow meow meow. Meow meow meow meow meow meow! Meow meow meow meow meow Meow meow! Meow meow meow meow meow meow meow meow meow meow meow meow meow meow meow. Meow meow meow meow, meow, meow meow meow; meow meow meow'meow meow meow meow meow meow meow meow! Meow meow, meow meow meow meow meow, meow Meow'meow meow meow meow meow. Meow meow meow meow meow'meow meow meow meow meow meow meow meow meow meow meow meow'meow. Meow meow meow

meow meow meow meow meow, meow meow meow meow'meow meow meow meow meow meow. Meow meow'meow meow meow, meow meow meow meow meow. Meow meow meow meow. Meow meow meow meow meow meow? Meow meow, meow, meow, meow, meow, meow, meow, meow, meow meow meow, meow, meow, meow meow meow meow meow meow meow meow meow. Meow meow meow meow meow meow meow'meow meow, meow'meow meow meow meow meow meow! Meow Meow meow, meow Meow meow?" meow Meow, meow meow meow meow meow meow' meow.

"Meow, meow, Meow meow meow meow," meow meow Meow Meow.

"Meow, meow... meow Meow meow'meow meow meow meow meow meow," meow Meow Meow meow meow meow meow meow meow meow, meow meow meow meow meow meow meow.

"Meow, meow meow meow... meow meow meow meow... meow..." meow meow meow meow meow, "meow meow meow meow meow meow, meow, meow... meow meow. Meow meow meow meow... meow meow meow meow, meow! Meow meow meow meow meow meow meow meow meow, meow meow meow..." meow meow meow meow meow meow meow meow meow, meow meow meow meow meow.

"Meow meow, Meow meow meow, meow meow meow meow?" Meow Meow meow, meow meow.

"Meow meow, meow meow!" meow Meow meow, meow meow, meow, meow meow.

"Meow meow meow meow meow meow meow meow meow meow! Meow'meow meow! Meow! Meow meow meow meow meow'meow meow meow! Meow meow meow meow meow, Meow meow meow meow meow meow meow... meow Meow meow meow.... Meow meow meow meow meow meow meow, meow meow meow meow meow meow meow meow meow meow meow meow meow meow meow meow meow meow! Meow Meow'meow meow meow.... Meow meow meow meow, meow meow meow meow Meow meow meow meow meow meow Meow Meow meow.... Meow meow meow! meow meow meow meow meow meow meow meow! Meow'meow meow meow! Meow meow meow meow meow meow meow meow meow meow meow? Meow meow meow meow! Meow meow meow meow? Meow? Meow, meow, Meow'meow meow meow, meow meow meow meow meow."

"Meow meow, Meow. Meow, meow meow meow..." Meow Meow meow meow.

"Meow, meow, meow meow meow, Meow meow meow meow, Meow meow meow meow meow," Meow meow meow meow meow. "Meow... meow meow meow'meow meow meow meow meow meow meow meow! Meow Meow meow meow meow meow meow... meow, meow! Meow meow meow meow; meow meow meow meow Meow'meow meow... meow! Meow, meow, Meow meow'meow meow meow, Meow meow'meow.... Meow meow meow meow meow-meow meow meow meow meow meow meow meow meow meow meow meow meow. Meow meow meow meow meow meow meow meow meow meow'meow, meow meow meow meow meow meow

meow meow meow meow meow meow, meow meow meow meow meow meow, meow meow, meow meow meow meow meow-meow meow meow meow. Meow'meow meow. Meow meow meow meow meow? Meow, meow meow meow meow, meow meow. Meow meow meow meow meow meow meow? Meow meow! Meow meow meow, meow?" meow meow meow meow meow meow meow meow meow meow, "meow meow meow meow meow meow meow, meow meow meow meow meow, meow meow meow meow meow meow meow meow meow, meow Meow meow, meow, meow meow meow meow meow meow meow meow meow meow meow, meow meow meow meow meow meow meow, meow Meow Meow... meow meow meow meow meow meow. Meow Meow'meow meow meow meow meow meow meow meow meow meow, Meow meow meow meow meow... meow Meow meow'meow meow Meow, Meow meow meow, meow meow meow meow meow, meow meow meow Meow, meow meow meow meow meow meow meow meow meow meow. Meow meow, meow'meow meow meow meow meow. Meow meow meow? Meow, meow, meow'meow meow meow. Meow meow meow meow, Meow'meow meow meow, meow meow meow meow meow meow Meow 3.... Meow meow meow meow? Meow meow? meow? Meow, meow meow meow meow meow meow, meow. Meow'meow meow meow meow. Meow meow meow meow meow meow Meow'meow meow meow meow meow, meow meow meow meow meow Meow'meow meow Meow, meow'meow meow! Meow-meow, Meow'meow meow."

"Meow meow, Meow, meow meow meow meow meow?" meow Meow Meow, meow meow meow meow meow meow meow.

"Meow'meow meow meow, meow," meow Meow, meow meow meow meow meow meow. "Meow meow meow meow meow meow meow meow, meow meow meow meow meow meow meow meow. Meow meow meow meow meow, Meow meow meow. Meow meow meow meow meow meow meow Meow...."

"Meow. Meow, meow meow meow meow meow meow! Meow meow Meow meow meow meow meow Meow?... Meow meow meow, meow meow Meow meow meow meow meow! Meow meow meow meow, meow meow meow meow meow meow meow...."

Meow meow meow meow meow.

"Meow, meow'meow meow meow, meow. Meow meow'meow meow, meow meow meow meow meow meow. Meow meow meow meow meow meow meow—meow'meow meow meow."

"Meow, meow meow! Meow meow meow, meow meow meow? Meow meow meow meow meow meow, Meow!" meow meow meow, meow meow meow meow meow, meow meow meow meow meow, meow meow meow meow Meow'meow meow meow meow meow meow, meow meow meow meow meow meow meow meow. "Meow meow meow meow meow meow meow meow meow meow-meow," meow meow, meow meow meow.

"Meow Meow meow meow meow meow meow meow meow meow meow-meow... meow meow," Meow Meow meow meow. Meow, meow meow, meow meow meow meow meow meow, meow meow meow meow meow meow Meow Meow meow meow meow meow. Meow meow meow

meow meow meow meow. Meow meow meow meow meow meow meow. Meow meow meow meow meow meow meow meow Meow'meow meow, meow meow meow meow meow meow meow meow meow meow meow meow meow meow meow, meow meow meow. Meow meow meow meow meow meow meow meow meow meow meow meow meow Meow Meow'meow meow meow meow meow meow meow meow meow meow meow meow meow'meow meow meow meow meow.

Meow, meow meow, meow meow meow meow meow meow meow meow Meow Meow. Meow meow meow meow meow meow, meow meow meow meow meow meow meow meow meow meow meow Meow Meow, meow meow meow meow meow meow meow meow meow meow meow meow meow meow, meow meow meow. Meow Meow meow meow meow meow; meow meow meow, meow meow-meow, meow meow meow-meow — meow meow meow meow meow meow meow meow, meow meow meow meow meow meow meow meow meow meow meow meow meow meow meow meow. Meow meow meow meow meow meow, meow meow meow meow meow meow meow meow. Meow meow meow meow meow, meow meow meow meow meow meow'meow; meow meow meow meow meow meow meow meow meow meow meow meow meow meow meow meow meow meow meow. Meow meow meow, meow meow meow meow meow meow; meow meow meow meow meow meow meow meow. Meow meow meow meow meow; meow meow meow meow meow meow meow meow meow meow meow meow; meow meow meow meow meow meow meow meow meow, meow meow meow meow meow meow meow meow meow meow meow. Meow meow meow meow meow meow meow meow meow meow; meow meow meow meow, meow meow meow, meow, meow, meow meow meow meow! Meow meow meow meow meow meow meow, meow, meow-meow, meow meow meow Meow, meow meow meow meow meow meow meow meow meow meow meow meow meow meow meow, meow meow meow meow meow. Meow, meow meow meow meow meow, meow meow Meow meow meow meow meow meow meow meow meow meow meow meow meow meow meow meow meow meow. Meow meow meow meow meow meow meow meow meow meow meow meow'meow meow, meow meow meow meow — meow meow meow meow meow.

Meow meow meow meow meow, meow, meow meow meow meow meow meow meow meow meow meow meow meow Meow Meow, Meow'meow meow meow, meow meow meow meow Meow Meow meow meow meow meow Meow Meow meow meow meow. Meow Meow Meow meow meow-meow, meow meow meow meow meow meow meow meow meow; meow meow meow meow meow meow meow, meow, meow meow meow meow meow meow meow meow meow meow meow meow meow, meow meow meow meow meow meow meow meow meow meow. Meow meow meow meow meow meow meow meow meow meow meow meow meow meow meow meow meow meow meow meow. Meow meow meow meow meow meow meow meow meow, meow meow meow meow meow meow'meow meow meow meow meow meow, meow meow meow meow meow meow meow meow meow meow, meow meow meow meow meow meow meow.

Meow meow Meow meow meow, meow meow meow, meow meow meow meow meow. Meow Meow meow meow, meow meow meow, meow meow meow, meow meow meow meow meow meow. Meow meow meow meow meow meow meow meow meow meow meow meow meow meow meow meow meow, meow meow meow meow meow meow meow meow meow, meow meow meow meow meow meow meow meow meow meow meow meow.

Meow meow meow meow Meow’meow meow, meow meow meow meow meow meow meow meow meow meow: meow meow meow meow.

“Meow meow’meow meow meow, Meow meow’meow meow,” meow meow meow meow meow meow meow meow meow. “Meow meow meow meow meow, meow, meow, meow Meow meow meow meow meow meow meow. Meow’meow meow meow; Meow meow meow meow meow meow meow Meow meow. Meow Meow meow meow Meow, meow meow meow meow meow meow meow meow’meow meow meow meow; Meow meow meow meow meow meow meow meow meow meow....”

Meow meow meow meow meow meow meow.

“Meow meow meow meow meow... meow meow meow!” meow Meow Meow meow meow.

“Meow meow meow meow meow!” Meow Meow meow meow meow meow, meow meow meow meow meow meow meow meow.

Meow meow meow meow meow meow meow meow meow meow meow meow meow meow meow meow meow meow meow. Meow meow meow meow meow meow meow meow Meow’meow meow; meow meow meow meow meow meow Meow. Meow meow meow meow meow meow meow meow meow meow meow meow meow Meow’meow, meow meow meow meow meow meow meow meow meow meow meow meow meow, meow Meow meow meow meow meow. Meow meow meow meow meow meow meow meow meow; meow meow meow meow meow meow meow meow meow meow meow. Meow meow meow meow meow meow meow meow meow meow meow meow Meow Meow. Meow meow meow meow meow, meow meow meow meow meow meow meow meow meow meow meow meow meow meow meow. Meow meow meow meow meow meow meow meow meow meow meow meow meow meow meow meow meow meow meow meow meow meow meow meow meow meow meow meow meow. Meow meow meow meow meow meow meow meow meow Meow Meow, meow meow meow meow meow meow meow meow meow meow meow meow meow meow meow meow Meow Meow. Meow meow meow meow meow meow. Meow meow meow meow meow meow meow meow meow meow meow meow meow meow. Meow meow meow meow meow meow’meow meow meow meow meow meow meow meow meow meow meow meow meow meow meow, meow meow meow meow meow meow meow meow, “meow, meow meow meow, meow meow meow meow meow meow meow meow, meow, meow, meow, meow meow... meow meow meow.” Meow meow meow Meow Meow meow meow meow meow meow meow meow, Meow meow meow meow meow meow meow meow. Meow Meow Meow’meow meow meow meow meow meow meow “meow meow meow

meow," meow meow meow meow meow meow meow meow meow meow meow meow meow meow; meow meow meow meow meow meow meow meow, meow meow meow meow—meow, Meow, meow meow meow meow meow meow meow meow meow—meow meow meow meow meow meow meow meow meow-meow meow meow meow meow meow meow meow... meow meow meow meow meow meow meow meow meow meow meow meow meow meow meow meow meow meow meow meow meow, "meow meow meow meow meow meow meow meow," meow meow meow. Meow meow meow meow, meow meow meow meow meow meow meow, meow meow, meow meow, meow meow meow meow meow meow, meow Meow Meow meow meow meow meow meow meow. Meow meow meow meow meow meow meow meow meow meow meow meow meow meow.

"Meow'meow meow meow-meow; meow meow meow meow meow!" Meow meow meow meow, meow Meow meow. "Meow'meow meow meow meow meow-meow meow meow meow meow meow meow meow meow."

"Meow'meow meow meow meow meow, Meow Meow," meow Meow, meow meow meow meow meow meow meow meow meow meow meow meow.

"Meow? Meow meow meow?" meow Meow meow meow meow meow Meow meow meow meow meow meow meow. "Meow meow meow meow.... Meow meow meow? Meow meow meow?" meow meow, meow meow meow meow meow meow meow meow meow meow meow. "Meow meow meow?"

"Meow meow meow, meow meow meow," meow Meow, meow meow meow meow meow meow meow meow, meow meow meow meow meow meow meow meow meow meow meow. Meow meow meow meow meow meow meow meow meow.

"Meow meow, Meow meow meow meow," meow meow, meow meow meow meow meow, "meow meow... meow meow meow." "Meow, meow, meow meow meow meow meow. Meow meow meow meow meow meow meow."

Meow meow meow meow meow meow meow meow meow meow meow meow Meow'meow meow, Meow meow meow meow meow meow meow.

"Meow," meow meow, "meow'meow meow meow-meow meow, meow meow meow meow meow, meow'meow meow meow meow, meow Meow meow, meow meow meow meow, meow. Meow meow meow meow, meow meow, meow meow meow meow meow, meow'meow meow meow meow meow meow meow'meow meow meow meow—meow Meow meow meow meow meow meow meow meow meow meow meow meow. Meow'meow meow meow meow meow meow meow Meow meow'meow meow meow meow meow meow meow meow meow meow, meow meow meow meow. Meow—meow meow—meow meow meow meow meow meow meow meow meow meow meow meow meow! Meow meow meow meow meow meow meow meow'meow meow meow meow meow meow... Meow meow meow meow, meow'meow meow meow meow!... Meow meow meow meow meow meow-meow meow meow meow'meow meow meow. (Meow meow Meow'meow meow meow meow meow!) Meow Meow'meow meow meow meow meow.

Meow meow'meow meow meow meow meow meow meow meow meow meow meow.... Meow'meow meow meow meow meow! Meow'meow meow meow meow meow meow meow meow meow, meow...!"

"Meow Meow meow'meow meow!"

"Meow meow meow meow, meow, meow, meow, meow meow meow... meow meow meow'meow meow meow meow meow meow, meow meow! Meow meow meow meow, meow meow meow'meow meow! Meow'meow meow meow... Meow'meow meow meow, Meow'meow meow meow...."

Meow meow meow meow meow meow.

"Meow, meow meow meow! Meow meow meow Meow meow meow meow meow?"

"Meow meow'meow meow meow meow, Meow meow meow. Meow meow meow meow meow meow meow, meow meow meow meow meow meow meow meow meow. Meow'meow meow meow, meow; meow meow meow meow meow. Meow meow meow meow'meow meow meow. Meow meow meow meow, meow meow meow, Meow meow meow meow. Meow meow meow meow meow, meow meow Meow meow: 'Meow meow meow meow.' Meow meow meow meow meow—meow meow, meow meow meow meow meow meow; Meow meow'meow meow meow meow, meow meow, meow Meow.... Meow meow meow, meow meow'meow meow meow!"

"Meow meow meow meow meow meow meow? Meow meow? Meow meow meow meow, meow?"

"Meow, meow, meow meow meow meow meow! Meow meow meow meow meow meow meow meow.... Meow meow meow...."

"Meow meow, meow meow!"

"Meow Meow meow'meow meow meow meow meow!"

"Meow meow'meow meow?"

"Meow, Meow meow'meow, meow'meow meow meow meow! Meow'meow meow meow meow meow meow, meow." "Meow meow meow meow meow meow?"

"Meow meow'meow meow meow; meow Meow meow meow meow meow meow meow. Meow meow meow'meow meow meow meow meow meow'meow meow meow Meow, meow meow meow meow meow meow meow, meow.... Meow meow'meow meow meow meow, meow... meow meow, meow meow meow meow meow, meow meow meow meow meow... meow meow meow meow meow meow; meow meow meow, Meow'meow meow meow, Meow'meow meow meow, meow'meow meow meow meow meow meow meow. Meow meow meow meow meow meow meow meow meow meow meow meow. Meow meow meow meow meow meow meow meow meow meow meow meow meow Meow Meow meow Meow (meow meow meow meow meow meow)— meow meow meow meow meow! Meow meow meow'meow meow meow meow—meow'meow meow meow meow—meow meow meow meow meow meow meow'meow meow meow meow—meow'meow meow. Meow'meow meow meow; meow'meow meow meow meow, meow meow meow, meow, meow meow, meow. Meow meow meow meow meow meow meow, meow meow'meow meow."

"Meow meow meow Meow meow meow meow?"

"Meow, Meow meow'meow meow meow meow! Meow meow, meow meow meow meow meow meow! Meow meow meow meow meow meow meow!... Meow'meow meow meow meow meow meow meow! Meow meow meow meow meow meow'meow meow meow meow? Meow'meow meow meow-meow meow meow, meow—meow! meow meow meow meow! Meow'meow meow meow meow—meow meow meow meow meow meow meow meow, meow meow, meow meow meow, meow meow meow meow meow, meow meow meow meow meow meow meow meow meow meow, meow meow meow meow, meow meow meow-meow, meow meow meow meow, meow meow meow meow meow meow, meow meow meow meow meow meow—meow meow meow meow meow meow meow, meow meow meow'meow meow—meow meow meow meow meow meow! Meow, meow meow, meow, meow meow Meow'meow meow, meow'meow meow! Meow. Meow meow meow meow meow meow; meow Meow'meow meow meow meow meow meow meow. Meow meow'meow meow meow, meow'meow meow meow. Meow'meow meow meow meow, meow meow meow meow, meow meow meow meow meow meow, meow. Meow meow meow meow meow— meow meow meow—meow meow meow meow. Meow meow meow'meow meow...."

MEOW II

Meow meow meow meow meow meow meow meow'meow, meow meow meow. Meow meow meow meow meow meow meow meow meow-meow meow. Meow meow meow meow meow meow meow meow meow meow meow meow meow. Meow meow meow meow meow meow meow meow meow meow meow meow meow meow meow meow meow meow meow, meow meow meow meow meow meow meow meow meow meow meow meow. Meow meow meow meow meow meow meow meow meow meow meow meow meow meow meow meow meow meow—meow meow meow meow meow meow meow meow meow, meow meow meow meow meow meow meow meow meow meow meow meow meow meow meow meow meow meow "meow meow meow."

Meow meow meow meow meow meow meow meow meow meow meow meow meow meow meow "meow meow meow," meow meow meow meow meow meow meow, meow meow meow meow meow meow meow meow meow meow'meow meow meow meow meow meow meow meow meow meow, meow meow meow meow meow meow meow meow meow meow meow meow meow meow meow meow. Meow meow meow meow meow meow meow meow meow meow meow meow meow meow? Meow meow meow meow meow meow? Meow meow meow meow meow meow meow meow Meow Meow meow meow meow meow meow meow meow meow? Meow meow meow meow meow meow meow. Meow meow? Meow meow meow meow meow meow meow meow meow meow meow meow? Meow meow meow meow meow... Meow! meow meow meow meow meow! Meow meow meow meow meow meow meow meow meow? Meow meow meow meow meow meow meow meow! Meow meow meow meow, meow meow meow meow meow meow meow, "meow meow, meow meow meow meow meow meow meow meow meow"! Meow meow meow meow meow meow meow meow meow meow, Meow? Meow meow meow meow meow meow meow—meow, meow meow meow meow meow meow meow? Meow meow meow meow meow meow meow meow meow meow meow? Meow meow meow meow meow meow meow meow meow meow meow meow meow meow meow meow meow meow meow meow meow meow meow meow meow meow meow meow meow meow meow meow meow meow meow Meow Meow... meow meow meow meow. Meow meow meow meow meow meow meow meow meow meow, meow meow meow meow meow meow meow meow meow meow.

"Meow meow," meow meow meow meow meow meow meow meow meow meow meow meow-meow, "meow meow, meow meow meow meow meow meow meow meow meow meow meow... meow meow meow'meow meow meow meow meow meow meow, meow Meow meow meow meow meow meow meow meow meow meow meow... meow meow, meow... meow meow meow meow, meow meow meow... meow meow meow meow meow!"

Meow meow meow meow meow meow meow meow meow meow meow meow meow. Meow meow'meow meow meow—meow meow meow meow, meow meow meow'meow meow meow meow meow. "Meow meow meow

meow meow meow meow meow meow meow meow." Meow meow meow meow meow meow meow meow meow meow meow meow meow meow; meow meow meow meow meow meow meow meow meow meow, meow meow meow meow meow meow meow meow meow meow meow meow meow meow meow. Meow meow meow meow meow. Meow meow meow meow meow; meow meow meow meow meow meow meow.

Meow meow meow meow meow—meow meow meow meow meow Meow—meow meow meow meow, meow meow meow meow meow meow. Meow meow meow meow meow meow meow meow meow meow meow meow meow meow (Meow Meow meow meow meow meow meow meow meow meow meow meow meow), meow meow meow meow meow meow meow meow. "Meow meow meow meow meow meow! Meow meow meow meow meow Meow meow meow meow meow...? Meow meow meow meow meow! Meow meow meow meow!"

"Meow... meow meow meow meow meow meow meow meow meow, meow meow, meow meow meow meow meow meow meow; meow... meow meow meow meow meow meow meow meow meow meow meow meow meow meow meow... meow meow meow meow meow meow meow meow meow? Meow meow meow meow meow meow meow meow meow meow... meow meow meow meow (meow meow) meow, meow, meow meow meow meow... meow meow meow, meow meow.... Meow meow meow meow meow meow; meow... meow meow meow meow meow meow Meow Meow! Meow meow! Meow meow meow! Meow, meow'meow meow meow meow meow meow meow meow, meow, meow meow meow meow meow meow meow'meow meow! Meow'meow meow meow!"

Meow meow meow meow meow meow meow Meow, meow meow meow meow meow meow Meow Meow'meow meow, meow meow.

Meow meow meow meow meow meow meow meow meow meow meow meow meow meow meow. Meow meow meow meow Meow meow meow meow meow meow. Meow meow meow meow meow meow'meow meow meow meow meow meow meow meow meow meow meow.

"Meow meow meow meow meow meow," meow meow. "Meow meow meow! Meow meow meow'meow meow meow'meow meow, meow meow meow meow meow meow? Meow meow meow meow meow meow meow meow, meow meow meow meow meow meow?"

"Meow meow meow, Meow meow," meow Meow, meow meow meow meow meow meow, "meow meow meow meow meow meow meow, meow meow. Meow'meow meow meow. Meow, meow meow meow, meow meow meow meow meow meow meow Meow."

"Meow Meow meow meow meow meow meow; Meow meow meow meow meow meow; Meow'meow meow meow meow meow meow meow meow."

"Meow meow meow meow," meow Meow, meow. "Meow meow meow meow Meow meow meow meow meow meow meow meow meow... meow meow meow meow... meow meow meow meow meow meow meow meow meow... meow meow meow."

"Meow meow meow meow meow, meow."

"Meow meow meow meow meow! Meow meow meow meow meow meow meow! Meow meow meow meow meow?"

"Meow'meow meow, Meow meow meow, meow meow Meow meow meow meow? Meow, meow, meow meow meow meow meow meow meow meow meow meow meow... meow meow meow meow meow meow meow meow, meow meow, meow meow, meow meow meow meow meow meow; meow meow meow meow meow, meow meow meow, meow, meow meow meow meow meow! Meow meow Meow'meow meow meow meow meow meow meow meow meow meow meow meow meow... meow meow meow meow meow meow! Meow... Meow meow meow meow meow meow meow meow. Meow meow meow meow meow meow meow meow meow meow-meow... meow meow meow meow meow meow meow.... Meow meow meow Meow meow, meow meow Meow'meow meow meow meow meow meow meow meow, meow meow meow. Meow, Meow meow meow meow meow meow meow meow, meow meow meow meow, meow meow meow meow meow meow meow meow meow, meow meow meow'meow meow meow meow meow meow meow meow meow meow! Meow meow meow meow meow meow, meow meow meow meow, meow meow meow meow meow! Meow meow meow meow meow meow meow meow meow meow, meow meow meow meow meow meow! Meow meow meow meow meow meow-meow meow meow. Meow, meow meow meow!... Meow, meow meow meow, meow Meow meow meow meow meow meow, meow meow... meow meow'meow meow meow meow meow meow meow. Meow meow meow meow meow!"

"Meow meow meow meow meow meow meow? Meow meow meow?"

"Meow Meow."

"Meow meow meow meow?"

"Meow, meow meow meow, meow meow meow meow meow meow, meow meow meow meow? Meow meow meow meow meow meow meow meow meow-meow...."

"Meow'meow meow meow meow meow!" Meow meow meow.

"Meow meow meow meow meow meow meow Meow? Meow meow meow meow meow meow meow'meow meow meow meow meow... meow meow meow'meow meow meow, Meow meow? meow?"

"Meow meow meow meow meow meow meow?" Meow meow meow meow. "Meow meow Meow meow meow meow'meow meow meow? Meow meow meow meow meow meow'meow meow meow...."

"Meow! meow meow meow meow meow meow! Meow meow'meow meow meow meow meow meow meow.... Meow-meow; meow meow Meow Meow meow meow meow meow meow'meow meow. Meow meow meow meow, meow meow meow meow meow meow meow meow meow; meow meow meow meow meow meow'meow, meow meow meow meow meow meow meow meow meow. Meow meow meow meow meow meow meow...."

Meow meow meow'meow meow Meow meow meow meow meow Meow'meow meow. Meow meow meow meow meow meow meow meow meow. Meow meow meow meow meow meow'meow meow meow. Meow meow meow meow meow meow meow, meow meow meow meow meow

meow meow meow meow meow meow. Meow meow meow meow meow meow: Meow Meow meow meow meow meow, meow meow meow meow meow meow meow meow meow meow. Meow meow meow meow Meow Meow, meow meow meow meow meow meow meow meow meow meow meow meow meow meow meow, meow meow meow meow-meow meow (meow meow meow meow meow meow meow meow-meow meow meow meow meow), meow meow meow meow meow meow meow meow meow meow meow meow meow meow meow. Meow meow meow meow meow meow meow, meow meow meow meow meow meow meow meow.

Meow meow meow meow meow meow meow meow Meow meow meow meow meow, Meow Meow meow meow meow meow meow meow meow meow, meow "meow meow meow meow meow meow meow, meow meow meow meow meow meow." Meow meow meow meow meow meow meow meow meow meow meow meow meow meow; meow meow meow meow meow meow meow meow. Meow Meow meow meow meow: meow meow meow meow meow meow meow meow, meow meow meow meow meow meow meow meow meow meow meow meow, meow meow meow meow meow meow meow meow meow meow meow meow meow. Meow meow meow meow meow, meow, meow Meow, meow meow meow meow meow meow meow meow Meow Meow'meow meow, meow meow meow meow meow meow meow meow.

Meow meow meow meow meow meow meow meow, meow meow meow meow meow meow, meow meow meow meow meow meow meow meow meow meow meow meow meow meow meow meow meow meow Meow'meow meow, meow meow meow meow meow meow meow meow. Meow meow, meow, meow meow, meow meow meow meow, meow meow meow meow meow meow meow meow meow meow meow. Meow meow meow meow meow meow, meow, meow meow meow meow meow meow meow meow meow, meow meow meow meow meow meow meow meow meow.

"Meow meow, meow meow! Meow meow meow meow...? Meow meow, Meow meow meow'meow meow meow meow!" Meow Meow meow meow meow.

"Meow Meow."

"Meow meow meow meow, meow meow meow meow, Meow Meow... meow meow meow... meow meow meow meow meow, meow meow, meow meow Meow meow, meow meow meow meow meow meow? Meow meow meow meow meow? Meow meow, meow meow meow, meow meow meow meow meow, meow meow meow, meow meow? Meow meow meow meow meow meow? Meow meow meow, Meow meow meow..."

"Meow, meow, meow meow meow meow meow meow meow meow?" meow Meow.

"Meow meow, Meow meow meow meow meow meow meow meow meow meow meow meow, Meow Meow!"

"Meow," meow Meow. "Meow meow meow meow, meow meow meow meow meow meow meow meow meow meow meow meow meow meow meow, meow meow meow, meow meow meow meow meow meow; meow

meow meow meow' meow meow meow meow meow. Meow meow Meow meow meow meow? Meow meow meow Meow meow meow meow meow meow meow; meow meow meow, meow, meow meow meow, meow meow meow— meow meow meow meow meow meow meow—meow meow meow meow meow meow. Meow meow meow meow meow meow meow meow meow. Meow meow meow meow meow meow meow meow meow meow meow meow meow meow meow meow meow meow meow. Meow, meow, meow meow meow meow meow meow, meow meow meow meow meow meow; meow'meow meow meow meow meow meow meow meow meow. Meow meow meow meow meow! Meow meow meow meow meow meow meow meow meow meow meow, meow meow meow meow meow meow meow meow. Meow meow'meow meow meow meow, meow meow meow meow'meow meow meow, meow meow meow meow meow'meow meow meow meow meow meow meow. Meow meow meow meow meow meow meow meow meow. Meow meow meow meow meow meow meow meow meow meow meow meow meow. Meow meow meow meow meow meow meow meow meow meow meow. Meow, meow meow? Meow meow meow meow meow meow meow meow meow meow meow meow."

"Meow meow meow meow," meow Meow Meow, meow meow Meow'meow meow meow meow Meow.

Meow Meow meow meow meow meow meow meow Meow Meow meow meow. Meow meow meow meow meow meow meow meow meow, meow meow meow meow meow meow meow meow meow meow meow. Meow Meow meow meow meow meow, meow meow, meow meow meow meow meow meow meow meow meow meow meow meow meow meow meow meow meow meow meow, meow meow meow meow meow, meow meow meow meow. Meow meow meow meow meow meow meow meow meow meow meow meow. Meow meow meow meow meow meow meow meow meow meow meow meow meow meow meow meow meow meow meow meow. Meow meow meow meow meow meow meow meow meow meow meow. Meow Meow Meow meow meow meow meow meow, meow meow meow meow meow meow meow meow meow meow, meow meow meow meow meow meow meow meow meow meow meow meow meow meow meow meow meow meow, meow meow meow meow meow meow meow meow meow meow meow meow meow meow meow meow meow, meow meow meow meow, meow meow meow meow meow meow meow meow meow meow meow.

"Meow'meow meow meow meow meow meow meow meow meow meow meow meow'meow meow... meow meow meow meow meow. Meow meow meow. Meow meow meow meow meow meow meow meow meow meow," meow Meow Meow meow meow meow. "Meow meow meow meow meow meow meow meow meow'meow meow," meow meow meow.

"Meow meow'meow meow meow; meow Meow meow meow meow meow, meow..."

"Meow?"

"Meow meow meow meow meow meow meow meow meow," Meow meow meow.

"Meow meow meow meow meow meow meow meow?"

"Meow meow meow, Meow Meow, meow meow meow meow meow meow, meow meow, meow!" meow meow meow meow meow meow meow meow, meow meow meow meow meow meow meow meow meow meow meow meow meow, meow meow meow meow meow meow meow meow meow meow meow meow. Meow Meow meow'meow meow meow meow meow meow meow meow.

"Meow meow meow meow meow meow Meow," Meow Meow meow, meow meow. "Meow meow meow meow meow meow meow meow, Meow. Meow Meow Meow meow meow meow meow meow meow meow meow Meow meow meow meow meow meow, meow meow meow'meow meow, Meow Meow, meow meow meow, meow meow meow, meow meow meow. Meow meow meow meow meow meow meow meow meow meow meow meow meow meow. Meow Meow meow meow meow meow meow meow meow meow meow meow meow meow meow meow meow... Meow, meow meow, meow meow meow meow meow meow meow meow meow meow meow meow meow meow meow meow meow meow meow meow meow meow, meow meow meow meow meow meow meow meow meow—meow meow meow meow—meow meow'meow meow?"

"Meow meow meow meow meow meow?" meow Meow Meow.

"Meow meow meow——" Meow Meow meow meow. "Meow meow meow meow meow meow, meow meow, meow meow, meow meow meow meow meow, meow meow meow meow meow meow meow? Meow, meow meow meow meow meow meow meow. Meow meow meow meow'meow meow meow meow'meow meow meow!"

"Meow meow meow meow meow meow meow meow meow meow meow," Meow meow meow. "Meow Meow meow meow meow meow Meow Meow meow, meow meow meow meow meow meow meow meow. Meow meow Meow meow meow meow meow meow."

"Meow meow meow meow meow?" meow meow meow meow meow meow.

"Meow, meow meow meow. Meow meow meow meow meow meow, meow meow meow meow meow meow meow meow meow'meow meow, meow meow meow meow meow Meow Meow'meow meow. Meow meow, meow, meow meow meow meow meow meow meow, meow meow Meow meow meow meow meow... meow meow meow meow... meow meow. Meow meow meow meow meow meow meow meow meow. Meow meow meow meow meow meow meow meow meow'meow meow meow.... Meow meow meow meow meow meow meow meow'meow meow meow meow meow.... Meow meow'meow meow meow meow meow meow meow meow."

"Meow meow meow meow meow meow meow meow," Meow Meow meow meow.

"Meow meow meow, Meow meow meow meow meow meow. Meow Meow meow'meow meow meow meow meow meow meow meow meow meow meow meow meow—meow meow meow meow meow meow meow," Meow Meow meow. Meow meow meow meow meow meow meow meow meow meow meow meow meow meow Meow, meow meow meow meow meow Meow, meow meow meow meow'meow meow. Meow meow meow

meow meow meow meow meow meow meow meow, meow meow. Meow meow meow meow meow meow, meow meow meow meow meow meow meow meow: meow meow meow Meow meow meow meow Meow Meow, meow meow meow meow meow meow meow meow meow meow meow.

"Meow meow meow meow meow meow meow," meow meow.

"Meow meow meow, meow," Meow Meow meow meow meow meow meow. Meow meow meow meow meow meow meow meow Meow meow meow meow meow meow meow meow meow meow meow meow Meow Meow. Meow Meow, meow, meow meow meow meow.

"Meow meow meow meow meow meow Meow Meow?" Meow Meow meow meow meow meow.

"Meow meow meow meow meow meow meow meow meow'meow meow meow," Meow meow meow meow meow meow, "meow Meow meow'meow meow meow meow meow meow meow, meow meow... meow meow Meow Meow meow meow meow meow meow meow meow meow meow meow meow. Meow Meow meow meow meow meow meow meow meow, meow meow meow Meow meow meow meow meow... meow meow; meow, meow, meow, Meow meow meow meow meow... meow meow meow Meow meow meow meow meow."

Meow meow meow meow meow. Meow Meow meow, meow meow meow meow meow meow. Meow meow meow meow meow meow meow meow meow meow meow meow meow meow Meow.

Meow meow meow Meow Meow meow meow meow meow meow meow meow. Meow meow, meow meow meow meow meow meow meow, meow meow meow meow meow meow meow meow meow meow.

"Meow meow, Meow Meow," meow meow. "Meow'meow meow meow meow meow Meow Meow, Meow?"

"Meow meow, meow," meow Meow Meow meow.

"Meow meow meow meow meow," meow meow meow meow, meow meow meow meow meow meow meow meow meow meow meow meow meow meow. "Meow meow meow meow meow meow meow meow meow Meow Meow meow meow meow meow meow meow meow meow. Meow meow meow meow meow meow meow meow, meow meow; meow meow meow meow meow meow meow meow meow meow meow meow meow meow meow meow meow meow meow meow meow; meow meow meow meow meow meow meow meow meow meow meow meow meow. Meow meow meow meow meow meow meow meow. Meow'meow meow meow meow meow; meow meow meow meow meow meow meow meow meow meow meow... meow meow meow meow meow meow meow, meow... meow meow meow meow meow, Meow Meow! Meow meow Meow'meow meow meow meow meow meow meow meow meow meow meow meow meow meow meow. Meow, Meow meow meow meow, meow meow meow meow meow, meow Meow meow meow'meow meow meow meow meow meow meow Meow... Meow'meow meow meow meow meow meow."

Meow meow meow meow meow meow meow meow meow meow meow meow meow meow:

"Meow Meow, Meow Meow, Meow meow meow meow meow meow meow meow meow meow meow meow Meow meow meow meow meow meow meow meow meow meow meow; Meow meow meow meow meow meow meow meow meow meow meow meow. Meow meow meow meow meow meow meow meow meow meow meow meow meow meow meow-meow meow meow meow meow meow Meow meow meow meow meow meow meow, meow meow meow Meow meow meow meow meow meow meow meow meow meow meow meow meow meow, meow Meow Meow meow meow. Meow meow meow meow meow meow meow meow meow meow meow meow meow meow meow meow meow meow meow meow-meow meow meow meow meow'meow meow, meow meow Meow meow meow meow meow meow meow, Meow meow meow, meow meow meow Meow Meow meow meow meow meow meow meow meow—meow meow meow meow meow meow meow meow meow meow meow meow meow meow meow meow meow meow meow meow meow meow, meow, meow, meow Meow meow meow meow meow meow meow meow meow meow meow meow meow meow, meow meow meow meow Meow meow meow meow meow meow meow. Meow meow meow meow meow meow meow, meow meow, meow meow, meow meow meow meow meow, Meow meow Meow Meow, Meow meow meow meow meow meow meow meow meow meow meow meow meow meow meow. Meow meow meow meow meow meow Meow Meow meow meow meow meow meow meow meow, meow meow meow meow meow meow meow, meow meow meow meow meow meow, meow meow meow meow. Meow meow meow meow meow meow meow meow meow meow meow meow meow meow meow meow meow meow meow meow meow meow meow meow meow meow meow meow meow meow, meow meow meow, meow meow meow meow meow meow, meow meow meow-meow meow meow meow meow meow meow meow, meow meow meow meow meow meow meow meow meow meow meow meow meow meow. Meow meow meow meow meow meow meow meow meow, Meow Meow, Meow meow meow meow meow meow meow meow meow meow meow meow meow.

"Meow. Meow."

"Meow meow Meow meow meow meow, Meow Meow?" meow Meow Meow, meow meow. "Meow meow Meow meow Meow meow meow meow? Meow meow meow meow meow meow meow Meow Meow meow meow meow meow meow meow meow meow Meow! Meow meow meow meow meow meow meow meow, meow... meow meow meow meow?"

"Meow meow Meow Meow'meow meow," Meow meow meow meow meow.

"Meow, meow meow! Meow meow... meow meow meow meow meow, meow meow'meow meow meow meow! Meow meow meow meow meow meow, meow meow, meow meow meow meow meow meow, meow meow meow'meow meow meow meow Meow meow meow meow meow meow meow meow meow meow meow'meow meow meow meow meow meow.... Meow meow'meow meow meow meow meow meow meow meow, meow meow meow meow meow meow meow meow meow meow meow

meow... meow meow meow meow meow.... Meow Meow meow'meow meow meow meow meow meow meow meow meow meow, meow meow meow meow meow meow meow meow meow meow meow... meow..."

"Meow meow meow meow meow, meow," meow meow Meow Meow.

"Meow meow meow meow meow," Meow meow meow, "meow meow meow meow meow meow meow meow meow meow meow meow meow, meow meow meow meow meow meow meow.... Meow! Meow meow meow meow, meow meow meow meow meow meow meow, meow meow meow meow meow meow meow, meow Meow meow'meow meow meow meow.... Meow meow meow, Meow meow..."

"Meow meow meow, meow, meow meow meow meow meow meow meow meow meow meow meow Meow meow meow meow meow meow meow meow meow'meow meow meow meow. Meow, meow'meow meow meow—meow meow, meow'meow meow meow," meow meow meow meow meow meow meow meow meow meow meow meow meow meow meow meow meow Meow meow, meow meow meow meow meow meow meow meow meow meow meow meow. "Meow meow meow meow meow," meow Meow.

"Meow meow meow, Meow, meow meow meow," meow meow meow meow meow meow.

"Meow meow meow meow meow meow meow meow meow meow, meow meow meow meow meow. Meow meow!"

Meow meow meow meow meow meow meow meow meow meow meow meow meow; Meow, meow, meow meow meow meow.

Meow meow, meow Meow meow, meow meow meow meow meow meow meow meow meow, meow meow meow meow meow meow meow meow meow meow meow meow meow meow, meow meow meow meow meow meow meow meow meow meow meow meow meow.

Meow meow meow meow Meow meow meow meow meow meow meow.

"Meow meow meow meow meow meow meow meow," meow meow, "meow meow meow meow meow meow meow meow meow meow meow meow meow meow meow meow meow meow meow."

"Meow Meow!" meow Meow Meow, "meow meow Meow meow meow Meow meow meow meow meow meow meow, meow meow, meow Meow! Meow meow meow, Meow Meow," meow meow, meow meow meow meow.

"Meow'meow meow meow, meow," meow Meow, meow meow, "meow meow meow meow meow."

"Meow, meow, Meow meow meow meow meow, meow Meow meow'meow meow meow meow," meow meow meow meow. Meow meow meow meow meow meow.

"Meow meow meow, Meow, meow Meow meow meow meow meow meow Meow meow meow Meow Meow... meow meow meow meow meow... meow meow meow meow meow, meow meow meow, meow meow meow meow meow meow, meow meow meow meow meow meow meow meow meow.... Meow meow meow meow meow? Meow, meow meow! Meow meow'meow meow, Meow Meow, meow Meow Meow'meow meow!"

"Meow, Meow meow'meow meow; meow meow Meow Meow?"

"Meow meow meow; meow meow meow..."

"Meow, meow," meow meow Meow. "Meow meow'meow meow meow Meow Meow meow."

"Meow, meow meow'meow meow? Meow Meow meow meow meow meow meow meow meow meow. Meow meow, Meow Meow, Meow meow'meow meow meow Meow meow meow meow meow meow meow meow. Meow meow meow meow meow meow meow meow meow meow, meow meow Meow meow meow meow meow meow meow meow meow meow meow. Meow meow meow meow meow meow meow.... Meow'meow meow meow meow meow meow meow meow. Meow meow, meow'meow meow meow meow meow meow meow? Meow meow meow meow?"

"Meow, Meow meow meow," meow Meow meow.

"Meow meow meow meow meow meow meow meow, meow meow Meow meow meow meow meow.... Meow, meow meow, meow meow meow meow meow meow! Meow meow meow meow meow meow? Meow meow meow, meow meow, meow meow meow meow? Meow, meow meow meow meow meow meow meow meow meow meow, meow meow Meow meow meow meow meow meow... meow? Meow meow meow, Meow Meow, meow meow Meow meow meow meow? Meow meow meow meow, meow meow."

"Meow'meow meow meow meow meow meow meow meow meow meow meow meow; meow'meow meow meow meow meow meow meow meow; meow meow'meow meow meow."

"Meow, Meow Meow, meow meow meow meow meow meow meow meow! Meow meow meow meow meow.... Meow meow meow meow!"

"Meow, meow meow meow meow, meow'meow meow meow, meow," meow Meow meow meow, meow meow meow meow meow meow: "Meow meow meow meow meow meow meow meow, meow meow meow meow meow meow."

"Meow, Meow'meow meow meow meow meow meow meow meow meow meow."

Meow meow meow meow Meow, meow meow meow meow, meow meow meow meow meow meow'meow meow meow meow meow meow, meow meow meow meow meow meow meow meow meow meow meow meow meow meow meow meow meow meow meow meow meow meow meow.

Meow meow meow meow, meow meow meow meow meow meow meow meow meow meow Meow Meow meow meow meow.

MEOW III

"Meow meow meow, meow meow!" Meow meow meow meow meow meow.

Meow meow meow meow meow meow meow meow meow meow meow meow meow meow meow meow, meow meow meow. Meow meow meow meow meow meow meow, meow meow meow meow meow meow meow, meow meow meow meow meow meow meow meow meow. Meow meow meow meow meow, meow Meow meow meow meow meow meow meow meow meow meow meow.

Meow meow meow meow meow, meow meow meow meow meow meow meow meow, meow meow meow meow meow, meow, meow meow. Meow meow meow meow meow meow meow meow meow meow meow meow meow meow meow. Meow meow meow meow, meow meow meow, meow meow meow. Meow meow meow meow meow, meow meow meow meow meow, meow meow meow meow meow meow meow meow.

Meow meow meow meow meow meow meow meow meow meow meow meow meow meow meow meow meow meow meow meow meow meow meow meow meow meow meow meow meow meow. Meow meow, meow meow meow meow meow meow meow meow meow meow meow meow meow, meow meow meow meow meow meow meow meow meow meow meow meow, meow meow meow meow meow meow. Meow meow meow meow meow, meow meow meow meow meow meow, meow Meow, meow meow meow meow meow meow meow meow meow meow meow meow meow meow meow meow, meow meow meow meow meow meow meow meow meow meow meow meow meow meow, meow meow meow meow meow, meow meow meow meow meow meow meow meow meow meow meow. Meow meow meow meow meow meow meow meow meow meow meow meow meow meow meow meow meow meow meow meow meow meow. Meow meow meow meow meow meow meow meow meow meow meow meow meow meow meow meow meow meow meow meow meow meow meow meow, meow meow meow, meow meow meow meow meow meow meow meow.

"Meow, Meow meow meow meow meow Meow meow meow meow," meow Meow, meow meow meow meow meow meow meow meow meow meow meow Meow Meow meow meow meow. "Meow Meow meow'meow meow

meow meow Meow meow meow," meow meow, meow Meow, meow meow meow meow meow meow meow.

"Meow, meow, Meow meow meow meow meow meow meow-meow," meow Meow, meow meow meow meow meow' meow, meow meow meow meow meow meow meow meow meow meow meow meow meow meow meow. "Meow meow meow meow meow meow, meow meow meow meow meow meow, meow meow meow meow meow, meow meow, meow meow meow meow meow meow meow, meow meow... meow meow meow meow. Meow meow meow meow meow meow meow meow.... meow? Meow, meow, meow meow meow meow meow meow meow meow?" meow meow, meow meow meow meow, meow meow meow meow meow meow meow.

"Meow meow meow meow," meow Meow meow.

"Meow meow meow, meow," meow Meow meow meow, "meow meow meow meow meow meow meow meow. Meow meow meow meow meow meow meow, Meow meow meow meow meow meow meow meow meow meow meow meow meow meow meow, meow meow meow, meow meow meow meow meow meow meow meow: meow meow meow meow meow meow meow, meow meow, meow meow meow meow meow meow meow. Meow meow meow Meow meow'meow meow, meow meow meow meow meow meow meow. Meow meow meow meow, meow meow meow meow meow, meow meow. Meow meow meow meow meow meow meow meow meow meow meow meow meow meow. Meow meow meow meow meow meow meow, meow meow, meow meow meow meow meow meow meow meow meow, Meow meow, meow meow meow."

"Meow, meow; meow meow meow meow.... Meow meow meow meow meow meow meow meow meow: meow meow meow meow meow meow...."

Meow, meow meow meow meow meow meow meow meow meow meow meow meow meow meow, meow meow meow meow, meow, meow meow meow meow, meow meow meow meow meow meow meow. Meow meow meow meow, meow. Meow Meow meow meow meow meow Meow, meow meow meow meow meow meow meow meow meow meow.

"Meow! meow meow meow meow meow?" Meow meow, meow meow meow. "Meow meow meow meow meow meow meow meow meow."

"Meow, Meow, meow meow meow meow meow meow'meow. Meow meow Meow meow meow meow meow meow meow meow meow."

"Meow meow'meow meow meow meow meow meow meow," Meow meow meow, meow meow meow meow meow. "Meow meow meow meow meow meow—meow meow meow meow meow meow (meow meow meow Meow)—Meow meow meow'meow meow meow Meow meow meow meow meow meow meow meow meow meow! Meow meow meow'meow meow meow... meow... meow... meow meow meow meow, meow, meow Meow meow'meow meow meow. Meow meow meow meow meow."

"Meow'meow meow meow." Meow meow meow meow meow. "Meow meow meow meow meow meow meow—meow—meow meow meow meow meow meow meow meow meow meow meow meow meow meow meow meow, meow meow meow meow meow meow meow meow. Meow, meow meow, Meow meow meow meow meow meow."

"Meow meow meow meow meow," meow Meow, meow meow Meow, "meow meow meow meow meow meow meow meow meow meow meow meow."

"Meow meow meow meow meow! Meow, meow meow meow meow meow meow meow-meow, meow meow?" meow Meow.

Meow meow meow meow meow meow meow meow meow meow meow meow meow meow meow meow meow meow meow, meow meow meow meow meow meow. Meow Meow Meow meow meow. Meow meow meow meow meow meow meow meow.

"Meow meow meow, meow, Meow meow'meow meow meow meow," meow meow meow, meow meow meow meow meow meow meow meow.

"Meow meow meow meow-meow meow Meow meow meow meow meow meow meow meow meow meow meow meow meow meow meow meow, meow meow meow meow meow meow."

Meow meow meow meow meow, meow meow meow meow meow meow meow meow meow, meow meow meow meow. Meow meow meow meow meow meow meow meow meow meow meow meow. Meow meow meow meow meow, meow meow meow meow meow, meow meow meow. Meow meow meow meow meow meow meow meow meow meow meow meow meow meow meow. Meow meow'meow meow meow meow meow meow meow meow meow meow meow meow meow meow meow. "Meow, meow meow meow Meow meow meow meow," Meow, meow meow meow, meow meow meow, meow meow meow meow meow meow meow. "Meow meow meow meow."

"Meow meow meow meow meow meow meow," meow meow meow meow meow meow. "Meow meow meow meow meow, meow meow meow, meow meow meow meow meow meow meow meow meow meow meow meow meow—meow meow meow meow meow meow meow meow meow meow meow meow meow meow meow meow.... Meow meow meow meow meow meow, meow meow meow meow meow meow meow!... Meow meow meow meow meow meow Meow.... Meow, meow meow, meow meow meow—meow meow meow'meow meow!... Meow, meow meow meow meow Meow Meow'meow meow, meow meow meow! Meow meow meow meow meow meow meow meow... meow meow meow—meow Meow meow meow.... Meow, meow, meow'meow meow meow! Meow'meow meow meow, meow Meow'meow meow! Meow, meow meow Meow meow meow?..."

"Meow, Meow, meow meow'meow meow," meow meow meow, meow meow meow meow meow meow meow meow, "meow meow Meow meow Meow meow meow! Meow meow meow'meow meow meow meow meow meow meow meow meow meow meow meow—Meow meow meow meow. Meow, meow meow meow meow meow meow meow meow meow meow meow meow meow meow—meow, meow meow meow! Meow meow, Meow!... Meow meow meow meow meow meow meow meow meow meow meow meow meow meow meow meow meow meow meow meow meow meow meow, meow meow meow meow meow meow meow meow meow. Meow meow'meow meow meow meow meow! Meow meow'meow meow meow meow meow meow meow meow Meow Meow, meow meow meow meow meow'meow—meow meow'meow meow meow, Meow—meow meow meow meow meow meow meow meow meow meow meow meow meow meow meow meow meow meow meow-meow meow meow meow'meow meow meow meow meow meow meow. Meow meow, meow meow meow. Meow meow meow meow meow meow meow meow meow Meow Meow meow meow meow meow meow.... Meow meow meow meow, meow meow," meow meow meow meow meow meow, meow, meow meow meow meow meow meow meow meow meow Meow Meow, meow "meow meow meow meow meow."

"Meow, meow.... Meow meow meow'meow meow meow...." Meow meow meow meow, meow meow meow meow meow meow meow meow meow Meow meow meow meow meow meow.

"Meow meow meow meow Meow meow meow meow?" Meow meow meow meow meow meow. "Meow, meow; meow, meow meow meow, Meow, meow meow'meow meow meow Meow meow'meow meow meow meow meow meow meow meow-meow meow meow meow meow meow meow meow meow."

"Meow meow meow meow, Meow?" meow Meow Meow. Meow, meow, meow meow.

"Meow meow meow meow meow meow meow?" Meow meow. "Meow meow meow meow meow meow meow meow meow meow meow meow meow meow meow meow meow meow?"

"Meow'meow meow meow meow meow, meow meow meow meow meow meow, meow meow meow meow meow meow meow; Meow meow meow meow meow meow... Meow... meow meow meow meow meow... Meow'meow meow meow meow."

"Meow! Meow meow?" Meow Meow meow meow meow.

"Meow, meow—meow'meow meow meow. Meow meow meow Meow meow meow meow meow, meow meow, Meow meow meow meow meow meow meow meow meow meow... meow meow..."

"Meow? Meow meow meow meow!" Meow meow.

"Meow'meow meow," Meow meow meow meow meow. "Meow meow meow meow meow meow meow meow, meow meow—meow Meow meow meow meow meow meow meow meow meow, Meow meow'meow meow meow meow."

"Meow meow meow," meow Meow, "meow meow meow meow meow meow meow meow meow meow meow, meow meow meow meow meow meow meow meow meow meow meow meow meow meow—meow'meow meow meow meow."

"Meow meow'meow meow meow meow meow meow meow meow meow meow meow meow meow," meow Meow.

"Meow, meow meow meow meow meow meow meow meow meow meow," meow Meow, meow meow meow Meow.

"Meow meow meow meow meow meow meow," meow meow meow. "Meow meow meow meow meow meow meow meow meow meow meow, meow meow meow meow meow meow meow meow meow meow meow, meow meow meow meow meow meow. Meow meow meow, meow meow meow, meow meow. Meow meow— meow meow meow meow—meow meow meow meow meow meow meow."

Meow meow meow "meow," meow meow meow Meow meow meow meow meow meow meow meow, meow meow.

Meow meow meow meow meow meow meow, meow meow meow meow meow meow meow meow meow meow meow. Meow meow meow meow meow meow.

"Meow, meow meow meow meow meow meow meow meow? Meow meow meow!" Meow meow meow.

“Meow?” Meow meow meow meow meow. “Meow... Meow meow meow meow meow meow meow meow meow meow meow meow. Meow meow meow, meow, Meow meow meow meow meow meow. Meow meow meow meow meow meow meow. Meow meow meow meow meow meow meow meow meow... meow meow meow meow meow meow. Meow’meow meow meow meow, meow meow, meow meow meow... meow meow meow, meow... meow meow meow meow... meow’meow meow meow, meow... meow meow’meow meow meow meow meow meow meow’meow meow meow. Meow Meow meow meow meow meow meow meow Meow meow, meow meow Meow meow meow meow meow meow meow meow. Meow meow meow meow meow meow meow meow meow meow meow, meow meow Meow, meow, meow meow meow’meow meow meow.” Meow meow, “Meow’meow meow, meow’meow meow, Meow?”

“Meow, meow’meow meow,” meow Meow meow.

“Meow! meow, meow, meow meow,” meow meow, meow meow meow meow meow meow, meow meow meow. “Meow meow meow meow meow meow.... Meow, meow’meow meow, meow meow’meow meow meow meow... meow meow meow meow meow meow meow meow’meow meow, meow meow meow meow... meow meow meow meow meow, meow meow meow meow meow meow.... Meow meow meow’meow meow,” meow meow meow, meow meow meow meow meow. “Meow meow meow meow meow meow Meow meow meow meow, meow,” meow meow, meow meow meow.

“Meow’meow meow, Meow, Meow meow meow meow meow meow meow meow meow meow,” meow meow meow, meow.

“Meow’meow meow meow meow,” meow meow, meow meow meow meow meow meow.

Meow meow meow. Meow meow meow meow meow meow meow meow meow, meow meow meow meow, meow meow meow meow, meow meow meow meow, meow meow meow meow meow.

“Meow meow meow meow meow meow meow meow meow,” Meow meow meow meow meow, meow meow meow meow meow meow meow. Meow Meow meow meow meow meow meow meow meow meow meow meow.

“Meow meow meow meow Meow meow meow meow meow meow meow,” meow meow meow meow.

“Meow meow meow, Meow, Meow Meow meow meow,” Meow Meow meow meow meow.

“Meow Meow Meow?”

“Meow, meow meow meow—Meow Meow Meow. Meow meow meow meow meow meow meow.”

“Meow-meow-meow! Meow, Meow meow.... Meow meow’meow meow! Meow, meow?” meow meow meow meow, meow meow meow meow. “Meow meow meow meow meow?”

“Meow meow, meow meow,” Meow Meow meow meow, meow meow meow meow. “Meow meow meow meow Meow meow meow meow meow meow! Meow meow meow meow, meow meow meow meow meow meow

meow meow meow meow meow meow. Meow meow meow meow meow meow."

"Meow, meow meow meow meow meow meow?" meow meow, meow meow meow.

"Meow meow meow. Meow meow meow meow. Meow meow, meow meow meow meow meow, meow meow. Meow meow, meow meow meow meow meow meow meow meow meow meow meow meow meow, meow meow meow meow, meow meow meow. Meow meow meow meow meow meow meow meow meow meow."

"Meow meow meow meow meow meow meow meow meow meow meow meow meow meow meow? Meow meow meow meow meow meow, Meow?"

"Meow, meow, meow'meow meow meow meow! Meow meow meow meow meow meow!" Meow meow, meow meow meow meow, meow meow meow, meow meow meow meow.

"Meow meow meow meow meow meow," Meow Meow meow meow meow. "Meow meow meow meow meow meow meow meow meow meow meow meow meow meow meow meow meow meow. Meow meow meow meow meow meow meow meow meow meow meow. Meow meow meow meow meow meow, Meow meow meow...."

"Meow meow meow?"

"Meow meow meow meow... meow; meow meow meow meow, meow meow meow meow meow meow meow meow, meow meow meow meow meow-meow.... Meow meow, meow meow meow meow meow meow meow. Meow meow meow meow meow meow, meow meow meow meow meow meow meow meow meow meow, meow meow meow meow meow meow meow meow meow meow meow meow meow meow meow!"

"Meow meow meow meow," meow Meow.

"Meow meow meow meow meow meow?"

"Meow meow meow meow!" meow meow Meow.

"Meow'meow! Meow Meow meow'meow meow meow meow meow meow meow meow meow meow, meow," meow Meow meow, meow meow meow meow meow meow meow.

"Meow, meow meow, Meow meow'meow meow meow meow meow meow," meow meow Meow Meow. "Meow, meow meow meow meow meow meow?" meow meow, meow meow meow meow.

"Meow'meow meow meow," meow Meow, meow meow meow meow meow meow meow. "Meow meow meow meow meow meow meow meow meow meow meow meow."

Meow meow meow, meow meow meow meow.

"Meow, meow meow meow meow, Meow! Meow'meow meow meow, meow, Meow.... Meow meow meow meow meow, Meow?" Meow Meow meow, meow—"Meow meow, meow meow, Meow meow meow meow meow meow, meow meow meow, meow meow meow meow, meow meow meow meow meow meow meow.... Meow Meow meow meow meow, Meow meow meow meow meow meow! Meow meow meow Meow meow? Meow meow meow meow.... Meow meow meow, Meow.... Meow meow meow meow—meow meow meow meow, Meow...."

"Meow, meow," meow meow meow meow, meow meow meow meow, meow meow meow meow. "Meow meow meow meow meow meow meow meow meow!"

Meow meow meow meow, meow meow meow meow meow meow meow meow meow. Meow meow meow meow meow meow meow meow meow meow meow meow meow meow meow. Meow meow meow meow meow meow meow meow meow meow meow meow meow meow meow meow—meow meow meow meow meow meow meow meow meow meow meow meow—meow meow meow meow meow meow meow meow meow meow meow meow meow. Meow meow meow meow meow meow meow meow meow meow meow meow meow meow. Meow meow meow meow meow meow, meow meow meow meow meow meow meow meow meow.

"Meow meow meow meow?" meow Meow, meow meow meow meow meow.

Meow meow meow meow, meow meow meow meow meow, meow meow. Meow meow meow meow meow meow meow meow.

"Meow meow meow meow meow meow meow meow?" meow meow, meow meow meow meow. "Meow meow meow! Meow'meow meow meow meow meow meow meow? Meow, meow meow. Meow meow meow.... Meow meow meow meow meow meow meow.... Meow, meow!"

"Meow Meow; Meow meow meow meow meow meow meow meow meow meow meow," meow Meow Meow, meow meow.

"Meow meow meow meow, Meow?" meow Meow Meow, meow.

"Meow, meow! Meow meow meow," meow meow, meow meow meow.

"Meow, meow meow meow meow; meow'meow meow meow!... Meow meow meow meow meow..." meow Meow, meow meow meow meow meow. "Meow meow meow meow meow meow meow meow. Meow meow meow meow meow meow... meow Meow meow..." Meow meow meow meow, meow meow meow.

"Meow meow meow meow!" meow Meow Meow.

"Meow, meow, meow, meow-meow, meow," Meow meow, meow meow meow meow meow, meow meow meow meow meow meow meow meow meow. "Meow meow'meow meow meow Meow meow meow meow meow meow.... Meow meow Meow meow meow meow meow— —... Meow meow meow meow meow meow, meow," meow meow meow Meow. "Meow meow meow meow, Meow?" meow meow meow; meow meow, meow meow meow meow, meow.

"Meow meow," meow Meow.

"Meow!—meow meow meow meow meow!" Meow meow, meow meow meow meow, meow meow meow meow meow meow meow. Meow Meow meow meow, meow Meow meow meow.

"Meow meow meow meow meow?"

"Meow meow meow."

"Meow meow meow meow meow. Meow. Meow meow meow, meow meow meow. Meow'meow meow. Meow'meow meow meow? Meow meow meow meow'meow? Meow meow meow meow meow meow meow, Meow.

Meow meow meow meow meow meow meow? Meow meow meow meow meow."

"Meow meow meow meow meow Meow Meow," meow Meow. "Meow meow meow meow meow!" meow Meow Meow. "Meow-meow! Meow meow meow meow! Meow meow meow meow'meow."

"Meow meow meow meow," meow Meow.

"Meow meow meow meow meow meow meow meow meow," meow Meow, meow meow meow meow. "Meow meow meow meow Meow'meow meow," meow Meow.

"Meow, meow meow meow meow Meow meow meow meow."

"Meow-meow! Meow meow meow, meow, Meow meow meow meow meow meow meow meow meow?" meow meow meow, meow meow meow meow, meow meow meow meow meow meow meow meow meow meow meow meow meow meow meow meow.

"Meow, meow, meow meow."

Meow Meow meow meow meow Meow meow Meow.

"Meow'meow, meow. Meow meow Meow meow meow? Meow meow'meow meow meow meow. Meow meow meow meow meow meow," meow meow meow, meow meow meow meow meow meow. "Meow meow meow. Meow meow meow meow meow meow meow meow meow, meow meow meow meow meow meow meow, meow meow meow meow meow meow meow meow meow meow meow meow meow meow. Meow, meow, Meow meow. Meow meow meow meow. Meow meow meow meow meow meow. Meow meow meow'meow meow meow meow meow meow meow meow—Meow meow meow meow meow meow meow meow meow. Meow meow meow meow meow meow meow, Meow meow Meow meow meow meow meow meow meow," meow meow meow. "Meow, meow meow meow meow meow meow meow."

"Meow, meow meow meow meow meow meow," meow Meow, meow meow meow.

Meow meow meow meow meow meow meow meow meow, meow meow meow meow meow meow meow meow meow meow. Meow, meow meow meow meow, meow meow meow, meow meow meow meow meow, meow meow, meow meow meow meow meow meow meow meow.

"Meow meow meow meow meow?" meow Meow Meow, meow.

"Meow? Meow? Meow, meow.... Meow meow meow meow? Meow... meow'meow meow meow, meow meow meow, meow meow meow... meow meow meow meow. Meow meow meow meow meow meow meow meow meow." Meow meow meow meow meow. "Meow, meow... Meow meow meow meow meow meow meow meow meow meow meow meow... meow, meow meow meow meow meow meow meow meow! Meow meow'meow meow meow meow meow meow meow?" meow meow meow meow, meow meow meow meow, meow meow meow meow meow.

"Meow meow meow meow meow meow, Meow! Meow'meow meow meow meow," meow Meow Meow, meow meow meow meow meow. "Meow meow meow meow'meow meow meow meow meow meow meow meow meow meow meow."

"Meow meow," meow meow, meow. "Meow, meow meow meow meow meow meow meow meow meow meow.... Meow meow meow, meow.... Meow meow meow meow, meow, meow meow meow meow meow meow meow meow, meow," meow meow, meow meow.

Meow meow meow, meow meow meow, meow meow meow meow meow, meow meow meow meow meow' meow, meow meow meow meow meow, meow meow meow meow meow meow meow meow meow meow meow, meow meow meow meow meow meow meow meow. Meow meow meow meow meow meow meow meow meow meow meow meow meow meow meow meow meow meow—meow meow meow meow meow meow meow. Meow meow meow meow meow meow meow, meow meow meow meow meow.

"Meow, Meow," meow meow, meow meow meow, "meow meow Meow meow meow meow meow meow, meow Meow meow meow meow meow meow meow meow meow meow Meow meow meow meow meow meow meow meow. Meow meow meow meow Meow. Meow Meow meow meow meow, meow meow meow meow. Meow meow meow. Meow meow meow Meow, Meow meow meow meow meow meow meow meow meow meow meow."

"Meow, Meow! Meow meow meow meow meow meow meow," Meow Meow meow, meow. "Meow meow meow meow meow meow meow meow? Meow meow'meow meow meow. Meow meow meow meow meow."

"Meow," Meow meow meow meow meow meow meow meow. "Meow meow meow meow meow meow meow meow meow meow. Meow meow meow meow meow meow, meow meow meow meow meow. Meow meow meow meow meow meow meow meow Meow meow meow meow meow meow meow meow meow. Meow meow meow meow meow meow meow. Meow meow meow meow meow meow meow meow, meow meow meow meow meow meow. Meow, meow meow, Meow meow meow meow meow Meow meow meow meow meow meow meow meow. Meow meow meow meow meow meow meow meow meow meow...."

"Meow meow meow," meow meow meow meow, meow meow meow meow. "Meow meow! Meow meow'meow meow meow meow meow meow meow meow meow meow! Meow meow! Meow, meow meow! Meow meow meow meow meow meow meow.... Meow, meow Meow... meow meow meow!"

"Meow meow," meow Meow, "Meow meow meow Meow Meow meow meow meow meow Meow meow meow meow. Meow meow meow meow meow meow meow meow meow meow, meow Meow meow meow meow meow.... Meow meow meow meow meow meow?" Meow, meow, meow, meow meow meow meow meow meow meow meow meow.

"Meow?" meow meow, meow meow meow meow.

"Meow meow meow. Meow meow meow meow meow meow Meow Meow'meow meow meow meow meow meow meow meow meow. Meow meow, meow meow, meow meow meow meow meow, meow Meow meow meow meow meow, meow.... Meow meow meow meow meow?"

"Meow meow meow meow meow meow? Meow meow meow, meow. Meow meow meow meow, meow meow meow meow, meow meow meow

meow meow meow meow.... Meow meow meow Meow. Meow meow meow meow meow meow meow meow. Meow meow meow meow meow meow meow, meow meow meow meow meow meow meow meow meow, meow Meow meow meow meow meow meow meow meow meow meow meow."

"Meow meow meow meow. Meow meow meow meow," meow Meow, meow meow meow. "Meow meow meow meow meow meow Meow meow meow meow meow meow meow meow meow meow meow meow meow. Meow meow meow meow meow meow meow meow meow meow Meow meow meow meow. Meow, Meow meow meow meow meow meow meow meow meow meow... meow meow meow meow meow meow meow meow, meow meow meow! Meow meow meow meow meow meow, meow Meow meow meow meow meow meow meow meow, meow meow meow meow meow meow meow meow meow meow meow meow meow? Meow meow meow meow meow meow meow meow meow meow meow meow meow meow? Meow meow meow; meow meow meow. Meow Meow meow meow, meow meow meow meow.... Meow meow meow meow meow meow. Meow meow meow meow meow meow meow meow? Meow meow meow meow meow? Meow, meow, meow'meow meow meow?"

"Meow meow! Meow meow meow meow meow," meow Meow Meow.

"Meow, meow, meow! Meow'meow meow. Meow meow meow—meow meow. Meow meow meow meow meow meow. Meow'meow, meow, meow meow Meow meow? Meow, meow. Meow meow meow meow meow meow meow meow meow- meow meow meow meow meow meow, meow meow meow... meow meow, meow meow meow. Meow meow meow meow meow-meow?"

"Meow, meow Meow Meow Meow'meow meow," meow Meow.

Meow meow meow, Meow Meow meow meow meow meow. Meow meow meow meow meow meow, meow, meow meow meow, meow meow meow meow meow meow meow meow meow Meow.

"Meow meow meow," meow meow, meow, meow meow meow meow meow meow meow. "Meow meow Meow meow meow meow meow meow? Meow meow meow meow meow? Meow meow meow meow!"

Meow meow meow meow meow meow meow, meow meow meow meow, meow meow meow meow meow meow meow meow, meow meow meow. Meow meow meow meow meow meow, meow meow meow meow meow meow meow meow meow meow meow. Meow, meow meow meow, meow meow meow, meow meow meow meow meow. Meow Meow meow meow meow, meow meow meow meow meow meow.

"Meow meow meow," meow meow, meow meow meow meow, meow meow meow meow meow meow, meow meow meow meow meow meow, "meow meow meow meow meow meow meow, meow meow, meow meow meow meow meow meow, meow meow meow meow meow meow meow meow."

Meow meow meow. Meow meow meow meow meow meow.

"Meow meow meow meow meow meow, meow meow," Meow meow, meow.

"Meow meow meow meow?"

"Meow."

"Meow meow meow, Meow. Meow... meow meow meow meow," Meow Meow meow, meow.

"Meow'meow meow meow meow meow meow meow," Meow meow meow. "Meow meow meow meow meow meow meow meow meow."

"Meow? Meow, meow'meow meow meow—meow meow—meow meow meow meow, meow meow meow meow—meow meow!"

"Meow Meow meow meow meow meow meow meow meow meow meow meow meow meow, meow meow meow meow meow meow meow meow meow meow," Meow Meow meow, meow meow meow meow meow'meow meow.

"Meow, meow meow'meow meow meow meow, meow meow meow, Meow meow'meow meow meow. Meow meow meow meow meow, meow, meow meow meow meow meow meow meow meow meow meow, meow meow meow meow Meow meow meow meow meow meow meow meow meow meow meow. Meow meow meow meow, meow meow meow meow meow meow meow meow meow meow meow meow meow meow meow meow meow meow. Meow meow meow meow, 'meow meow' meow meow meow meow meow meow, meow meow meow meow meow meow meow meow meow meow meow meow meow Meow meow meow. Meow meow meow meow meow meow meow meow meow meow meow meow meow meow meow meow meow meow, meow meow meow meow meow meow meow meow meow Meow. Meow, meow meow meow meow? Meow meow meow meow meow meow meow Meow, meow meow meow meow meow (meow meow meow Meow) meow meow meow, meow Meow, meow meow meow meow?"

"Meow-meow," meow Meow, meow meow meow. "Meow meow meow meow meow meow meow meow meow, meow meow meow meow meow meow meow meow meow meow... meow meow meow meow meow, meow. Meow meow meow meow, meow..."

"Meow meow meow meow meow meow, meow meow meow meow meow meow meow. Meow Meow meow meow meow meow meow. Meow meow meow meow meow meow meow, meow meow meow meow, meow meow meow meow meow. Meow meow meow meow meow meow meow meow meow, meow meow meow meow, meow meow meow, meow meow 'meow meow meow meow meow meow,' meow meow meow meow meow meow meow, meow meow meow meow meow—meow meow meow, meow meow meow, meow meow meow (meow Meow meow meow meow meow meow meow meow meow meow meow)—meow meow meow meow. Meow meow meow Meow meow meow meow meow meow meow meow meow meow meow meow meow meow meow. Meow meow meow meow meow meow, meow meow meow meow, meow meow meow meow meow meow meow meow, meow meow meow meow meow meow. Meow meow meow meow meow meow, meow meow meow meow, meow meow meow meow. Meow meow meow meow meow meow... Meow meow'meow meow meow meow meow meow meow meow meow. Meow meow meow meow meow meow meow meow, meow Meow meow meow meow meow meow..."

Meow meow meow meow. Meow meow meow meow meow. Meow meow meow meow meow meow.

"Meow meow meow meow meow, Meow?" meow Meow Meow, meow meow meow meow meow meow meow meow meow, meow meow meow meow meow meow.

"Meow meow?"

"Meow meow Meow Meow meow meow meow meow meow meow meow meow meow meow meow, meow meow meow meow meow meow meow meow meow. Meow meow meow... meow?"

"Meow, meow meow, meow meow meow meow meow meow, meow meow meow meow, meow meow meow meow meow meow meow meow meow; meow meow, meow Meow, meow meow, meow, meow meow meow. Meow meow meow meow meow meow meow," meow meow, meow.

"Meow meow meow meow, meow Meow meow meow meow meow," Meow Meow meow meow meow.

"Meow meow meow meow meow, Meow, meow meow meow meow meow meow meow meow meow meow meow meow meow," meow Meow. "Meow meow meow?"

"Meow."

"Meow meow meow meow, meow, meow meow meow meow meow meow meow'meow," meow meow, meow Meow. "Meow, Meow meow meow meow, meow."

"Meow meow, Meow. Meow, meow meow meow meow," meow Meow Meow, "meow meow meow. Meow meow meow meow meow. Meow meow meow meow meow meow meow. Meow meow meow meow meow meow meow.... Meow Meow meow meow meow meow meow, meow!"

MEOW IV

Meow meow meow meow meow meow meow meow, meow meow meow meow meow meow meow meow, meow meow meow meow. Meow meow meow meow meow meow meow meow. Meow meow meow, Meow meow meow meow meow. Meow meow Meow Meow Meow. Meow meow meow meow meow meow meow meow meow, meow meow meow meow meow, meow meow meow meow meow meow meow meow, meow meow meow meow meow meow meow meow meow meow meow. Meow meow meow meow meow meow- meow meow meow, meow meow, meow, meow meow meow meow, meow meow meow meow meow meow, meow meow meow meow meow meow-meow meow. Meow meow meow meow meow meow meow meow, meow meow meow meow meow meow-meow meow, meow meow meow meow meow meow. Meow meow meow meow meow meow meow, meow meow meow meow meow meow meow meow meow meow meow, meow meow meow meow. Meow meow meow meow meow meow.

"Meow... meow'meow meow!" meow Meow, meow meow, meow meow, meow, meow meow. Meow meow meow meow meow meow meow meow meow meow meow Meow'meow meow meow "meow meow meow meow meow meow." Meow meow meow meow meow meow meow Meow'meow meow meow meow meow meow meow meow meow meow meow meow meow meow meow meow, meow meow meow meow meow. Meow

meow, meow, meow meow meow meow meow meow meow meow "meow meow meow." Meow meow meow meow meow meow meow meow meow, meow meow meow meow meow meow, meow meow meow meow meow meow meow meow meow meow meow meow meow meow meow meow. Meow meow meow meow meow meow meow meow meow, meow meow meow meow meow meow meow.

"Meow meow meow meow meow," meow meow, meow, meow meow meow meow meow meow meow. "Meow meow meow. Meow meow, meow meow, meow Meow Meow. Meow meow—meow meow. Meow meow...."

Meow Meow'meow meow, Meow, meow meow meow meow meow meow meow Meow'meow meow meow, meow meow meow meow, meow meow meow meow meow meow meow. Meow meow meow meow meow meow meow meow meow meow meow meow Meow meow meow meow, meow meow meow meow meow meow meow meow meow meow meow, meow meow meow meow meow, meow meow meow meow meow Meow'meow meow.

"Meow meow meow," meow meow meow Meow, meow meow meow meow meow.

Meow meow meow, meow meow meow meow, meow meow meow meow meow meow meow. Meow meow meow meow meow meow meow meow meow meow meow meow meow meow. Meow meow meow meow meow, meow meow meow meow meow meow meow meow meow meow, meow meow meow meow meow Meow.

"Meow... Meow... meow meow meow meow meow. Meow meow meow meow meow," meow meow meow. "Meow meow meow Meow Meow, meow meow meow meow meow meow meow. Meow Meow meow meow meow meow meow... meow meow meow meow meow... meow meow meow... meow Meow... meow meow... meow meow... meow meow... meow meow meow meow meow... meow meow meow meow meow meow..." Meow meow meow meow meow.

"Meow meow meow, meow, meow meow," meow Meow. Meow, meow, meow meow, meow meow, meow, meow meow meow meow meow meow meow. "Meow meow meow," meow meow, meow. "Meow meow meow meow meow meow. Meow meow meow meow meow meow, meow meow, meow meow meow, meow meow meow meow," meow meow meow meow meow meow meow meow.

Meow meow meow meow, meow meow meow meow meow meow meow, meow meow meow meow meow meow, meow meow meow meow. Meow'meow meow meow meow, meow meow meow meow meow, meow meow meow.

"Meow," meow meow, meow meow meow, "meow meow Meow Meow Meow, meow meow meow meow meow Meow. Meow, meow meow meow meow meow meow meow meow, meow meow meow Meow meow meow meow meow." Meow Meow meow meow Meow, meow meow meow meow meow meow. Meow meow meow meow meow meow Meow'meow meow meow meow meow, meow meow meow meow meow meow meow. Meow meow meow meow meow meow meow meow meow'meow meow, meow

meow meow meow meow. Meow, meow meow meow, meow meow meow meow meow meow, meow meow meow meow meow meow.

"Meow meow meow meow meow," meow Meow, meow, "meow meow meow meow meow. Meow meow meow meow meow meow, meow meow?"

"Meow, meow meow meow meow... meow meow meow meow, meow meow meow meow... meow meow meow meow meow... meow meow meow meow meow."

"Meow?"

"Meow meow meow'meow meow meow meow. Meow meow meow meow meow meow. Meow meow, meow-meow, meow meow meow meow meow meow meow, meow meow meow, meow meow-meow. Meow meow Meow Meow meow meow, meow meow meow meow meow meow meow'meow meow..."

"Meow-meow, meow?"

"Meow meow meow meow meow meow meow meow meow meow meow meow meow meow-meow meow meow meow, meow meow meow meow meow meow meow meow meow."

"Meow meow meow meow meow meow?"

"Meow... meow meow meow.... Meow meow meow meow meow meow meow meow meow meow meow meow. Meow meow meow, meow meow meow meow meow meow meow meow."

Meow meow meow meow meow meow meow meow meow, meow, meow meow meow, meow meow meow, meow meow meow.

Meow meow meow, Meow meow meow meow. Meow meow meow meow, meow meow, meow meow meow, meow meow meow meow, meow meow meow meow meow meow meow. Meow meow meow meow meow meow meow, meow meow meow meow meow meow meow, meow meow meow meow meow, meow meow meow meow meow meow meow meow meow meow meow meow meow meow meow meow meow. Meow meow, meow meow meow meow meow, meow meow meow meow. Meow meow meow meow meow meow, meow meow meow meow meow meow—meow meow meow. Meow meow meow meow meow meow, meow meow meow meow meow.

"Meow meow Meow Meow meow meow meow meow meow meow meow meow? Meow meow meow meow meow meow meow meow meow?" Meow meow, meow meow meow meow meow.

"Meow meow meow meow meow, meow meow... meow meow meow meow meow, meow meow meow'meow meow meow. Meow Meow meow Meow meow meow meow meow meow, meow meow meow meow meow meow meow... meow Meow Meow meow meow meow meow meow meow meow. Meow meow meow meow'meow... meow'meow meow meow meow meow... meow meow meow meow, meow meow...."

"Meow meow, Meow meow... meow meow... meow meow meow meow meow meow meow meow meow? Meow meow meow meow meow meow meow meow meow meow."

"Meow meow meow meow meow," Meow meow meow, meow meow, meow meow meow meow meow; meow meow meow meow meow meow meow. Meow meow meow meow meow meow meow meow. Meow meow meow meow meow meow meow Meow'meow meow meow, meow meow meow meow meow meow meow. Meow meow meow. Meow meow meow meow meow Meow'meow meow, meow meow Meow Meow meow meow meow Meow.

"Meow," meow meow, meow meow, "meow meow meow meow meow, meow meow. Meow, Meow.... Meow meow, Meow, meow meow meow meow meow meow meow, meow meow meow meow meow meow meow meow meow meow meow meow.... Meow meow meow meow meow meow meow...."

"Meow, meow, Meow'meow meow," meow meow, meow meow meow. "Meow Meow meow meow meow meow meow."

"Meow meow meow meow meow meow meow?" meow Meow, meow meow meow meow Meow. "Meow meow meow meow?"

"Meow, meow, Meow meow meow... meow meow, meow meow! Meow meow meow meow meow. Meow meow meow meow meow meow meow, meow meow, meow? Meow meow Meow meow meow meow meow meow?"

"Meow, meow, meow. Meow meow meow, Meow Meow, meow meow meow meow meow meow meow meow?"

"Meow meow," meow Meow.

Meow meow, meow meow. Meow meow meow, meow meow meow meow meow.

"Meow-meow, Meow, meow meow meow meow meow. Meow meow meow meow meow meow-meow. Meow-meow, Meow. Meow, Meow meow meow meow-meow meow."

Meow Meow meow meow meow Meow, meow; meow meow meow meow meow meow meow, meow meow meow meow meow meow meow meow meow meow.

Meow Meow Meow meow meow meow meow meow, meow meow meow meow meow, meow Meow meow meow, meow meow. Meow, meow meow, meow meow meow, meow meow. Meow meow meow meow meow meow meow meow meow meow, meow meow Meow Meow'meow meow meow meow meow meow meow meow meow meow.

"Meow, meow-meow," meow Meow, meow meow meow. "Meow meow meow meow."

"Meow, Meow meow meow meow meow meow. Meow meow meow?" meow Meow, meow meow meow meow meow meow.

"Meow meow, meow meow meow meow meow." Meow meow meow meow meow meow. Meow meow, meow, meow meow meow meow, meow meow meow meow meow.

"Meow, meow'meow meow," meow meow meow Meow, meow meow meow meow meow meow meow. "Meow meow meow meow meow meow, meow meow meow meow meow meow. Meow meow meow, meow'meow meow?"

Meow meow meow meow meow meow meow meow meow meow. Meow meow meow meow meow meow meow meow meow. Meow meow meow meow meow meow meow meow meow meow meow meow meow meow....

"Meow, Meow," Meow Meow meow, meow meow meow meow meow meow meow meow, "Meow meow meow meow meow meow meow meow—meow meow meow. Meow meow meow Meow meow meow meow meow meow meow Meow meow meow meow meow meow meow."

"Meow meow meow meow, meow, meow meow meow meow meow. Meow'meow meow meow meow? Meow meow meow meow meow meow. Meow meow meow meow, meow meow, meow meow meow meow."

"Meow, meow meow meow meow meow!" Meow Meow meow meow meow, meow meow meow. "Meow meow meow, Meow, Meow meow meow meow meow meow. Meow meow meow meow meow meow meow, meow meow meow meow meow meow meow meow meow. Meow meow meow meow, meow meow meow meow-meow, meow meow meow meow meow.... Meow meow meow'meow meow meow meow, Meow. Meow? Meow Meow meow meow meow meow meow meow meow meow meow meow, meow meow meow!"

"Meow'meow meow meow, meow. Meow meow meow, meow meow."

"Meow, meow meow meow meow meow meow meow meow! Meow meow Meow Meow meow meow meow?" meow Meow Meow meow meow, meow.

"Meow meow'meow meow meow meow meow meow meow," meow Meow, meow meow meow.

"Meow meow meow meow meow meow," Meow Meow meow meow meow. "Meow meow meow meow meow meow meow meow meow meow. Meow meow meow meow meow meow meow meow meow meow... meow meow meow meow meow meow meow.... Meow meow meow meow meow meow meow meow meow meow meow? Meow meow meow meow meow meow-meow meow. Meow meow! meow meow meow!... meow... meow meow... meow meow meow meow—meow meow. Meow, meow meow meow meow meow meow meow, Meow meow... meow meow meow!... Meow meow meow meow meow meow meow meow meow, meow."

"Meow meow meow, meow?

"Meow, meow Meow Meow, meow meow meow meow meow."

"Meow?"

"Meow meow meow meow, Meow. Meow, meow meow meow meow meow meow, meow meow meow meow meow meow meow, meow meow meow, Meow meow meow meow meow meow meow meow meow meow meow...."

"Meow meow meow meow!" meow Meow, meow meow. "Meow meow, meow meow meow, meow! Meow meow meow meow meow meow meow, meow meow meow meow meow meow meow meow meow meow."

"Meow, meow meow meow.... Meow meow meow; meow meow meow meow, meow meow meow! Meow meow meow meow. Meow meow meow meow meow meow meow meow. Meow meow meow meow meow meow meow meow meow meow meow meow meow, meow meow meow? Meow

meow meow meow, meow Meow Meow meow meow meow meow meow, meow meow meow meow meow meow—meow meow! Meow meow meow meow meow meow meow meow meow."

"Meow meow meow meow. Meow meow meow meow meow meow meow, meow. Meow meow meow? Meow meow meow meow meow meow meow meow meow, meow meow meow meow meow meow."

"Meow meow meow meow meow!"

"Meow Meow Meow meow meow meow meow," Meow meow meow, meow.

Meow Meow meow meow; meow meow meow meow meow.

"Meow meow meow meow meow Meow meow meow meow," meow Meow, meow Meow meow meow meow.

"Meow Meow meow meow Meow Meow meow meow meow meow," Meow meow meow, meow meow meow.

"Meow meow, Meow Meow. Meow meow meow meow. Meow meow meow meow meow meow. Meow meow meow meow meow meow meow meow meow meow. Meow!" meow meow meow meow Meow meow. "Meow meow meow... meow'meow meow meow... Meow Meow?"

"Meow meow meow meow! Meow meow meow meow. Meow?" meow meow meow, meow meow.

"Meow meow meow meow meow meow... meow meow, meow meow meow? Meow meow meow meow meow meow."

"Meow... meow?" Meow'meow meow meow meow.

"Meow meow meow meow meow meow meow meow meow, meow Meow meow meow meow meow, meow— meow—meow meow meow meow meow meow meow meow meow meow Meow meow meow, meow meow meow'meow meow meow—meow meow meow meow meow meow meow meow meow... meow Meow meow meow. Meow meow meow Meow meow meow meow? Meow meow meow meow meow meow meow meow, meow meow meow. Meow meow meow meow meow, meow meow meow meow meow meow meow meow meow, meow meow meow meow Meow'meow meow. Meow meow meow meow meow meow meow'meow meow meow. Meow meow meow meow meow meow meow meow. Meow meow meow meow meow. Meow meow meow meow meow meow. Meow meow Meow meow meow meow meow meow meow meow meow meow, meow meow meow meow meow meow meow meow meow meow Meow? Meow? Meow meow meow meow? Meow meow meow meow meow meow meow. Meow meow, meow meow meow meow meow meow meow."

"Meow meow meow meow meow meow. Meow meow Meow," Meow meow meow meow meow. "Meow, meow meow Meow meow. Meow meow meow meow meow. Meow meow meow meow meow meow. Meow meow meow meow meow meow meow."

"Meow meow, meow meow meow."

"Meow meow meow meow meow, meow meow meow meow meow meow. Meow meow meow meow meow meow meow meow meow meow meow. Meow meow meow meow meow meow. Meow meow meow. Meow

meow meow meow meow meow? Meow meow'meow meow! Meow meow meow meow meow meow.... Meow, meow, Meow Meow..."

"Meow Meow," meow Meow. "Meow Meow, meow meow meow meow Meow, meow meow meow meow meow meow."

"Meow meow meow meow meow meow," Meow meow meow, meow meow meow Meow meow meow, meow meow meow meow.

"Meow meow meow," meow Meow. "Meow meow meow meow meow meow-meow, Meow Meow. Meow meow meow meow meow meow."

Meow meow meow meow meow meow meow, meow meow meow, meow meow meow meow. Meow meow meow meow, meow meow meow meow meow meow. Meow meow meow meow meow.

"Meow'meow meow meow meow?" meow Meow, meow meow meow meow meow meow.

"Meow," meow Meow. "Meow meow meow meow meow meow meow meow meow meow meow meow. Meow meow meow meow meow meow meow meow meow," meow meow, meow, meow Meow. Meow meow meow meow meow meow.

"Meow meow meow meow meow meow, Meow Meow? Meow meow meow meow meow, meow meow meow?" meow meow, meow meow meow meow meow meow meow meow meow. Meow meow meow meow meow meow meow meow meow, meow meow meow meow meow.

"Meow, meow meow meow meow meow Meow meow."

"Meow? Meow, meow; Meow, meow meow meow meow meow. Meow meow meow meow? Meow Meow meow meow meow meow?"

"Meow, meow meow meow?" "Meow, Meow meow."

"Meow meow meow meow meow meow meow meow... meow Meow meow meow meow meow meow, meow meow meow meow meow meow. Meow meow Meow meow... meow meow Meow meow meow meow meow, Meow meow meow-meow, 'Meow meow Meow. Meow meow?' Meow meow meow meow meow meow meow meow meow meow.... Meow-meow, Meow meow meow Meow Meow."

Meow meow meow meow meow meow meow meow; meow meow meow meow meow, meow meow meow meow meow meow meow meow meow meow, meow meow meow meow meow meow meow meow meow meow meow meow meow meow meow meow meow, meow meow meow meow meow, meow meow meow meow, meow meow, meow meow, meow meow, meow meow meow meow meow, meow meow. Meow, meow meow meow meow meow meow meow. Meow meow meow meow meow meow meow meow meow meow. Meow meow meow meow Meow meow meow meow meow meow meow meow, meow meow meow!

"Meow meow meow-meow, meow, meow meow-meow!" meow meow meow meow meow meow meow, meow meow meow meow, meow meow meow meow. "Meow! meow meow... meow meow meow... meow meow meow... meow, meow!"

Meow meow meow meow meow meow meow meow meow meow meow meow meow meow meow meow meow meow meow meow. Meow meow meow meow meow meow meow. Meow meow meow meow Meow,

Meow, meow meow meow meow meow meow meow meow meow, meow meow, meow meow meow meow, meow meow meow Meow'meow meow: "meow Meow meow meow Meow. Meow meow?" Meow meow meow meow meow meow meow meow meow meow, meow meow Meow, meow meow Meow meow meow; meow meow meow meow meow meow meow. Meow meow meow meow meow meow meow meow meow meow, meow meow meow meow meow meow meow, meow meow meow meow meow meow meow meow meow meow. Meow meow meow meow Meow; meow meow meow meow meow meow, meow meow Meow meow meow meow. "Meow? Meow? Meow'meow meow meow meow meow," meow meow. "Meow meow meow meow."

Meow meow meow meow meow meow, meow meow, meow meow Meow meow meow meow meow, meow meow. Meow meow meow meow. Meow meow meow meow meow meow meow. Meow meow meow meow meow meow meow meow, meow meow meow meow meow meow meow meow meow meow. Meow meow meow meow meow meow, meow meow meow meow meow, meow meow meow meow meow meow meow meow meow meow meow meow meow meow. Meow meow meow meow meow meow, meow meow meow meow meow meow meow. Meow meow meow meow meow, meow meow meow meow meow meow meow meow meow; meow meow meow meow. Meow meow meow meow, meow meow meow meow meow meow-meow meow meow meow meow, meow meow meow meow Meow. Meow meow meow meow meow meow, meow meow meow meow meow meow meow meow, meow meow meow meow meow meow meow meow meow meow. Meow meow meow meow meow meow meow meow meow meow meow; meow meow meow meow. Meow meow meow meow meow- meow meow meow meow meow meow meow meow meow. Meow Meow meow meow meow meow meow meow, meow meow meow meow meow meow meow meow meow. Meow meow meow meow meow meow. Meow meow meow meow meow meow meow, Meow meow meow meow meow meow; meow meow meow, meow meow meow. Meow meow meow meow meow meow meow meow meow. "Meow!" meow meow meow meow, meow meow meow meow meow meow. Meow meow Meow meow meow. Meow meow meow meow meow, meow meow meow meow, meow meow meow Meow. 9. Meow meow meow meow meow meow meow, "Meow, Meow." "Meow!" meow meow meow, meow meow meow meow meow, meow meow meow meow meow, meow Meow. 8. Meow meow meow meow meow meow meow meow.

"Meow meow meow Meow'meow," meow meow, meow meow Meow meow meow. "Meow meow meow meow meow meow meow. Meow meow meow meow meow meow Meow Meow'meow. Meow meow!" Meow meow meow meow meow.

"Meow meow meow," meow meow meow meow. "Meow meow meow meow meow meow meow meow meow. Meow-meow meow meow meow."

Meow meow meow meow; meow meow meow meow meow meow meow. Meow meow meow meow meow meow meow meow.

Meow meow meow meow Meow'meow, Meow meow meow meow.

"Meow'meow meow, meow," meow meow meow meow, "meow Meow meow meow! Meow meow meow!"

"Meow meow meow meow meow?" Meow meow meow meow.

"Meow meow'meow meow meow meow meow meow meow meow meow meow'meow, meow. Meow... meow meow meow meow? Meow meow, meow meow meow meow meow meow meow?"

"Meow meow meow-meow meow meow meow!"

"Meow meow meow?" Meow meow meow meow meow. "Meow meow meow meow meow meow meow meow meow meow meow. Meow Meow meow meow meow meow meow meow meow meow," meow meow meow meow meow meow meow meow meow meow meow meow meow meow. "Meow'meow meow meow meow meow meow meow meow... meow meow meow'meow meow meow!"

Meow meow meow meow meow meow meow.

"Meow, meow," Meow meow meow meow—meow meow meow meow meow. "Meow meow'meow meow meow... meow meow... meow... meow meow meow meow meow meow meow meow meow meow meow meow meow! Meow, meow... meow'meow meow, meow'meow meow meow meow."

"Meow! Meow meow meow meow meow meow meow meow meow. Meow meow meow meow meow meow meow meow meow meow, meow Meow meow meow meow meow meow meow meow meow meow Meow meow meow meow meow meow meow! Meow meow meow meow meow meow meow meow meow meow meow!"

"Meow meow meow meow?" meow meow meow.

"Meow, meow," Meow meow meow. "Meow meow meow meow meow, meow meow meow, meow. Meow meow, meow meow meow meow, meow meow meow meow meow meow meow, meow Meow meow meow meow meow meow meow. Meow meow meow meow meow, meow meow meow meow, meow meow meow meow meow meow meow meow.... Meow meow meow, meow, meow... meow meow meow meow meow meow, meow meow meow meow meow meow meow. Meow meow meow meow, meow meow.... Meow meow meow meow meow... meow.... Meow meow meow meow meow meow meow meow meow meow meow meow meow meow meow meow. Meow meow meow, meow meow meow meow meow meow!"

"Meow meow meow meow meow meow meow?"

"Meow, meow'meow meow meow... meow meow, meow meow'meow meow meow Meow meow meow meow meow meow meow meow.... Meow, meow meow meow meow meow... meow meow meow meow meow meow meow meow meow meow meow meow meow, meow meow, 'Meow meow meow!' Meow meow Meow meow... meow meow meow, meow meow meow; meow Meow... meow meow, Meow, Meow meow meow meow meow meow meow meow meow meow meow, meow Meow meow meow... Meow meow meow, meow, meow meow meow meow, meow meow."

"Meow? Meow meow meow Meow meow meow meow? Meow meow meow meow," meow meow meow meow meow meow.

"Meow, meow.... Meow meow, meow, meow!... Meow meow meow Meow meow (meow meow meow meow meow meow) meow meow meow meow, meow meow."

"Meow meow meow meow meow? Meow meow meow meow meow meow meow!" Meow meow meow meow meow. Meow meow meow meow, meow.

"Meow meow, Meow meow, Meow meow. Meow meow, Meow meow. Meow'meow meow meow meow meow meow." "Meow meow meow meow, meow meow'meow meow meow meow."

Meow meow meow. Meow meow meow meow meow meow Meow meow meow meow meow. Meow meow meow, meow, meow meow Meow meow meow meow meow Meow.

"Meow meow meow meow meow meow meow meow meow meow meow," meow meow, meow meow meow meow, meow meow meow meow, "meow meow meow meow, meow. Meow meow meow meow meow meow meow meow meow meow meow meow. Meow meow meow meow meow! Meow, meow meow meow meow meow meow.... Meow, meow, meow meow meow meow meow meow meow.... Meow meow meow... meow. Meow meow meow meow meow meow meow meow meow? Meow meow meow meow meow meow. Meow meow meow meow, meow'meow meow'meow meow!"

"Meow meow meow meow," meow Meow.

"Meow meow meow meow, meow Meow meow meow Meow meow meow meow meow meow'meow meow meow... meow meow meow meow meow? Meow meow meow meow meow meow, meow meow meow Meow meow meow, meow meow meow meow meow; meow... Meow'meow meow meow, meow meow'meow meow meow."

"Meow meow, meow," meow meow meow, meow Meow, meow meow meow meow, "Meow meow meow meow meow meow meow meow meow meow meow meow meow. Meow'meow meow meow?"

"Meow? Meow meow meow meow meow," meow Meow, meow meow meow meow.

"Meow, meow, Meow meow meow meow'meow meow. Meow, meow meow meow meow meow meow meow meow meow meow meow meow, meow meow meow meow, meow meow meow meow meow meow meow meow meow. Meow meow meow meow meow meow. Meow meow meow meow meow, meow meow meow meow meow meow meow meow meow. Meow meow meow; meow meow meow meow meow meow meow, meow meow meow."

"Meow meow meow meow, meow! Meow meow meow meow?"

"Meow meow meow meow meow meow meow meow, meow meow meow? Meow Meow, meow meow'meow meow meow."

"Meow meow meow meow meow!"

"Meow meow meow meow meow meow meow meow? Meow! Meow, Meow'meow meow meow meow meow-meow. Meow-meow-meow! Meow'meow meow meow meow, meow meow meow, meow..."

“Meow, meow, meow, meow meow meow.... Meow meow, meow meow!” Meow meow meow meow, meow meow meow meow. “Meow meow meow meow meow? Meow, meow... meow! meow meow meow meow meow!”

“Meow meow meow meow meow meow. Meow meow meow meow meow meow meow meow meow; meow Meow meow meow meow meow! Meow meow meow’meow meow meow-meow—meow meow meow meow, Meow meow. Meow? Meow’meow meow meow meow! Meow, Meow meow meow meow’meow meow meow meow meow meow! Meow meow.”

“Meow!”

Meow meow meow meow meow meow meow meow meow. Meow meow, meow meow Meow Meow’meow meow. Meow meow meow Meow meow: meow meow meow meow meow meow meow meow meow meow meow, meow meow meow meow meow.

“Meow meow meow meow meow Meow’meow... meow meow!” Meow meow meow, meow Meow meow meow meow.

MEOW V

Meow meow meow meow meow meow. Meow meow meow meow meow meow meow meow meow meow meow meow meow meow meow meow meow. Meow meow Meow meow meow meow meow meow, meow meow meow meow meow meow, meow meow meow meow meow meow meow. Meow meow meow meow meow meow meow meow meow meow meow meow meow meow Meow'meow meow. Meow, meow meow meow meow meow, meow meow Meow Meow, meow meow meow meow meow meow meow meow meow meow meow meow. Meow meow meow meow meow meow meow meow, meow meow meow meow meow meow meow meow meow meow meow meow meow meow meow meow meow. Meow meow meow meow meow meow meow meow meow meow meow meow meow meow meow meow meow meow meow meow meow meow meow meow Meow, meow meow meow meow meow meow: meow meow meow meow meow meow meow meow meow meow meow meow meow meow meow. Meow meow meow meow meow Meow meow meow "meow" meow meow meow meow meow meow meow meow meow meow meow meow meow. Meow meow meow meow meow meow meow meow.

"Meow! Meow meow," meow meow, meow meow meow meow meow meow meow meow meow meow meow meow meow meow meow-meow meow meow. Meow meow meow meow meow meow.

"Meow meow meow meow, meow? Meow meow meow'meow meow meow meow meow Meow," Meow Meow meow meow.

Meow meow meow meow, meow meow meow meow Meow Meow'meow, meow meow meow meow meow meow, meow meow meow meow meow meow meow meow meow meow meow. Meow, meow meow meow meow meow meow meow meow meow meow meow, meow meow meow meow meow, meow meow meow meow meow meow meow meow meow meow meow meow meow meow meow meow meow meow meow meow meow meow meow meow, meow meow. Meow Meow meow meow meow meow meow meow meow meow, meow meow meow meow meow. Meow meow meow meow meow meow meow, meow meow meow meow meow meow' meow meow meow meow meow meow meow meow meow meow meow meow, meow meow meow meow meow meow meow meow meow meow meow meow meow meow meow meow Meow meow meow meow meow. Meow'meow meow meow meow Meow meow.

"Meow'meow meow meow meow meow meow," meow meow. "Meow meow, meow," meow meow, meow meow meow. "Meow."

"Meow meow meow, meow meow meow meow meow... meow meow meow meow'meow meow meow.... Meow, meow'meow meow meow meow meow-meow?" Meow Meow meow meow Meow.

"Meow meow meow Meow meow'meow meow meow meow meow meow meow meow meow meow meow. Meow meow meow meow meow meow meow meow meow meow meow Meow... meow meow meow. Meow meow meow meow, Meow meow!"

"Meow!" meow Meow, meow meow meow.

"Meow meow meow meow meow meow meow meow meow, meow meow meow meow meow meow meow meow," Meow meow.

"Meow, meow meow meow!... Meow meow meow!" meow Meow, meow meow meow meow meow meow, meow meow meow meow Meow meow meow meow meow meow meow meow meow meow meow. "Meow'meow meow! Meow meow meow meow. Meow meow meow meow. Meow meow meow meow Meow Meow Meow; meow meow meow meow meow meow meow meow meow meow meow meow meow meow meow, meow meow, meow meow meow meow meow meow meow meow meow. Meow! Meow, meow meow meow meow? Meow meow meow meow? Meow meow meow meow meow meow?"

"Meow meow meow meow?" meow Meow meow.

Meow meow meow meow, meow meow meow meow meow.

"Meow, meow meow meow meow meow meow meow meow," meow meow meow.

"Meow Meow meow meow meow meow meow. Meow meow meow meow meow meow meow meow meow meow meow meow. Meow meow meow meow meow meow meow meow meow meow. Meow meow meow meow?"

Meow Meow meow meow meow meow-meow, meow meow meow, meow meow-meow meow. Meow meow meow meow meow meow meow meow meow, meow, meow meow meow meow, meow meow meow. Meow meow meow meow meow meow meow meow meow meow meow meow, meow meow meow meow meow. Meow meow, meow, meow meow-meow meow meow meow meow meow meow meow, meow meow meow meow meow meow meow meow. Meow meow meow meow meow-meow meow meow meow meow meow meow meow, meow meow meow meow meow, meow meow meow meow meow, meow meow. Meow meow meow meow meow meow meow meow meow meow meow meow meow meow meow, meow meow meow meow meow meow meow meow meow meow meow meow meow meow.

Meow meow meow Meow Meow meow meow meow meow meow meow meow meow meow meow meow meow, meow meow meow meow meow meow meow meow meow meow meow meow meow meow meow meow meow, meow meow meow meow meow meow meow, meow meow meow meow meow-meow meow meow meow meow meow meow meow meow, meow meow meow meow, meow meow meow meow meow meow meow meow meow meow meow meow meow meow meow meow meow meow meow meow meow. Meow meow meow meow meow meow Meow meow meow meow meow meow meow, meow meow meow meow meow meow meow meow meow meow meow meow meow meow meow meow meow meow Meow. Meow Meow meow meow meow meow meow meow meow meow. Meow, meow meow meow meow meow meow, meow meow meow meow, meow meow meow meow meow meow meow meow meow meow meow meow.

"Meow," Meow meow meow meow.

"Meow meow meow meow meow meow meow meow," Meow meow, meow meow meow meow meow, "meow meow meow meow meow meow,

meow meow meow meow meow, meow meow meow meow meow meow meow meow meow meow meow meow meow meow meow meow meow meow meow, meow meow meow meow meow meow meow... meow... meow meow meow meow meow meow."

"Meow'meow meow meow meow, meow meow meow meow meow," Meow meow meow meow meow meow meow, "Meow meow meow meow meow meow... meow meow meow meow meow meow meow meow... Meow meow meow, meow meow, meow meow meow meow meow meow meow meow meow meow, meow meow meow Meow meow meow...."

"Meow'meow meow meow," meow Meow Meow, meow meow meow meow meow meow meow meow, "meow meow meow, meow meow meow, meow meow meow meow, meow meow, meow meow meow meow meow meow meow, meow meow meow meow meow meow meow meow, meow meow..."

"Meow meow meow meow meow meow?" Meow meow meow, meow meow meow meow meow meow meow meow meow.

"Meow, meow meow meow," meow meow Meow Meow meow meow meow meow meow meow, meow meow meow meow meow, meow meow meow, meow meow meow. Meow meow meow meow Meow'meow meow, meow meow meow meow meow meow meow. Meow meow meow meow meow meow meow, Meow meow meow meow meow meow meow meow, meow meow meow.

"Meow meow," meow meow meow meow meow meow.

"Meow meow meow meow meow meow meow," meow meow meow, meow meow meow, "meow meow meow meow meow meow meow, meow Meow meow meow meow meow meow meow meow meow meow meow meow meow meow, meow Meow meow meow meow Meow meow meow meow Meow meow..."

"Meow'meow meow meow meow meow meow meow meow Meow meow meow Meow meow Meow meow meow meow meow meow meow meow!" Meow meow meow meow meow meow.

Meow meow meow meow. Meow meow meow meow meow meow meow meow meow meow meow meow meow meow meow meow meow, meow meow meow meow.

"Meow meow meow meow meow meow meow, meow?" meow meow meow meow, meow meow meow-meow meow. "Meow meow meow Meow meow meow meow meow meow meow meow meow meow; meow meow meow'meow meow meow meow meow meow meow meow, meow meow meow meow meow meow meow meow meow meow meow meow. Meow meow meow meow meow meow meow meow meow, meow meow'meow meow meow meow meow, meow meow meow meow meow meow meow meow meow'meow. Meow meow meow meow meow, meow meow meow meow meow," meow meow meow meow Meow, "meow meow meow meow," meow meow meow meow meow Meow, meow meow meow meow meow, "meow meow meow meow meow, meow meow meow meow meow! Meow meow meow meow meow!"

"Meow meow meow meow meow! Meow meow'meow meow meow meow meow! Meow meow meow!" meow Meow meow.

"Meow meow meow? Meow meow meow? Meow Meow meow meow?" Meow meow meow meow meow meow. "Meow meow Meow meow meow meow meow?"

"Meow, meow meow meow meow meow?" Meow Meow meow. "Meow."

"Meow meow meow meow?"

"Meow meow."

Meow meow meow meow meow.

"Meow meow meow meow meow meow meow meow meow," meow meow meow meow meow meow. "Meow meow meow meow meow meow meow meow meow."

Meow meow meow meow meow meow meow meow meow meow, meow meow meow meow meow-meow meow Meow, meow meow meow meow meow meow meow meow meow. Meow meow, meow Meow meow meow meow meow meow meow meow meow, meow meow meow meow meow Meow'meow meow.

"Meow? Meow meow? Meow, meow meow meow meow meow meow meow?" meow Meow. Meow Meow meow meow meow Meow.

"Meow meow, meow meow meow meow meow, meow meow meow meow, meow meow meow meow meow meow meow meow meow meow, meow meow meow meow meow meow meow meow meow meow..."

"Meow meow meow meow!" Meow meow meow, meow meow meow meow meow meow meow meow meow meow meow, meow meow meow, meow meow meow:

"Meow meow meow meow Meow meow meow meow meow meow meow meow... meow meow meow meow meow meow meow meow meow.... Meow meow meow meow meow meow meow, meow... meow..."

"Meow! Meow!" meow meow. "Meow meow Meow meow meow?"

"Meow meow meow meow meow meow meow, meow meow meow meow meow meow meow meow'meow meow meow," Meow meow meow meow meow meow.

"Meow meow'meow meow meow meow."

"Meow meow meow meow. Meow meow, meow, meow meow meow meow meow meow meow meow. Meow meow meow meow."

"Meow meow meow meow meow meow.... Meow, Meow meow meow meow," Meow meow meow meow meow meow, meow meow meow meow. Meow meow meow meow, meow meow meow meow meow. "Meow meow meow meow Meow meow meow meow," meow meow meow meow meow. "Meow meow meow meow meow?"

"Meow meow meow!" Meow meow meow meow. "Meow meow! Meow meow meow meow meow meow meow. Meow meow meow, Meow, meow meow meow meow meow meow meow, meow meow, meow meow meow meow meow, meow meow meow meow meow meow meow meow meow meow meow meow meow meow, meow meow meow meow! Meow meow meow meow! Meow!"

"Meow meow? Meow meow'meow meow meow!" Meow meow meow meow meow meow meow meow.

"Meow! Meow'meow meow meow meow! Meow meow meow'meow meow meow meow," Meow meow meow meow meow meow. Meow Meow Meow meow meow meow meow meow meow meow meow.

"Meow meow meow meow meow meow meow meow meow meow'meow meow meow?" Meow meow meow meow. "Meow meow meow meow meow meow? Meow meow meow meow meow meow? Meow meow meow meow meow? Meow meow meow meow meow meow meow meow meow? Meow meow meow meow meow meow Meow meow meow meow."

"Meow meow meow meow meow meow meow." Meow meow Meow meow meow meow meow meow meow meow, "Meow meow meow meow meow meow meow meow meow meow'meow meow meow, meow meow meow meow meow meow meow meow. Meow. Meow meow meow meow. Meow meow, Meow. Meow, meow Meow meow meow meow meow; meow meow meow."

Meow meow meow meow Meow meow meow meow, meow meow meow meow meow meow meow meow meow meow.

"Meow meow meow meow meow meow meow meow meow, meow meow meow meow meow," Meow meow meow.

"Meow Meow Meow meow meow meow meow-meow," meow meow Meow Meow, "meow meow meow meow meow meow meow meow meow meow meow meow meow meow meow meow meow meow meow."

"Meow meow," meow Meow, "meow'meow meow meow meow? Meow meow meow meow meow meow meow meow meow meow meow. Meow meow meow meow meow, meow meow meow meow meow, meow meow meow meow meow meow meow meow, meow meow meow meow meow meow meow-meow meow meow!"

"Meow Meow meow meow meow meow meow meow meow meow meow meow? Meow meow'meow meow Meow meow meow meow.... Meow. Meow meow Meow'meow meow meow meow! Meow meow, meow, meow meow meow meow meow meow meow meow meow meow," meow meow, meow meow Meow Meow, meow meow meow. "Meow meow meow meow, meow'meow meow?"

"Meow meow, meow meow meow, meow meow meow! Meow meow meow meow meow meow meow meow! Meow'meow meow meow meow meow meow meow... meow Meow meow meow meow meow meow meow meow meow meow."

"Meow meow meow meow meow meow meow! Meow meow'meow meow," meow Meow.

"Meow meow! Meow meow meow meow meow meow meow. Meow'meow meow meow... meow meow meow meow meow?"

"Meow meow meow meow!"

Meow Meow meow meow meow meow meow.

Meow'meow meow meow meow meow meow. Meow meow meow meow meow.

"Meow meow meow meow meow meow meow'meow meow meow; meow meow'meow meow meow meow meow meow! Meow meow meow meow meow'meow meow meow meow meow, meow meow meow meow meow meow Meow Meow meow meow? Meow meow meow'meow meow meow meow meow meow meow meow meow meow meow meow meow. Meow meow meow meow meow meow." Meow meow meow meow meow. "Meow, meow meow meow, meow'meow meow meow meow meow meow meow meow meow meow. Meow'meow meow meow, Meow Meow, meow meow Meow meow'meow meow meow! Meow meow meow meow meow meow meow meow meow meow meow meow, meow meow'meow meow meow Meow meow meow." Meow meow meow meow. "Meow meow meow meow'meow meow meow meow? Meow meow Meow meow meow, meow meow meow Meow meow meow meow meow'meow meow meow meow meow meow? Meow meow'meow meow meow. Meow meow meow meow meow meow meow, meow meow meow meow meow meow.... Meow meow meow meow meow, meow meow meow meow. Meow meow meow meow meow, 'Meow meow'? Meow meow Meow meow meow Meow meow meow? Meow meow meow meow meow meow meow? Meow, meow meow.... Meow meow meow meow, meow meow meow meow meow? Meow meow meow meow meow meow meow! Meow meow! Meow Meow meow meow meow meow meow? Meow meow meow'meow meow! Meow meow meow meow meow? Meow meow meow meow meow meow meow meow meow meow meow meow? Meow meow'meow meow meow meow meow meow! Meow Meow meow meow.... Meow Meow meow? Meow meow meow meow meow. Meow meow meow meow meow meow meow! Meow meow meow meow meow, meow meow'meow meow meow meow. Meow meow meow meow meow meow meow; meow meow meow meow meow meow. Meow'meow meow meow meow meow, meow meow, meow meow! Meow meow meow meow meow meow meow meow meow meow meow. Meow meow meow meow meow meow? Meow meow meow'meow meow meow! Meow Meow meow meow Meow meow meow meow meow meow meow meow meow meow meow.... Meow meow meow meow meow meow meow meow, meow meow meow meow meow meow.... Meow, meow... meow-meow-meow! Meow meow meow meow meow! Meow meow'meow meow meow meow meow'meow meow! Meow meow meow meow meow meow meow meow meow! Meow meow meow, meow meow'meow meow meow! Meow meow meow meow... meow'meow meow meow! Meow meow meow! Meow meow meow meow'meow meow meow meow meow. Meow meow meow meow meow meow meow.... Meow meow meow meow meow meow? Meow meow'meow meow meow meow meow. Meow meow Meow meow meow? Meow meow meow meow meow, meow meow meow meow! Meow, meow meow Meow meow! Meow meow'meow meow; meow meow meow meow.... Meow meow meow meow. Meow meow meow meow meow meow. Meow meow Meow meow?"

Meow meow meow meow meow meow meow meow.

Meow Meow meow meow. Meow meow meow meow meow.

"Meow meow meow, meow, meow meow meow meow meow.... Meow Meow meow meow meow meow meow," meow meow meow meow meow meow meow, meow meow Meow.

"Meow meow meow? Meow meow meow meow meow meow meow meow meow. Meow meow meow meow meow meow?" "Meow, meow meow, meow meow. Meow meow meow meow meow meow, meow meow meow meow."

"Meow meow, Meow, meow meow meow meow meow meow. Meow meow meow meow meow meow meow meow. Meow meow meow meow meow meow meow meow meow."

"Meow meow meow meow? Meow'meow meow meow meow meow," Meow meow meow. "Meow meow meow'meow meow meow meow meow," meow Meow.

"Meow meow, meow'meow meow," Meow meow meow meow, meow meow meow meow meow meow. "Meow, Meow, meow meow meow meow meow, Meow meow meow meow meow. Meow meow meow meow meow meow meow meow meow meow meow meow meow meow. Meow meow meow meow meow meow.... Meow meow meow meow meow meow. Meow meow meow meow; meow meow meow meow meow meow meow meow meow meow meow meow meow meow, meow meow meow; meow meow meow meow!..."

"Meow meow meow meow," meow Meow Meow; meow meow meow meow meow meow meow meow meow meow meow Meow, meow meow meow meow meow meow meow.

"Meow meow meow," Meow meow meow meow.

"Meow meow meow meow. Meow'meow meow meow meow meow. Meow meow meow meow 'meow meow meow meow,' meow meow meow. Meow meow meow! Meow meow meow meow meow, meow meow meow meow meow, meow meow meow meow meow meow, meow meow meow meow meow meow meow meow meow meow meow meow meow meow meow meow meow. Meow meow meow meow meow meow meow, meow meow meow, meow'meow meow meow meow meow! Meow meow'meow meow meow meow, meow meow meow meow meow meow, meow meow meow meow meow meow meow, meow meow meow meow meow meow meow meow meow meow meow meow meow meow meow meow meow meow meow meow meow meow meow meow meow meow meow meow meow meow meow meow meow meow meow, meow meow meow meow meow! Meow'meow meow meow meow meow meow, 'meow meow meow meow meow meow,' meow meow meow meow meow meow meow! Meow'meow meow meow meow meow meow meow meow meow; meow meow'meow meow meow meow meow! Meow meow meow meow meow, meow meow meow'meow meow meow meow meow meow, meow meow meow meow meow meow meow, meow meow meow meow! Meow meow meow meow meow meow meow meow meow meow meow meow meow meow Meow-meow, meow meow meow meow meow, meow meow meow, meow meow meow meow'meow meow! Meow meow meow meow meow meow meow meow meow meow meow meow meow meow meow meow meow meow

meow meow meow meow meow meow meow! Meow meow meow meow, meow, meow meow meow meow meow meow meow meow meow meow—meow meow meow, meow meow'meow meow meow meow meow, meow'meow meow meow meow meow meow! Meow meow'meow meow meow meow meow meow. Meow meow meow meow, meow meow meow meow! Meow meow meow meow, meow meow meow meow meow meow meow meow meow! Meow'meow meow meow meow meow meow meow! Meow'meow meow meow meow meow meow'meow meow meow meow. Meow'meow meow meow meow, meow meow'meow meow! Meow meow meow meow meow meow meow meow meow meow!"

"Meow meow meow meow, meow meow meow! Meow meow meow meow, meow!" meow Meow. "Meow meow meow," meow meow meow Meow, "meow meow meow meow meow meow meow meow, meow meow meow, meow meow meow meow meow! Meow, meow, meow meow meow, meow meow meow meow meow meow meow meow; Meow meow meow meow meow meow."

"Meow, Meow meow meow meow, meow meow meow meow: meow meow meow meow meow meow meow meow meow; meow meow meow meow meow meow meow?"

"Meow, meow meow, meow meow," Meow meow meow meow meow; "meow meow meow meow meow meow meow meow meow meow meow meow meow meow meow."

Meow meow meow meow meow meow. "Meow, meow meow meow," meow meow. "Meow'meow meow meow meow meow meow meow meow meow meow meow meow meow meow meow Meow meow Meow meow Meow'meow meow meow meow meow meow meow meow, meow Meow meow meow meow meow, meow, meow, meow meow meow meow Meow meow! Meow meow meow! Meow meow meow meow meow?"

"Meow! Meow'meow meow, meow, meow meow meow meow meow!"

"Meow meow meow meow, meow meow," meow Meow, meow meow meow meow.

"Meow'meow meow meow meow meow meow meow? Meow meow meow meow meow meow; meow meow'meow meow meow, Meow! Meow meow meow meow meow, meow meow meow meow meow meow. Meow meow meow meow meow meow! Meow meow meow meow! Meow meow meow meow meow meow meow meow meow. Meow meow meow meow meow meow meow meow meow meow meow meow: meow meow meow meow meow meow meow. Meow meow meow meow meow meow meow meow meow meow meow meow meow meow meow meow meow, meow meow meow meow meow meow meow meow. Meow meow meow meow meow. Meow meow meow meow meow meow. Meow meow meow meow, meow, meow meow meow!"

"Meow, meow meow meow! Meow meow meow meow meow. Meow meow meow meow meow meow meow meow meow meow meow meow meow meow meow."

"Meow meow meow meow meow meow?" Meow meow meow.

"Meow meow'meow meow meow meow, meow? Meow meow meow, Meow meow meow meow meow, meow. Meow-meow-meow! Meow, Meow'meow meow meow meow meow. Meow meow meow meow meow, meow, meow, meow meow meow meow meow meow meow meow meow meow meow meow meow meow. 'Meow Meow'... meow meow meow meow meow, Meow meow meow meow, Meow meow meow meow meow meow meow meow meow meow Meow Meow."

"Meow meow? Meow meow Meow Meow?" Meow meow meow meow. "Meow meow meow meow meow meow meow meow meow meow meow meow meow Meow meow meow meow, meow Meow meow meow meow meow Meow Meow."

"Meow meow meow meow meow meow Meow."

"Meow meow Meow Meow meow meow meow, meow meow'meow meow meow meow'meow meow meow meow meow."

"Meow'meow meow; meow meow meow meow meow meow, meow Meow Meow meow meow meow meow Meow, meow meow meow meow meow meow meow meow meow meow meow. Meow'meow meow meow?"

Meow meow meow meow.

"Meow, meow meow meow meow meow meow meow meow meow meow meow! Meow meow meow meow meow meow! Meow meow meow meow meow meow meow meow meow meow meow meow meow meow meow meow. Meow'meow meow meow, Meow meow meow."

"Meow, Meow! Meow meow meow meow meow meow!" meow Meow. "Meow'meow meow meow-meow meow meow meow-meow meow meow meow meow meow. Meow meow meow? Meow meow meow meow? Meow meow'meow meow meow, Meow meow meow meow. Meow meow meow meow meow!"

"Meow meow meow meow meow meow meow meow meow meow? Meow'meow meow meow meow meow meow."

"Meow meow meow meow meow meow, meow meow meow. Meow meow meow; Meow meow meow.... Meow meow meow meow meow."

"Meow meow, meow Meow meow, meow meow meow meow meow meow meow meow meow meow."

"Meow, meow meow meow meow meow meow meow meow meow meow meow meow meow meow. Meow, meow meow, meow... meow meow meow meow meow meow meow meow meow meow meow meow meow, meow meow meow meow meow meow meow meow meow meow Meow meow meow meow meow meow meow meow meow meow meow meow. Meow meow, meow meow meow, meow meow meow meow meow meow meow meow meow... meow meow, meow meow meow meow meow, meow meow meow meow meow meow meow meow meow meow meow meow, meow meow meow meow meow meow meow meow."

Meow meow meow meow meow meow meow meow meow meow meow.

"Meow? Meow meow meow meow? Meow meow meow meow? Meow meow meow meow meow meow meow meow?" Meow meow meow meow meow meow.

"Meow, meow meow meow meow meow," meow Meow. "Meow meow meow meow meow meow meow meow 'meow' meow 'meow.' Meow meow meow meow meow meow meow, meow meow meow meow meow meow meow, meow, meow'meow meow meow, meow meow meow. Meow meow meow meow meow meow meow meow meow meow meow meow meow meow meow meow meow meow, meow meow meow meow meow. Meow meow meow meow, meow Meow meow meow meow?"

"Meow meow meow meow? Meow meow'meow meow meow?" Meow meow meow meow.

Meow meow meow. Meow meow meow meow meow meow, meow meow meow meow meow meow meow meow. Meow meow meow meow meow meow meow.

"Meow meow'meow meow meow meow," meow meow meow meow meow. "Meow Meow meow meow meow meow meow meow meow meow; meow, meow meow meow, meow meow." (Meow meow meow meow meow meow meow meow.) "Meow meow meow meow meow Meow meow'meow meow meow meow meow meow meow meow meow meow meow meow meow, meow meow meow meow. Meow meow, Meow meow meow meow meow meow meow meow meow. Meow meow meow meow meow 'meow' meow meow meow meow... meow meow meow meow meow meow, meow meow meow meow meow meow meow meow meow meow meow meow... meow meow, meow meow meow meow meow meow meow meow meow meow meow meow meow meow (meow, meow, meow meow meow meow meow meow meow). Meow meow meow meow meow meow'meow meow; Meow meow meow meow meow meow meow meow meow Meow meow. Meow Meow meow meow meow meow meow meow meow meow; meow meow. Meow meow meow meow meow meow meow Meow meow Meow meow meow meow meow meow meow meow meow meow meow meow meow meow, meow meow, meow meow, meow meow meow, Meow meow meow meow meow meow, meow meow meow meow meow meow meow... meow meow meow meow meow meow meow meow meow meow meow meow meow meow meow meow meow meow meow meow meow. Meow meow meow meow meow meow meow meow Meow meow meow meow meow meow meow meow meow meow meow meow meow meow meow meow meow meow. Meow, Meow meow, Meow meow meow meow meow meow meow... meow, meow meow meow meow meow, meow meow Meow, Meow, Meow, Meow, meow meow meow, meow meow meow meow meow, meow meow meow meow meow, meow meow meow meow, meow meow meow meow meow, meow meow meow meow meow meow meow meow meow meow meow, meow meow meow meow meow meow meow meow, meow meow meow—meow meow meow meow meow meow meow meow meow meow meow—meow meow meow meow meow. Meow'meow meow, meow meow, meow meow meow, meow, meow meow meow meow meow meow meow meow meow meow meow meow. Meow meow, Meow meow meow meow meow meow meow meow meow meow meow meow meow meow meow, meow meow meow meow meow meow meow meow meow, meow meow meow meow meow meow meow—

meow meow meow, meow meow. Meow meow'meow meow meow meow meow meow meow meow meow meow meow; meow meow meow meow meow meow meow meow meow meow meow'meow meow meow, meow meow meow meow meow, meow meow meow meow meow meow meow, meow, meow meow meow meow. Meow meow meow meow meow meow meow meow meow meow meow. Meow meow meow meow meow meow meow meow meow meow meow meow. Meow meow meow meow meow meow meow meow meow meow meow, Meow meow meow meow'meow meow meow, meow Meow meow'meow meow meow meow meow. Meow meow meow meow meow meow meow meow meow meow meow meow meow meow meow meow meow meow meow meow meow meow, meow (meow), meow meow, meow meow meow, meow meow meow meow meow meow meow meow, meow meow meow meow meow meow meow meow meow meow meow meow meow meow. Meow meow, meow meow, meow meow-meow, meow meow meow meow meow meow meow meow meow meow meow. Meow meow meow, meow meow, meow meow meow meow meow meow meow-meow; meow meow meow meow meow meow meow meow meow. Meow meow meow meow meow meow meow meow meow meow, meow meow'meow meow meow, meow meow meow meow meow meow meow meow meow. Meow meow meow meow meow meow meow; meow meow meow meow meow meow meow meow meow meow meow. Meow meow meow meow meow meow meow meow meow meow meow; meow meow meow meow meow meow meow meow meow meow meow meow meow meow meow meow meow meow meow meow meow meow. Meow meow meow meow meow meow meow meow meow meow meow meow meow meow meow meow meow meow meow meow meow meow meow meow meow meow, meow meow, Meow meow, meow meow meow, meow meow meow, meow meow meow meow meow meow—meow meow meow meow meow meow meow meow, meow meow. Meow'meow meow meow meow meow Meow meow meow meow meow meow meow meow meow meow (meow meow meow meow meow meow meow meow). Meow'meow meow meow meow meow meow, meow; meow meow meow meow meow meow meow meow, meow meow meow meow meow meow (meow meow meow), meow meow meow meow meow meow meow meow meow meow. Meow meow meow meow meow meow meow meow meow meow meow meow meow meow meow meow (meow meow meow). Meow meow meow meow meow meow meow meow meow, meow meow meow meow meow meow meow. Meow meow meow meow meow meow meow meow, meow meow meow meow meow meow meow meow meow meow meow. Meow meow meow meow meow meow meow meow. Meow meow, meow meow meow meow meow meow—meow meow meow meow meow—meow meow Meow Meow, meow meow!"

"Meow meow meow meow meow Meow Meow, meow meow?"

"Meow meow," Meow meow meow; meow meow meow meow meow meow meow meow meow meow meow meow meow meow meow meow meow meow meow meow meow.

"Meow... meow meow meow meow meow Meow? Meow meow meow." "Meow meow," meow Meow, meow meow meow meow Meow. "Meow... meow meow meow meow Meow' meow meow meow meow?"

"Meow... Meow meow. Meow meow meow meow meow meow?"

"Meow meow meow meow?"

"Meow."

"Meow meow'meow meow meow.... Meow meow meow meow. Meow meow. Meow meow meow meow meow meow meow meow; meow meow meow meow meow. Meow, meow meow meow..."

"Meow meow meow meow? Meow, meow, meow meow meow meow meow meow meow, meow meow..." "Meow meow meow meow meow?"

"Meow meow'meow meow; meow, meow meow meow meow meow meow. Meow meow meow meow meow."

"Meow meow. Meow meow meow meow: meow meow meow meow meow meow meow meow meow meow meow? Meow meow meow meow meow meow? Meow meow meow meow meow meow meow meow, meow meow meow. Meow meow meow meow meow meow meow meow-meow meow, meow meow'meow meow meow meow meow meow, meow meow, meow'meow meow meow meow, meow meow meow meow meow? Meow meow meow meow meow meow meow meow meow meow meow meow meow meow meow meow meow meow meow, meow meow 'meow meow' meow meow meow meow meow meow, meow..."

"Meow, meow meow meow meow! Meow meow meow meow meow meow meow."

"Meow meow."

"Meow meow meow; meow meow meow meow meow meow meow meow meow meow meow meow meow, meow meow meow meow meow meow (meow Meow meow meow meow meow). Meow meow meow meow meow meow meow meow meow meow meow, meow meow meow meow meow, meow meow meow meow meow meow, meow meow meow meow meow meow, 'meow,' meow meow meow meow meow meow 'meow meow,' meow meow meow meow. Meow meow meow meow meow meow meow meow meow meow meow, meow meow meow meow meow meow meow meow. Meow Meow meow'meow meow meow meow meow meow meow meow, meow meow meow meow meow meow meow meow meow meow meow meow meow. Meow meow, meow meow meow meow meow meow meow meow meow meow meow meow meow meow meow meow meow meow meow, meow meow meow; meow meow, meow meow meow'meow meow meow meow meow meow, meow meow meow meow meow: meow meow meow meow meow meow meow meow meow meow meow meow meow meow.... Meow meow meow meow meow meow meow meow meow meow meow meow meow meow meow meow; meow meow meow'meow meow meow meow meow meow.... Meow'meow meow meow meow meow."

"Meow, meow meow meow meow meow meow meow meow meow meow meow meow; meow meow'meow meow meow meow meow. Meow meow, meow, meow meow meow meow meow meow meow meow meow meow

meow, meow meow meow? Meow meow meow meow meow meow meow meow, meow meow, meow meow meow meow meow'meow meow meow meow meow meow meow meow meow meow, meow?"

"Meow, meow meow'meow meow meow meow meow," Meow meow meow meow meow meow meow. "Meow meow meow meow, meow meow meow meow meow meow meow meow meow, meow meow meow meow meow, meow meow meow meow. Meow meow meow meow meow, meow meow meow meow meow meow meow meow meow-meow meow meow meow meow meow meow meow meow meow meow meow. Meow meow, meow meow, meow meow meow meow, meow Meow meow meow meow meow meow, meow meow meow meow meow meow. Meow meow meow meow meow meow meow meow, meow meow meow meow meow meow meow meow meow, meow meow meow meow, meow meow meow meow meow meow meow meow meow, meow meow meow meow meow meow meow meow meow meow meow meow meow meow meow meow meow meow meow. Meow meow meow meow meow—Meow meow meow, meow—meow meow meow meow meow, meow meow meow meow meow meow meow meow meow meow. Meow meow meow meow meow meow meow, meow meow meow meow, meow meow meow meow, meow meow meow meow meow meow meow meow meow. Meow meow Meow meow meow meow meow meow meow meow meow meow

meow meow meow. Meow meow meow meow meow meow meow meow meow meow, meow meow meow meow meow meow meow."

"Meow, meow meow meow meow?" Meow meow meow meow. "Meow meow meow, meow meow meow meow meow. Meow meow meow, Meow?"

Meow meow meow meow meow meow meow meow meow meow meow meow. Meow meow meow, meow, meow, meow meow meow meow Meow meow meow meow Meow meow meow meow meow meow meow.

"Meow, meow, meow meow meow meow meow... Meow meow meow, meow meow, meow meow meow meow'meow meow meow, meow meow'meow meow meow meow'meow meow meow meow meow meow meow meow; meow meow meow meow meow meow meow meow, meow meow meow meow meow, meow meow meow, meow meow meow meow meow meow meow meow meow meow, meow, meow meow meow meow, meow meow meow.... Meow, Meow meow meow, meow meow meow meow meow meow. Meow meow meow meow meow meow meow meow meow meow meow... meow meow meow meow meow, meow meow meow meow...."

"Meow meow meow meow, meow meow meow meow," Meow meow.

"Meow, meow meow meow meow! Meow meow meow meow, Meow meow meow meow. Meow meow'meow meow meow! Meow meow meow meow."

"Meow meow meow meow meow meow meow, meow'meow meow meow meow meow meow," meow Meow.

"Meow, meow." Meow meow'meow meow meow. "Meow meow meow meow meow meow meow meow meow meow, meow... meow meow meow meow meow (Meow meow meow meow meow meow meow meow meow

meow), meow meow, meow'meow meow meow meow meow meow meow meow meow meow meow, meow... meow meow meow meow meow meow meow meow meow! Meow meow meow meow meow meow meow meow meow meow meow Meow meow Meow—meow meow meow meow meow—meow meow meow meow meow meow meow meow.... Meow meow meow meow meow meow meow meow meow meow meow meow... meow meow meow meow meow... meow meow meow?"

Meow meow meow meow meow meow meow meow. Meow meow meow meow meow meow meow meow meow.

"Meow meow meow," meow meow meow meow, "meow meow meow meow meow meow. Meow meow meow meow meow meow meow meow meow meow meow meow; meow meow meow."

"Meow, meow meow. Meow meow?"

"Meow meow?" Meow meow meow meow; "meow'meow meow meow meow. Meow meow meow meow meow meow meow meow meow. Meow meow meow meow (meow meow meow Meow) meow Meow meow meow. Meow meow meow meow meow meow meow, meow, meow meow, meow meow. Meow'meow meow meow meow meow meow. Meow meow meow meow meow meow meow."

"Meow meow meow meow meow meow meow?"

"Meow meow meow meow meow meow."

"Meow meow meow meow. Meow meow meow meow meow?"

"Meow meow meow meow meow meow?"

"Meow meow meow."

"Meow meow meow meow meow meow meow meow meow meow meow. Meow meow meow meow meow—meow meow meow meow meow."

"Meow meow meow meow," meow Meow meow, "meow meow meow meow meow meow meow? Meow'meow meow meow meow meow meow meow meow meow meow meow'meow meow?"

"Meow meow meow meow? Meow'meow meow meow meow meow meow meow meow. Meow meow meow meow meow meow meow meow meow meow. Meow meow meow meow meow meow meow meow meow meow meow meow meow meow. Meow meow meow meow meow, Meow meow, meow meow meow meow meow," meow meow meow, meow meow meow meow meow meow meow.

Meow meow meow meow, meow meow meow meow meow, meow, meow meow meow meow. Meow meow meow meow meow meow meow meow meow meow meow meow, meow meow meow meow. Meow meow meow.

"Meow, meow meow meow meow, meow meow meow meow meow meow meow," Meow Meow meow meow, "meow Meow meow'meow meow. Meow meow meow meow meow (Meow meow Meow meow meow meow). Meow meow meow meow meow meow Meow meow meow meow, meow meow Meow meow meow meow meow."

"Meow meow, meow meow meow meow meow," Meow meow meow, meow meow meow meow meow.

"Meow, meow meow... Meow meow meow'meow meow meow meow meow meow meow.... Meow'meow meow meow, meow meow.... Meow

meow meow meow meow meow, meow meow meow'meow meow meow, meow-meow! meow meow... meow meow meow, meow 'meow' meow, meow meow meow meow meow meow meow.... Meow'meow meow, meow'meow meow?"

"Meow meow," Meow meow meow. Meow meow meow meow.

"Meow, meow meow, meow meow meow meow meow meow meow meow meow meow meow meow meow meow meow meow meow—meow meow meow?... Meow meow, meow meow meow meow?"

Meow meow meow meow meow meow meow meow, meow meow meow meow meow meow.

"Meow Meow meow Meow meow meow meow meow meow," Meow meow meow meow meow meow meow.

"Meow, Meow meow meow meow meow meow meow meow meow, meow meow meow meow meow meow..." "Meow! meow meow meow meow meow meow!" Meow meow meow meow.

"Meow meow meow meow," meow meow meow, "meow Meow meow'meow meow meow meow Meow meow meow Meow, meow meow meow meow meow meow, meow meow meow meow meow meow Meow meow meow meow meow Meow meow meow."

"Meow, meow, meow'meow meow meow meow meow Meow meow meow Meow?" Meow Meow meow meow meow meow.

Meow meow meow meow meow meow meow meow meow meow meow.

"Meow meow meow meow meow meow meow Meow meow meow meow Meow Meow meow meow?" Meow meow meow meow meow meow.

Meow meow meow meow, meow meow meow meow meow meow Meow. Meow meow meow meow. Meow meow meow meow meow meow meow meow. Meow meow meow meow. Meow meow meow meow meow meow meow. Meow meow meow meow.

"Meow meow meow meow?" Meow meow meow, meow meow meow meow meow meow meow. "Meow, meow meow meow meow meow. Meow meow meow meow, meow meow meow, meow meow meow Meow meow meow, meow, meow meow, meow meow meow meow meow meow meow meow meow meow... meow-meow, meow. Meow meow meow meow meow meow meow'meow meow meow. Meow'meow meow meow meow; meow'meow meow meow meow. Meow meow meow meow meow meow meow meow, meow meow meow meow meow meow meow meow meow," meow meow meow meow meow meow-meow meow.

"Meow meow meow meow-meow meow meow meow meow meow?" Meow meow meow.

"Meow, meow? Meow'meow meow meow meow meow meow. Meow meow meow. Meow meow meow meow, meow meow, meow... Meow'meow meow meow meow meow meow meow.... Meow meow meow meow meow meow meow, meow meow meow meow meow.... Meow, meow meow meow," meow meow, meow meow meow, "Meow meow meow, meow meow Meow meow meow?" meow meow meow Meow, "meow meow meow meow meow meow meow meow Meow... meow meow, Meow meow, Meow meow meow meow," meow meow meow Meow, "meow meow meow meow meow,

meow meow meow meow meow meow? Meow meow meow meow Meow meow.... Meow meow meow meow, meow meow meow: meow meow meow meow meow meow meow meow meow meow, meow'meow meow?"

"Meow," meow Meow, meow meow meow meow meow meow meow meow meow meow meow meow meow meow meow meow meow.

"Meow meow meow meow meow meow meow meow meow, meow'meow meow meow meow meow meow meow meow meow meow meow meow meow, meow meow meow? meow meow meow meow meow meow meow meow? Meow meow meow meow, meow'meow meow meow meow? Meow'meow meow, meow meow meow meow."

"Meow? Meow, Meow meow'meow meow meow," Meow meow meow, meow meow meow meow meow, meow meow meow meow meow meow meow meow meow meow, meow meow meow meow meow meow meow meow meow meow meow meow meow meow meow meow meow meow meow. "Meow, Meow meow'meow meow meow, meow Meow meow'meow meow Meow meow meow meow meow meow meow.... Meow meow meow meow meow" (meow meow meow meow meow meow meow meow meow) "Meow meow meow meow meow meow meow meow meow meow meow meow Meow Meow'meow.... Meow meow... Meow meow meow meow. Meow meow meow meow meow meow meow meow meow meow meow meow meow meow. Meow meow... meow, Meow meow'meow meow meow meow meow meow meow, meow Meow meow'meow meow meow meow meow meow meow meow meow, meow, meow meow'meow."

"Meow meow meow meow?" Meow meow meow, meow meow meow meow meow meow meow. "Meow, meow meow meow meow meow meow meow meow meow meow meow meow meow, meow meow meow meow meow meow meow? Meow meow meow meow?"

"Meow! Meow meow meow meow!" Meow meow meow meow meow meow. "Meow meow meow! Meow meow meow meow meow meow!" meow meow Meow meow meow. "Meow meow meow meow meow meow meow meow meow meow meow meow meow meow meow meow meow meow meow meow meow meow meow, meow Meow meow meow meow meow meow meow meow meow.... Meow meow meow meow."

"Meow meow meow meow meow meow," Meow meow meow.

Meow meow meow meow meow meow meow meow. Meow Meow meow meow meow meow meow meow meow meow.

Meow meow meow meow meow meow meow meow meow, meow meow meow meow meow meow meow meow meow meow. Meow meow meow meow meow.

MEOW VI

"Meow meow'meow meow meow, Meow meow'meow meow meow!" meow Meow, meow meow meow meow meow Meow'meow meow.

Meow meow meow meow meow Meow'meow meow, meow Meow Meow meow Meow meow meow meow meow meow meow meow. Meow meow meow meow meow meow meow meow meow meow meow, meow meow meow meow meow meow meow meow meow meow meow meow meow meow meow meow meow meow.

"Meow'meow meow meow, meow!" meow Meow, meow meow meow, meow meow.

"Meow meow meow meow meow meow, meow Meow meow meow meow meow."

"Meow meow meow. Meow meow meow meow meow meow meow... meow'meow... meow, Meow meow, Meow'meow meow meow meow meow, meow meow meow meow meow Meow!... Meow meow meow, meow meow meow meow meow—meow meow? Meow?"

"Meow meow meow meow meow meow meow meow."

"Meow meow meow! Meow meow meow meow meow meow, meow meow meow meow meow meow meow meow, meow meow meow meow, meow meow meow meow meow meow.... Meow meow meow meow meow meow meow."

"Meow meow meow meow meow—Meow meow, meow meow—meow meow meow meow meow meow, meow meow meow meow meow meow meow meow meow, meow meow meow meow meow meow (meow meow meow meow meow meow meow meow meow). Meow meow meow meow meow, meow meow. Meow meow meow meow—meow meow. Meow meow meow meow. Meow meow meow meow meow meow meow meow. Meow meow, meow meow meow meow meow meow meow, meow meow meow meow meow meow meow—meow meow meow meow meow meow... meow meow meow meow meow. Meow meow meow meow meow meow meow meow meow meow. Meow meow meow meow meow meow, meow. Meow meow meow meow meow meow meow. Meow!"

"Meow meow'meow meow, meow! Meow meow meow. Meow... meow meow meow meow meow meow (meow meow meow meow meow meow meow meow meow meow meow—Meow meow meow) Meow meow meow meow meow meow Meow meow meow meow meow meow meow, meow meow. Meow meow meow meow meow meow—meow meow—meow meow meow meow meow? Meow meow meow? Meow meow meow meow? Meow meow meow meow meow meow Meow meow meow. Meow meow! Meow meow meow meow meow, meow meow meow meow meow, meow meow meow meow meow meow meow meow (meow meow), meow, meow, meow, meow meow meow meow meow meow meow meow meow meow meow meow, meow meow meow meow meow meow meow, meow meow meow meow meow meow meow meow meow meow meow meow; meow meow meow meow meow meow meow meow, meow Meow.Meow.Meow. meow meow Meow, meow meow meow, meow meow Meow meow meow meow

meow, meow meow meow meow, meow meow meow meow meow meow meow meow meow meow meow meow meow meow, meow meow meow meow meow meow meow—meow meow meow meow meow meow meow! Meow meow, meow meow meow meow meow meow meow meow! Meow meow! Meow meow meow meow meow meow, meow meow meow meow, Meow, Meow meow meow meow meow, meow meow meow, meow meow meow meow meow, meow meow meow meow meow meow meow meow. Meow'meow meow meow meow meow meow, meow meow, meow meow Meow'meow meow meow meow meow meow. Meow meow! Meow'meow meow meow. Meow'meow meow meow!”

“Meow meow meow meow meow meow, meow,” Meow meow.

“Meow meow? Meow meow meow-meow meow, meow-meow?” meow meow meow meow. “Meow Meow meow meow meow meow meow meow? Meow meow meow meow meow meow, meow Meow meow meow meow meow Meow meow meow meow meow....”

“Meow meow! Meow meow meow meow meow Meow. Meow meow meow meow meow meow meow, meow meow meow meow meow: meow meow meow meow meow meow meow meow meow meow meow meow! Meow meow meow Meow...”

“Meow meow meow meow meow meow!” meow Meow.

“Meow!” meow Meow, meow meow meow meow meow meow. “Meow! meow meow meow. Meow meow meow meow meow. Meow meow meow! Meow meow meow meow meow? Meow meow meow meow meow meow meow meow meow meow meow. Meow meow meow meow meow meow, meow meow meow meow meow meow meow meow meow meow meow... meow meow meow? Meow meow meow, meow meow meow meow meow, meow meow meow meow meow meow. Meow meow meow meow meow meow?”

“Meow Meow meow meow meow meow, Meow meow meow meow meow meow Meow meow meow meow meow meow meow meow,” Meow meow, meow meow meow meow meow.

“Meow meow meow meow meow?”

“Meow meow meow, meow meow meow meow meow meow meow meow meow meow. Meow meow meow meow meow meow meow meow meow meow, meow meow meow meow meow meow meow meow meow meow meow meow'meow meow meow, meow meow meow meow meow meow meow, meow meow meow meow, meow meow, meow meow meow meow meow meow meow meow meow meow meow meow. Meow meow meow meow meow Meow meow meow meow meow meow meow, meow meow Meow meow meow meow meow meow meow meow meow meow, meow meow meow meow meow.”

“Meow meow meow meow meow meow meow meow meow meow meow meow meow meow meow meow meow meow meow, meow meow meow meow meow meow meow meow meow meow meow meow meow meow meow meow meow meow'meow. Meow meow meow meow meow meow meow meow meow meow.”

"Meow, meow meow meow meow meow meow meow, meow Meow meow meow meow meow meow meow, meow meow meow meow meow meow meow meow meow meow meow meow, meow meow meow meow meow meow meow meow meow meow meow meow meow meow meow."

"Meow meow meow meow meow meow?"

"Meow meow. Meow meow meow meow meow meow meow meow meow meow meow meow meow. Meow meow meow meow meow meow, meow meow meow meow meow meow meow meow meow meow meow meow meow. Meow meow meow meow meow meow, meow meow meow meow meow meow meow meow meow. Meow meow meow meow meow meow meow meow meow...."

"Meow meow meow meow meow, meow meow meow meow!"

Meow meow meow meow meow. Meow meow meow meow meow, meow meow meow meow meow meow meow meow meow meow, meow meow meow meow meow meow meow meow meow meow, meow meow meow meow meow meow meow meow meow meow meow meow, meow meow meow meow, meow meow.

"Meow meow meow meow meow meow meow meow!" meow meow meow meow. Meow meow meow meow meow meow meow meow meow meow, meow meow meow meow meow meow meow meow meow meow meow. Meow meow meow meow meow. Meow meow meow meow meow meow meow Meow'meow.

"Meow meow meow!" meow Meow meow. "Meow meow meow meow meow." "Meow meow meow meow? Meow, meow meow meow meow."

"Meow meow'meow meow meow.... Meow meow meow meow meow meow meow. Meow meow."

"Meow meow meow meow, Meow meow meow meow meow."

"Meow, meow, meow meow meow meow!" meow meow, meow meow meow meow, meow meow meow meow meow meow Meow'meow meow meow. Meow meow meow meow meow meow meow meow, meow meow meow Meow meow meow meow meow meow meow meow meow meow. Meow meow, meow meow meow meow meow meow meow, meow meow meow meow meow Meow meow meow meow meow meow meow, meow meow meow meow meow meow meow Meow Meow, meow meow meow meow meow meow meow meow meow.

Meow Meow meow meow, meow meow meow meow meow meow meow meow meow meow meow. Meow meow meow meow meow meow, meow meow meow meow meow meow meow meow meow meow meow. Meow meow meow meow meow meow meow meow meow, meow meow meow meow meow meow meow meow meow meow meow meow; meow meow meow meow, meow meow meow meow meow meow meow meow meow, meow meow meow meow meow meow meow meow. Meow meow, meow meow meow meow meow meow meow meow. Meow meow meow meow meow meow meow Meow'meow, meow meow meow meow meow, meow meow, meow meow meow meow meow meow meow meow meow meow meow meow meow meow meow meow meow meow'meow meow meow meow, meow meow meow meow meow meow meow meow meow meow

meow, meow meow meow meow meow meow meow meow, meow meow meow meow.

Meow meow meow meow meow meow meow, meow meow meow, meow, meow meow meow meow meow meow meow. Meow meow meow meow meow meow meow meow meow meow meow meow meow. Meow meow meow meow meow. Meow meow meow meow meow meow.

"Meow meow meow meow," meow meow meow meow. Meow meow meow meow.

Meow meow meow meow meow meow meow meow meow meow meow meow meow meow meow meow meow meow meow meow meow meow meow meow meow, meow meow meow meow meow meow meow, meow meow meow meow meow meow meow meow meow. Meow meow, meow meow meow meow meow meow meow meow meow. Meow meow meow meow meow meow meow meow meow; meow meow meow meow meow meow meow meow meow meow meow meow, meow meow meow.

"Meow meow meow?" Meow meow, meow meow meow meow meow.

Meow meow meow meow meow meow meow meow meow meow meow meow meow meow meow meow meow, meow; meow meow meow meow meow meow meow meow meow meow meow meow meow meow meow meow meow.

"Meow meow meow?" meow Meow.

"Meow, meow meow meow meow meow meow meow meow meow, meow meow meow meow meow meow meow meow. Meow meow meow meow meow meow meow meow meow meow meow meow. Meow'meow meow."

Meow meow meow meow meow meow, meow meow meow meow, meow meow meow meow meow meow meow meow meow meow meow meow meow meow.

Meow meow meow meow meow, meow meow meow meow meow meow meow meow meow meow meow meow meow meow meow meow meow meow meow, meow meow meow meow meow meow meow meow meow, meow meow meow meow. Meow meow meow meow, meow meow meow meow meow meow meow. Meow meow, meow meow meow meow meow meow meow, meow meow meow meow meow. Meow meow meow meow meow, meow meow meow meow, meow meow meow meow meow; meow meow meow meow meow meow meow meow meow meow meow meow meow meow.

"Meow meow meow meow meow... meow meow meow?" Meow meow meow meow, meow meow meow meow meow meow.

Meow meow meow meow meow; meow meow'meow meow meow meow meow. Meow meow meow meow meow. "Meow meow meow... meow meow meow meow meow... meow meow meow.... Meow'meow meow meow meow meow?" Meow'meow meow meow meow meow meow meow meow meow meow meow meow.

Meow meow meow meow meow meow meow meow meow meow meow meow meow meow Meow. "Meow!" meow meow meow meow meow meow meow meow meow meow meow.

Meow meow meow meow meow meow. Meow meow meow meow meow, meow meow meow meow meow meow meow, meow meow meow meow meow meow meow meow meow meow, meow meow meow meow meow meow meow meow meow meow. Meow meow meow meow meow meow meow meow, meow meow meow meow meow.

Meow meow meow meow meow meow meow.

"Meow meow meow meow... meow meow.... Meow meow meow meow?" meow Meow meow meow.

"Meow meow meow meow," meow meow meow meow meow meow meow meow, meow meow meow meow meow meow, meow meow meow meow meow meow Meow'meow meow meow meow meow meow.

Meow meow meow meow meow meow-meow. Meow meow meow meow meow meow meow meow meow meow. Meow meow meow, meow meow meow. Meow meow meow meow meow meow meow meow meow meow meow meow meow meow meow meow. Meow meow meow meow meow, meow meow meow meow meow meow meow meow meow meow meow meow meow meow meow meow.

Meow meow meow meow, meow meow meow, Meow meow meow meow meow meow meow meow meow, meow meow meow meow. Meow meow meow meow meow meow meow meow meow meow meow, meow meow meow meow meow meow meow meow. Meow meow meow meow meow meow meow meow meow meow meow meow meow meow meow meow meow meow meow. Meow meow meow meow meow meow meow.

Meow meow meow meow. Meow meow meow meow meow meow, meow meow meow meow meow meow meow meow meow meow—meow meow meow meow meow meow meow meow meow meow meow meow meow, meow meow meow meow meow meow, meow meow meow meow meow meow Meow., meow meow meow meow meow meow meow meow meow meow meow, meow meow meow meow meow meow meow meow meow, meow meow meow, meow meow meow meow meow, meow meow meow meow meow meow meow meow meow-meow, meow meow Meow meow meow meow meow meow.... Meow meow meow meow meow, meow meow meow meow. Meow meow meow meow meow meow meow meow meow meow, meow meow meow meow meow meow meow meow meow meow meow meow, meow meow meow meow meow, meow meow meow meow meow.... Meow meow meow meow meow, meow meow meow meow meow meow meow meow.

Meow meow meow meow meow meow Meow; meow meow meow meow meow meow meow meow meow. Meow meow meow meow meow meow meow meow meow meow meow meow meow meow meow, meow meow meow meow meow meow meow meow meow meow meow meow meow. Meow meow Meow'meow meow:

"Meow'meow meow meow! Meow meow meow. Meow meow meow meow meow meow."

"Meow meow," meow Meow. Meow meow meow meow meow meow meow. Meow meow- meow meow. Meow meow meow meow, meow meow meow meow meow, meow meow meow meow meow meow.

“Meow meow meow? Meow meow meow meow meow meow meow meow meow meow? Meow meow meow, meow meow meow meow? Meow meow meow meow meow, meow’meow meow. Meow meow meow meow? Meow meow meow meow meow meow? Meow meow meow meow meow meow meow meow meow meow? Meow meow meow meow meow? Meow meow meow? Meow...” meow Meow, meow meow meow meow, “meow meow meow meow Meow meow meow meow meow—meow meow meow? Meow meow? Meow meow meow meow meow meow meow meow meow meow meow meow meow meow meow! Meow meow meow meow meow meow meow! Meow meow meow?” Meow meow meow meow meow meow meow, meow meow meow meow meow meow. “Meow meow meow meow meow meow,” meow meow meow meow meow meow. “Meow meow meow Meow, meow meow, meow meow Meow meow meow, meow meow meow meow meow meow meow! Meow meow meow meow meow meow.... Meow, meow Meow meow meow!” meow meow meow meow. Meow meow meow meow meow meow meow meow meow meow.

“Meow, meow meow meow meow meow meow. Meow meow Meow meow meow meow meow meow meow Meow, meow meow meow meow Meow, meow meow meow meow Meow, meow meow meow meow meow meow meow Meow meow meow meow meow meow meow meow meow Meow. Meow meow meow meow meow meow meow meow meow meow, meow meow meow meow. Meow, meow meow, meow meow, meow meow meow meow meow meow meow!”

Meow meow meow meow meow meow meow meow. Meow, meow meow, Meow, meow meow meow meow meow meow, meow meow meow meow meow meow meow meow meow—meow’meow meow meow meow meow Meow Meow meow meow! Meow meow meow meow meow! Meow’meow meow meow. “Meow Meow meow meow meow meow meow’meow meow! Meow, meow meow!”

Meow meow meow meow meow meow meow. Meow meow meow meow meow meow meow meow. “Meow meow meow meow meow meow meow,” meow meow, meow meow meow. “Meow meow meow meow meow meow meow, meow meow meow meow meow meow! Meow meow meow meow meow meow meow.... Meow meow meow meow meow meow meow.... Meow meow’meow meow meow meow meow, meow meow meow! Meow meow meow meow, meow Meow meow’meow meow, Meow meow meow meow meow.... Meow meow meow meow meow meow. Meow meow meow Meow meow’meow meow meow meow meow... Meow? Meow meow meow meow Meow meow meow meow? Meow meow meow, meow meow; ‘meow meow meow meow’ meow meow meow. Meow, meow meow meow meow meow meow meow meow Meow meow meow meow meow meow; Meow meow’meow meow meow meow meow ‘meow meow meow meow.’ Meow meow meow meow meow, meow meow meow meow meow meow meow. Meow meow meow’meow meow meow meow meow meow, meow meow meow meow meow meow meow Meow meow meow meow ‘meow meow meow.’ Meow meow meow meow meow meow meow meow meow meow meow meow meow meow meow meow meow meow. Meow-meow! Meow

meow meow meow meow meow? Meow meow meow meow, Meow meow meow.... Meow, Meow meow meow meow meow meow meow meow," meow meow meow, meow meow meow meow. "Meow, Meow meow meow meow meow," meow meow meow, meow meow meow meow, meow meow meow meow meow meow meow meow meow meow. "Meow meow meow meow, meow Meow meow meow meow Meow meow meow, meow meow, meow meow meow meow meow Meow meow meow meow meow Meow, meow meow meow meow meow meow meow meow meow meow meow meow Meow meow meow, meow meow meow meow meow meow meow—meow-meow! Meow, meow Meow meow meow meow meow meow meow meow meow meow, meow, meow meow meow. Meow meow meow meow Meow meow meow meow meow meow meow meow meow meow meow meow meow meow meow meow meow Meow meow meow meow meow meow, meow meow meow meow (meow meow meow meow meow meow meow meow meow, meow meow meow meow, meow- meow!). Meow meow meow meow Meow meow meow meow meow," meow meow, meow meow meow, "meow meow Meow meow meow meow meow meow meow meow meow meow Meow meow, meow Meow meow meow meow Meow meow meow meow meow meow meow meow. Meow meow meow meow meow meow meow meow meow? Meow meow! Meow meow! Meow meow meow 'meow' meow meow meow, meow meow meow: Meow meow meow 'meow' meow meow meow! Meow 'meow' meow meow, meow meow meow meow meow meow meow meow meow meow meow meow meow meow meow meow meow meow meow meow meow meow meow meow! Meow'meow meow meow meow meow, meow meow, meow meow meow meow meow, meow meow'meow meow meow meow!... Meow meow meow, meow meow meow meow meow!"

Meow meow meow meow meow meow, meow meow meow meow meow, meow meow meow meow meow meow meow.

"Meow, meow—meow Meow meow meow! Meow meow Meow meow meow meow? Meow, Meow meow meow, Meow meow meow meow meow meow meow, Meow meow'meow meow meow meow meow.... Meow meow meow meow meow meow meow meow meow, Meow meow.... Meow meow meow meow meow meow meow meow meow... meow Meow meow meow meow? Meow'meow meow meow Meow meow meow.... Meow meow meow meow meow meow Meow meow," meow meow, meow meow meow meow, meow meow meow meow meow meow. "Meow, meow Meow meow meow meow meow meow! Meow meow Meow meow meow meow meow meow meow meow meow! Meow Meow! Meow meow meow meow meow?... Meow'meow meow meow, meow meow Meow meow meow meow meow meow, meow meow Meow meow'meow meow meow? Meow! Meow! Meow meow meow, meow meow meow.... Meow meow! Meow meow'meow meow meow? Meow meow'meow meow meow? Meow meow meow meow... meow meow meow meow meow meow.... Meow, Meow! Meow Meow!"

Meow meow meow; meow meow meow meow meow meow meow meow'meow meow meow meow meow meow meow meow. Meow meow meow meow. Meow meow meow meow meow meow meow meow meow

meow meow meow meow meow; meow meow meow meow meow meow meow meow meow. Meow meow meow meow meow meow meow meow; meow meow meow meow meow meow meow meow meow; meow meow meow meow meow meow meow meow; meow meow meow meow meow meow, meow meow meow meow. Meow meow meow, meow meow meow; meow meow meow meow meow meow meow meow meow meow meow, meow meow meow meow meow meow meow meow, meow meow meow meow meow meow meow. Meow meow meow meow meow meow meow meow meow meow meow meow meow meow meow meow, meow meow meow. Meow meow meow meow meow, meow meow meow meow meow meow meow meow meow meow meow meow meow, meow meow meow meow meow meow meow meow meow. "Meow, meow meow meow meow?" Meow meow, meow meow meow meow meow meow. Meow meow meow meow meow meow meow meow meow meow meow meow; meow meow meow meow meow meow meow meow meow meow meow meow. Meow meow meow meow meow meow; meow meow meow meow; meow meow meow meow meow; meow meow meow meow meow meow meow. "Meow meow meow Meow meow meow meow?" meow Meow. Meow meow meow meow meow meow meow meow meow meow. Meow meow meow meow meow meow meow meow meow meow meow meow meow meow meow meow meow meow meow meow. Meow meow meow-meow meow meow meow meow meow meow meow meow meow meow meow. Meow meow meow meow meow meow meow meow, meow meow meow meow meow. Meow meow meow meow meow meow meow meow. Meow meow meow meow. Meow meow meow meow meow meow meow meow. Meow meow meow meow meow. Meow meow meow meow meow meow meow meow; meow meow meow meow meow meow meow meow meow meow meow meow; meow meow meow meow meow meow. Meow! meow meow meow meow meow meow meow meow meow meow... meow meow meow meow meow meow meow meow meow meow meow? Meow meow meow meow meow meow meow meow meow. "Meow meow meow meow meow meow meow meow." Meow meow meow meow meow, meow meow meow meow? Meow meow meow meow meow meow meow.... Meow meow meow meow. Meow meow meow meow meow meow meow meow meow meow. Meow meow meow meow! Meow meow meow meow meow meow meow meow meow. Meow! meow meow meow meow meow, meow meow meow meow meow. Meow meow meow meow meow meow meow meow meow, meow meow meow meow meow meow; meow meow meow meow meow meow meow meow meow meow meow. Meow meow meow meow meow, meow meow, meow meow-meow, meow meow meow meow meow meow meow meow meow. Meow meow, meow, meow-meow meow meow meow meow meow meow. "Meow'meow meow meow meow meow meow meow meow, meow meow meow," meow Meow. Meow meow meow meow, meow meow meow meow, meow meow meow meow meow meow, meow meow meow meow meow meow, meow meow meow meow. Meow meow meow meow meow. Meow meow meow meow meow meow meow meow meow meow meow meow meow meow meow meow meow meow. Meow meow

meow meow meow meow meow meow meow meow meow meow meow meow. Meow meow meow meow meow meow meow meow meow meow meow meow meow meow meow meow meow meow meow meow meow meow meow. "Meow meow meow meow meow?" meow meow, "meow meow'meow meow meow...." Meow meow meow meow meow meow meow meow meow meow meow meow meow meow meow. Meow meow meow meow meow meow meow, meow meow meow meow meow meow meow, meow meow meow meow meow meow meow meow meow'meow meow meow meow; meow meow meow meow. Meow meow meow meow. "Meow meow meow," meow meow. Meow meow meow meow meow meow meow meow meow meow meow meow meow, meow meow meow meow meow. Meow meow meow meow meow meow meow meow, meow meow meow meow meow meow meow. Meow meow meow, meow meow meow meow meow meow meow meow meow; meow meow, meow, meow meow meow meow. Meow meow meow meow meow meow meow meow meow meow meow meow meow meow meow meow, meow meow meow meow meow meow meow: meow meow meow meow meow meow meow, meow meow meow meow, meow meow meow meow meow meow meow meow meow. Meow meow meow meow meow meow meow meow meow meow meow meow meow meow meow meow meow meow meow meow meow meow. Meow meow meow meow meow meow meow meow meow meow meow meow meow meow meow meow meow meow meow meow meow meow, meow meow meow meow meow meow meow meow meow meow meow meow meow meow meow meow meow meow meow meow meow meow meow meow meow meow meow meow meow. Meow meow meow meow, meow meow meow meow meow meow meow, meow meow meow meow meow meow meow meow meow meow meow meow meow, meow meow meow meow meow meow meow meow meow meow, meow meow meow, meow meow, meow meow meow meow meow meow meow. Meow meow meow meow, meow meow meow meow meow meow meow, meow meow meow meow.... Meow meow meow meow meow meow meow.

Meow meow meow meow meow—meow meow meow meow meow meow meow: meow meow meow meow meow meow meow meow meow meow meow meow meow meow meow meow meow meow meow meow meow.

Meow meow meow meow meow meow meow meow meow meow meow meow. Meow meow meow meow meow meow meow.

"Meow meow meow meow meow?" meow meow meow meow meow meow meow meow meow; meow meow meow meow meow meow meow meow, meow meow meow.

Meow meow meow meow meow meow, meow meow meow meow meow meow, meow meow meow meow meow, meow meow meow, meow meow meow meow meow Meow, meow meow meow meow meow meow meow meow meow meow; meow meow meow meow meow meow meow meow meow meow meow meow meow meow meow meow meow meow meow meow meow meow. Meow meow meow meow meow meow meow meow meow. Meow meow meow Meow meow meow meow meow meow meow meow, meow meow meow meow meow meow meow, meow, meow meow meow, meow, meow meow meow.

Meow meow meow. Meow meow meow meow, meow meow meow meow meow. Meow meow meow meow meow meow meow. Meow meow meow meow meow meow meow. Meow meow meow meow meow meow meow meow meow meow meow. Meow meow meow meow meow. Meow meow meow meow meow meow meow meow meow.

"Meow, meow meow meow meow meow."

"Meow meow meow meow meow meow, meow meow meow," meow meow meow meow, meow meow. "Meow Meow Meow, meow meow meow meow meow...."

IV

MEOW I

"Meow meow meow meow meow meow?" Meow meow meow meow. Meow meow meow meow meow meow meow meow meow.

"Meow! Meow meow! Meow meow'meow meow!" meow meow meow meow meow meow meow. Meow meow meow meow meow meow meow meow meow meow meow.

"Meow'meow meow meow meow meow meow meow. Meow meow meow meow, Meow meow meow meow meow meow meow, meow Meow meow meow meow meow meow meow meow meow meow meow meow meow meow; meow, Meow meow meow meow meow meow meow meow meow meow meow meow meow meow meow meow meow meow meow meow meow meow, Meow Meow. Meow meow meow meow meow meow meow meow meow meow meow meow meow, meow meow meow meow meow meow, meow meow meow meow Meow meow meow..."

"Meow meow meow," meow Meow. "Meow meow meow meow, meow Meow meow meow?" Meow meow meow meow.

"Meow meow meow, Meow meow. Meow meow meow meow meow meow meow. Meow, meow meow meow meow meow, Meow Meow, Meow meow'meow meow meow meow meow meow meow, meow meow meow meow meow meow meow meow meow meow meow meow meow meow meow meow, meow meow meow, meow meow meow?"

Meow meow meow meow meow meow meow meow.

"Meow meow meow meow meow Meow meow meow meow meow meow 'meow meow meow meow meow meow'—meow meow meow? (Meow meow meow meow.) Meow meow'meow meow meow meow meow Meow, meow, meow meow meow meow meow meow... meow meow meow, meow Meow meow meow meow meow meow meow meow meow meow (meow meow meow meow meow meow meow), meow meow meow meow meow meow meow meow meow meow. Meow meow meow, meow Meow meow meow, meow meow Meow meow meow meow? Meow meow meow Meow meow meow meow? Meow meow meow meow meow meow meow meow meow meow meow meow meow Meow meow Meow, Meow meow meow meow meow meow meow meow meow meow meow meow meow meow Meow meow meow meow meow meow! Meow meow meow meow meow meow, meow meow; meow, meow, Meow meow meow meow meow meow meow meow meow!"

"Meow meow'meow meow meow meow," Meow meow meow meow. "Meow'meow meow meow meow meow meow meow meow meow, meow meow meow. Meow meow'meow meow meow meow meow meow meow meow. Meow meow meow meow meow. Meow meow!"

Meow meow meow meow meow meow.

"Meow meow'meow... meow meow'meow meow meow meow meow," meow meow, meow meow meow meow meow. "Meow meow meow meow meow meow, meow meow meow meow meow meow meow meow meow!"

"Meow meow meow meow meow meow meow meow meow!"

"Meow meow meow? Meow meow meow?" meow Meow, meow meow. "Meow meow meow meow meow Meow meow meow meow, meow meow meow meow meow meow meow!... Meow meow meow meow meow meow; meow meow meow meow, Meow meow meow: meow meow meow meow meow meow meow meow meow meow meow meow meow meow. Meow Meow..."

"Meow meow meow meow meow Meow Meow, meow, meow meow meow?" Meow meow meow.

"Meow, meow'meow meow meow, meow, meow? Meow'meow meow meow meow, meow.... Meow meow meow meow meow, Meow meow meow'meow meow meow meow meow, meow meow meow meow meow meow meow meow meow meow meow. Meow'meow meow meow Meow meow meow meow meow meow meow. Meow meow meow meow meow meow; meow meow meow meow meow meow meow meow meow meow meow meow meow meow meow meow meow meow, meow meow meow meow meow meow meow meow. Meow Meow'meow meow meow meow Meow meow meow meow meow meow meow meow, meow meow meow meow meow meow meow, meow: meow'meow Meow meow meow meow meow... meow, meow, meow meow meow, meow meow meow meow meow meow meow. Meow Meow meow meow meow meow meow meow, meow, meow meow meow meow meow meow."

Meow meow.

"Meow meow meow meow meow meow meow!"

"Meow meow meow meow meow meow? Meow meow, Meow meow meow meow meow meow meow meow—meow meow meow meow meow... meow'meow meow meow meow meow meow, meow; Meow meow meow meow meow meow meow meow meow meow meow meow meow; meow Meow meow meow meow, meow, meow Meow Meow meow meow meow meow meow meow, meow meow meow, meow. Meow meow meow meow meow meow meow meow meow meow meow meow meow; meow meow meow meow meow Meow Meow meow meow meow meow meow meow meow; meow meow meow meow meow meow meow meow meow meow. Meow, meow meow meow meow meow meow meow meow (meow meow meow meow meow meow meow). Meow meow meow meow meow meow meow meow meow meow meow! Meow meow meow meow meow meow meow meow meow meow meow meow.... Meow meow meow meow meow meow meow meow meow meow meow meow meow meow, meow meow meow meow meow meow meow meow meow meow meow meow meow. Meow meow meow meow meow meow meow; meow meow meow meow, meow, meow meow meow meow meow, meow meow meow meow? Meow meow'meow meow meow meow meow. Meow meow meow meow meow'meow meow meow meow."

Meow meow meow Meow meow meow meow meow meow meow meow meow meow meow meow meow. Meow meow meow meow meow meow meow meow meow meow meow meow meow meow meow.

"Meow meow meow meow meow?" meow meow meow.

“Meow, meow meow,” Meow meow, meow. “Meow Meow Meow meow Meow meow meow meow. Meow meow meow meow, meow meow meow meow meow meow meow.

Meow meow meow meow meow meow meow meow meow meow meow (meow meow meow meow meow meow meow meow meow meow). Meow meow meow, meow meow meow meow meow, meow meow meow meow meow meow meow, meow meow meow meow meow meow meow meow meow meow meow. Meow meow meow Meow meow meow meow meow, meow meow meow, meow meow meow meow? Meow, meow! Meow meow meow, meow meow meow, Meow Meow, meow meow meow meow meow, meow meow meow meow meow meow, meow meow, Meow’meow meow meow meow, meow meow meow meow meow, meow meow meow meow, meow meow meow meow Meow meow meow meow meow meow. Meow meow? Meow meow meow meow meow, meow meow meow Meow meow, meow ‘meow meow meow meow Meow’ meow meow (meow meow, ‘Meow Meow Meow,’ meow meow meow, meow meow? Meow meow meow, meow meow! Meow, meow meow meow meow meow meow, meow meow meow?). Meow, meow meow meow meow meow meow meow Meow, Meow meow meow meow meow meow, meow meow meow meow meow meow meow meow meow? Meow Meow meow meow meow meow meow meow meow meow ‘Meow’ meow Meow meow’meow meow meow meow meow meow meow meow meow meow meow meow. Meow meow meow meow meow meow meow meow meow meow meow meow, meow meow’meow meow meow meow meow meow meow, Meow meow meow.”

Meow meow meow, Meow meow meow meow meow meow meow. Meow meow meow meow meow meow meow meow meow meow meow meow meow meow meow meow meow meow meow meow meow meow.

“Meow meow meow’meow meow meow meow meow meow meow meow?” meow meow.

“Meow meow. Meow meow meow meow meow meow meow meow meow meow meow meow?” “Meow, Meow meow meow meow meow meow meow meow meow meow meow.”

“Meow Meow meow meow meow meow meow meow meow meow meow? Meow meow meow? Meow meow meow meow? Meow meow meow, meow Meow meow,” meow meow, meow meow meow meow meow meow. “Meow meow, meow’meow meow meow Meow meow meow meow,” meow meow meow, meow meow meow meow, “meow meow, Meow’meow meow meow meow.... Meow meow meow meow meow meow meow meow meow Meow meow meow meow meow meow meow meow meow, meow meow Meow meow meow Meow meow meow meow meow meow meow meow. Meow Meow’meow meow meow, Meow meow meow meow meow. Meow meow meow meow meow, meow Meow meow meow meow meow meow.... Meow’meow meow meow, Meow Meow, meow meow meow meow meow meow meow meow meow. Meow meow meow meow, meow’meow meow meow meow meow, meow meow, meow... meow meow meow meow, Meow meow, meow meow, meow.... Meow, meow, Meow meow’meow, Meow

meow'meow, meow'meow meow! Meow meow meow meow meow meow, meow meow, meow meow meow."

Meow meow meow meow meow.

"Meow meow meow meow meow, meow, meow meow," meow meow. "Meow meow meow meow meow meow meow meow meow meow meow meow, meow meow meow meow meow meow meow meow meow meow meow."

"Meow meow meow meow meow meow meow'meow meow," Meow meow, meow meow meow meow meow meow meow meow, "meow meow meow meow meow meow meow meow meow meow meow meow meow meow meow meow meow meow... meow meow meow meow meow meow meow meow meow meow," meow meow, meow meow.

"Meow Meow'meow meow meow meow meow meow meow. Meow meow, meow meow meow, 'meow meow meow.' Meow meow meow meow meow meow, meow, meow meow'meow meow meow meow?"

"Meow'meow meow meow Meow meow meow meow," Meow meow, meow meow meow meow meow meow. "Meow'meow meow meow meow. Meow'meow meow meow meow meow meow meow meow meow, meow Meow'meow meow meow, meow meow'meow meow meow. Meow'meow meow meow meow meow. Meow meow meow meow meow meow meow meow meow meow; meow meow meow meow meow meow'meow meow meow; meow meow meow meow meow meow meow meow meow. Meow meow meow meow meow meow; meow... Meow meow meow meow meow meow meow, Meow meow meow meow meow meow meow. Meow'meow meow meow meow meow meow meow meow meow meow meow.... Meow meow meow meow meow! Meow meow meow meow meow meow meow meow, meow meow meow? Meow meow meow meow meow meow meow meow meow. Meow, meow'meow meow meow meow Meow meow'meow meow meow Meow meow meow meow meow meow, meow meow meow meow.... Meow meow meow meow meow meow meow, meow Meow, meow meow!"

"Meow?"

"Meow meow meow meow meow, Meow, meow, meow meow, meow, meow—meow, meow meow meow meow meow meow meow," meow meow meow, meow meow meow meow meow. "Meow, meow meow meow meow meow meow-meow?"

"Meow, meow meow meow meow meow-meow meow?"

"Meow meow Meow meow meow? Meow meow meow meow meow meow meow, meow meow meow meow meow, meow meow meow; meow meow meow meow meow. Meow meow meow meow meow, meow meow, meow, meow meow meow. Meow meow meow meow meow meow meow Meow meow meow meow meow meow meow meow meow'meow meow meow, meow meow meow meow? Meow'meow meow meow meow meow. Meow Meow meow meow meow meow meow meow, meow meow meow Meow meow meow meow Meow. Meow Meow Meow meow meow; meow meow meow meow meow meow meow meow meow meow meow meow (Meow meow meow meow). Meow meow meow meow meow

meow meow meow meow meow meow meow meow meow meow meow meow. Meow meow meow meow meow meow meow meow Meow. Meow meow meow meow meow meow. Meow meow meow Meow meow meow meow meow. Meow, meow meow, meow meow meow meow meow meow meow meow meow meow, meow Meow meow meow meow meow, meow meow Meow meow meow meow meow meow meow meow meow Meow meow meow meow meow meow! Meow meow meow meow meow meow! Meow meow meow meow meow meow."

"Meow meow meow'meow meow meow meow, meow meow meow meow meow meow meow?"

"Meow meow'meow meow meow meow meow. Meow meow meow meow meow meow meow. Meow meow'meow meow meow meow meow meow. Meow Meow meow meow meow meow meow meow, meow Meow meow meow, meow Meow'meow meow meow meow, meow meow meow meow meow. Meow meow meow, meow meow meow, meow meow meow Meow, meow meow—meow meow meow meow meow meow meow meow meow. Meow'meow meow meow meow meow meow meow meow meow! Meow, meow'meow meow meow meow. Meow meow meow meow meow meow meow meow meow meow meow. Meow meow meow meow meow meow meow meow meow meow Meow Meow, meow meow'meow meow meow meow meow meow meow, meow meow'meow meow meow meow meow. Meow meow meow meow. Meow, Meow meow, Meow'meow meow meow Meow meow meow meow meow meow meow meow meow Meow meow meow Meow Meow meow meow meow meow meow meow meow meow. Meow meow meow?"

"Meow, meow meow meow meow?"

"Meow... Meow, meow, meow," meow Meow meow meow meow meow meow meow meow. "Meow meow meow meow? Meow meow meow meow?" Meow meow.

"Meow, meow meow meow'meow meow meow," Meow meow meow, meow. "Meow meow meow meow meow, meow meow meow meow, meow meow meow meow meow Meow Meow meow meow meow meow meow meow meow meow-meow meow meow meow meow meow meow meow meow meow meow meow meow, meow. Meow meow meow meow, meow meow. 'Meow meow meow Meow meow meow, Meow Meow'—meow meow meow meow meow. Meow meow'meow meow meow meow meow? Meow meow meow meow Meow meow meow meow meow meow, meow meow meow meow meow meow. Meow meow meow, meow. Meow Meow meow meow meow, meow meow meow meow meow meow meow meow-meow."

"Meow meow meow meow meow Meow Meow meow meow?"

"Meow meow? Meow. Meow, meow Meow meow. Meow, meow meow meow, meow meow meow meow meow?" "Meow meow?"

"Meow, meow meow."

"Meow meow meow meow meow?"

"Meow meow, meow meow meow.... Meow meow'meow meow meow meow."

"Meow meow meow meow, meow?"

Meow meow meow meow meow meow.

"Meow Meow meow meow meow meow meow," meow meow, meow meow meow meow meow meow meow. "Meow meow meow meow 'meow meow meow meow meow meow'?"

"Meow meow meow meow meow. Meow meow meow meow meow meow meow meow meow meow meow, meow meow meow meow meow meow. Meow meow meow meow meow Meow meow meow meow meow. Meow meow meow meow meow meow meow meow, meow meow, meow meow meow meow meow meow meow Meow Meow, meow meow meow meow meow meow meow meow meow meow meow meow Meow meow meow. Meow meow meow."

"Meow meow meow?"

"Meow meow. Meow meow meow meow meow meow. Meow meow, meow meow meow meow meow meow meow meow meow meow meow meow—meow meow meow meow. Meow meow meow meow meow."

"Meow meow meow meow meow meow meow meow meow meow meow meow meow meow?" Meow meow meow.

Meow meow meow meow meow meow meow meow meow meow meow. Meow meow meow meow.

"Meow! Meow meow meow meow?" Meow meow meow meow. "Meow meow meow? Meow'meow Meow meow meow meow meow meow meow meow meow meow, meow?"

"Meow meow meow meow!" Meow meow meow meow meow meow.

"Meow'meow Meow?"

"Meow!"

"Meow meow Meow meow. Meow Meow meow meow meow meow meow meow meow meow meow meow, meow, Meow meow meow meow meow meow, 'Meow'meow meow meow.'"

"Meow meow meow meow meow 'meow meow?' Meow meow meow meow meow?" meow Meow.

"Meow meow Meow meow? Meow meow meow'meow meow...." Meow meow meow, meow meow meow, meow, meow meow.

Meow meow meow meow meow meow. Meow meow meow meow meow'meow meow.

"Meow'meow meow meow!" Meow meow meow meow. "Meow meow meow meow meow meow meow meow meow?"

"Meow! Meow meow meow meow, meow meow meow meow meow meow meow—meow meow meow meow meow—meow meow meow meow. Meow meow meow meow meow meow (Meow meow meow meow meow: meow meow meow, meow meow meow, meow meow meow. Meow meow Meow meow meow meow meow meow meow. Meow meow meow meow meow meow meow meow), meow meow meow meow meow meow. 'Meow'meow meow meow meow meow-meow, Meow Meow, meow meow meow meow meow meow meow-meow meow,' meow meow. Meow meow meow meow Meow'meow meow meow meow meow meow, meow meow Meow meow meow meow meow meow meow meow. Meow meow meow Meow meow meow meow meow meow meow. Meow meow meow meow

meow meow meow meow; Meow'meow meow meow, meow meow, meow meow meow meow meow, Meow meow meow meow meow. Meow meow meow meow meow meow meow Meow Meow meow meow meow meow meow meow meow meow meow meow meow. 'Meow Meow meow meow meow meow meow meow, Meow Meow?' Meow meow meow meow meow meow meow meow. Meow meow meow meow meow meow meow meow meow meow. Meow meow meow meow meow meow, meow, meow, meow meow meow. Meow meow meow meow-meow, meow meow meow meow meow meow meow meow meow meow; Meow meow meow meow, meow meow meow meow Meow Meow meow. Meow meow meow meow meow meow meow meow meow meow meow meow meow meow meow. 'Meow meow, Meow Meow! Meow meow meow meow meow meow? Meow meow'meow meow meow meow.' (Meow meow meow meow meow meow meow, meow meow meow meow meow meow meow meow meow meow meow Meow, meow meow meow.) Meow meow meow meow meow meow. Meow meow meow meow meow, meow meow Meow meow meow, meow meow, meow meow meow. 'Meow meow meow meow meow meow meow meow meow meow meow, Meow Meow.' 'Meow meow, meow meow'meow meow meow meow meow meow meow!' Meow meow meow Meow meow, 'Meow meow meow meow meow, Meow Meow.' 'Meow'meow meow meow meow, Meow Meow; meow meow meow meow meow meow meow meow meow meow meow meow meow meow'meow meow meow meow meow. Meow meow meow meow meow meow meow meow, meow meow, meow Meow meow meow meow'meow meow meow meow meow meow meow, meow meow meow meow meow meow-meow meow meow meow meow.' Meow meow meow meow meow meow meow meow meow meow. Meow'meow meow meow, meow?"

"Meow meow meow meow meow meow?" Meow meow meow.

"Meow meow meow," meow Meow meow, meow meow meow meow meow meow meow meow.

"Meow meow meow meow, meow meow meow meow meow meow?"

"Meow-meow, Meow meow meow meow, meow meow meow meow meow meow, meow meow meow. Meow meow meow meow, Meow; meow meow meow meow Meow meow meow meow 'Meow, meow meow!' Meow meow meow meow meow meow meow meow meow meow meow meow. Meow meow meow meow meow 'meow meow meow meow meow meow,' meow meow meow meow meow meow meow meow meow meow. 'Meow meow meow meow meow meow meow meow meow meow meow?' Meow meow. 'Meow meow, meow meow!' Meow meow meow meow meow, meow meow meow meow. Meow meow'meow meow Meow Meow meow meow meow. Meow meow meow meow meow meow meow meow meow, meow Meow meow meow."

"Meow meow meow meow meow meow."

"Meow meow Meow meow meow meow, meow meow meow meow, meow Meow meow'meow meow meow'meow meow; Meow meow Meow meow meow meow meow meow meow meow meow. Meow meow'meow

meow meow meow meow meow meow meow meow meow, meow meow meow meow meow meow meow."

"Meow, Meow meow'meow meow meow!" Meow meow, meow meow meow.

"Meow meow meow meow meow?" meow Meow, meow meow meow meow meow, meow meow meow meow meow meow. "Meow meow, 'Meow meow meow, meow meow meow meow meow meow meow meow.' Meow meow'meow meow meow meow. Meow meow meow meow meow meow meow meow meow, meow meow meow meow meow meow meow meow meow meow meow meow meow meow, meow meow meow meow'meow meow."

"Meow meow meow meow," Meow meow meow.

"Meow? Meow meow'meow meow meow?" Meow meow meow, meow meow meow meow. "Meow meow meow meow meow meow meow meow (meow meow meow meow): meow meow, meow meow meow, meow meow meow meow meow meow, meow meow meow meow. Meow meow meow meow meow, meow meow, meow meow meow meow meow, meow meow meow meow meow meow meow meow meow meow meow meow meow meow meow meow meow meow meow meow meow meow meow meow meow meow meow meow. Meow meow meow meow meow meow meow, meow meow meow meow meow meow meow meow meow meow meow meow, meow meow meow meow meow meow meow meow meow; meow meow meow meow meow meow meow, meow meow meow meow'meow meow meow meow meow meow, meow meow meow meow meow meow meow meow meow meow meow meow meow meow. Meow meow meow meow meow meow. Meow meow meow meow meow meow meow, meow meow meow meow meow, meow."

"Meow meow'meow meow meow meow meow meow," meow Meow.

Meow meow meow meow meow.

"Meow meow meow meow meow meow meow meow, meow meow meow meow meow," meow meow meow. "Meow meow meow meow," meow Meow.

"Meow meow meow meow meow meow meow meow meow, meow meow, meow! Meow meow meow meow meow meow? Meow meow meow meow, meow meow meow'meow meow meow meow, meow meow meow meow meow meow meow, meow meow meow meow meow meow meow meow, meow meow'meow meow meow meow? Meow meow meow meow meow meow."

"Meow meow meow meow meow meow meow meow meow meow meow meow meow?" Meow meow, meow meow meow meow meow.

"Meow? Meow meow meow meow meow, meow meow meow meow, meow meow meow meow meow'meow meow Meow meow meow meow meow meow," meow Meow, meow meow meow meow.

Meow meow meow meow meow meow meow meow Meow. Meow meow meow meow, meow meow meow, meow meow meow meow.

"Meow meow," meow meow, "meow meow meow meow meow meow meow meow meow meow, meow meow meow meow meow meow; meow

meow meow meow meow meow meow; meow′meow meow meow meow, meow meow meow′meow meow meow meow meow! Meow′meow Meow meow meow meow meow meow meow meow meow meow meow?"

"Meow meow meow," Meow meow meow meow, "meow meow meow meow meow meow meow meow meow meow meow meow meow... meow... meow Meow meow meow meow meow, Meow meow meow meow meow meow. Meow meow meow meow meow."

"Meow meow meow, meow meow meow. Meow meow, Meow Meow, meow meow meow meow meow meow Meow. Meow, Meow Meow?"

"Meow meow meow meow meow meow meow meow meow meow meow meow meow meow? Meow meow′meow meow meow meow meow meow meow meow meow meow meow, meow meow meow meow Meow."

"Meow, meow Meow′meow meow meow meow meow meow; meow meow Meow meow meow meow?" "Meow meow, meow, meow meow meow."

"Meow meow meow meow meow meow meow meow meow meow meow meow meow Meow. Meow, meow meow meow meow meow meow meow meow meow, meow meow meow meow meow meow meow meow meow meow, meow meow meow meow meow meow. Meow meow meow meow meow Meow Meow. Meow meow Meow Meow meow meow meow meow meow meow meow meow meow meow... meow meow meow meow meow meow. Meow meow meow meow Meow meow meow meow meow meow meow meow meow meow meow meow meow meow meow meow meow meow meow meow meow meow meow meow meow. Meow Meow meow meow meow, Meow meow meow meow meow."

"Meow meow meow meow meow... meow meow, Meow meow meow meow meow meow meow meow," meow Meow.

"Meow meow meow meow meow Meow meow meow meow meow meow. Meow′meow meow meow, Meow Meow, meow Meow meow meow meow meow meow meow, Meow meow meow meow meow meow meow meow. Meow meow meow meow meow meow. Meow meow meow meow meow meow meow meow: meow meow, meow meow meow meow Meow Meow, Meow meow Meow meow meow meow meow. Meow, meow meow meow meow meow Meow′meow meow meow meow meow meow, meow meow meow, meow meow Meow meow meow meow, meow Meow meow meow meow meow..."

"Meow meow meow meow," Meow meow meow.

"Meow meow meow meow meow meow, meow meow meow meow meow meow meow meow Meow meow meow meow meow meow meow meow. Meow meow′meow meow meow, meow Meow meow meow meow."

"Meow meow meow meow meow?"

"Meow meow meow meow meow meow meow meow, meow meow meow meow meow meow meow meow meow meow meow, meow meow meow meow Meow meow meow Meow. Meow meow meow meow Meow, meow, meow Meow meow meow meow meow meow meow Meow Meow′meow meow meow meow meow meow Meow. Meow."

"Meow meow meow meow meow; meow meow meow, meow meow meow meow meow meow meow meow. Meow meow meow meow meow, Meow meow meow meow meow..."

"Meow meow meow meow. Meow meow meow meow meow meow meow meow... meow, Meow meow meow meow meow meow meow meow. Meow meow meow meow meow meow meow; meow meow meow meow meow; meow meow meow meow meow meow meow meow. Meow meow meow meow Meow meow meow, meow! Meow meow meow meow meow meow Meow Meow meow meow meow meow meow.

Meow'meow meow meow meow. Meow meow, Meow meow meow meow meow meow meow. Meow meow meow meow meow meow meow, Meow meow meow meow Meow. Meow, meow. Meow'meow meow meow Meow meow meow meow meow, meow meow meow meow meow Meow meow meow Meow Meow meow Meow meow meow meow meow meow meow meow meow. Meow meow meow meow Meow Meow meow meow meow, meow meow meow meow meow meow meow, meow meow meow meow meow meow meow meow meow meow meow meow meow meow meow meow meow Meow. Meow. Meow, meow meow meow meow meow meow meow, meow meow meow meow meow meow meow meow meow meow meow meow meow meow meow Meow. Meow, meow meow meow meow Meow meow meow meow meow meow meow, meow meow meow meow meow meow meow meow."

"Meow meow meow meow," meow Meow meow meow meow meow meow meow. "Meow meow meow meow meow meow!"

"Meow meow meow meow meow meow meow; meow meow meow meow meow, meow Meow meow meow meow, meow meow meow meow meow meow meow; Meow meow meow meow meow meow meow. Meow Meow Meow meow meow meow meow, Meow meow meow meow meow meow meow meow meow. Meow'meow meow meow meow. Meow, meow meow meow meow meow; Meow meow meow meow meow meow meow meow. Meow meow meow meow meow, meow meow meow meow Meow Meow meow meow meow meow. Meow meow meow, meow Meow meow meow meow meow meow, meow Meow meow meow, meow meow meow meow, meow meow, meow meow meow, Meow meow—meow meow meow, meow meow meow meow meow meow meow, meow meow meow meow meow meow meow meow, meow meow meow Meow meow meow, meow meow, meow meow meow meow meow meow. Meow meow meow meow meow meow meow meow-meow meow meow meow, Meow meow meow meow meow meow meow meow; meow Meow meow meow meow meow meow meow meow meow, meow meow meow meow Meow meow meow meow, Meow, Meow meow, meow, meow meow meow meow meow meow, meow meow meow meow meow meow meow meow meow meow meow Meow Meow. Meow meow, meow meow meow meow meow meow Meow. Meow, meow meow meow meow meow meow meow, meow meow meow meow. Meow'meow meow meow, Meow Meow, meow meow meow meow meow meow."

Meow meow meow meow meow meow meow meow meow meow meow meow.

"Meow meow meow meow meow meow meow," meow Meow. "Meow meow meow meow meow meow meow."

"Meow meow meow meow. Meow meow meow meow meow meow meow meow meow meow meow meow meow meow, meow meow meow meow meow meow meow meow meow meow meow meow meow meow. Meow'meow meow. Meow Meow meow, meow meow, meow meow meow meow meow meow meow meow meow meow, meow meow meow'meow meow meow?"

"Meow meow meow meow."

"Meow, meow, meow. Meow, meow meow meow meow, meow meow meow, meow meow meow meow meow meow meow meow meow meow meow. Meow meow meow Meow meow meow meow meow meow Meow meow meow meow Meow Meow."

"Meow, Meow meow'meow."

"Meow meow meow, Meow Meow, Meow meow meow meow meow meow meow meow meow meow meow meow meow meow meow meow."

"Meow meow Meow meow meow meow, meow meow meow meow meow meow meow?"

"Meow meow'meow meow meow meow meow meow. Meow meow meow meow meow meow meow meow meow meow." "Meow'meow meow meow meow."

"Meow'meow meow. Meow meow meow'meow meow meow. Meow meow meow meow meow meow." "Meow meow meow meow meow meow?"

"Meow meow meow?" Meow meow, meow. Meow meow meow meow meow meow meow. "Meow meow'meow meow meow meow meow meow meow Meow meow meow meow meow meow meow... meow Meow meow meow meow meow meow meow meow meow meow."

"Meow meow meow meow meow meow meow?" Meow meow meow.

"Meow meow meow meow meow.... Meow meow meow meow meow meow meow meow meow meow.... Meow meow'meow meow meow. Meow meow meow meow; Meow meow meow meow meow meow meow meow meow-meow, meow Meow meow meow Meow Meow, meow meow meow meow meow meow meow meow meow meow, meow Meow meow meow meow Meow'meow Meow meow Meow Meow'meow meow, meow Meow meow meow Meow Meow'meow meow meow meow meow, meow Meow meow meow meow meow meow meow Meow'meow meow meow meow Meow Meow meow meow meow meow, meow Meow meow meow meow meow meow meow meow Meow, meow."

"Meow, meow meow. Meow meow meow meow meow meow meow, meow Meow meow?" "Meow meow?"

"Meow, meow meow 'meow'; meow meow meow meow meow."

"Meow meow? Meow, meow. Meow meow meow meow meow meow. Meow, meow'meow meow meow meow.... meow meow meow meow meow meow meow meow," meow meow, meow meow meow meow, meow, meow

meow. "Meow Meow'meow meow meow meow meow meow meow. Meow'meow meow meow meow meow meow."

"Meow?"

"Meow."

"Meow meow meow meow meow meow meow?"

"Meow Meow meow meow meow meow meow Meow Meow meow. Meow meow meow meow. Meow, meow-meow meow meow meow. Meow, meow. Meow meow meow meow. Meow meow meow, Meow Meow, meow Meow Meow meow meow meow meow meow meow meow meow meow meow meow. Meow'meow meow meow. Meow Meow meow meow meow meow meow meow meow, meow meow meow meow meow meow meow. Meow Meow meow meow meow meow meow meow meow meow meow meow meow meow."

"Meow meow meow meow meow?"

"Meow, meow meow. Meow, meow meow. Meow meow meow meow meow meow."

Meow meow meow meow, Meow meow meow meow Meow meow meow meow.

MEOW II

Meow meow meow meow meow'meow. Meow meow meow meow meow meow Meow'meow, meow meow meow Meow.

"Meow, meow meow meow?" meow Meow, meow meow meow meow meow meow meow meow.

"Meow meow Meow, meow meow meow meow meow meow meow meow meow meow meow meow meow meow. Meow meow meow meow meow meow meow, meow meow meow meow meow meow meow, Meow Meow. Meow Meow Meow meow Meow'meow meow meow, meow meow'meow meow meow meow. Meow meow meow meow meow meow meow meow meow. Meow meow'meow meow meow Meow'meow meow meow meow meow. Meow meow meow meow meow meow meow meow'meow meow. Meow meow meow meow, meow meow meow meow meow meow.... Meow meow meow Meow meow meow... meow'meow meow Meow meow meow meow meow, meow meow meow?"

"Meow meow! Meow meow meow meow meow meow Meow Meow? Meow meow, Meow, meow meow meow meow meow meow.... Meow meow, meow meow meow meow. Meow meow meow meow?"

"Meow meow'meow meow."

"Meow meow'meow meow meow? Meow meow meow! Meow'meow meow meow, meow."

"Meow meow meow meow?" meow Meow meow meow meow.

"Meow, Meow meow meow, Meow meow meow meow."

"Meow meow meow meow meow? Meow meow meow meow?" Meow meow.

"Meow, Meow meow meow meow, Meow meow meow meow meow meow meow; Meow meow meow meow meow meow meow."

Meow meow meow meow.

"Meow!... meow'meow meow meow," meow Meow. "Meow meow meow, Meow meow... Meow meow meow meow meow meow meow meow meow meow."

"Meow meow meow meow? Meow meow'meow meow meow."

"Meow, meow meow meow," Meow meow meow, meow meow meow meow meow meow, "meow Meow meow meow. Meow meow meow meow meow meow Meow meow meow meow, meow meow meow meow meow meow."

"Meow meow meow meow?"

"Meow, meow meow meow? Meow Meow meow meow meow, meow meow meow meow meow meow meow meow meow meow meow meow."

"Meow, Meow, meow meow meow meow meow!... Meow meow meow meow meow, meow meow meow meow meow?" Meow meow meow meow. Meow meow meow meow.

"Meow meow meow meow meow meow meow," meow meow, "Meow meow meow meow, meow meow meow. Meow meow meow meow meow meow Meow meow meow Meow'meow, Meow meow meow meow meow.

Meow meow meow meow, meow meow meow meow meow. Meow meow'meow meow meow meow meow meow. Meow meow'meow meow meow meow meow meow'meow meow, meow meow meow meow meow meow. Meow meow Meow meow meow meow, meow meow meow meow meow, meow meow meow meow meow meow. Meow meow meow meow Meow meow meow. Meow meow Meow meow meow meow meow meow meow meow, meow meow meow meow meow meow Meow'meow meow meow. Meow meow meow meow meow, Meow meow meow meow meow. Meow meow meow. Meow meow meow meow. Meow Meow Meow meow'meow meow meow meow. Meow, meow meow, Meow meow Meow'meow meow meow meow meow meow, meow meow Meow meow meow meow meow meow meow meow: meow meow meow meow? Meow meow meow meow meow meow meow meow meow meow, meow meow meow meow meow? Meow meow'meow meow meow meow meow meow. Meow meow meow meow meow meow meow meow, meow meow Meow meow meow meow meow Meow'meow meow meow meow meow meow. Meow meow meow'meow meow meow! Meow meow! Meow meow meow meow meow, meow meow'meow meow meow meow meow!"

"Meow meow meow," meow Meow. "Meow meow meow meow meow meow-meow?" meow meow meow meow. Meow meow meow, meow meow meow meow meow meow meow meow meow meow meow meow Meow meow meow meow meow meow. Meow meow meow meow, Meow meow meow meow. Meow'meow meow meow meow meow meow Meow meow meow meow meow meow meow, meow meow meow meow meow meow meow meow.

Meow meow meow meow meow meow Meow; meow meow meow meow meow meow, meow meow meow meow meow meow, meow meow meow meow meow meow meow meow meow meow meow meow meow meow. Meow meow meow meow meow meow, meow Meow Meow, meow meow meow, meow meow meow meow meow meow, meow meow meow meow. Meow Meow meow meow meow meow meow meow meow meow meow meow, Meow meow meow meow meow. Meow Meow meow meow meow meow meow, meow meow meow meow, meow meow meow meow. Meow meow, meow, meow meow meow meow meow meow meow meow meow meow meow meow meow meow. Meow Meow, meow meow meow meow meow meow, meow meow meow meow meow meow meow meow meow meow meow meow meow meow meow meow. Meow meow Meow meow meow meow meow meow meow meow meow meow meow. Meow meow Meow meow meow Meow Meow, Meow meow meow meow Meow meow Meow meow meow meow meow.

Meow meow'meow meow meow. Meow Meow meow meow meow meow meow meow meow meow meow meow meow meow meow meow meow meow meow meow meow meow meow meow meow meow meow, meow meow meow meow meow meow meow meow meow. Meow meow meow meow meow meow meow meow meow meow meow meow meow meow meow meow meow meow, meow meow meow meow meow meow meow meow meow meow meow meow meow meow meow meow meow meow meow meow meow.

Meow meow meow meow meow meow meow meow meow. Meow, meow meow meow meow meow, meow meow meow meow meow: meow meow meow meow meow meow meow meow, meow meow meow meow meow, meow meow meow meow meow meow meow meow meow meow meow meow; meow meow meow meow meow meow meow meow meow meow meow meow meow meow meow.

"Meow meow meow meow meow meow meow," meow meow meow meow Meow Meow.

"Meow, meow, Meow Meow."

"Meow meow meow meow meow meow. Meow Meow Meow meow meow meow-meow meow?"

"Meow meow meow meow meow, Meow meow'meow meow meow, meow meow meow meow meow meow meow meow," meow Meow.

"Meow'meow meow! meow meow meow meow meow meow meow. 'Meow Meow,' meow meow meow, meow meow meow meow.... Meow meow meow meow meow meow meow meow meow, Meow meow meow meow meow meow meow. Meow Meow meow meow meow meow meow meow?"

"Meow, meow, Meow Meow, meow meow meow meow meow," Meow Meow meow meow meow meow meow meow, "meow meow Meow Meow meow meow meow meow meow, Meow meow meow meow Meow Meow, meow meow meow meow meow meow. Meow, meow meow! Meow Meow Meow," meow meow, meow meow meow Meow.

"Meow meow meow meow... meow," meow Meow Meow meow meow meow meow meow meow Meow; meow meow meow meow meow meow.

Meow Meow meow meow meow meow meow meow, meow meow meow meow meow meow meow, meow meow meow meow meow meow meow, meow meow, meow meow meow meow meow meow, meow meow meow, meow meow meow meow meow meow meow meow meow meow meow meow meow meow. Meow meow meow meow; Meow meow meow meow, Meow Meow meow meow meow meow meow meow meow meow. Meow meow meow meow meow, meow Meow Meow meow meow meow.

"Meow Meow meow meow, meow meow meow?" meow meow meow meow meow meow meow meow meow meow.

"Meow meow meow, Meow meow meow. Meow meow meow meow, meow Meow meow meow meow meow meow meow meow meow meow meow Meow Meow Meow meow meow meow meow meow Meow meow meow meow meow'meow meow. Meow meow meow Meow meow meow meow meow meow."

"Meow Meow? meow?" Meow meow meow meow meow meow meow meow meow.

"Meow, meow, meow meow meow meow meow meow, meow meow meow meow meow meow meow meow, meow meow meow meow meow meow."

"Meow meow! meow'meow meow meow Meow meow meow meow meow?" meow Meow Meow.

"Meow meow meow meow meow meow Meow Meow meow meow meow meow meow, meow, meow meow, meow meow meow meow meow meow meow meow meow meow. Meow meow meow Meow meow meow meow meow, meow meow meow meow meow meow meow meow."

"Meow, Meow Meow, meow meow meow meow meow meow meow meow meow meow meow," Meow Meow meow meow: "Meow'meow meow meow meow meow, meow Meow meow meow meow, meow! Meow meow meow meow meow meow meow meow meow Meow Meow'meow meow."

"Meow'meow meow meow meow meow meow meow. Meow meow meow meow.

Meow meow meow meow meow meow meow meow meow meow meow meow meow meow meow meow meow meow meow, meow meow meow, meow meow meow; meow meow meow meow meow meow meow meow meow meow meow meow, Meow meow meow meow meow meow. Meow meow meow meow meow meow meow meow meow meow, meow meow meow Meow Meow meow meow; meow meow meow meow meow meow meow meow meow meow; meow meow meow meow meow Meow, meow meow meow meow meow meow, meow meow meow meow meow meow meow meow meow. Meow meow meow meow meow, meow meow meow meow meow meow meow meow meow. Meow meow meow meow meow meow meow Meow Meow, meow meow meow meow meow meow meow meow meow meow meow meow meow meow meow meow meow meow meow, meow meow meow meow meow meow meow meow meow. Meow meow meow meow meow meow, meow meow meow, meow meow meow meow meow meow meow meow meow meow meow meow meow meow meow meow meow Meow, meow meow meow. Meow'meow meow meow meow meow meow meow, meow meow meow meow meow."

"Meow meow!" meow Meow Meow. Meow meow meow.

"Meow meow meow meow meow meow meow meow meow meow meow meow meow meow meow?" Meow meow meow meow meow.

"Meow meow meow meow Meow meow meow meow meow meow Meow Meow. Meow meow meow meow meow meow meow meow meow meow meow meow meow meow meow meow. Meow meow, meow Meow meow meow meow, meow meow meow meow meow Meow, meow meow, meow meow meow meow meow meow meow meow, meow meow meow meow, meow meow meow meow Meow meow meow meow meow meow meow meow meow meow. Meow meow meow meow, meow meow Meow meow, meow meow meow, meow meow meow meow meow meow meow, meow meow meow meow meow meow. Meow meow meow meow, meow meow meow meow meow; meow meow meow meow meow meow. Meow meow meow meow meow meow meow meow meow meow. Meow meow meow meow meow meow meow. Meow meow meow meow meow meow meow, meow, meow meow, meow meow meow meow meow meow meow meow... meow meow meow Meow. Meow meow meow, meow meow meow meow meow, meow meow meow meow meow meow Meow meow meow meow meow meow meow meow meow meow meow; meow meow meow meow meow meow meow meow, meow meow Meow Meow'meow meow meow

meow; meow meow meow meow meow meow. Meow meow meow meow meow meow meow meow meow. Meow meow, meow meow, Meow Meow, meow meow meow meow meow meow meow meow meow meow Meow meow meow meow meow meow meow meow meow meow meow, meow meow meow meow meow."

"Meow meow, meow meow meow, meow meow Meow meow meow."

"Meow meow, meow meow meow meow, meow meow meow meow meow, meow meow meow meow meow meow meow meow meow Meow, Meow."

"Meow meow'meow meow meow," meow Meow, meow. "Meow meow meow meow meow meow meow Meow meow meow meow meow meow, meow meow meow meow meow, meow meow meow meow meow, 'meow meow meow meow,' meow meow meow meow meow meow meow meow meow Meow. Meow' meow meow meow meow meow meow meow meow. Meow Meow meow meow meow meow meow meow meow meow, meow meow meow meow meow meow meow, meow meow meow meow meow meow meow Meow'meow meow."

"Meow meow, Meow Meow, meow meow meow meow meow meow meow meow meow meow meow meow," Meow meow, meow meow meow meow meow meow meow, "meow'meow meow meow meow meow meow meow meow meow, meow meow meow meow meow meow, meow meow Meow Meow, meow meow meow meow meow, meow meow meow meow. Meow meow meow meow meow meow meow meow meow meow meow meow meow meow meow meow meow, meow meow meow meow meow meow meow meow meow meow meow meow meow. Meow meow meow meow'meow meow meow meow, meow meow meow meow meow meow meow'meow meow meow. Meow Meow meow meow meow meow meow meow meow meow meow meow meow, meow meow meow meow meow'meow meow, meow, meow meow meow meow meow, meow meow meow meow meow meow meow, meow meow meow meow, meow meow meow meow meow meow meow meow meow meow meow meow."

"Meow Meow, Meow meow meow," meow Meow, "meow meow meow meow Meow Meow. Meow meow meow meow."

"Meow meow meow meow meow meow meow," meow Meow, meow meow meow meow meow meow meow.

Meow meow meow meow meow, meow meow meow meow meow meow. Meow Meow Meow meow meow.

"Meow meow meow meow meow meow, meow meow meow meow Meow meow meow, meow meow, meow meow meow," Meow meow. "Meow meow meow meow meow meow meow, meow meow meow meow meow meow meow meow. Meow meow meow meow, meow meow meow, Meow, meow meow meow meow meow, meow meow meow meow meow meow meow. Meow meow meow meow meow meow meow meow, meow meow meow meow meow meow. Meow meow meow, meow, meow meow meow meow meow meow Meow Meow meow meow meow meow meow meow meow meow, Meow, meow meow meow meow meow meow meow meow meow."

"Meow Meow!" meow Meow Meow, meow meow. "Meow meow meow meow, Meow!" "Meow'meow meow meow!" meow meow Meow.

"Meow meow, meow meow?" Meow meow Meow.

"Meow meow meow meow meow meow'meow meow meow meow meow meow meow meow meow meow meow meow meow meow meow meow meow, meow meow meow meow meow meow meow meow meow meow, meow meow, Meow meow'meow meow, Meow meow'meow meow...."

"Meow meow, meow meow meow meow meow meow meow Meow?" meow Meow Meow meow meow meow. "Meow meow meow meow?"

"Meow."

"Meow meow meow?"

"Meow'meow meow meow meow."

Meow meow meow meow meow meow meow meow meow meow.

Meow Meow meow meow meow meow.

"Meow meow meow meow meow meow meow meow, meow meow Meow meow meow meow meow meow meow," meow meow meow meow meow meow meow meow meow meow meow meow meow.

"Meow'meow meow, Meow Meow," meow Meow, "meow meow meow meow meow meow. Meow, meow meow meow meow meow meow meow meow meow meow meow meow."

"Meow meow, Meow Meow," Meow Meow meow meow, meow meow meow, meow meow meow meow meow. "Meow meow meow meow meow meow meow meow meow meow meow meow meow meow meow meow. Meow meow meow meow meow meow meow meow meow meow meow meow meow meow Meow. Meow, Meow, meow, meow meow meow meow meow meow meow meow meow meow... meow meow meow meow... meow meow meow meow meow meow meow. Meow, meow meow meow meow meow meow meow meow meow...."

Meow meow meow meow, Meow meow meow meow meow.

"Meow meow meow meow meow meow meow meow meow meow meow meow meow meow meow meow meow meow," meow Meow. "Meow meow meow meow meow meow meow meow meow meow; Meow meow meow meow meow meow meow meow meow, meow meow meow meow meow. Meow meow Meow meow meow meow meow, meow meow meow meow meow meow."

Meow Meow meow meow meow meow.

"Meow meow meow, Meow Meow, meow meow meow meow meow meow meow. Meow meow meow meow meow meow meow meow meow meow meow meow; meow meow meow meow meow meow, meow meow meow meow."

"Meow meow'meow meow Meow meow meow meow meow, Meow Meow," Meow meow meow meow meow. "Meow meow meow meow meow meow meow meow meow meow meow meow meow meow meow meow meow meow meow meow. Meow meow meow meow meow meow meow meow Meow meow meow meow meow meow meow meow meow, meow meow meow meow meow meow meow meow meow, meow meow meow meow meow meow meow-meow, meow meow meow meow meow.

Meow meow meow meow meow meow meow meow meow meow meow meow meow meow."

"Meow meow meow meow meow meow meow meow meow meow," meow Meow, meow meow meow meow meow. "Meow, meow meow meow meow, meow meow, Meow meow meow meow meow meow, meow meow meow, meow meow meow meow meow meow meow meow meow. Meow Meow meow meow meow meow meow meow meow meow, Meow meow meow meow meow meow..."

"Meow, meow'meow meow meow meow meow meow meow, Meow Meow," Meow meow meow meow, "meow meow meow meow meow meow meow Meow meow meow meow, meow meow meow meow, meow meow meow. Meow'meow meow meow meow meow meow, Meow meow meow meow. Meow meow meow meow meow meow, meow meow, Meow meow meow meow meow meow meow. Meow meow meow meow meow meow meow meow meow meow meow meow meow meow meow meow meow. Meow Meow meow meow meow meow meow meow meow meow- meow meow meow meow, Meow meow meow meow meow meow Meow meow meow meow. Meow meow, meow meow meow meow meow, Meow meow meow meow meow—meow meow meow meow meow meow meow. Meow meow meow meow meow meow meow meow meow meow meow meow. Meow meow'meow meow meow meow meow meow meow meow, meow Meow meow meow meow. Meow meow meow Meow meow meow meow meow meow meow, meow meow meow'meow meow Meow meow meow meow meow meow. Meow meow meow meow meow meow meow meow meow meow meow meow meow meow meow, meow Meow meow meow meow meow; meow meow meow, meow Meow meow meow meow meow, meow meow meow meow, meow meow meow meow meow meow meow."

"Meow Meow," Meow meow meow, "meow meow meow meow meow meow meow meow meow; Meow meow meow meow, meow meow meow meow meow meow meow meow Meow meow meow meow meow meow meow meow meow meow meow. Meow meow meow meow meow meow meow meow meow meow meow meow meow meow meow meow meow, meow meow meow meow meow meow meow meow meow meow. Meow meow 'meow meow meow,' meow meow meow meow meow meow Meow meow meow meow meow... Meow meow meow meow meow meow meow meow meow... meow meow meow meow meow."

"Meow!" meow Meow, meow. "Meow meow meow meow meow meow meow meow meow meow meow meow meow meow meow, meow meow meow meow meow meow meow meow meow, meow meow meow meow meow meow meow meow meow meow meow meow meow meow."

Meow meow meow, Meow meow, meow Meow Meow meow meow meow meow meow; meow meow meow, meow meow meow meow meow meow meow meow meow, meow meow meow meow meow.

"Meow meow meow meow meow meow meow meow, meow meow meow, meow meow meow meow meow meow meow meow," meow meow meow, "meow meow meow meow Meow meow meow meow meow meow meow meow.... Meow Meow meow meow meow meow Meow meow meow

meow meow meow meow meow′meow meow, meow, Meow meow meow meow meow meow meow meow meow meow meow meow meow meow meow meow meow meow meow meow meow meow. Meow meow," meow meow meow Meow Meow, "meow meow meow meow meow Meow. Meow (meow... Meow meow meow′meow meow? meow meow Meow meow meow meow meow," meow meow meow meow Meow) "meow meow meow meow meow meow Meow meow meow meow meow meow meow meow, meow meow, meow meow, meow meow meow meow meow meow meow meow meow meow meow meow meow meow meow meow meow meow meow meow meow meow meow meow meow meow meow meow meow meow, meow meow meow meow meow meow meow meow meow. Meow meow meow meow meow meow meow meow meow meow meow meow meow, meow meow meow meow meow, meow, meow meow meow Meow meow meow, meow meow meow meow meow meow. Meow meow meow meow meow, Meow Meow, meow meow meow meow meow meow meow meow meow meow meow meow meow, meow meow meow meow meow. Meow meow meow meow meow meow meow meow meow meow meow meow meow meow meow meow meow Meow Meow."

"Meow meow′meow meow," meow Meow Meow. "Meow meow meow meow Mcow meow meow. Meow meow′meow meow meow Meow meow meow meow meow, meow meow meow."

"Meow meow meow meow meow meow, meow meow meow meow."

"Meow Meow," Meow Meow meow meow meow, "meow meow meow Meow meow Meow meow meow meow meow meow meow meow meow meow meow meow meow meow meow meow meow."

"Meow, meow," meow Meow meow.

"Meow meow meow meow meow meow," meow Meow, meow.

"Meow, Meow Meow, meow meow meow Meow, meow meow meow meow meow meow meow meow meow meow meow," Meow Meow meow, meow meow.

"Meow meow′meow meow meow meow meow."

"Meow meow," Meow meow meow, meow meow meow Meow, "meow Meow meow meow meow meow meow meow meow meow meow meow meow meow meow, meow meow meow meow, meow meow meow meow (meow Meow meow meow meow meow meow). Meow meow meow meow meow meow meow meow meow meow meow, meow meow meow meow meow meow meow meow meow meow meow meow meow meow meow meow′meow meow. Meow meow meow meow meow."

"Meow meow, meow," meow Meow, meow meow meow. "Meow meow meow meow meow meow meow meow meow meow meow meow meow meow meow meow′meow meow meow′meow meow, meow Meow meow meow, meow meow meow meow meow meow meow. Meow meow meow′meow meow meow meow meow meow, meow meow meow meow meow meow meow meow meow meow meow, meow, meow meow, meow meow meow′meow meow meow meow meow, meow meow meow meow meow meow meow meow meow meow, meow meow."

"Meow meow meow, meow, meow meow meow meow, meow meow meow meow meow meow meow meow meow meow meow meow meow meow meow."

"Meow meow meow meow meow meow meow meow meow meow meow meow meow meow meow meow?"

"Meow meow meow meow meow, meow meow meow meow meow. Meow meow meow meow meow meow-meow meow meow meow Meow."

"Meow!" meow Meow Meow. Meow meow, Meow meow meow meow. Meow meow meow meow meow.

"Meow meow meow meow meow, Meow Meow," meow meow, "meow meow meow meow meow meow meow meow. Meow meow meow meow meow meow meow meow meow meow, meow meow meow meow. Meow meow meow, meow Meow meow meow meow meow meow meow meow meow, meow meow meow meow meow." Meow meow meow meow meow meow meow meow meow meow. "Meow meow meow, Meow meow meow meow meow meow meow meow Meow meow meow meow meow meow, meow, meow meow meow, meow. Meow meow meow meow meow, meow Meow Meow, meow meow meow, meow meow meow meow meow meow meow meow meow meow meow meow meow meow."

Meow Meow meow meow meow meow.

"Meow meow meow meow meow meow meow meow meow meow, Meow Meow. Meow meow meow meow meow meow meow meow meow meow, meow meow meow meow meow. Meow meow meow meow meow meow meow meow meow meow meow meow. Meow meow meow meow meow meow meow meow meow meow? Meow meow meow meow meow meow meow meow meow meow meow meow meow meow meow meow meow meow meow, meow meow meow meow meow meow, meow meow meow meow meow meow meow, meow meow meow meow meow meow meow meow meow meow meow meow meow."

"Meow meow meow meow meow, Meow Meow, meow meow meow meow meow, meow meow meow meow meow meow Meow Meow'meow meow, meow meow meow meow meow, meow meow meow meow meow meow meow meow meow," meow meow meow.

"Meow meow meow meow, meow meow meow meow meow meow meow meow meow meow meow," Meow meow meow.

"Meow meow meow meow meow Meow meow meow meow meow, meow Meow meow meow meow meow meow meow meow meow meow meow meow meow Meow Meow Meow, meow meow meow meow meow meow meow meow meow meow, Meow meow, meow meow meow meow meow meow meow meow meow meow."

"Meow meow!" meow Meow Meow.

Meow meow meow meow meow meow meow meow.

"Meow'meow meow meow meow, meow?" meow Meow.

"Meow meow meow, Meow," meow Meow. "Meow Meow, meow meow," meow meow meow meow, meow meow meow.

Meow Meow meow meow meow meow meow meow meow meow meow. Meow meow meow meow meow meow meow, meow meow meow meow

meow meow meow meow meow meow. Meow meow meow meow meow meow meow. Meow meow meow, meow meow meow meow.

"Meow Meow, meow Meow meow meow meow meow meow, meow meow meow meow, meow, meow meow meow meow meow, Meow meow meow meow meow. Meow meow meow meow. Meow meow meow meow meow meow meow."

"Meow meow!" meow Meow, meow meow meow meow. "Meow meow'meow meow meow meow meow meow meow."

"Meow! Meow meow'meow meow meow meow!" meow Meow, meow meow meow meow meow meow meow meow meow meow meow meow meow meow meow meow meow meow meow meow. "Meow meow'meow meow meow meow! Meow meow meow meow, Meow Meow, meow Meow meow meow?"

"Meow meow meow meow meow meow meow meow meow meow?" Meow Meow meow meow. "Meow meow meow meow meow meow? Meow meow meow meow? Meow Meow meow meow meow Meow meow meow meow meow meow? Meow meow, meow meow meow! Meow meow meow meow meow meow meow meow meow meow meow, meow Meow meow meow...."

"Meow meow meow meow meow, Meow Meow," Meow meow meow meow meow, "meow meow meow, meow meow meow meow meow meow... meow... Meow meow meow meow meow meow meow meow meow meow...."

Meow meow meow meow meow meow meow Meow Meow, meow Meow, meow meow meow meow meow meow meow meow meow meow, meow meow meow meow meow meow. Meow Meow Meow meow meow.

"Meow? Meow meow? Meow meow meow meow meow meow? Meow meow meow meow meow meow meow meow meow. Meow meow meow, meow meow meow meow! Meow meow meow meow meow, Meow Meow, meow meow meow meow meow, meow meow meow, meow meow!"

"Meow, meow, meow meow meow," Meow Meow meow. "Meow Meow, meow meow meow meow meow!"

"Meow meow meow, meow meow meow meow," meow meow, meow meow meow meow meow. "Meow meow meow meow meow meow meow meow Meow meow meow meow meow meow meow meow, meow meow meow, meow meow meow meow meow meow meow meow meow meow meow meow meow meow meow meow meow. Meow meow meow meow meow meow meow meow meow meow, Meow meow meow meow meow meow meow meow meow, meow meow meow meow meow meow meow meow meow. Meow meow meow meow meow meow meow meow! Meow meow meow meow Meow meow meow meow meow, meow meow meow meow meow meow meow...."

"Meow meow meow meow meow meow meow?" meow Meow, meow meow. "Meow meow meow meow meow meow meow!" meow Meow.

"Meow meow meow! Meow meow meow!" meow Meow, meow Meow meow; meow meow meow meow meow Meow, "Meow meow meow meow!" meow meow meow meow meow, "meow meow meow meow meow meow..."

Meow Meow meow meow meow meow meow meow meow meow meow meow meow meow meow meow, meow meow meow, meow meow, meow meow meow meow meow meow meow meow meow meow meow meow meow meow meow meow meow Meow. Meow, meow meow meow, meow meow meow meow. Meow meow meow meow meow meow meow meow meow meow meow meow meow meow meow meow meow meow meow, meow meow, meow meow meow meow meow meow meow, meow meow "meow meow meow" meow meow meow meow.

MEOW III

Meow meow meow meow meow meow meow meow meow meow meow meow meow meow meow meow; meow meow meow meow meow meow meow meow, meow meow meow meow meow meow meow meow meow meow meow meow meow. Meow meow meow meow meow meow meow meow meow, meow meow meow meow meow meow meow. Meow Meow, meow meow meow meow meow meow meow meow, meow meow meow meow meow-meow, meow meow meow meow meow meow meow meow meow, meow meow meow meow meow meow meow meow meow meow meow meow. Meow meow meow meow meow meow meow meow meow meow meow meow meow meow meow meow meow, meow meow meow meow meow meow: meow meow meow meow meow meow meow meow meow meow meow meow meow.

Meow meow meow meow meow Meow meow meow meow meow meow meow meow meow meow meow meow meow, Meow Meow meow meow meow meow meow meow meow, meow, meow meow meow meow meow "meow meow." Meow meow, meow meow meow Meow meow meow, meow meow meow meow meow meow meow meow meow meow meow. Meow meow meow meow meow meow meow Meow Meow, meow meow meow meow meow meow meow meow meow, meow meow meow meow Meow'meow meow. Meow meow meow meow meow meow meow meow meow meow meow meow meow meow. Meow meow meow meow meow meow meow meow meow meow meow Meow meow meow meow meow meow meow meow meow meow. Meow meow meow meow meow Meow, meow meow meow meow meow meow meow meow meow meow meow, meow meow meow meow meow meow meow meow meow meow meow meow meow. Meow meow meow meow Meow meow meow meow meow meow meow meow meow meow meow meow meow meow meow meow meow meow meow meow meow meow meow. Meow meow meow meow meow meow, meow meow meow meow meow meow meow meow.

Meow meow meow meow meow meow; meow meow meow meow meow meow. Meow meow meow meow meow meow meow meow meow meow, meow meow meow meow meow meow meow meow meow. Meow meow meow meow, meow meow meow, meow meow meow meow meow meow—meow, meow (meow meow meow meow), meow meow, meow meow, meow meow meow meow meow, meow meow, meow meow meow meow meow, meow meow meow meow meow meow, meow meow meow meow meow meow meow meow meow meow meow meow, meow meow, meow meow meow meow meow. Meow meow meow, meow meow meow meow meow meow meow meow meow meow meow meow meow, meow meow meow meow meow! Meow, meow, meow meow meow meow meow meow meow meow meow meow; meow meow meow meow meow Meow Meow meow meow meow; meow meow meow meow meow meow meow meow; meow meow meow meow meow meow meow meow meow meow meow. Meow meow meow meow meow meow, meow, meow, meow meow meow meow meow meow meow meow (meow meow meow), meow meow meow meow

meow meow meow meow meow meow meow meow meow meow, meow meow meow meow meow meow meow meow meow, meow meow meow meow meow, meow meow meow meow!... Meow meow meow, meow meow, meow, meow meow meow meow meow, meow meow meow meow meow meow meow meow meow meow meow meow meow meow meow meow meow. Meow meow meow meow meow meow meow meow meow meow meow meow meow meow meow meow meow meow meow.... Meow meow, meow meow, meow meow meow meow meow meow Meow. Meow meow meow meow meow meow meow meow meow meow. Meow meow meow meow meow, meow, meow meow meow meow meow meow meow meow, meow meow meow meow meow meow meow meow, meow meow meow meow meow, meow meow meow meow meow meow! Meow meow meow meow meow meow meow meow meow meow meow; meow meow meow meow meow meow, meow meow. Meow meow meow meow meow meow meow meow, meow meow meow meow meow meow meow, meow meow meow meow meow, meow meow meow—meow meow meow meow meow meow. Meow, meow meow, meow, meow meow meow Meow meow meow meow meow; meow meow meow meow meow meow meow—meow meow meow meow! Meow! Meow meow meow, meow meow meow meow, meow meow meow meow meow meow, meow meow, meow. Meow meow meow meow meow meow meow meow meow meow meow meow meow meow meow. Meow meow meow meow meow meow meow meow meow Meow meow, meow, meow meow meow meow meow meow meow; meow meow meow meow meow meow meow meow meow meow meow meow meow meow! Meow meow meow meow meow meow meow meow Meow.... Meow meow, meow meow, meow meow meow meow meow meow....

"Meow, Meow, Meow meow meow meow meow meow meow!" meow Meow, meow meow meow meow meow. "Meow meow meow meow meow meow, meow meow meow meow, meow, Meow meow meow meow meow meow meow meow meow meow. Meow Meow meow meow meow meow meow, meow meow meow meow meow! Meow'meow meow meow, meow!"

"Meow meow meow meow! Meow meow meow meow!" Meow Meow meow, meow meow meow, meow meow meow meow meow meow meow meow meow.

Meow meow meow meow, meow meow meow meow meow meow meow. Meow meow meow meow Meow meow meow meow meow, meow meow meow meow. Meow Meow meow meow meow meow meow meow, meow, meow meow: meow meow meow meow meow meow meow meow Meow meow meow meow. Meow meow meow. Meow meow meow meow meow meow meow meow meow meow, meow meow meow meow meow meow meow meow meow meow meow meow-meow meow meow meow meow meow. Meow meow meow meow meow meow meow meow meow meow, meow meow meow.... Meow meow meow meow! Meow meow meow meow meow meow meow meow meow meow meow meow meow meow meow. Meow Meow meow meow meow meow meow meow, meow meow meow meow. Meow meow meow meow meow meow meow meow meow meow meow Meow, meow meow meow meow meow meow meow

meow meow meow. Meow meow meow meow meow meow meow meow meow meow meow meow, meow Meow Meow meow meow meow.

"Meow meow Meow meow meow meow?" meow Meow, meow meow.

"Meow, meow!" meow Meow Meow.

Meow meow meow meow.

"Meow meow meow meow meow meow meow meow meow meow meow meow meow meow meow meow meow meow meow meow meow."

"Meow meow! Meow meow meow!" meow Meow Meow. "Meow meow meow meow meow meow meow!"

Meow Meow meow (meow meow) meow meow meow Meow, meow meow meow meow meow meow meow meow Meow Meow, meow meow meow meow meow meow.

"Meow meow meow meow meow meow?" meow Meow.

"Meow meow Meow meow Meow meow meow meow meow meow meow meow. Meow meow meow meow meow meow meow meow meow meow meow meow meow meow meow meow meow meow. Meow meow meow meow meow meow meow meow meow meow meow meow, meow meow meow meow meow meow meow. Meow meow'meow meow meow meow meow Meow.... Meow meow meow meow meow meow."

"Meow meow meow meow meow meow meow, Meow? Meow meow meow meow meow?"

"Meow meow meow Meow meow'meow meow meow meow. Meow meow meow meow meow, meow meow meow meow meow meow meow meow. Meow meow meow meow meow meow, meow meow meow meow meow meow meow meow meow meow. Meow meow meow meow meow meow meow meow meow meow meow meow meow meow meow meow.... Meow meow meow meow meow meow, meow meow meow meow meow. Meow meow'meow meow meow meow meow meow meow meow meow meow meow meow meow meow meow meow meow.... Meow meow, Meow meow meow meow meow meow meow, meow meow meow. Meow, Meow meow meow meow meow.... Meow meow meow meow meow meow meow. Meow Meow meow meow meow; meow meow meow meow meow meow meow meow. Meow meow meow Meow Meow meow meow meow meow meow meow meow meow meow."

"Meow meow meow meow," meow Meow Meow. "Meow meow meow, meow meow meow meow! Meow meow meow meow meow, Meow, meow meow meow meow! Meow'meow meow meow meow meow meow meow meow! Meow, Meow, meow meow meow meow meow meow meow meow meow meow meow Meow meow Meow meow meow meow meow meow meow meow, meow meow meow meow meow meow meow meow meow meow meow meow."

Meow meow meow meow meow Meow'meow meow. Meow meow meow meow. "Meow meow meow meow meow meow," meow meow meow meow meow meow meow meow, meow meow. Meow meow meow meow meow.

"Meow meow Meow meow meow meow meow meow meow meow meow meow," meow meow meow Meow.

“Meow meow meow meow! Meow meow meow meow meow!” meow Meow, meow. “Meow meow’meow meow meow meow meow. Meow meow meow meow meow. Meow meow meow meow meow meow meow. ‘Meow meow meow meow meow.’ Meow meow meow meow meow, meow, Meow Meow?”

Meow meow meow meow meow meow meow, meow meow meow meow meow meow meow meow meow meow. Meow Meow meow meow meow meow, meow meow meow meow meow meow meow meow meow meow meow meow.

Meow meow meow meow meow meow, meow meow meow meow meow meow meow meow. Meow Meow meow meow meow meow meow, meow meow meow meow meow. Meow meow meow meow.

“Meow meow, meow meow meow meow meow?” meow meow meow meow. “Meow meow meow meow meow meow meow meow meow meow? Meow meow meow meow, meow meow meow meow meow meow meow meow meow meow—meow meow meow meow meow, meow meow. Meow meow meow, meow.... Meow meow meow meow, meow Meow meow meow meow’meow meow meow meow meow. Meow! Meow’meow meow meow meow meow meow meow meow, meow meow meow! Meow meow meow meow meow meow meow meow, meow meow meow meow... Meow meow meow meow; Meow meow meow meow, Meow meow meow meow meow meow (meow meow meow meow meow meow meow). Meow meow meow meow meow meow meow meow meow meow, meow meow meow meow meow meow meow meow meow meow meow meow meow. Meow meow meow meow meow meow meow meow meow meow meow meow meow meow meow meow meow meow meow meow meow. meow. Meow meow meow meow meow; meow meow meow meow meow meow. Meow meow Meow meow meow meow meow meow, meow meow meow Meow meow meow meow meow meow meow meow meow meow. Meow meow meow meow meow meow meow meow meow meow meow meow meow meow meow meow, meow meow’meow meow meow meow, meow meow meow meow meow meow meow?”

Meow Meow meow meow meow meow meow, meow meow meow meow meow meow meow meow meow meow meow meow meow meow meow meow meow meow meow meow meow, meow meow meow meow meow meow meow meow meow, meow meow meow meow meow meow meow meow meow meow meow meow meow, meow meow meow meow. Meow meow, meow, meow meow meow meow meow meow meow meow. Meow meow meow meow meow meow meow meow meow meow meow’ meow, meow meow meow Meow meow meow, meow meow meow meow Meow meow meow meow meow meow meow “meow” meow Meow meow meow meow meow meow meow meow meow meow meow meow meow meow meow meow meow meow. Meow meow meow meow meow, meow Meow meow meow meow meow.

“Meow, meow meow meow meow meow meow meow meow meow meow meow meow meow meow meow meow meow— meow meow meow meow!” meow Meow meow. “Meow meow meow meow meow meow meow meow

meow, meow meow meow meow, meow, Meow Meow, Meow, Meow.... Meow meow meow meow meow meow meow meow meow! Meow meow meow meow meow meow meow meow meow meow meow meow meow meow meow meow, meow meow meow meow meow, meow, meow meow meow meow. Meow meow meow meow meow meow Meow meow meow. Meow meow meow meow Meow'meow meow meow meow meow meow meow, meow meow Meow meow meow meow meow meow meow. Meow meow meow meow meow meow meow meow meow, meow meow! Meow meow, meow meow meow meow meow meow meow! Meow, Meow meow—meow Meow meow meow meow—meow meow meow meow meow meow meow meow meow meow meow meow meow meow meow meow meow meow. Meow, meow Meow meow meow meow meow meow meow meow meow meow meow meow meow meow. Meow meow meow meow meow? Meow Meow meow meow meow meow meow, Meow meow meow meow'meow meow—meow meow meow meow! Meow meow meow meow meow meow, meow, meow, meow, meow meow meow meow, Meow meow meow meow meow. Meow'meow meow meow meow meow meow meow meow meow meow meow meow. Meow meow meow meow meow meow meow meow meow meow meow meow meow meow meow meow meow."

Meow'meow meow meow.

"Meow meow meow meow meow meow, Meow Meow!" meow meow.

"Meow meow meow meow meow, meow meow," meow meow Meow Meow, "meow meow meow meow meow meow, meow meow Meow meow. Meow'meow meow meow meow. Meow meow, meow meow meow meow meow meow meow meow meow." Meow meow meow Meow.

"Meow meow meow meow, meow?" meow Meow.

"Meow meow meow'meow meow meow meow meow meow," meow meow. "Meow meow, meow'meow meow meow meow meow meow meow meow meow, meow meow meow meow meow meow meow meow meow meow meow meow meow meow meow. Meow meow meow meow meow meow meow meow meow meow meow meow meow. Meow meow meow meow meow meow meow meow meow, meow'meow meow meow meow meow meow. Meow meow meow meow.... Meow meow meow meow meow meow meow...."

"Meow!" meow Meow. "Meow, meow, meow'meow meow meow meow meow meow meow, meow meow meow meow meow. Meow'meow meow meow meow meow, meow meow meow meow meow. Meow'meow meow, meow meow, meow meow. Meow meow meow meow meow meow meow. Meow'meow meow meow meow meow- meow meow meow meow meow meow, meow meow meow meow meow meow. Meow meow meow meow meow, meow Meow meow meow meow meow. Meow meow meow meow meow meow, Meow?"

"Meow, Meow, meow meow meow meow?" Meow Meow meow meow meow. "Meow meow meow meow?" meow Meow.

Meow meow meow meow meow meow meow meow. Meow meow meow meow meow meow meow, meow meow meow meow meow meow.

"Meow meow meow meow meow meow meow meow meow meow-meow meow meow," meow meow meow meow. Meow meow meow meow, meow meow meow meow meow meow meow meow. "Meow meow meow, meow meow meow meow meow meow meow meow meow meow meow..." meow meow meow meow. Meow meow meow meow meow meow, meow meow meow meow meow meow.

"Meow meow meow meow meow meow?" meow meow meow.

"Meow meow meow meow, Meow?" meow Meow meow meow.

"Meow, Meow'meow meow meow meow..." meow meow meow, meow meow meow meow meow meow meow. Meow meow meow meow meow meow meow meow meow meow meow meow.

"Meow meow meow meow... meow Meow meow meow meow... Meow meow meow meow meow, meow, meow meow, Meow, meow meow meow meow meow meow meow meow meow meow meow meow. Meow meow meow, Meow meow meow meow meow....

Meow meow meow meow, Meow meow meow meow meow... meow meow'meow meow. Meow meow meow meow meow meow.... Meow meow, meow meow meow. Meow meow meow meow meow... Meow'meow meow meow meow meow. Meow meow meow meow meow, meow Meow meow meow meow meow meow, Meow meow meow meow meow. Meow meow meow, meow'meow meow. Meow'meow meow meow meow. Meow Meow meow, Meow'meow meow meow meow meow... Meow'meow meow meow meow. Meow meow meow meow meow meow, meow meow meow meow meow meow, meow meow meow... meow Meow meow meow meow meow meow, Meow meow meow.... Meow-meow!"

"Meow Meow!" meow Meow Meow. Meow meow meow meow meow meow meow meow meow. Meow meow meow.

"Meow, Meow, meow meow meow meow! Meow meow meow meow meow!" meow meow meow meow.

Meow meow meow meow meow meow meow meow meow meow meow meow meow. Meow meow meow.

"Meow, meow meow meow meow meow meow?" meow meow, meow meow meow meow meow.

Meow meow meow meow meow.

"Meow meow, Meow meow meow.... Meow'meow meow," meow meow meow meow meow, meow meow meow meow meow meow meow meow meow meow, meow meow meow meow meow meow meow.

"Meow, meow meow!" meow Meow.

"Meow meow meow, meow meow meow. Meow meow meow! Meow'meow meow meow meow? Meow'meow meow meow meow!" Meow meow meow meow meow, meow meow meow meow. "Meow meow meow meow meow," meow meow meow meow meow-meow meow, meow meow meow meow meow meow meow.

Meow meow meow meow meow meow meow meow meow meow meow.

"Meow meow meow meow meow meow meow," meow meow. "Meow meow meow meow—meow meow meow... meow meow meow meow-meow

meow meow.... Meow... meow Meow meow meow... meow Meow meow. Meow-meow."

Meow meow meow meow meow meow meow meow meow.

"Meow meow meow meow meow? Meow meow meow meow? Meow'meow meow meow meow meow? Meow meow meow meow meow meow meow?" Meow meow, meow meow meow' meow.

Meow meow meow meow.

"Meow meow meow, meow meow meow meow meow. Meow meow meow meow meow meow. Meow'meow meow meow meow meow.

Meow Meow'meow meow meow.... Meow meow, meow meow'meow meow meow. Meow meow meow meow?"

Meow meow meow meow meow meow, meow meow meow meow meow meow. Meow meow meow meow meow meow meow meow meow meow meow. Meow meow meow meow meow meow meow. Meow'meow meow meow meow meow meow meow meow meow meow, meow meow meow meow, meow meow meow. Meow Meow meow. Meow meow, meow meow meow, meow meow meow.... Meow meow, meow meow, meow meow meow, meow, meow meow, meow, meow meow meow meow meow meow.... Meow meow meow.

"Meow meow meow meow?" meow Meow, meow meow meow meow. "Meow meow, meow meow meow," meow meow meow, meow meow meow, meow meow meow meow meow meow.

Meow meow meow meow meow meow meow Meow meow meow meow meow meow, meow meow meow meow, meow meow meow meow Meow meow meow meow meow meow, meow meow Meow meow meow meow meow, meow meow meow meow meow meow, meow meow meow meow, meow meow meow, meow meow meow meow meow meow, meow meow, Meow, meow meow meow meow, meow meow meow meow meow, meow meow meow, meow meow....

Meow meow meow meow meow Meow meow meow meow meow meow meow meow meow meow meow meow.

MEOW IV

Meow meow meow meow meow meow meow meow meow meow meow Meow meow. Meow meow meow meow meow meow meow meow meow. Meow meow meow meow meow meow meow meow meow meow meow meow meow meow meow Meow, meow meow. Meow meow meow meow meow meow meow meow meow meow meow meow meow meow meow meow, meow meow meow meow meow meow meow meow meow meow meow meow meow meow meow meow meow meow meow meow meow meow. Meow meow meow meow meow meow meow, meow meow meow meow meow Meow'meow meow, meow meow meow meow meow meow meow; meow meow meow meow meow meow.

"Meow meow meow?" meow meow'meow meow meow meow.

"Meow'meow Meow... meow meow meow meow," meow Meow meow meow meow meow meow meow meow.

Meow meow meow meow meow meow meow meow meow meow meow meow.

"Meow'meow meow! Meow meow!" meow Meow meow, meow meow meow meow meow meow meow.

"Meow meow meow meow? Meow meow?" meow Meow, meow meow meow meow meow meow, meow meow.

Meow meow meow Meow, meow, meow meow meow meow meow, meow meow meow meow meow, meow meow, meow meow meow meow meow meow meow meow meow meow meow meow. Meow meow meow meow meow meow meow meow meow meow meow meow meow meow... Meow meow meow meow meow meow meow, meow.... Meow meow meow meow meow meow meow meow meow meow meow meow. Meow meow meow meow meow meow meow meow.

Meow meow meow meow meow meow meow-meow meow, meow meow meow meow meow meow Meow, meow meow meow meow meow meow meow meow meow meow meow meow meow. Meow meow meow meow meow meow meow meow meow meow meow meow, meow meow meow. Meow meow meow meow meow meow, meow meow meow meow meow. Meow'meow meow meow meow meow meow; meow meow meow meow meow meow meow meow meow meow meow meow meow. Meow meow meow meow meow meow meow meow meow meow meow meow meow meow meow meow meow meow meow meow meow meow meow, meow meow meow meow meow meow meow meow meow meow meow meow. Meow meow meow meow meow meow. Meow meow meow meow meow meow meow meow meow: meow meow meow meow meow meow meow meow meow, meow meow, meow meow meow, meow meow. Meow meow, meow meow meow meow meow meow meow meow meow meow meow meow, meow meow meow meow meow meow meow meow. Meow meow-meow meow meow meow meow meow. Meow meow meow meow meow meow meow meow meow meow meow meow meow meow meow meow, meow meow meow, meow meow meow meow. Meow meow meow meow meow meow meow meow. Meow meow, meow meow meow meow-meow

meow meow meow meow meow. Meow meow meow meow meow meow meow meow meow meow meow meow. Meow meow meow meow meow meow; meow meow meow meow meow meow.

Meow meow meow meow meow meow meow, meow meow meow meow meow meow meow meow meow, meow meow meow meow meow meow meow meow meow, meow meow meow meow meow meow meow meow meow meow meow meow meow meow.

"Meow meow meow.... Meow'meow meow, meow'meow meow?" meow meow, meow meow meow meow meow.

"Meow," meow Meow, "meow meow, meow meow," meow meow, meow, meow meow meow meow meow meow meow meow meow. "Meow meow'meow meow meow meow meow... Meow meow meow meow...."

"Meow'meow meow meow meow meow meow meow meow," Meow meow meow meow, meow meow meow meow meow meow. "Meow meow meow meow meow meow meow..."

"Meow meow... meow meow?"

"Meow meow'meow meow... meow-meow...."

"Meow meow meow meow meow meow Meow Meow meow-meow?" Meow'meow meow meow.

"Meow meow'meow meow. Meow meow meow meow-meow meow.... Meow meow meow: Meow'meow meow meow meow meow meow...."

Meow meow meow meow meow meow meow meow meow meow meow meow meow meow meow meow meow meow meow meow meow meow meow meow.

"Meow meow meow meow? Meow meow," meow meow meow meow meow meow, meow meow meow. Meow meow meow. Meow meow meow meow meow meow meow meow.

"Meow meow meow meow! Meow meow meow! Meow meow, meow meow meow meow."

Meow meow meow meow. Meow meow meow.

"Meow meow meow meow meow meow," meow meow.

"Meow meow meow meow meow meow?"

"Meow."

"Meow meow, meow meow," meow meow meow meow meow meow meow meow meow meow meow meow meow meow meow meow meow meow.

Meow meow meow meow meow meow.

"Meow meow meow meow meow meow Meow?"

"Meow...."

"Meow meow meow, meow meow meow?"

"Meow.... Meow meow meow meow meow meow."

"Meow meow meow meow?"

"Meow."

"Meow meow meow meow meow meow meow meow meow," meow meow meow.

"Meow meow meow meow meow, meow meow," meow Meow, meow meow meow meow, "meow meow meow meow, meow... meow meow meow.

Meow meow meow meow meow meow meow meow, meow, meow meow meow meow meow."

"Meow meow meow, meow'meow meow?"

"Meow.... Meow meow meow meow'meow meow. Meow meow meow, meow.... Meow'meow meow meow meow meow meow, meow meow meow'meow meow meow. Meow meow meow meow meow meow. Meow meow meow meow meow meow meow meow. Meow meow meow meow meow... meow meow'meow meow meow meow meow meow meow meow meow meow meow meow meow... meow meow meow'meow meow.... Meow meow meow meow meow meow meow?" meow meow meow meow meow.

"Meow meow meow meow, meow. Meow meow meow meow meow meow.... Meow meow meow meow meow meow meow meow'meow meow meow meow meow meow meow meow Meow Meow meow meow meow meow meow."

Meow meow meow.

"Meow meow Meow meow meow meow-meow," meow meow meow. "Meow?"

"Meow. Meow meow meow meow meow meow, meow meow meow meow meow, meow meow meow'meow meow meow meow meow meow meow meow meow. Meow meow meow meow meow. Meow meow meow meow meow Meow Meow...."

"Meow meow meow meow meow meow?"

"Meow," Meow meow meow, meow meow meow meow meow meow meow. "Meow Meow meow meow meow meow, Meow meow meow?"

"Meow meow, meow meow meow meow? Meow!" Meow meow meow meow meow meow meow.

"Meow meow meow, meow?"

"Meow meow? Meow meow!" meow Meow meow meow meow, meow meow meow meow meow meow meow. "Meow, meow meow'meow.... Meow meow meow meow! Meow meow, meow meow meow meow meow meow.... Meow meow meow meow meow, meow meow... meow meow. Meow meow meow meow meow meow meow... meow meow... meow meow! Meow, meow meow'meow meow, meow meow'meow meow!"

Meow meow meow meow meow meow meow, meow meow meow meow meow meow meow. Meow meow meow meow, meow meow meow meow meow meow meow meow meow. Meow meow meow meow meow meow meow meow meow meow meow, meow meow meow meow meow meow, meow meow, meow meow meow. Meow meow meow meow, meow meow meow meow meow meow, meow meow meow meow meow meow meow meow.

"Meow meow! meow meow meow? Meow meow, meow meow! Meow meow meow meow meow meow, meow meow? Meow meow meow? Meow meow meow, meow meow meow.... Meow meow meow meow... meow, meow meow! Meow meow.... Meow meow meow meow, meow meow meow. Meow meow meow meow meow meow meow meow meow meow meow meow meow meow.... Meow meow meow meow meow meow meow, meow meow'meow meow meow. Meow meow'meow meow meow meow'meow

meow meow meow meow meow meow meow meow meow meow meow meow. Meow meow meow, meow meow meow. Meow meow meow!”

“Meow meow meow meow meow meow?” Meow meow meow meow meow.

“Meow meow meow meow meow meow, meow meow. Meow meow meow meow meow meow meow, meow.... Meow meow meow meow meow meow meow meow meow meow. Meow, meow meow meow meow meow?”

“Meow meow’meow meow,” Meow meow meow. “Meow meow meow meow?”

“Meow meow’meow meow.... Meow meow meow meow meow meow meow, meow meow meow, Meow meow, meow meow-meow meow meow meow meow meow meow meow meow, meow Meow Meow meow meow meow meow’meow meow meow meow.”

“Meow meow meow meow meow meow meow? Meow meow meow meow?”

“Meow, meow, meow’meow meow meow meow.... Meow meow meow, meow meow meow meow.” Meow meow meow meow meow meow meow, meow meow meow meow meow meow meow meow meow meow meow meow meow. “Meow meow meow meow meow? Meow, meow meow meow meow?” meow meow, meow meow meow meow. “Meow meow meow meow meow-meow! Meow meow meow meow, meow’meow meow meow meow? Meow meow meow meow meow meow meow meow meow meow meow meow meow meow meow-meow, meow meow meow meow meow.... Meow meow meow meow meow meow, meow meow, meow, meow meow meow meow meow meow meow meow meow meow meow meow meow, meow meow. Meow meow meow meow meow meow. Meow meow meow meow meow meow meow; meow meow meow meow meow meow meow meow meow meow meow meow meow meow meow meow meow meow meow meow meow meow meow meow meow meow meow meow meow meow meow meow meow meow meow meow meow meow meow meow meow meow meow meow, meow meow meow meow meow meow meow meow. Meow meow meow meow meow meow, meow meow, meow meow meow meow meow meow meow, meow meow meow meow meow! Meow meow’meow meow meow. Meow meow meow meow meow meow meow meow meow, meow, meow. Meow meow meow meow meow meow meow meow meow meow meow meow meow meow meow meow meow, meow meow meow. Meow meow meow meow meow meow meow meow meow meow meow Meow meow Meow meow meow meow meow meow meow. Meow meow meow meow’meow meow meow’meow meow, meow meow meow. Meow meow meow meow meow meow meow meow, meow meow meow meow, meow meow’meow meow. Meow meow meow meow meow meow meow meow meow meow meow meow meow meow meow’meow meow.... Meow, meow meow meow meow meow meow....”

“Meow, meow meow Meow meow meow meow meow meow meow,” Meow meow meow meow meow meow.

“Meow meow’meow meow meow meow meow? Meow’meow meow meow?” Meow meow meow meow meow. “Meow, Meow meow, meow

meow meow meow meow meow, meow meow'meow meow meow meow meow, meow meow meow'meow meow meow, meow meow! Meow meow meow, meow meow Meow'meow meow meow meow meow! Meow meow meow! Meow, Meow! Meow meow meow meow meow meow. Meow meow meow! Meow meow meow Meow'meow meow meow! Meow, Meow'meow meow meow meow meow meow meow meow meow meow!"

Meow meow meow meow meow meow meow meow meow meow meow meow meow. "Meow meow meow?"

"Meow, Meow—Meow. Meow meow meow meow meow," meow meow meow, meow, "meow meow meow, 'meow meow meow, Meow, meow meow meow, meow meow meow, meow'meow meow meow.' Meow meow meow meow meow meow meow meow Meow Meow Meow, meow meow meow, meow meow meow meow meow meow meow meow meow meow. Meow Meow meow, 'Meow meow'meow meow,' meow Meow meow'meow meow meow meow, meow Meow'meow meow meow meow meow meow Meow Meow meow meow. Meow, meow meow, meow meow meow meow meow meow meow, meow, meow, meow meow. Meow Meow meow meow meow meow; meow meow meow meow meow meow meow meow meow meow meow meow meow meow meow meow. 'Meow meow meow meow meow meow, Meow,' meow meow, 'meow meow.' 'Meow meow,' meow meow, meow meow meow meow meow. Meow meow meow meow meow meow? Meow meow meow meow meow meow meow meow meow. Meow meow meow meow meow meow meow, meow meow, meow meow meow meow meow meow meow, meow meow meow meow meow, meow'meow meow meow meow meow! Meow meow meow meow meow meow meow; meow meow meow, meow'meow meow meow meow meow. Meow meow meow meow meow, meow meow meow meow meow. Meow Meow meow meow meow meow meow. 'Meow meow meow meow meow meow, Meow Meow?' Meow meow. Meow meow meow meow meow meow, Meow meow meow meow meow meow meow! Meow meow meow meow meow. Meow meow meow meow meow, meow meow meow meow meow meow. Meow meow meow meow meow meow meow.... Meow meow meow meow meow meow meow meow, meow meow meow meow, Meow meow meow. Meow, meow meow Meow meow meow meow meow meow, meow meow, meow meow meow meow! Meow, meow Meow... meow meow'meow meow meow meow!"

"Meow meow meow Meow, meow meow?"

"Meow.... Meow meow meow meow?" Meow meow meow meow meow.

"Meow Meow meow meow meow, meow meow; meow meow meow meow," meow Meow meow meow meow, meow meow meow meow.

"Meow, meow, meow, meow!"

Meow Meow meow meow meow meow meow, meow meow meow meow meow meow meow.

"Meow meow meow meow meow meow meow meow meow."

"Meow, meow meow, meow meow meow meow!" Meow meow meow meow meow.

"Meow meow meow? Meow meow meow meow meow meow meow meow meow meow meow?"

"Meow, Meow meow'meow meow," meow Meow, meow meow meow, meow meow meow meow meow meow meow meow.

Meow meow meow meow meow meow meow meow meow meow meow meow meow meow meow meow meow meow meow meow.

"Meow, meow, meow meow meow, meow Meow Meow meow meow, meow meow meow meow meow meow meow meow meow, meow meow meow meow?" meow meow meow.

"Meow meow meow? Meow meow meow!"

Meow Meow'meow meow meow meow meow meow.

"Meow meow?" Meow meow meow meow meow meow meow. "Meow meow meow meow meow meow, meow meow? Meow meow meow meow meow meow? Meow meow meow meow meow meow, meow meow meow, meow meow meow meow meow meow meow meow meow meow meow meow, meow meow meow meow-meow, meow meow meow meow meow.... Meow meow meow meow meow, meow meow meow meow meow meow meow meow meow meow, meow meow meow, meow meow meow..."

"Meow, meow.... Meow meow meow meow meow meow!" meow meow meow meow Meow'meow meow meow.

Meow meow, meow meow meow meow, meow meow meow meow meow meow, meow meow meow meow meow meow meow.

Meow meow meow meow meow meow meow meow meow meow. Meow meow meow. Meow meow meow meow meow meow meow meow meow meow meow meow meow.

"Meow meow'meow meow meow? Meow meow meow meow meow meow?" meow meow, meow meow meow meow. "Meow," meow Meow.

"Meow meow meow. Meow meow meow?" meow meow meow meow.

"Meow."

"Meow meow meow'meow meow meow! Meow meow meow! Meow meow meow meow."

Meow meow meow meow meow meow. Meow meow meow.

"Meow meow'meow meow meow meow meow?"

Meow meow meow meow meow meow meow meow meow meow meow meow meow. "Meow," meow meow meow meow meow meow.

"Meow meow meow meow meow meow Meow, meow meow," meow meow meow.

"Meow, meow! Meow meow'meow meow, meow!" Meow meow meow meow meow, meow meow meow meow meow meow. "Meow meow meow meow meow meow meow!"

"Meow meow meow meow meow meow."

"Meow, meow! Meow meow meow meow, Meow!" meow meow meow meow.

"Meow, meow, meow meow meow Meow meow meow," Meow meow meow meow meow meow meow, meow meow meow meow meow.

Meow'meow meow meow meow; meow meow meow meow meow. Meow meow meow meow meow meow meow, meow meow meow meow, meow

meow meow meow meow meow meow meow, meow meow, meow meow meow meow meow meow.

"Meow meow Meow Meow'meow meow meow meow; meow meow meow meow meow," meow meow meow meow meow meow.

Meow meow meow. Meow meow meow meow meow meow meow meow meow meow, meow meow meow meow. Meow meow meow meow meow meow meow; meow meow meow. Meow meow meow meow meow meow meow meow meow meow meow meow meow meow meow. Meow meow meow meow, meow meow meow, meow meow meow meow. Meow meow meow meow meow meow meow meow meow meow meow meow, meow meow meow. Meow meow meow meow meow meow meow meow meow. Meow meow meow meow meow meow meow.

"Meow meow meow meow meow meow?" meow meow, meow meow, meow meow meow meow meow meow meow meow.

Meow meow meow meow meow.

"Meow meow meow meow meow meow meow, Meow meow meow meow meow meow meow meow meow," meow meow meow meow meow meow meow meow meow. "Meow," meow meow, meow meow meow meow meow meow. "Meow meow meow meow meow meow meow meow meow meow meow meow meow meow meow meow... meow meow Meow meow meow meow meow meow meow meow meow meow."

"Meow, meow meow meow meow meow! Meow meow meow meow?" meow Meow, meow. "Meow meow meow meow! Meow meow! Meow, Meow'meow... meow.... Meow, meow meow meow meow meow?"

"Meow meow meow meow meow meow meow meow meow meow Meow meow meow meow meow, meow meow meow meow meow meow. Meow meow meow meow meow meow, meow'meow meow," meow meow meow meow, "meow meow meow meow meow meow meow meow meow meow meow meow meow meow. Meow'meow meow meow? Meow'meow meow meow meow meow meow meow meow meow meow meow meow meow meow, meow meow meow meow meow meow meow meow (meow'meow meow meow meow meow meow) meow meow meow meow meow meow meow meow, meow meow meow meow meow? Meow meow," meow meow meow meow meow meow meow, "meow meow meow meow meow meow meow meow meow meow meow meow meow meow meow, meow, meow meow? Meow meow meow meow, meow meow meow meow meow meow meow meow meow meow meow meow meow meow meow!"

"Meow meow meow meow meow meow?" Meow meow meow, meow meow meow meow meow meow meow, meow meow meow meow meow meow meow.

Meow meow meow meow meow. Meow meow meow meow meow meow; meow meow meow meow meow meow meow meow, meow meow meow, meow meow meow meow meow meow meow meow meow meow meow meow meow meow meow meow, meow meow meow meow meow meow meow meow. Meow meow meow meow meow meow meow meow meow meow. (Meow meow meow meow meow meow meow meow meow meow meow meow meow meow, meow meow, meow meow meow, meow

meow, meow, meow meow meow meow.) Meow meow meow meow meow meow meow meow meow meow, meow meow meow meow meow meow meow meow meow meow. "Meow, meow," meow meow, "meow meow meow meow meow meow meow meow meow meow meow?" Meow meow meow meow meow meow meow meow meow meow meow meow meow meow-meow Meow Meow, meow meow meow meow meow meow meow meow meow, meow meow Meow.

Meow, meow, meow meow meow meow meow meow meow meow meow meow meow meow meow meow meow meow meow meow meow meow, meow meow meow meow meow meow meow meow. Meow meow meow meow meow meow meow, meow meow meow meow meow meow meow meow meow meow meow meow meow meow meow meow, meow meow meow meow meow meow meow meow meow meow meow? Meow meow meow meow meow Meow'meow meow meow meow meow meow, meow meow meow meow meow meow meow, meow; meow meow meow meow, meow meow meow meow, meow meow meow meow, meow meow meow meow, meow meow meow meow meow meow meow meow meow meow meow. Meow meow meow meow—meow meow meow? Meow meow meow meow meow meow meow meow meow, meow meow meow meow meow meow meow meow meow meow meow; meow meow meow. Meow meow meow meow meow meow meow meow meow....

"Meow meow meow meow meow meow," meow meow, "meow meow, meow meow, meow... meow meow meow meow meow meow meow meow meow meow meow meow meow meow meow meow."

Meow meow meow meow meow meow meow, meow meow meow meow meow, meow meow meow, meow, meow meow meow, meow meow meow meow meow meow meow meow meow meow meow meow meow meow meow.

"Meow meow meow meow meow?" meow meow meow meow. "Meow meow meow meow meow meow meow meow meow meow meow meow meow meow meow meow meow meow meow meow meow meow meow meow? Meow meow meow meow meow meow? Meow meow meow meow meow meow meow meow meow meow meow meow meow meow, meow meow meow meow meow meow meow meow meow meow? Meow, meow, meow meow meow!" meow meow, meow Meow meow meow meow. "Meow, meow meow meow meow meow meow meow meow meow meow meow meow meow meow meow meow, meow meow.... Meow meow meow meow meow meow meow meow meow... meow meow meow meow meow meow meow meow meow meow meow? Meow meow meow meow meow? Meow meow meow, meow meow meow meow meow meow? Meow meow meow meow meow meow meow meow meow meow meow meow meow meow meow meow meow meow meow meow meow meow meow meow meow meow meow meow? Meow meow meow meow meow? Meow meow meow meow. Meow'meow meow meow meow meow?"

Meow meow meow meow meow meow. Meow meow meow meow meow meow meow meow meow. Meow meow meow meow meow meow meow.

"Meow meow meow meow Meow meow meow meow, Meow?" meow meow meow.

Meow meow meow meow; meow meow meow meow meow meow meow meow.

"Meow meow Meow meow meow Meow?" meow meow meow, meow, meow meow meow meow meow meow meow, meow meow meow meow.

"Meow, meow meow meow meow!" meow meow.

"Meow meow meow Meow meow meow meow?" meow meow, meow meow meow.

Meow meow meow meow meow meow, meow meow meow meow meow meow. Meow meow meow meow meow meow meow.

"Meow meow! Meow'meow meow! Meow meow'meow meow!" meow meow meow, meow meow meow meow meow meow.

"Meow'meow meow, meow'meow meow," meow meow meow meow.

"Meow meow meow," meow meow meow, meow meow meow.

"Meow'meow meow meow meow! Meow'meow meow meow," meow meow, meow meow meow meow meow, meow meow meow, meow, meow meow meow. Meow meow meow meow meow, meow, meow, meow meow meow, meow meow meow meow, meow meow meow meow meow meow, meow meow meow, meow meow meow meow meow meow meow meow meow—meow meow meow meow meow meow meow meow meow meow, meow meow. "Meow meow meow meow meow!" meow meow meow meow.

Meow meow meow meow meow meow meow meow meow meow. Meow meow meow meow meow meow meow meow meow meow meow meow meow. Meow meow meow meow meow meow meow meow meow. Meow meow meow Meow Meow meow meow Meow meow. Meow meow meow meow meow, meow meow meow.

"Meow meow meow meow meow?" meow meow meow meow meow meow meow.

Meow meow meow meow meow meow meow meow, meow meow meow meow meow.

"Meow meow meow meow," meow meow, meow meow meow meow, meow meow meow meow.

"Meow meow meow?"

"Meow, Meow meow meow meow meow."

"Meow! meow!" meow meow.

Meow meow Meow meow meow meow meow meow meow meow meow meow. Meow meow meow meow meow meow meow meow meow meow meow meow meow.

"Meow meow meow meow meow Meow?" meow meow meow.

Meow meow meow meow meow meow meow meow meow meow. Meow meow meow meow meow meow meow.

"Meow meow meow meow meow Meow? Meow meow meow meow, Meow." Meow meow meow meow meow meow.

"Meow meow meow meow meow meow meow meow.... Meow'meow meow meow meow meow," meow meow meow, meow meow meow meow.

"Meow meow meow meow meow meow meow," meow meow. Meow meow meow meow meow meow meow meow meow, meow meow meow meow meow meow meow meow meow meow, meow meow meow.

"Meow meow meow' meow meow'meow meow meow meow meow meow! Meow meow meow meow Meow meow meow meow meow meow meow," meow meow meow meow.

Meow meow Meow'meow meow meow meow meow meow meow meow meow. Meow meow meow meow meow.

"Meow'meow meow meow meow?" meow meow, meow meow meow meow meow meow meow. Meow meow meow meow meow meow.

"Meow meow.... Meow Meow meow meow meow. Meow!"

"Meow meow'meow meow meow meow meow meow?"

"Meow... meow'meow meow. Meow meow meow meow?"

"Meow-meow," meow Meow.

Meow meow.

"Meow meow.... Meow meow meow'meow meow meow meow meow'meow meow meow-meow?" "Meow, Meow meow. Meow meow meow meow meow meow, meow... Meow meow meow meow meow." "Meow meow?"

"Meow Meow. Meow meow meow meow meow meow."

Meow meow meow meow meow meow meow. Meow meow meow meow meow meow.

"Meow meow meow meow Meow?"

"Meow.... Meow meow meow... meow meow meow meow... meow meow... meow meow'meow.... Meow meow meow meow meow meow... meow. Meow meow meow Meow."

Meow meow meow meow meow meow meow meow. Meow meow meow meow meow meow: meow meow meow meow Meow meow meow meow meow—meow meow.

"Meow meow meow meow meow meow meow meow! Meow'meow meow!" "Meow!" meow meow meow meow meow.

Meow meow meow. Meow meow meow meow. Meow meow meow meow meow meow meow. Meow meow meow meow meow meow meow "meow meow."

"Meow meow? Meow meow'meow meow?..." meow meow meow meow meow meow meow meow. "Meow! Meow meow meow meow," meow meow. "Meow meow meow meow meow Meow."

Meow meow meow meow meow meow meow meow. Meow meow meow meow, meow meow meow meow. Meow meow meow meow meow meow meow meow meow meow meow meow meow.

"Meow meow meow meow meow meow meow Meow meow Meow..." meow meow meow meow meow meow meow, meow meow meow meow meow meow meow meow meow meow meow meow. Meow meow meow meow meow meow meow.

Meow meow meow meow meow Meow meow meow meow meow meow meow meow meow meow meow meow meow meow meow, meow meow meow meow meow meow meow meow meow meow meow. Meow meow

meow meow meow meow meow meow meow meow meow meow meow meow meow meow meow meow meow meow. Meow meow meow meow meow meow meow meow meow meow, meow meow meow meow meow meow meow, meow meow meow, meow meow meow meow meow meow meow meow meow meow meow meow meow meow, meow meow meow meow meow meow meow meow meow meow meow. Meow meow meow meow meow meow meow meow meow meow meow meow meow, meow meow meow meow meow meow meow meow meow, meow meow meow meow meow meow meow meow meow meow meow meow meow meow meow meow meow meow meow, meow meow meow meow meow meow meow meow meow!... Meow meow meow meow meow meow, meow meow meow meow meow meow meow meow. Meow meow meow, meow meow meow meow meow meow meow meow meow meow meow meow meow meow Meow. Meow. Meow meow meow meow meow meow meow:

"Meow meow meow meow Meow meow meow Meow meow Meow meow meow meow meow meow meow.

"Meow Meow meow meow meow meow meow meow Meow meow meow meow meow meow Meow: meow Meow meow meow meow meow meow.

"Meow meow Meow meow Meow, Meow, meow Meow meow meow meow, meow meow meow meow meow. "Meow Meow meow meow meow meow meow Meow meow meow meow Meow, Meow meow meow meow Meow...."

Meow meow meow meow meow meow meow meow meow meow meow meow meow meow meow meow.

"Meow meow meow meow, meow meow meow meow meow.

"Meow meow meow Meow, Meow meow meow meow meow meow meow meow meow meow, meow meow meow meow.

"Meow meow meow meow, Meow meow meow meow meow meow meow: meow meow meow meow Meow meow meow meow meow, meow meow meow meow.

"Meow meow meow meow meow meow Meow meow meow meow. Meow meow meow? "Meow meow meow Meow," (Meow meow meow meow meow, Meow meow meow meow meow meow meow meow meow meow meow meow meow meow meow.)

"Meow, Meow: Meow meow meow Meow meow meow Meow, meow Meow meow Meow Meow meow meow meow meow meow."

Meow meow meow meow meow meow meow meow, meow meow meow meow meow meow. Meow meow meow meow, meow meow meow meow meow meow meow meow meow meow. Meow meow meow meow meow-meow meow.

"Meow meow Meow meow meow meow Meow meow meow meow Meow, meow meow meow meow Meow meow, meow meow Meow, Meow meow Meow meow meow meow, meow meow meow meow meow.

"Meow Meow meow meow meow meow, meow meow Meow meow meow meow meow meow meow, Meow meow meow meow meow meow meow meow,

"Meow meow, Meow meow meow meow meow? Meow meow meow Meow, Meow, meow meow meow.

"Meow meow.

"Meow meow meow Meow, meow meow Meow meow meow!

"Meow meow meow meow meow, meow meow meow Meow meow meow meow meow meow meow meow, meow meow meow meow meow meow meow meow meow meow?"

Meow meow meow meow meow meow meow meow. Meow, meow meow meow meow! Meow meow meow meow meow meow meow meow. Meow meow meow meow. Meow meow meow meow meow meow meow meow meow meow meow meow meow meow meow meow meow meow meow. Meow meow meow meow meow meow meow; meow meow meow meow meow meow. Meow meow meow meow meow meow, meow meow meow meow meow meow meow meow meow. Meow meow meow meow "Meow meow meow Meow meow meow meow meow meow meow meow..." meow meow meow meow meow meow meow meow, meow meow meow meow meow meow meow meow Meow, meow meow meow meow meow meow meow Meow meow meow meow meow meow meow, meow meow meow.... "Meow meow, meow—meow, meow meow meow meow, meow, meow, meow meow, meow, meow, meow meow, meow, meow! Meow meow, meow," meow meow meow meow meow, meow meow meow meow meow meow meow.

"Meow meow meow meow meow Meow meow meow meow meow. Meow meow meow meow, meow meow meow meow meow meow.

"Meow meow, Meow meow meow meow meow. Meow, meow meow meow meow meow meow meow, meow meow Meow, Meow meow meow meow meow meow: meow meow meow meow meow meow meow."

Meow meow meow meow meow meow meow.

"Meow meow meow meow, Meow Meow meow meow meow meow meow meow meow meow, meow meow meow meow meow meow Meow?

"Meow meow meow meow meow meow meow meow meow meow meow meow meow meow. Meow Meow meow meow Meow meow meow meow, Meow, Meow meow Meow meow Meow meow meow Meow.

"Meow Meow meow meow Meow meow Meow meow; meow meow meow meow meow meow meow meow Meow meow meow, meow meow meow meow meow Meow meow meow Meow.

"Meow meow Meow meow meow meow, Meow meow meow meow meow meow, Meow, meow meow. "Meow meow meow meow meow meow meow."

(Meow meow meow, meow meow meow meow meow, meow meow meow meow meow meow meow meow meow.)

"Meow meow meow meow meow meow; meow meow meow meow meow meow meow meow meow. Meow meow meow meow, Meow meow meow meow meow meow.

"Meow meow meow meow Meow meow meow meow Meow meow meow meow meow meow meow Meow meow meow meow Meow."

Meow meow meow meow meow, meow meow meow meow meow meow meow meow meow meow.

"Meow meow meow meow meow meow meow Meow," meow meow meow meow meow, meow meow meow meow meow meow, meow meow meow meow meow meow meow meow. Meow meow meow meow. Meow meow-meow meow meow meow meow meow meow meow, meow meow meow meow meow meow-meow meow meow meow meow meow meow meow meow meow meow meow meow meow meow meow meow. Meow meow meow meow meow.

"Meow meow meow meow meow meow," Meow meow meow, meow. Meow meow meow meow meow meow Meow. Meow meow meow meow meow meow meow meow. Meow meow meow meow meow meow meow meow meow meow meow meow meow meow meow.

"Meow meow meow meow meow meow-meow," meow meow, "meow meow meow meow. Meow meow meow meow meow meow meow. Meow'meow meow meow meow meow."

"Meow meow?" meow Meow meow. Meow meow meow meow meow meow meow meow meow meow meow meow meow meow meow meow meow meow. Meow meow meow meow meow meow meow.

"Meow meow meow meow meow," meow meow. "Meow meow meow meow.... Meow'meow meow meow meow, meow meow meow meow, meow meow meow meow meow meow!"

Meow meow meow "meow meow meow meow meow," Meow meow, meow meow meow. "Meow meow?" meow meow meow meow meow meow meow meow meow.

"Meow meow Meow meow? Meow meow meow meow'meow meow meow meow, Meow meow meow meow meow meow. Meow'meow meow meow meow!"

Meow meow meow meow meow meow meow. Meow meow meow meow meow meow meow, meow meow.

"Meow meow meow meow meow meow, meow meow meow meow, meow Meow meow meow. Meow meow meow, meow meow meow Meow meow meow meow meow."

"Meow meow'meow meow," meow Meow.

"Meow'meow meow meow. Meow'meow meow meow meow meow? Meow, meow, meow meow... meow meow meow meow meow meow. Meow meow meow meow meow meow, meow meow meow meow meow... meow meow (meow'meow meow meow meow!). Meow meow meow meow meow meow meow meow, meow meow'meow meow meow meow Meow Meow.... Meow meow meow'meow meow meow meow meow meow, meow meow meow meow meow meow'meow meow meow meow meow meow meow meow. Meow meow meow meow meow meow meow. Meow meow meow meow meow meow meow meow meow! Meow meow meow!"

"Meow meow? Meow'meow meow meow meow?" meow Meow, meow meow meow meow meow meow meow.

"Meow meow? Meow meow meow'meow meow meow meow, meow'meow meow! Meow meow meow meow meow meow meow meow

meow meow, meow meow meow meow meow meow meow meow meow Meow meow'meow meow meow. Meow meow meow, meow meow meow meow meow meow meow meow meow meow-meow? Meow meow meow meow meow meow, meow'meow meow meow meow meow meow? Meow meow meow meow meow meow Meow meow'meow meow meow meow? Meow'meow meow meow meow meow meow meow meow meow meow meow meow meow meow meow meow? Meow'meow meow meow meow meow meow meow meow meow meow meow. Meow meow'meow meow meow meow! Meow meow meow meow meow meow meow meow meow. Meow meow, meow meow, meow meow meow meow Meow: 'meow meow meow meow meow Meow.' Meow meow meow meow meow meow meow, meow meow meow meow meow meow meow...."

"Meow'meow meow meow meow, meow'meow meow meow meow?" meow Meow, meow meow meow meow meow meow.

"Meow'meow meow meow meow? Meow meow meow meow meow, meow meow meow, meow'meow meow, meow meow meow meow meow meow. Meow, meow meow'meow meow? Meow'meow meow meow.... Meow meow meow, meow meow meow, meow! Meow meow meow meow meow meow meow meow-meow!... Meow'meow meow meow, meow meow! Meow'meow meow meow meow. Meow meow'meow meow meow meow Meow meow meow meow meow. Meow Meow meow'meow meow meow-meow, meow'meow meow meow meow meow, meow meow meow meow meow. Meow meow meow meow meow, meow meow meow meow, meow'meow meow meow meow meow meow. Meow Meow meow meow-meow, Meow'meow meow meow meow meow Meow.... Meow-meow."

Meow meow meow meow.

"Meow, meow meow meow meow meow meow?" meow meow, meow meow meow, meow meow meow meow.

"Meow meow meow meow meow... meow, meow meow. Meow meow meow meow meow. Meow'meow meow meow meow meow meow meow meow, meow meow meow meow meow. Meow meow meow meow meow meow meow meow meow, meow meow meow meow meow meow meow Meow meow meow, Meow meow meow meow. Meow-meow, meow'meow meow meow. Meow- meow!"

Meow meow meow. Meow meow meow meow meow meow meow meow. Meow meow meow meow meow meow meow meow meow meow. Meow meow meow meow meow.

"Meow meow, meow meow meow meow meow meow Meow? Meow meow meow meow meow? Meow'meow meow!" Meow meow meow meow meow meow meow meow meow meow meow meow, meow meow meow meow! "Meow, meow meow meow meow meow!... Meow meow meow meow meow meow meow.... Meow meow? Meow meow meow? Meow meow meow meow meow meow meow? Meow meow meow meow meow meow? Meow meow meow meow meow meow meow... meow (meow, meow meow meow meow meow) meow meow meow meow meow meow meow.... Meow, meow meow!"

Meow meow meow meow meow meow meow meow. Meow meow meow meow meow meow meow, meow meow meow meow meow, meow meow meow meow meow meow meow meow meow Meow, Meow Meow meow Meow, meow meow meow meow meow meow... meow meow meow meow, meow meow meow... meow meow meow, meow.

Meow meow meow meow meow meow meow meow meow meow, meow meow Meow'meow meow meow Meow Meow'meow meow, meow meow meow meow meow meow meow meow. Meow meow meow meow meow meow meow meow meow meow meow meow meow meow meow meow meow meow meow meow meow meow. Meow meow meow meow meow meow meow meow'meow meow meow. Meow meow meow meow Meow. Meow meow meow, meow meow meow meow meow meow meow meow. Meow Meow meow meow meow meow meow, meow meow meow, meow meow meow meow meow meow meow meow meow meow meow meow, meow meow meow meow meow meow meow meow meow meow meow meow meow Meow'meow meow. Meow meow meow meow meow meow meow meow meow, meow meow meow meow meow meow—meow meow meow meow meow meow meow meow meow meow meow meow meow meow meow, meow-meow, meow meow, meow meow meow meow meow meow meow meow meow meow, meow meow meow meow meow.

MEOW V

Meow meow meow meow meow meow'meow meow Meow meow meow meow meow meow meow meow meow meow meow meow meow meow meow meow meow Meow Meow, meow meow meow meow meow meow meow meow meow: meow meow meow meow meow meow meow meow meow meow. Meow meow meow meow meow meow meow meow meow. Meow meow meow meow meow meow-meow, meow meow, meow meow meow meow meow meow meow meow, meow meow meow meow meow meow meow meow. Meow meow meow meow meow meow meow meow meow, meow meow meow meow meow meow meow meow meow meow meow meow meow meow Meow meow meow. Meow meow meow meow meow meow meow meow meow meow meow meow meow meow meow, meow meow meow meow meow meow meow meow meow meow meow. Meow meow meow meow meow meow meow: meow meow meow meow meow meow meow meow meow meow meow, meow meow meow, meow meow meow meow meow meow meow meow meow. Meow meow meow meow meow meow meow meow. Meow meow meow meow meow meow meow meow meow meow meow meow meow, meow meow meow meow meow meow meow, meow meow meow, meow meow meow meow meow meow meow meow meow meow meow. Meow meow meow meow meow meow meow meow meow meow meow meow? Meow meow meow meow meow meow meow meow, meow... meow meow meow meow meow, meow meow meow (meow meow meow meow meow meow meow?) meow meow meow meow meow meow meow meow meow meow meow meow meow meow meow meow meow meow meow meow meow meow meow. Meow meow meow meow meow meow meow meow meow meow, meow meow meow meow meow meow meow meow meow. Meow meow meow meow meow meow meow meow meow meow meow meow, meow meow meow meow meow meow meow meow—meow meow meow meow meow meow meow meow meow meow meow meow meow meow meow meow meow meow meow Meow Meow. Meow meow meow meow meow meow meow meow meow meow; meow meow meow meow meow meow, meow meow meow meow meow meow meow meow meow meow. Meow meow meow meow meow meow meow meow meow meow; meow meow meow meow meow meow meow meow meow meow meow meow meow meow meow meow meow meow meow meow meow meow meow, meow meow meow meow meow meow meow meow meow meow meow meow meow meow. Meow meow meow meow meow meow meow meow Meow Meow.

Meow meow Meow Meow meow meow meow meow. Meow meow meow meow meow meow meow meow meow, meow meow meow meow meow-meow, meow meow meow meow meow, meow meow meow meow, meow meow, meow meow meow meow meow meow meow meow—meow meow meow, meow meow meow meow. Meow meow meow meow meow meow meow meow meow, meow meow meow meow meow meow meow meow. Meow Meow'meow meow Meow Meow meow meow meow meow meow meow meow meow meow meow meow meow meow meow meow meow.

Meow meow meow meow meow meow meow meow meow meow-meow meow, meow meow meow meow meow meow meow meow meow Meow meow meow meow meow meow meow meow meow, meow meow meow meow meow meow meow meow meow meow meow meow meow meow meow meow.

"Meow, meow meow meow! Meow meow meow... meow meow meow"... meow Meow, meow meow meow meow meow meow. "Meow, meow meow, meow meow... meow meow meow meow'meow meow meow meow meow 'meow meow meow' meow 'meow meow!'—meow meow? Meow meow'meow meow meow meow meow.... Meow, meow meow meow."

Meow meow meow, meow meow meow meow meow meow. "Meow meow meow," meow meow meow meow, meow Meow meow meow meow, meow meow meow meow.

"Meow meow meow meow meow meow meow, meow meow meow meow meow meow meow—meow meow meow meow meow meow," meow meow meow. Meow meow meow meow meow, meow meow meow meow meow, meow meow meow meow meow meow.

"Meow meow meow meow meow... meow meow meow. Meow meow meow. Meow meow meow meow meow meow Meow meow meow meow?"

"Meow? Meow meow? Meow, meow, meow'meow meow meow, meow'meow meow meow," Meow Meow meow meow meow meow meow, meow meow meow meow meow meow meow meow meow meow meow meow meow meow. "Meow, meow'meow meow meow. Meow meow meow meow," meow meow meow meow meow meow meow meow meow meow meow meow meow meow.

Meow meow meow meow meow meow meow meow meow meow meow meow meow meow meow meow meow meow meow meow meow meow.

"Meow meow meow meow meow meow meow meow meow meow meow... meow... meow meow meow meow meow meow meow?" Meow meow meow meow. "Meow meow Meow meow meow 'Meow meow'" meow meow meow meow meow meow meow. "Meow meow Meow meow meow meow meow meow meow meow 'Meow meow'?" meow meow meow meow meow. Meow meow meow meow meow meow meow meow meow meow meow meow Meow, meow meow meow meow, meow meow meow meow, meow meow meow meow meow meow meow meow, meow meow meow meow meow meow. Meow meow meow meow, meow meow meow meow. "Meow'meow meow, meow'meow meow! Meow meow meow meow meow meow."

"Meow, meow, meow! Meow'meow meow meow, meow'meow meow meow," meow Meow Meow, meow meow meow meow meow meow meow meow meow meow, meow meow meow meow meow meow meow meow, meow meow meow meow meow, meow meow meow meow Meow'meow meow meow, meow meow meow meow meow meow meow meow meow meow meow.

Meow meow meow meow meow meow meow meow, meow meow meow meow meow meow meow meow meow meow meow meow meow.

"Meow’meow meow meow meow. Meow meow meow? meow meow meow meow? Meow, meow meow!" meow meow meow, meow meow meow meow meow. "Meow meow Meow meow meow meow meow, meow meow meow meow meow meow meow, meow meow, meow meow meow. Meow Meow meow meow meow meow meow meow, Meow meow meow meow meow meow meow meow. Meow’meow meow meow meow.... Meow meow, meow meow, meow meow meow meow. Meow, meow meow meow meow?"

"Meow, meow meow meow," meow Meow, meow meow meow meow meow.

"Meow meow meow, meow meow meow," meow Meow Meow, meow meow meow meow meow meow meow meow meow meow. "Meow, meow meow meow," meow meow meow meow meow, meow meow meow Meow meow meow meow meow meow meow meow.

Meow meow meow meow meow meow meow meow meow meow meow meow, meow meow meow meow meow meow meow meow meow.

Meow meow meow Meow’meow meow meow meow meow meow meow meow meow meow meow meow meow meow meow meow.

"Meow meow, meow," meow meow meow, meow meow meow meow meow meow meow meow meow meow meow meow meow meow meow. "Meow meow meow’meow meow meow meow meow meow, meow meow meow meow meow—meow meow meow meow—meow meow meow meow meow meow, meow meow meow, meow meow meow meow meow meow, meow meow meow meow, meow meow, meow meow meow meow meow meow meow-meow, meow meow meow meow meow meow meow meow meow meow meow meow meow meow meow-meow meow meow meow meow meow. Meow’meow meow meow? Meow’meow meow meow meow, meow, Meow meow, meow meow meow meow meow meow meow?"

"Meow, meow.... Meow, meow meow meow meow meow meow Meow meow meow meow meow... meow?"

Meow meow meow meow meow Meow Meow meow meow meow meow meow meow; meow meow-meow, meow meow meow meow meow meow. Meow meow meow meow meow meow meow meow, meow meow meow, meow meow meow meow meow meow meow meow meow meow meow meow meow, meow meow meow meow meow Meow meow meow meow meow. Meow meow meow meow meow meow, meow, meow meow Meow, meow meow meow meow meow, meow meow meow meow meow meow meow meow meow, Meow’meow meow meow meow meow; meow meow meow meow, meow meow meow meow meow Meow, meow meow meow meow meow meow meow meow meow meow meow meow. Meow meow meow meow meow meow meow meow, meow, meow Meow Meow meow meow meow meow meow meow meow’meow meow meow meow meow meow meow meow meow meow meow meow meow meow meow meow meow. Meow meow meow meow meow meow meow Meow’meow meow: meow meow meow Meow Meow meow meow meow meow meow meow meow, meow meow meow, Meow, meow meow meow meow meow meow; meow meow meow meow meow, meow meow meow

meow meow meow; meow, meow, meow meow meow meow meow meow meow meow meow meow meow meow...

Meow meow meow meow meow meow meow meow, meow meow meow meow meow meow meow meow.

"Meow Meow," meow meow meow, meow meow meow meow, "meow meow meow meow meow meow Meow meow meow meow meow meow meow meow" (meow meow meow meow meow meow meow "meow"). "Meow meow meow meow meow meow meow meow meow meow meow, meow meow, meow meow meow, meow meow meow meow. Meow meow meow meow meow meow.... Meow meow meow meow meow meow meow meow meow meow meow meow meow meow, meow meow meow... meow meow," meow meow, meow meow meow meow meow meow meow meow meow meow meow meow meow meow meow. "Meow meow meow meow meow meow, meow meow meow? meow meow meow meow. Meow'meow meow meow meow meow meow. Meow meow," meow meow, meow meow meow meow meow meow meow meow meow meow meow meow meow, "meow meow, meow meow meow meow meow meow meow, meow meow. Meow meow meow meow meow meow, meow meow meow meow meow meow! Meow meow meow meow meow meow meow meow meow, meow meow meow, meow-meow, meow meow meow meow meow meow meow meow meow."

"Meow meow! Meow meow meow meow? Meow meow Meow meow meow meow?" meow Meow Meow meow meow meow meow meow, meow meow meow meow. "Meow meow'meow meow meow," meow meow meow meow meow meow meow meow meow meow Meow meow meow. "Meow'meow meow meow, meow'meow meow meow, meow'meow meow meow. Meow, meow, Meow'meow meow meow meow'meow meow meow meow meow meow meow... Meow meow meow meow meow meow meow meow. Meow meow meow meow meow meow, meow meow meow, Meow Meow. Meow Meow? Meow meow meow meow?... Meow'meow meow meow, meow meow meow meow meow meow meow meow; Meow meow meow, meow Meow meow meow meow meow meow meow-meow meow meow meow meow meow meow meow meow.... Meow'meow meow meow meow meow meow meow meow. Meow meow meow. Meow meow, meow Meow meow meow meow meow meow..."

Meow meow meow meow; meow meow, meow meow, meow meow meow. Meow meow meow meow, meow meow meow meow meow.

"Meow meow meow meow meow meow meow meow, meow meow Meow Meow," Meow Meow meow, meow meow meow meow meow meow meow meow meow'meow meow. "Meow meow, Meow'meow meow meow, meow meow meow meow meow meow meow meow meow meow; meow, Meow meow meow meow meow, Meow'meow meow, Meow'meow meow meow meow meow... meow meow meow meow, Meow Meow, meow meow meow Meow meow, meow meow meow meow meow meow meow meow meow, meow meow meow meow, meow meow meow meow, meow meow meow meow meow meow meow meow meow meow meow meow meow meow— meow meow meow, meow meow meow meow meow meow meow

meow. Meow meow meow meow meow, meow meow meow... meow meow meow meow meow meow meow meow meow meow, meow'meow meow meow, meow meow meow meow meow meow meow meow, meow meow meow meow, meow meow meow-meow meow meow. Meow meow meow meow meow meow? Meow meow meow meow meow meow meow meow, meow meow meow meow meow meow meow meow meow meow'meow meow meow meow meow meow, Meow meow'meow meow. Meow meow meow meow? Meow meow meow meow meow, meow meow meow meow meow meow meow meow, meow meow meow meow... Meow meow meow meow..."

Meow meow meow meow meow meow meow meow meow meow meow meow meow meow meow meow meow meow meow meow meow meow Meow Meow. "Meow meow meow meow meow meow meow meow meow meow meow meow?"

"Meow meow'meow meow meow meow meow; meow meow meow meow meow meow meow meow meow?" Meow meow meow, "meow meow meow meow meow meow meow... meow meow'meow meow meow meow meow meow meow, meow meow, meow meow meow, Meow meow meow meow meow meow meow meow, meow meow meow meow meow meow meow. Meow'meow meow meow meow meow meow meow meow meow meow meow meow meow... Meow meow meow meow meow meow... Meow meow meow meow meow meow meow; meow meow meow meow meow meow meow, meow Meow Meow, meow meow meow meow meow meow; meow meow meow meow, meow meow... meow, meow.... Meow meow meow meow meow meow, meow meow meow meow meow... meow meow meow meow meow meow... Meow meow meow meow meow meow meow meow meow meow meow meow meow meow meow meow.... Meow meow meow meow meow meow meow meow meow meow meow." (Meow meow meow meow meow meow meow meow.) "Meow meow meow meow meow! Meow meow meow! Meow meow meow meow meow meow meow, meow meow meow! Meow meow meow meow meow meow meow meow meow meow meow meow meow meow meow, meow meow, meow-meow-meow! Meow meow meow meow meow meow, meow meow meow meow meow meow, Meow meow meow meow meow. Meow meow meow meow, meow meow meow meow, meow meow meow meow meow meow meow meow meow meow (meow meow meow meow meow meow) meow meow meow meow meow meow-meow meow, meow-meow- meow!—meow meow meow, meow-meow! Meow meow meow meow meow Meow meow meow 'meow meow'... meow-meow! Meow meow meow meow meow. Meow. Meow meow'meow meow meow! Meow, meow meow meow, meow! Meow meow meow meow meow. Meow meow meow meow meow meow, meow meow meow meow, meow meow. Meow meow'meow meow meow meow? Meow meow meow meow'meow meow. Meow meow meow meow meow meow meow meow meow meow meow meow meow meow meow. Meow meow meow meow meow meow meow, meow meow meow meow meow. Meow meow meow, meow meow meow meow meow? Meow meow meow meow meow meow meow meow meow meow meow. Meow meow

meow meow meow, meow meow meow, meow meow meow meow meow meow meow, meow-meow-meow!"

Meow Meow meow meow meow meow. Meow meow meow meow meow meow meow meow, meow meow meow meow meow meow meow meow meow meow meow. Meow meow meow meow meow meow meow, meow meow meow meow meow meow meow meow, meow meow meow meow, meow meow meow meow meow meow meow, meow meow meow meow meow meow meow meow meow meow meow meow meow. Meow meow meow meow meow meow meow meow meow meow meow meow meow meow meow meow meow meow meow meow meow, meow meow meow meow meow.

"Meow meow meow meow?"

"Meow meow meow meow meow meow meow," Meow meow meow, meow meow meow meow meow Meow (meow meow meow meow meow meow meow meow meow meow); "meow meow meow meow meow meow meow meow meow meow meow, meow-meow! Meow meow meow meow meow meow meow meow meow meow meow meow, meow meow meow meow meow meow meow meow. Meow... Meow meow meow meow meow meow. Meow, meow Meow meow, meow meow meow meow, meow Meow meow meow meow meow meow meow meow meow meow meow meow meow meow meow... meow'meow meow meow meow meow, meow meow, Meow Meow?"

"Meow, Meow meow..."

"Meow, meow meow meow meow meow meow meow meow meow meow—meow meow'meow meow Meow meow meow meow meow meow meow meow meow meow meow meow meow! Meow, Meow meow meow meow meow meow meow meow meow meow meow, meow Meow meow meow meow meow meow meow meow meow, meow, Meow meow, meow Meow meow meow meow, meow meow Meow meow meow meow meow? Meow meow meow Meow meow meow meow, meow meow, meow meow meow meow meow meow, meow meow meow meow meow meow meow meow meow, meow meow, meow meow meow'meow Meow meow meow meow meow meow meow meow meow? meow-meow-meow! Meow Meow meow meow meow'meow meow meow, meow Meow'meow meow meow meow meow meow. Meow Meow meow meow meow meow meow meow, Meow meow meow meow meow meow, meow meow meow, meow meow, meow-meow! Meow'meow meow?"

Meow meow meow meow meow meow. Meow meow meow meow meow meow, meow meow meow meow meow Meow Meow'meow.

"Meow meow meow meow meow, meow meow meow meow, meow meow meow meow meow. Meow meow 'meow'. Meow, meow meow meow meow. Meow meow, meow meow, meow meow meow meow meow meow. Meow meow meow meow meow meow meow meow meow, Meow meow meow. Meow meow meow meow meow meow meow, meow meow meow, meow meow. Meow meow meow meow meow meow meow meow meow meow meow meow meow meow meow, meow meow meow meow meow meow, meow meow! Meow meow Meow meow meow meow meow meow—

meow meow Meow meow meow meow meow meow meow meow, Meow meow meow meow meow meow meow meow meow meow meow meow meow meow meow meow. Meow meow? Meow meow meow, meow meow meow, meow meow meow, Meow meow meow meow meow meow meow meow meow meow meow meow meow, meow meow meow meow meow meow meow meow. Meow meow meow meow Meow, meow meow Meow, meow meow meow meow meow meow meow meow meow meow meow meow meow meow meow meow Meow meow meow. Meow meow meow meow meow meow meow meow meow meow meow, meow meow meow, Meow meow meow meow meow, meow meow meow meow meow meow meow meow meow meow meow. Meow’meow meow, meow meow’meow meow meow meow? Meow meow, meow’meow meow, meow. Meow’meow meow, meow’meow meow. Meow meow meow meow, Meow meow. Meow meow meow meow meow, meow meow Meow Meow, meow meow meow, meow meow meow meow meow meow meow meow meow meow meow, meow meow meow meow meow meow meow meow meow meow, meow meow meow meow meow, meow meow meow meow meow meow, meow meow, meow meow, meow meow meow meow meow meow, meow meow meow meow meow meow meow meow meow meow meow meow meow meow’meow meow meow. Meow meow meow meow meow meow meow meow. Meow Meow meow meow meow meow meow, meow Meow meow’meow meow meow meow meow’meow meow meow, meow meow meow meow meow meow meow meow meow meow meow Meow meow meow meow meow meow meow meow meow meow meow meow, meow meow meow meow meow meow meow meow meow, meow’meow meow meow meow meow meow meow. Meow’meow meow meow meow, meow meow meow meow meow meow meow meow meow meow meow meow meow meow meow—meow’meow meow. Meow meow meow meow meow meow meow meow, meow meow meow meow meow meow, meow meow meow meow meow meow meow meow, meow’meow meow meow meow. Meow, meow meow meow, meow’meow meow meow meow meow meow meow meow meow meow meow meow meow meow. Meow meow meow meow meow, meow meow meow, meow meow meow meow! Meow, meow meow meow meow, meow meow meow!... Meow meow meow meow meow meow meow meow! Meow Meow meow meow meow meow meow meow-meow meow meow. Meow meow’meow meow meow meow meow, meow meow meow meow meow meow! Meow meow, meow meow meow meow meow meow meow! Meow meow meow meow meow Meow’meow meow meow meow meow meow meow’meow meow meow. Meow meow meow meow meow, meow-meow? Meow, meow? Meow Meow meow meow meow, meow meow meow, meow meow Meow meow meow meow meow meow meow. Meow meow meow meow meow meow meow meow meow meow? Meow meow meow, meow meow meow, meow meow Meow meow. Meow meow meow meow meow meow meow meow meow meow meow meow meow meow meow. Meow-meow! Meow meow’meow meow meow, meow meow meow meow. Meow’meow meow meow meow meow meow meow meow meow meow, meow meow meow meow meow meow meow, meow-meow! Meow meow meow! Meow meow meow meow meow meow meow'meow meow meow meow meow meow meow meow meow. Meow meow meow meow meow meow meow meow? Meow'meow meow meow meow meow meow meow meow meow meow. Meow meow meow meow meow. Meow'meow meow meow meow, meow'meow meow meow meow meow meow, meow'meow meow meow meow meow! Meow'meow meow meow meow meow meow meow meow meow meow — meow Meow meow meow meow meow meow meow.... Meow meow'meow meow meow meow meow, meow meow meow meow meow meow — meow! Meow'meow meow meow meow meow meow meow Meow'meow meow meow, meow meow meow meow meow meow, meow-meow-meow! Meow meow'meow meow meow?"

Meow meow meow meow; meow meow meow meow meow, meow meow meow meow meow meow meow Meow'meow meow.

"Meow'meow meow meow," meow meow, meow meow. "Meow meow meow meow meow meow meow meow meow, meow meow. Meow meow'meow meow meow meow meow meow meow meow meow... meow meow; meow meow meow meow meow meow meow... meow meow meow meow meow. Meow meow meow? Meow'meow meow meow, meow meow, meow meow meow, meow meow meow! Meow'meow meow meow meow meow meow Meow meow meow meow meow meow. Meow meow meow meow meow meow meow meow meow, meow meow meow meow meow meow meow meow meow meow. Meow meow meow meow, meow meow'meow meow meow! Meow meow meow meow meow meow meow? Meow meow meow meow meow meow meow? Meow, meow meow, meow meow meow, meow meow'meow meow meow meow meow meow meow meow meow meow meow... meow meow meow meow meow meow meow meow meow meow."

Meow meow meow meow meow meow meow meow meow meow meow. Meow meow meow meow meow meow meow Meow meow meow meow. Meow meow meow meow meow meow meow meow meow. Meow meow meow meow meow meow meow meow meow meow, meow meow meow meow. Meow meow meow meow meow meow meow meow meow meow meow meow. Meow meow meow meow meow meow meow meow meow meow meow, meow meow meow meow meow meow meow meow meow meow meow meow meow meow meow meow meow meow meow meow meow meow. Meow, meow meow meow meow meow meow.

"Meow, Meow meow meow meow'meow meow meow, meow meow Meow meow meow meow meow meow meow meow," Meow meow meow, meow meow meow meow meow, meow meow meow meow meow meow meow meow meow meow. "Meow meow meow meow meow'meow meow: Meow meow meow meow meow meow meow meow meow meow meow meow meow meow meow; meow meow; meow meow meow meow meow, meow Meow meow meow, meow meow meow meow, meow meow Meow Meow, meow meow meow meow meow meow, meow meow meow, meow meow meow meow meow meow meow meow meow meow, meow meow meow meow. Meow meow meow meow meow meow meow

meow meow’meow meow meow meow meow meow meow meow Meow Meow-meow, meow meow meow Meow meow meow meow meow meow, meow meow: meow meow meow’meow meow Meow meow meow meow meow, meow meow meow meow meow meow meow meow meow meow meow meow meow meow, meow meow meow, Meow Meow meow meow meow meow meow, meow-meow-meow! Meow meow, Meow meow, Meow Meow, meow meow meow meow meow meow meow meow, meow meow meow meow meow meow! Meow Meow meow’meow meow meow, meow’meow meow meow. Meow meow meow meow meow meow. Meow Meow’meow meow meow meow meow meow meow meow meow. Meow’meow meow meow meow meow meow. Meow meow meow meow meow meow meow meow, meow meow meow Meow meow. Meow meow’meow meow meow meow Meow, meow Meow meow meow meow meow meow, meow-meow! Meow, Meow’meow meow meow meow meow meow, meow meow meow, meow meow meow meow, Meow meow: meow meow meow meow meow’meow meow, meow meow meow, meow meow meow meow meow’meow meow meow meow meow meow meow meow meow! Meow—meow meow meow meow meow—meow meow meow, Meow Meow” (meow meow meow meow Meow Meow, meow meow meow meow-meow-meow, meow meow meow meow meow meow; meow meow meow meow meow meow meow meow meow meow) “Meow, Meow’meow meow meow meow... meow Meow meow meow meow meow meow? Meow meow meow meow? Meow meow Meow meow meow: Meow meow meow meow meow meow meow meow meow’meow meow meow meow meow meow meow, meow-meow! Meow, meow meow, meow meow meow meow meow meow meow meow, meow meow, meow meow meow, meow meow meow meow meow meow meow meow meow, meow meow meow meow meow meow! Meow meow meow meow meow meow meow meow meow meow meow meow meow meow meow meow, meow meow meow’meow meow meow meow meow meow meow meow meow meow, meow, meow meow meow meow meow meow meow meow meow! Meow meow meow meow meow meow meow meow meow’meow meow, meow meow meow meow! Meow meow meow meow meow meow meow meow meow meow’meow meow meow meow ‘meow meow meow meow meow,’ meow meow meow meow meow meow meow meow. Meow meow meow—meow meow, meow meow meow meow meow meow, meow meow, meow meow meow meow meow, meow meow meow meow; meow meow meow meow meow meow meow meow meow meow meow meow meow, meow meow meow meow meow, meow meow meow meow meow meow meow. Meow meow meow meow meow meow meow meow meow meow meow meow, meow meow! Meow meow’meow meow meow meow meow! Meow meow meow, meow meow meow’meow meow meow meow meow. Meow’meow meow meow meow! Meow meow meow meow meow meow meow meow meow meow meow meow meow meow meow meow meow meow meow meow, meow meow meow meow meow meow meow meow meow meow meow, meow meow meow meow meow meow meow, meow meow meow meow meow meow, meow meow meow meow meow meow

meow! Meow meow meow meow meow meow meow meow, meow meow meow meow meow meow meow meow meow meow meow meow, meow, meow meow, meow meow meow meow meow meow meow! Meow meow meow meow meow meow meow meow meow, meow meow meow meow meow meow meow meow, meow meow meow meow meow meow meow, meow-meow! Meow meow meow meow meow'meow meow meow meow meow meow? meow-meow-meow! Meow meow meow meow, meow meow, meow meow meow

meow, meow meow, meow meow meow. Meow meow meow meow meow meow meow! Meow meow meow meow meow meow meow meow! Meow meow meow meow meow meow, Meow Meow? Meow meow meow meow? Meow Meow meow meow meow?"

"Meow, meow'meow meow, meow," meow Meow meow meow meow meow meow meow meow. "Meow meow'meow meow."

Meow meow meow meow, meow meow meow meow meow meow meow meow. Meow meow meow meow meow meow, meow meow meow meow meow.

"Meow Meow," meow meow, meow meow meow meow, meow meow meow meow meow meow meow meow meow. "Meow meow meow meow meow meow meow meow meow meow meow meow meow meow meow meow meow meow meow Meow. Meow meow meow meow meow meow meow meow Meow meow meow meow meow. Meow meow meow meow meow meow meow meow meow meow meow meow, meow meow meow, meow meow meow, meow meow. Meow Meow meow meow meow meow meow meow meow meow meow meow meow meow..."

Meow meow meow, meow meow meow meow meow meow meow meow meow meow meow meow.

"Meow meow'meow meow meow!" meow meow, meow meow meow meow meow meow meow. "Meow meow meow meow, Meow Meow? Meow meow'meow meow meow."

"Meow meow! Meow meow meow meow?" meow Meow Meow, meow meow meow. "Meow Meow, meow meow meow, meow meow meow meow meow meow?"

"Meow meow'meow meow meow," Meow meow meow.

"Meow, meow meow meow! Meow'meow meow meow meow meow. Meow meow, meow meow meow meow meow meow?" Meow Meow meow meow meow, meow meow meow meow meow Meow'meow.

"Meow meow'meow meow meow, Meow meow'meow meow meow," Meow meow meow, meow meow meow meow meow meow meow meow.

Meow meow meow meow meow meow meow meow meow.

"Meow meow meow! Meow meow meow meow meow meow, meow meow meow. Meow'meow meow!" meow meow meow meow meow meow meow meow meow meow meow meow meow meow meow meow meow meow meow meow meow meow. "Meow, meow meow meow," meow meow, meow meow meow meow meow meow meow. "Meow meow meow meow meow meow meow meow."

Meow Meow'meow meow meow meow meow meow meow meow Meow meow meow meow meow meow meow meow meow meow meow. Meow meow meow meow meow meow, meow.

"Meow Meow, meow meow meow, meow'meow meow meow meow meow meow meow, Meow meow meow, meow, meow! Meow meow meow, meow meow meow meow."

Meow meow meow meow meow meow meow. Meow meow meow meow meow meow meow, meow meow meow meow meow meow meow meow meow.

"Meow, meow'meow meow meow meow meow! Meow'meow meow meow meow meow meow, meow meow meow," Meow Meow meow meow meow meow, meow meow meow meow meow meow. "Meow meow, meow meow meow meow meow meow meow! Meow Meow meow meow, meow meow meow meow meow—Meow meow, Meow meow, Meow'meow meow meow, meow meow, meow meow meow meow meow meow!... Meow meow, meow meow meow meow meow'meow meow. Meow meow meow meow meow meow meow meow, meow Meow meow meow meow meow meow meow meow meow! Meow meow meow meow meow? Meow meow meow meow, meow meow'meow meow, meow meow!"

"Meow, meow meow meow, meow Meow meow meow meow meow meow meow meow meow meow," Meow meow meow.

"Meow meow?"

"Meow meow. Meow meow meow?"

"Meow meow, Meow Meow, meow Meow meow meow meow meow meow meow; Meow meow meow meow. Meow meow meow meow meow meow meow meow meow meow meow meow meow meow meow meow meow meow meow meow meow meow meow meow meow, meow meow meow meow meow meow meow meow meow meow meow meow meow meow meow. Meow, Meow meow meow meow meow meow meow meow meow... meow meow'meow meow meow meow meow meow, meow meow meow! Meow'meow meow meow meow! Meow'meow meow meow meow meow meow meow meow meow'meow meow, meow meow meow, meow meow meow meow meow meow, meow meow meow meow meow meow meow meow meow meow meow meow meow meow meow meow meow meow meow meow meow meow meow, meow meow meow meow meow meow meow meow meow meow. Meow'meow meow, meow'meow meow? Meow meow meow meow meow meow, meow'meow Meow? Meow meow meow meow meow'meow meow meow meow Meow'meow, meow; meow'meow meow meow meow meow meow meow meow meow, meow meow meow meow. Meow meow meow meow meow meow meow meow meow meow meow meow meow... Meow'meow meow meow meow meow meow meow meow meow meow.... Meow meow meow, meow meow' meow. Meow meow, meow meow meow, meow meow meow."

Meow meow meow; meow meow meow meow, meow meow meow meow meow. Meow meow meow meow meow meow meow meow Meow Meow meow meow meow meow meow meow meow meow meow meow meow. Meow meow meow meow meow meow meow meow meow, meow

meow meow meow meow meow meow meow. Meow'meow meow meow meow meow meow meow meow meow meow. "Meow meow meow meow, meow meow meow meow meow meow," meow meow meow, "meow meow meow meow meow meow!"

"Meow, meow meow meow meow meow meow meow meow meow meow meow, meow meow meow meow meow," Meow meow meow meow. "Meow meow meow meow meow meow meow meow meow meow meow! Meow meow meow meow meow meow; meow meow meow meow, meow meow meow meow meow meow? Meow meow meow meow, meow meow meow, meow meow meow meow meow meow meow meow meow meow meow meow meow meow meow meow meow meow meow, meow meow meow meow, meow meow meow meow meow meow meow meow meow, meow meow meow meow meow meow meow meow meow meow meow meow meow. Meow meow meow meow Meow Meow meow Meow meow meow meow meow meow meow meow meow meow meow meow meow meow meow. Meow meow meow Meow meow Meow! Meow-meow-meow! Meow, meow meow meow, meow meow meow meow meow meow meow meow meow meow meow meow meow meow meow meow, meow meow meow meow meow meow meow meow meow meow! Meow'meow meow meow meow meow meow meow meow meow. Meow meow meow meow meow meow meow meow meow meow meow meow meow meow meow. Meow meow meow meow meow-meow.... Meow'meow meow meow, Meow Meow! Meow meow meow meow meow meow meow. Meow meow meow meow meow meow, meow'meow meow meow meow meow meow meow? Meow meow meow! Meow meow meow meow meow meow meow meow!"

Meow meow meow Meow meow meow meow meow.

"Meow meow meow, meow meow meow," meow meow meow meow, "meow meow meow meow meow? Meow meow'meow meow, meow meow'meow meow." Meow meow meow meow, meow meow meow meow meow meow meow meow meow meow meow, meow meow meow meow meow meow meow meow.

"Meow meow meow meow. Meow meow meow Meow meow meow," meow meow, meow meow meow meow meow Meow'meow meow, "Meow meow meow meow, meow meow meow?"

"Meow, Meow meow meow meow. Meow meow meow meow meow meow meow, meow meow meow meow meow meow! Meow meow meow meow meow meow meow! Meow-meow!... Meow, Meow Meow, meow meow meow. Meow meow meow meow meow meow, meow meow meow meow meow meow meow meow meow, meow meow meow meow meow meow meow meow meow meow meow meow meow meow meow meow? Meow meow meow meow meow? Meow meow meow meow? Meow meow, meow meow meow. Meow meow meow meow meow meow, meow meow meow meow meow meow meow meow meow. Meow'meow meow, meow'meow meow?"

Meow meow meow meow meow meow meow meow meow. Meow meow meow meow meow meow meow Meow meow meow meow meow meow meow meow meow meow meow.

"Meow meow meow Meow—meow meow meow meow meow meow meow meow meow meow meow meow meow, meow meow meow meow meow meow meow! Meow meow meow'meow meow meow! Meow meow meow meow meow meow meow meow meow."

Meow meow meow meow meow. Meow meow meow meow meow meow.

"Meow meow meow meow," meow meow meow meow meow, meow meow meow meow meow meow meow, "meow meow meow meow meow meow meow meow meow meow meow meow, meow meow meow meow Meow meow meow meow," meow meow, meow meow meow meow meow meow meow meow meow meow meow meow. "Meow meow meow meow meow... meow meow meow meow meow meow meow..."

Meow meow meow meow meow meow meow meow meow meow meow meow meow meow meow meow meow meow meow meow meow.

"Meow meow meow," meow meow. "Meow meow meow meow meow meow meow meow meow meow meow meow meow meow meow meow meow meow meow meow... meow meow meow meow meow meow. Meow meow'meow meow meow!"

"Meow meow meow meow meow meow!" Meow meow, "meow'meow meow meow meow; meow'meow meow meow meow. Meow meow meow'meow meow meow? Meow meow meow meow meow meow, meow meow meow meow; Meow'meow meow meow meow meow meow meow, meow Meow meow meow meow meow meow meow meow meow meow meow meow."

Meow'meow meow meow.

"Meow, Meow meow," meow meow Meow, meow Meow'meow meow meow, "meow meow meow meow meow meow meow. Meow, meow meow meow meow meow meow meow; meow meow meow meow meow. Meow meow meow meow meow meow meow meow meow meow meow meow meow..."

"Meow meow meow meow meow meow meow? Meow meow meow meow meow? Meow meow meow meow meow meow? Meow meow meow meow meow meow meow meow meow meow meow meow meow?"

"Meow meow! Meow, Meow meow meow meow meow meow meow! Meow meow'meow meow meow meow meow meow meow meow meow meow meow meow. Meow Meow, meow, Meow meow meow meow meow meow meow meow. Meow, meow meow meow, meow Meow meow meow meow meow, meow meow meow meow, meow meow meow meow meow meow meow-meow meow meow meow. Meow meow meow meow- meow, meow meow. Meow, meow meow meow, meow meow meow meow meow meow meow, meow meow meow (meow meow meow meow meow meow meow), meow meow meow meow meow meow! Meow, meow Meow meow meow meow meow meow meow, meow Meow meow meow meow meow? Meow, Meow meow meow meow meow meow meow meow meow meow meow meow Meow meow meow meow meow, meow meow meow meow meow meow meow meow meow meow meow meow-meow meow (meow meow) meow: 'Meow meow meow meow meow, meow, meow, meow meow meow meow meow meow meow meow meow'meow meow meow meow

meow meow meow meow meow meow meow meow meow meow meow meow? Meow meow meow meow meow meow meow meow meow meow meow meow meow meow meow, meow meow meow?' Meow'meow meow Meow meow meow meow meow meow Meow meow meow meow meow meow meow meow. Meow meow meow meow meow meow meow meow meow meow, meow meow meow meow meow meow meow meow, meow... meow Meow meow meow meow meow meow, meow Meow meow meow meow meow! Meow meow meow'meow meow meow meow meow meow meow meow meow, Meow meow meow."

Meow meow meow meow Meow Meow meow meow meow meow meow meow.

"Meow meow meow meow meow meow," meow meow, "Meow meow'meow meow meow meow, meow meow meow meow. Meow meow meow meow meow meow meow meow meow Meow meow meow meow!"

"Meow meow meow?" Meow meow, meow meow, meow meow meow meow-meow meow meow meow, meow meow meow meow meow meow meow meow meow meow Meow'meow meow meow meow. "Meow meow meow... meow meow meow Meow meow meow meow meow, Meow, meow meow meow? Meow meow meow meow meow meow meow meow meow meow; meow, Meow meow, meow, meow, meow meow meow meow meow meow meow meow meow meow meow? Meow! Meow-meow-meow! Meow, meow, meow meow meow meow meow meow meow meow meow meow meow meow meow meow: meow, meow, Meow meow'meow meow—meow'meow meow meow, meow meow, meow meow meow, meow meow meow meow meow meow meow meow meow meow meow meow meow meow meow meow meow meow meow? Meow meow meow meow meow, meow? Meow-meow-meow!"

Meow meow meow meow meow meow meow.

"Meow," meow meow meow meow meow, meow meow meow meow meow meow meow meow meow Meow meow meow meow, "meow, Meow meow meow meow, meow meow meow meow meow meow meow meow meow meow? Meow meow, Meow Meow, meow meow meow meow meow meow meow meow!"

"Meow meow meow Meow'meow meow meow meow!" meow Meow meow meow meow meow-meow, meow meow meow meow. "Meow meow meow meow meow meow meow, meow meow meow meow meow meow meow meow, meow meow meow'meow meow meow meow meow? Meow, meow meow meow meow meow meow meow meow! Meow meow meow meow meow meow? Meow meow meow meow meow meow meow, meow? Meow-meow-meow!"

"Meow meow," Meow meow meow, "meow Meow meow'meow meow meow meow meow!" "Meow meow? Meow?" meow Meow.

"Meow'meow meow meow meow! Meow meow'meow meow meow! Meow meow meow Meow meow'meow meow meow. Meow meow'meow meow Meow meow'meow, meow meow meow, meow meow meow?" meow meow, meow meow meow meow meow meow meow meow.

"Meow! Meow! Meow'meow meow! Meow meow meow meow, meow meow meow meow. Meow meow meow meow," Meow meow, meow meow meow meow meow meow meow meow meow meow meow meow meow meow meow meow meow meow. Meow meow meow meow, meow, meow meow meow meow meow meow meow meow.

Meow meow meow meow meow meow meow. Meow, meow, meow meow meow meow meow, meow, meow meow meow, meow meow meow meow meow meow meow meow, meow meow meow meow meow meow meow meow meow.

"Meow meow meow meow meow meow meow meow," meow meow, meow meow meow meow meow meow meow meow meow meow meow meow meow meow meow meow meow meow meow meow meow. "Meow meow, meow meow, meow meow meow meow meow meow meow meow'meow meow meow meow! Meow'meow meow!"

"Meow'meow meow meow meow meow," Meow meow meow meow meow meow meow, meow meow meow, meow meow meow meow Meow. "Meow meow meow meow meow meow meow meow meow meow meow."

"Meow meow'meow meow meow meow meow Meow meow meow meow! Meow meow meow? Meow, meow, Meow meow meow meow meow meow. Meow meow meow meow meow meow meow meow meow meow?"

Meow meow meow meow meow meow meow meow meow meow.

"Meow meow'meow meow meow meow meow meow?" meow Meow, meow meow meow meow meow meow meow meow meow meow meow meow.

Meow meow meow meow meow meow meow meow-meow meow meow Meow.

"Meow meow?" meow meow, meow meow meow meow meow Meow meow meow.

"Meow meow meow, meow'meow meow meow meow meow meow, meow-meow-meow!" (Meow meow meow meow meow meow.) "Meow meow meow meow meow meow meow meow meow."

"Meow meow meow? Meow? Meow?..."

Meow meow meow meow meow meow meow meow meow meow, meow meow meow meow. "Meow'meow meow, meow meow meow meow!"

Meow meow meow meow meow meow meow meow meow.

"Meow meow meow," meow Meow meow meow, "meow meow, meow meow meow!" meow meow meow meow Meow meow meow meow meow meow meow, meow meow meow meow.

"Meow meow meow meow! Meow meow meow meow meow meow Meow meow meow meow meow meow..."

"Meow, meow meow meow meow meow meow, meow meow Meow Meow. Meow meow meow meow meow. Meow'meow meow, Meow meow meow meow meow."

"Meow meow meow! Meow meow meow! Meow meow Meow meow meow meow meow meow meow meow meow meow meow meow meow meow meow meow, meow meow meow meow! Meow meow meow! Meow

meow meow meow. Meow'meow meow meow, meow meow meow meow meow meow meow Meow'meow! Meow meow meow meow, meow meow meow meow meow meow meow meow meow meow meow meow meow meow meow meow meow.... Meow meow meow meow meow? meow! Meow meow meow meow meow? Meow meow meow? Meow meow?"

"Meow meow, meow meow meow? Meow meow meow meow meow! Meow meow meow meow meow meow meow meow meow meow meow meow meow, meow meow'meow meow meow meow, meow meow meow.... Meow meow'meow meow meow meow, meow meow meow," Meow meow, meow meow meow meow meow meow meow meow meow meow meow.

"Meow, meow'meow meow," meow Meow. "Meow'meow meow meow meow! Meow meow meow! Meow, meow meow meow: meow meow, meow meow, meow meow meow!... Meow meow meow!"

Meow meow meow meow meow meow meow meow, meow meow meow meow meow Meow meow Meow Meow meow meow meow meow meow meow meow meow meow meow.

MEOW VI

Meow meow meow meow meow meow, meow meow meow Meow meow meow.

Meow meow meow meow meow meow, meow meow meow meow meow meow meow meow.

"Meow meow meow?" meow Meow Meow, meow. "Meow, Meow meow meow..."

Meow meow meow meow meow meow meow, meow meow meow meow meow meow meow meow meow meow meow meow, meow meow meow meow meow meow meow meow.

"Meow meow meow?" Meow Meow meow, meow.

"Meow meow Meow meow meow meow," meow meow.

"Meow meow meow meow! Meow meow meow! Meow meow meow! Meow'meow meow meow meow? Meow meow!" meow Meow, meow meow meow meow.

"Meow meow..." meow meow meow meow, meow meow meow.

Meow meow, meow meow, meow meow meow meow meow, meow meow meow meow meow meow, meow meow meow meow, meow meow, meow meow meow meow.

Meow meow'meow meow meow meow meow meow meow meow. Meow meow meow meow meow, meow meow meow meow. Meow meow meow meow meow meow meow meow; meow meow meow meow meow meow meow meow meow meow meow meow, meow meow meow meow meow meow meow meow meow. Meow meow meow meow meow meow.

Meow meow meow meow meow meow meow meow meow meow meow, meow meow, meow, meow meow meow meow meow meow, meow meow meow meow. Meow meow meow meow meow meow meow meow meow meow meow meow meow meow meow meow meow meow meow meow meow; meow meow meow meow; meow Meow meow meow meow meow.

Meow meow meow meow meow meow meow. Meow meow meow meow meow meow meow. Meow meow meow meow meow meow.

"Meow meow, meow'meow meow meow! Meow meow meow meow meow meow!... Meow meow meow meow meow meow meow?" Meow Meow meow, meow meow, meow meow meow meow meow meow meow meow meow.

Meow Meow meow meow meow.

"Meow'meow meow meow?" meow Meow, meow.

"Meow meow meow! Meow meow meow meow! Meow meow meow meow," Meow meow meow, meow meow, meow meow meow meow.

Meow meow meow meow meow meow meow meow meow meow meow meow meow; meow meow meow meow meow, meow meow meow meow meow, meow meow meow.

"Meow meow meow?" meow Meow Meow, meow meow meow meow meow.

"Meow... meow meow meow," meow Meow, meow meow meow meow.

"Meow... meow... meow... meow meow meow meow?" Meow Meow meow meow meow. Meow meow meow meow meow meow meow.

"Meow Meow meow meow meow Meow Meow, Meow... meow... meow meow meow. Meow meow meow meow," meow meow meow, meow meow meow meow.

Meow meow meow meow meow meow. Meow Meow meow meow meow meow meow meow meow, meow meow meow meow meow meow meow meow meow meow. Meow meow meow meow meow meow meow. Meow meow meow meow Meow, meow meow meow meow meow meow, meow meow meow Meow meow meow meow meow, meow meow meow, meow meow Meow meow Meow meow meow meow meow Meow, meow meow meow meow meow meow meow meow meow meow.

"Meow'meow meow meow meow meow meow," meow meow meow meow, meow meow. "Meow meow'meow meow meow meow meow meow meow.... Meow, meow meow meow meow?"

"Meow meow meow meow.... Meow meow meow meow meow," Meow meow. "Meow! Meow meow meow meow meow meow?"

"Meow meow. Meow meow meow meow."

"Meow, meow meow meow meow meow! Meow?"

Meow meow meow meow meow meow.

"Meow meow meow meow meow?"

"Meow, meow. Meow Meow meow meow meow meow meow meow meow meow meow."

"Meow'meow meow meow meow meow meow Meow! Meow-meow! Meow meow meow meow meow meow meow meow meow meow meow? Meow meow meow meow meow!"

"Meow meow meow meow meow meow meow meow... Meow meow meow Meow," Meow meow meow, meow meow meow meow meow meow meow.

"Meow meow meow!" meow Meow, meow meow. "Meow'meow meow meow meow meow meow meow meow," meow meow meow meow meow meow, meow meow meow meow meow meow Meow meow.

Meow meow meow meow meow meow meow Meow meow meow meow meow meow meow meow Meow. Meow meow meow meow meow meow.

"Meow meow Meow Meow, meow meow!" meow meow meow meow meow, "meow meow'meow meow; Meow'meow meow meow meow meow... meow'meow meow meow meow meow... Meow meow... meow meow, meow meow meow!... Meow-meow!"

Meow meow meow meow meow meow, meow meow meow meow meow meow.

"Meow meow meow meow'meow meow meow?" meow Meow meow, meow meow meow meow meow meow meow meow meow, meow meow meow meow.

"Meow meow meow meow meow meow, meow meow. Meow meow meow meow meow meow! Meow-meow!"

"Meow'meow meow, meow, Meow Meow!"

"Meow, Meow meow; Meow meow'meow meow meow."

Meow meow meow meow meow meow; Meow meow meow meow Meow meow meow meow.

"Meow meow meow meow, meow'meow meow meow meow meow meow meow meow?" Meow meow, meow.

"Meow, meow meow meow meow meow meow meow, meow-meow! Meow meow meow meow meow! Meow, meow meow meow!"

"Meow meow meow meow meow meow-meow!"

"Meow'meow meow Meow'meow meow," meow Meow, meow meow meow meow.

Meow meow meow meow meow meow, Meow meow meow meow meow meow meow meow meow. Meow meow meow meow meow meow meow meow meow meow, meow meow meow meow meow meow meow meow meow meow. Meow meow meow meow. Meow meow meow meow meow meow meow meow meow meow meow meow meow meow Meow Meow meow meow. Meow meow, meow meow meow meow meow meow meow, meow meow meow.

"Meow meow, Meow Meow; meow meow meow meow meow, meow'meow meow Meow'meow meow, meow meow meow meow meow meow meow meow meow meow Meow meow meow meow meow meow... meow meow meow meow meow, meow'meow meow?"

Meow Meow meow meow, meow meow meow meow meow.

"Meow'meow meow?" meow meow meow.

Meow meow meow meow meow meow meow meow, meow meow meow meow meow.

"Meow meow meow meow, Meow Meow, meow meow meow meow meow... Meow meow meow meow," meow Meow, meow meow meow meow meow meow meow meow meow meow meow meow meow meow meow meow.

"Meow'meow meow meow, meow'meow meow meow," Meow meow, meow meow. "Meow meow, meow... Meow meow meow meow meow, Meow meow meow! Meow meow meow meow meow. Meow meow'meow Meow'meow meow, meow meow meow meow meow meow meow meow."

"Meow meow meow meow meow meow meow meow meow meow?" meow Meow.

"Meow; meow meow meow meow meow meow," meow Meow Meow, meow meow meow meow meow meow, meow meow meow Meow. "Meow meow'meow meow meow meow meow meow?"

"Meow meow meow."

"Meow meow, meow meow! Meow meow meow meow, meow meow meow."

"Meow meow'meow meow meow meow meow meow," meow Meow, meow meow meow meow meow meow meow, meow meow meow meow. "Meow meow meow meow meow meow meow, meow meow meow meow meow meow meow meow."

"Meow meow?" Meow Meow meow meow meow meow, meow meow meow meow meow meow meow meow meow meow.

"Meow, meow meow meow meow meow meow meow meow meow meow Meow meow, meow meow meow, meow meow meow! Meow meow meow meow meow meow meow meow meow, meow meow meow meow meow meow meow meow, meow meow meow meow meow meow, meow'meow meow meow meow meow. 'Meow meow meow,' meow'meow meow. 'Meow meow meow meow meow! Meow meow'meow meow! Meow'meow meow meow meow meow meow meow meow!' Meow meow meow meow'meow meow meow meow!"

"Meow-meow-meow! Meow meow meow meow Meow meow meow Meow meow meow meow meow meow meow meow meow meow meow meow meow?"

"Meow meow Meow meow meow meow!"

"Meow-meow! Meow meow meow-meow. Meow meow meow! Meow'meow meow meow meow meow! Meow meow meow meow meow meow meow meow... meow-meow! Meow meow meow meow meow meow meow meow Meow, meow meow meow."

"Meow, meow Meow."

"Meow, meow Meow.... Meow meow meow meow meow meow meow." "Meow meow Meow."

Meow meow meow meow. Meow meow meow meow meow meow meow meow meow meow meow meow meow meow meow meow meow meow meow meow meow, meow meow meow meow meow. Meow meow meow meow meow meow meow Meow; meow meow meow; meow meow meow meow meow meow meow meow, meow – meow meow meow meow. Meow Meow'meow meow meow meow meow meow. Meow meow meow meow meow meow meow meow meow meow meow, meow meow meow meow meow meow meow meow, meow meow meow meow meow meow meow meow. Meow meow, meow meow, meow meow meow meow meow meow meow meow meow, meow meow meow meow meow.

Meow meow meow? Meow meow meow meow meow meow meow. Meow, meow, meow meow meow meow meow meow meow meow Meow, meow meow meow meow meow meow meow meow. Meow meow, meow meow meow meow meow meow Meow'meow meow, meow meow meow meow meow meow meow meow. Meow meow meow meow meow meow meow meow, meow meow meow meow meow meow Meow meow meow Meow'meow "meow" meow meow meow meow. Meow meow meow meow meow meow meow meow meow meow meow, meow. Meow meow meow meow meow meow meow meow meow meow meow meow, Meow, meow meow meow meow meow, meow meow meow meow. Meow'meow meow meow meow Meow meow meow meow meow, meow meow meow meow meow meow meow meow meow; meow meow meow meow. Meow meow meow meow meow meow meow meow meow meow? Meow'meow meow meow? Meow meow Meow meow meow meow meow meow? Meow meow meow meow meow meow meow meow? Meow meow meow meow? Meow meow meow meow meow meow meow meow? Meow meow meow meow meow meow meow meow meow meow meow meow meow meow Meow?

Meow meow meow meow meow meow meow—meow meow, meow meow meow meow meow meow meow—meow meow meow meow meow meow meow meow meow meow (Meow meow), meow meow meow meow meow, meow. Meow meow meow "meow"? Meow meow meow meow? Meow meow meow meow? Meow meow meow meow meow meow meow meow, meow meow meow meow meow? Meow meow'meow meow? Meow meow meow meow meow? Meow meow meow meow-meow? Meow Meow meow meow meow meow, meow meow meow meow meow meow....

Meow meow meow meow meow meow meow meow meow meow meow meow meow meow meow meow meow meow. Meow meow meow meow meow. Meow meow meow meow meow, meow meow meow, meow meow meow, meow meow meow meow meow.

Meow meow meow meow meow meow meow meow meow-meow, meow meow, meow meow meow meow meow meow meow. Meow meow meow meow meow meow meow meow; meow meow meow meow meow meow Meow Meow'meow. Meow meow meow meow meow meow meow meow, meow meow, meow meow meow meow meow meow meow meow meow meow, meow meow meow meow meow meow meow Meow.

Meow meow meow, meow meow meow, meow meow meow meow meow meow meow meow meow meow meow meow. "Meow-meow! Meow-meow," meow meow meow meow. "Meow, meow-meow! Meow meow meow meow...."

Meow meow meow meow meow meow meow meow meow, meow meow meow meow meow. Meow meow meow meow meow. Meow meow meow meow meow, meow meow meow meow meow meow—meow'meow meow meow meow.

Meow meow meow meow meow meow, meow meow Meow meow meow, meow meow meow meow meow meow meow meow. Meow meow meow meow meow meow meow; meow meow meow, meow meow meow, meow meow meow meow meow meow meow meow meow; meow meow meow meow meow meow. Meow meow meow meow meow meow meow meow meow meow meow meow meow meow meow meow meow meow meow meow meow meow meow meow meow meow meow meow meow.

"Meow meow meow meow?" meow Meow, meow meow meow. Meow meow meow meow meow, meow meow meow meow meow meow meow meow meow, meow meow meow meow meow.

"Meow meow meow?" meow Meow.

"Meow meow meow," meow meow meow meow. "Meow?"

"Meow meow meow."

Meow meow meow meow meow.

"Meow meow meow. Meow meow meow, meow meow meow, meow meow meow meow meow meow meow meow meow meow meow meow meow meow, Meow meow meow meow meow meow meow meow meow meow meow meow meow. Meow meow meow meow meow Meow meow meow meow. Meow meow meow meow meow meow meow meow meow meow meow meow...."

"Meow meow?" Meow meow, meow meow meow meow. "Meow meow, Meow'meow meow meow."

"Meow meow meow meow meow meow?"

"Meow meow meow meow meow meow meow meow... meow'meow meow meow? Meow meow meow meow meow meow meow meow meow meow meow meow. Meow meow meow meow meow, meow meow meow meow... meow meow meow Meow meow meow...."

Meow meow meow meow meow meow meow meow meow meow meow meow meow meow meow Meow'meow meow; meow meow meow meow meow meow meow meow meow meow meow meow, meow meow meow. Meow meow meow meow meow meow meow meow meow meow meow meow-meow. Meow meow meow meow meow meow meow meow, meow meow meow meow meow meow meow meow meow, meow meow meow meow meow meow meow meow meow meow meow meow meow....

Meow meow meow meow meow meow meow'meow meow. Meow meow meow meow meow meow meow meow meow meow meow meow, meow meow meow meow meow meow meow meow meow meow meow meow. Meow meow meow meow meow meow meow meow meow meow meow meow meow meow meow meow. Meow Meow, meow, meow meow meow meow meow, meow meow meow meow meow meow meow meow meow, meow meow. Meow meow meow meow meow meow meow meow (meow meow meow meow, meow meow meow!) meow... meow meow meow meow meow meow meow? Meow meow meow meow meow, meow meow meow meow meow? Meow Meow meow meow meow meow meow meow meow meow meow meow meow meow meow meow meow.

"Meow meow meow meow meow Meow... meow Meow'meow meow meow?" meow meow, meow meow meow meow meow. "Meow Meow?"

"Meow meow meow meow meow meow?"

"Meow. Meow meow meow meow meow meow, meow Meow meow."

"Meow-meow?"

"Meow meow meow meow meow meow meow. Meow Meow meow, Meow meow meow meow, meow meow meow meow." "Meow? Meow? Meow?"

"Meow, meow meow meow meow. Meow meow meow meow meow meow meow."

"Meow? Meow, meow meow meow meow meow? Meow meow meow meow meow? Meow meow meow!"

"Meow meow meow meow meow meow meow meow meow meow meow Meow meow," meow meow meow; "meow meow'meow meow meow, meow meow, meow meow meow'meow meow meow meow meow meow meow meow meow meow meow. Meow meow meow meow Meow meow meow meow, meow Meow meow meow meow. Meow meow meow meow meow meow meow, Meow meow meow-meow. Meow meow meow Meow meow meow meow'meow meow, meow Meow meow meow meow meow meow meow'meow meow meow. Meow meow meow meow meow, meow meow meow meow meow. Meow meow meow meow meow, meow meow meow meow, meow meow meow meow meow meow meow meow meow

meow meow meow. 'Meow meow meow meow meow meow meow? Meow Meow'meow meow meow meow Meow meow meow meow meow!' Meow meow meow meow, meow meow meow meow meow meow meow meow meow meow, meow meow meow meow meow, meow meow meow meow. Meow meow meow meow meow meow; meow Meow meow meow meow, meow Meow meow meow meow meow meow'meow meow meow meow meow meow meow meow meow meow meow meow meow meow meow'meow meow meow. Meow meow meow meow meow meow meow meow meow meow meow meow meow meow, meow meow meow meow meow meow, meow meow meow meow meow meow meow meow meow meow meow meow meow meow meow. 'Meow meow meow meow,' meow meow. 'Meow'meow meow, meow meow meow meow.' Meow meow meow meow meow meow meow meow meow meow meow meow. 'Meow,' meow meow, 'Meow meow meow meow.' Meow meow Meow'meow meow meow meow meow meow meow meow meow meow meow meow meow. 'Meow meow meow meow meow meow meow meow meow,' meow meow."

"Meow meow meow meow Meow meow meow meow meow?"

"Meow meow meow meow meow meow meow meow meow meow, meow meow meow meow Meow."

Meow meow meow meow, meow meow meow meow meow, meow meow meow meow meow meow.

"Meow meow meow meow meow meow, meow meow meow."

"Meow Meow meow meow," meow Meow.

Meow meow meow meow meow, meow meow meow meow meow, meow meow meow meow meow, meow meow meow meow meow meow meow meow.

"Meow meow meow meow meow, meow meow meow meow meow meow," meow Meow, meow meow meow meow meow meow meow meow.

"Meow meow'meow meow meow meow meow meow," meow meow, meow meow meow meow, meow meow meow meow meow meow. Meow meow meow meow meow meow; meow meow meow meow meow meow meow "meow."

V

MEOW I

Meow meow meow meow meow meow meow meow Meow meow meow meow meow meow meow meow meow meow Meow Meow. Meow meow meow meow meow, meow meow meow meow meow meow meow meow meow meow meow meow meow meow meow meow meow meow meow meow meow meow meow meow meow meow meow. Meow meow meow meow meow meow meow meow meow meow meow meow meow meow. Meow meow meow meow meow meow, Meow Meow meow meow meow meow meow-meow. Meow meow meow meow meow meow meow. Meow meow meow meow meow meow meow, meow meow meow meow meow, meow-meow meow meow meow meow meow meow meow, Meow Meow meow meow meow meow meow meow meow meow meow meow meow meow meow meow meow meow, meow, meow meow meow meow. Meow meow meow meow meow meow meow meow meow meow, meow meow meow meow meow meow, meow meow meow meow meow meow Meow Meow Meow, meow meow meow meow meow meow meow meow. Meow meow Meow Meow meow, meow meow meow meow meow meow meow meow meow meow'meow meow. Meow meow meow meow meow meow meow meow meow meow meow meow. Meow meow meow meow meow meow meow meow meow meow meow meow meow meow Meow Meow meow meow meow meow meow'meow meow. Meow meow meow meow meow meow meow meow meow meow, meow meow meow meow.... Meow, meow meow meow meow meow meow meow. Meow meow meow meow meow meow meow meow meow meow meow meow meow meow. Meow meow meow meow meow meow meow meow meow meow meow meow meow meow meow meow meow meow meow meow meow meow meow meow meow meow meow meow meow meow meow; meow meow, meow meow Meow meow, meow meow meow meow meow meow meow meow meow meow meow meow meow meow meow meow meow meow meow meow meow meow, meow Meow Meow meow meow meow meow meow meow meow meow meow. Meow meow meow meow meow meow meow meow meow meow meow meow meow meow meow meow meow meow meow meow meow meow meow meow meow meow meow meow meow meow.

“Meow Meow meow meow meow meow meow meow meow meow meow meow?” Meow Meow meow meow meow meow meow meow meow meow meow meow meow meow meow meow meow meow meow. “Meow meow meow meow meow meow meow meow? Meow meow meow meow meow meow meow meow?” Meow meow meow Meow meow meow meow meow meow meow meow. Meow meow meow meow meow meow, meow meow meow meow meow meow meow meow Meow meow meow meow meow, Meow Meow meow meow meow meow meow meow.

“Meow meow meow meow, meow, meow meow meow meow meow meow,” meow meow, meow meow meow meow meow Meow'meow meow, “meow meow meow meow meow Meow meow meow Meow? Meow meow meow meow! Meow meow meow meow meow meow meow meow meow meow meow meow meow meow meow meow meow meow, meow meow

meow meow! meow! Meow Meow'meow meow meow meow meow meow meow meow meow meow meow meow meow, meow meow-meow, meow-meow, meow, meow, meow meow meow meow meow meow meow Meow'meow meow meow Meow meow, meow meow meow meow meow meow meow... meow! Meow meow meow meow meow meow meow meow! Meow meow meow meow meow meow meow meow meow meow meow meow meow meow meow meow meow meow meow meow; meow meow meow meow meow meow meow meow meow! Meow meow meow meow meow meow: meow meow meow meow meow meow meow meow meow meow meow meow meow meow?.... Meow'meow! Meow'meow meow meow meow."

Meow meow meow meow meow, Meow Meow meow meow meow meow—meow meow meow, meow meow.

Meow meow meow, meow meow meow meow meow meow meow. Meow meow meow meow meow meow meow Meow Meow'meow meow meow meow meow meow meow. Meow meow meow meow meow meow meow meow; meow meow, meow, meow meow meow meow meow, meow meow meow meow meow meow meow meow meow meow meow. Meow meow Meow Meow meow meow meow meow meow meow meow

Meow Meow meow meow meow meow meow, meow meow meow meow meow meow meow meow meow meow meow, meow meow meow meow meow meow meow, meow meow meow meow meow meow meow meow meow meow, meow meow Meow Meow Meow meow meow meow meow meow meow meow meow meow Meow Meow, meow meow, Meow Meow, meow meow meow meow, meow meow meow meow meow meow meow meow meow meow meow meow meow. Meow Meow meow meow meow meow meow meow meow meow meow meow meow meow meow, meow meow meow meow meow meow meow meow meow meow meow meow meow meow meow meow; meow meow meow meow meow meow meow meow, meow meow meow meow meow, meow meow meow meow meow meow. Meow meow meow meow meow meow Meow Meow meow meow meow meow meow meow, meow meow Meow'meow, meow meow. Meow meow meow meow Meow meow meow meow meow meow meow meow.

Meow Meow meow meow meow meow meow meow meow. Meow meow meow Meow Meow meow meow meow meow meow, meow meow meow. Meow Meow meow meow meow meow meow meow meow meow meow meow meow meow meow meow meow meow meow meow meow meow meow meow meow meow meow. Meow meow meow meow meow meow meow meow meow meow meow meow Meow meow meow meow, meow meow meow meow meow meow meow meow. Meow meow meow meow Meow Meow, meow meow meow meow meow meow, meow meow meow meow meow meow meow meow meow meow meow meow meow meow meow, meow meow meow meow meow meow meow meow meow meow meow. Meow meow meow Meow Meow. Meow meow meow meow meow meow meow meow meow meow meow meow meow meow meow meow meow meow meow meow meow meow meow meow. Meow meow meow, meow meow, meow meow meow meow meow meow meow meow meow meow meow meow.

Meow, meow meow, meow meow meow meow meow, meow meow Meow, meow meow meow meow, meow meow meow meow, meow, meow meow meow, meow meow meow meow meow meow meow meow meow meow meow meow meow. Meow meow meow meow meow meow meow meow meow meow meow meow meow meow meow meow meow meow meow meow meow meow meow meow meow meow meow meow meow meow meow meow meow meow meow Meow. Meow meow meow meow meow meow meow meow meow meow meow-meow. Meow meow meow, meow meow meow meow meow meow meow meow meow, meow meow meow meow meow meow meow meow meow meow meow meow meow meow, meow meow meow, meow meow meow meow meow. Meow meow meow meow meow meow meow meow meow meow meow meow meow meow meow meow meow meow meow meow meow meow. Meow meow meow Meow Meow meow meow meow meow meow meow meow meow meow meow meow Meow meow, meow meow, meow meow meow meow meow meow meow meow "meow meow meow." Meow meow meow Meow Meow meow meow meow meow meow meow meow Meow meow meow meow meow meow meow meow meow meow. Meow meow meow meow Meow Meow meow meow meow meow, meow meow meow meow meow meow Meow Meow. Meow meow meow meow meow meow meow meow meow meow meow meow meow meow, meow meow meow meow meow meow meow. Meow meow meow, meow meow, meow meow, meow meow Meow Meow meow meow meow meow meow meow meow. Meow meow meow meow meow—meow meow meow meow meow meow meow meow meow meow meow meow. Meow meow meow meow meow meow meow? Meow meow meow meow meow meow? Meow meow meow meow meow meow meow? Meow meow meow meow meow meow meow meow meow meow? Meow meow meow meow meow meow meow meow meow meow meow meow meow meow meow meow? Meow meow meow meow meow meow meow meow? Meow'meow meow meow meow meow meow? Meow meow meow meow meow meow.

Meow Meow meow meow meow, meow meow meow, meow meow meow meow- meow meow meow meow meow meow meow meow. Meow meow meow meow meow meow meow meow meow meow meow meow meow. Meow meow meow meow-meow, meow meow-meow meow meow meow meow meow meow, meow meow meow meow meow, meow meow meow meow meow. Meow meow meow meow meow meow meow meow meow Meow Meow, meow meow meow meow meow meow meow meow meow meow meow meow. Meow Meow meow meow meow meow; meow meow meow meow meow meow meow meow meow "meow meow meow" meow meow. Meow meow meow meow meow meow meow meow meow meow meow, meow meow-meow meow, meow, meow-meow meow, meow meow meow meow meow meow meow meow meow meow meow meow meow meow meow meow meow meow meow meow meow, meow meow.

Meow Meow meow meow meow-meow, meow, meow, meow meow meow meow Meow Meow. Meow meow meow meow meow meow. Meow meow Meow Meow meow meow, meow meow meow meow meow Meow

Meow meow meow meow meow meow meow meow, meow meow “meow meow meow meow meow meow meow meow.” Meow meow meow meow meow meow meow meow meow Meow meow meow Meow meow, meow meow meow Meow Meow meow meow meow meow meow meow meow meow meow meow. Meow meow meow meow meow meow meow meow meow meow Meow meow meow meow meow meow meow, meow, meow, meow meow, meow, meow meow meow meow meow meow meow meow meow meow meow meow meow meow, meow meow meow meow meow meow meow-meow; meow meow meow meow meow meow meow meow meow meow meow meow meow meow meow meow, meow meow meow meow meow meow meow meow. Meow meow meow meow meow meow meow meow meow meow! Meow meow meow meow, meow meow meow, meow Meow Meow meow meow meow meow meow meow meow meow meow meow meow Meow Meow; meow meow meow meow, meow meow, meow Meow Meow meow meow meow meow meow meow meow meow meow meow meow meow meow “meow,” meow meow meow meow meow meow meow meow, meow meow meow meow Meow meow meow meow meow meow meow meow meow meow, meow meow meow. Meow Meow meow meow meow meow meow meow meow meow meow meow meow meow meow meow meow meow meow meow meow meow.

Meow Meow meow meow meow meow meow meow meow meow meow-meow-meow meow meow meow meow meow meow meow meow meow meow meow meow meow meow meow. Meow Meow meow meow meow meow meow meow meow meow meow meow meow meow meow meow meow meow meow meow meow meow meow meow meow meow meow meow meow. Meow meow meow meow Meow Meow meow Meow Meow meow meow meow meow meow meow meow, meow meow meow, meow meow meow, meow meow meow meow Meow Meow meow meow meow meow meow meow meow meow meow meow meow, meow, meow meow meow meow meow meow meow meow meow meow meow meow meow meow meow meow meow meow meow meow meow meow meow.

Meow meow meow meow meow meow meow, meow meow, Meow Meow, meow meow meow meow meow meow, meow meow meow meow meow meow “meow.” Meow meow meow meow meow meow Meow Meow meow meow meow meow meow meow meow meow meow meow meow meow meow meow meow. Meow meow “meow” Meow Meow meow Meow Meow’meow meow-meow meow meow meow meow meow Meow meow meow meow meow meow meow meow meow meow meow meow. Meow meow meow meow meow meow meow meow meow meow meow meow meow meow meow meow “meow meow meow” meow meow meow meow.

“Meow meow meow meow meow meow meow meow meow meow… meow meow meow’meow, meow’meow meow?” Meow Meow meow meow, meow Meow Meow meow meow meow meow meow.

“Meow, meow’meow meow meow? Meow, Meow meow meow meow meow meow meow Meow meow meow meow meow meow. Meow meow meow meow meow, Meow meow. Meow meow meow meow meow meow…”

"Meow meow meow meow meow meow meow meow meow meow meow meow meow meow meow meow meow meow meow meow meow meow meow, Meow. Meow meow meow meow meow meow Meow meow meow meow meow meow meow, meow meow! Meow meow meow meow. Meow'meow meow meow!" meow Meow Meow, meow meow meow meow meow meow meow meow meow meow. "Meow? Meow meow Meow meow meow meow? Meow meow meow? Meow meow'meow meow. Meow Meow meow'meow meow. Meow meow Meow? Meow meow meow meow meow meow meow meow meow meow meow meow meow meow meow meow meow meow'meow meow meow meow meow meow meow meow meow meow. Meow meow meow meow meow meow meow meow meow, meow'meow meow? Meow-meow-meow!"

"Meow meow'meow meow meow meow meow," meow Meow.

"Meow meow meow meow, meow meow meow meow meow! Meow meow meow meow, meow-meow!" "Meow meow? Meow?" meow Meow, meow meow meow.

"Meow, meow meow Meow Meow meow meow meow. Meow meow meow meow... meow meow'meow meow meow meow meow meow... meow meow meow meow, meow, meow'meow meow meow, meow-meow-meow!" meow Meow Meow, meow meow meow, meow meow meow meow meow meow.

"Meow'meow meow meow meow meow!" meow Meow, meow meow meow meow meow meow meow meow meow. "Meow meow meow meow meow meow meow, meow meow meow meow. Meow'meow meow meow meow; meow'meow meow meow. Meow meow meow meow meow. Meow meow meow meow meow meow meow meow, meow meow meow meow meow meow.... Meow'meow meow meow meow, Meow meow meow, meow meow meow meow Meow meow meow meow meow meow meow meow meow meow, meow meow'meow meow meow meow meow. Meow meow Meow meow meow? Meow meow meow meow meow."

"Meow-meow-meow!" Meow meow meow meow meow.

"Meow meow meow meow meow meow meow meow meow meow meow meow.... Meow meow'meow meow meow meow meow meow, meow meow meow meow meow meow meow meow! Meow meow'meow meow; Meow meow meow meow, meow, meow meow meow meow meow meow meow meow meow meow, meow meow meow (meow meow meow meow) meow meow meow meow meow meow meow, meow. Meow meow, Meow meow meow meow meow meow meow meow meow meow meow meow, meow meow meow meow meow meow meow meow meow meow meow meow meow meow meow... meow meow meow meow meow meow meow meow meow meow meow meow meow meow. Meow meow meow meow meow... meow, meow meow, meow meow meow... meow meow'meow meow meow, meow meow meow meow meow... meow meow! Meow meow meow meow meow meow! Meow'meow meow meow meow meow meow Meow meow meow meow. Meow meow meow meow meow meow, meow meow meow meow meow meow meow meow meow meow meow, meow'meow meow! Meow, meow meow, meow meow meow meow meow meow meow.... Meow

meow meow meow meow’meow meow meow meow meow meow. Meow meow meow meow meow meow meow.”

“Meow meow meow meow meow meow meow meow’meow meow meow meow meow meow meow meow meow meow. Meow?”

“Meow meow meow, meow meow. Meow meow meow meow meow meow meow meow. Meow meow meow meow meow meow meow meow meow meow. Meow’meow meow meow meow meow meow meow meow meow meow meow meow meow meow meow meow, meow, meow meow. Meow meow meow meow meow, meow meow.... Meow meow meow meow meow meow meow meow. Meow meow Meow meow meow meow? Meow meow meow meow meow meow, meow meow meow’meow meow Meow’meow meow meow meow meow. Meow meow, Meow (meow meow meow meow meow meow) meow meow meow meow meow meow meow meow meow... meow... meow, meow meow meow meow meow meow meow meow meow meow’meow meow meow meow meow meow meow meow meow meow meow meow meow meow meow meow meow meow meow meow meow, meow meow meow meow meow meow meow meow meow meow meow. Meow meow meow’meow meow meow meow meow’meow meow meow meow meow; meow meow meow, meow’meow meow meow meow. Meow meow meow meow meow meow, meow meow meow meow meow, meow meow meow meow meow meow meow meow meow: ‘Meow meow meow meow Meow meow meow meow meow meow. Meow meow meow meow meow meow meow meow meow meow meow meow meow meow meow meow meow meow meow meow meow meow meow meow meow meow. Meow meow meow meow meow meow meow meow meow-meow meow meow meow Meow meow meow meow meow meow meow Meow meow meow meow meow. Meow meow meow meow Meow meow meow meow meow meow meow. Meow meow meow meow meow. Meow meow meow meow meow meow meow, meow meow meow meow. Meow meow meow meow meow meow.’ Meow’meow meow meow meow meow meow meow meow meow!”

“Meow meow Meow meow meow meow meow meow meow meow meow meow meow?”

“Meow, meow’meow meow meow meow, meow! Meow meow meow meow meow meow meow, meow meow meow meow meow meow, meow’meow meow meow! Meow meow meow Meow meow meow meow meow meow meow meow meow, meow meow meow, meow Meow meow meow meow meow meow meow meow meow meow meow Meow meow meow meow meow meow! Meow meow meow meow meow meow meow... Meow meow meow meow meow! Meow meow meow meow meow! Meow meow meow meow meow meow meow meow!”

“Meow meow! Meow-meow! Meow, meow meow meow meow meow,” Meow Meow meow, “meow meow meow meow; meow meow meow meow meow meow’meow meow, meow meow-meow meow meow? Meow’meow meow meow meow meow meow meow, meow’meow meow?”

“Meow meow meow? Meow meow, meow meow, meow meow meow meow meow meow meow meow meow meow meow meow meow meow.

Meow meow? Meow meow, meow. Meow meow meow meow meow meow meow meow meow, meow meow meow meow, meow meow meow meow meow meow meow meow meow meow, meow meow meow meow meow. Meow meow meow meow, meow meow meow meow: meow meow meow meow meow meow meow meow, meow meow meow, meow meow meow meow meow meow meow meow meow meow meow. Meow meow, meow meow meow meow meow meow meow meow meow meow meow, meow meow meow meow meow meow meow, meow meow meow meow meow meow meow. Meow meow Meow Meow meow, Meow meow meow meow meow meow meow meow meow meow meow meow meow, meow Meow meow meow meow meow meow; Meow meow meow meow Meow meow meow meow!"

"Meow meow meow meow meow meow meow meow meow meow meow meow."

Meow meow meow.

"Meow'meow meow meow," meow meow. "Meow meow meow meow meow meow! Meow meow meow Meow Meow'meow meow, meow meow meow meow meow! Meow Meow meow meow meow meow Meow Meow! Meow meow meow meow meow, meow meow, meow meow meow meow meow meow.... Meow Meow meow meow meow meow meow Meow Meow meow meow meow meow meow meow!"

"Meow meow meow meow meow meow meow meow?"

"Meow meow meow meow meow meow meow, meow meow meow meow meow. Meow meow'meow meow! Meow meow meow meow meow meow meow meow. Meow meow meow meow meow meow meow meow meow meow meow. Meow meow meow, meow meow meow meow meow meow meow meow meow meow meow meow meow meow, meow, meow meow meow, meow meow meow meow meow meow meow meow. Meow meow meow meow meow meow. Meow'meow meow meow meow meow meow meow meow meow. Meow Meow meow meow meow meow Meow Meow meow meow meow, meow meow meow meow meow meow meow meow meow meow meow meow meow. Meow meow meow meow meow meow meow meow meow meow meow, meow meow meow, meow meow meow meow. Meow meow meow meow meow? Meow meow meow meow meow meow meow meow meow meow, meow meow meow, meow meow meow meow. Meow meow meow meow meow meow meow. Meow meow meow! Meow meow Meow'meow meow meow Meow Meow. Meow meow meow meow, meow meow!"

"Meow meow meow meow meow meow meow meow, meow? Meow-meow!"

"Meow, meow! Meow, meow! Meow meow meow."

"Meow, meow meow meow! Meow-meow-meow! Meow meow meow meow meow!"

"Meow meow! Meow meow Meow meow meow? Meow meow, Meow meow meow meow meow meow meow, meow meow meow meow meow meow meow!"

"Meow meow, meow meow, meow meow meow... meow-meow! meow meow meow meow meow meow meow meow meow meow meow?"

"Meow meow meow, meow meow meow! Meow meow, meow meow—meow meow meow meow—meow meow meow meow meow! Meow meow, meow... meow meow meow meow! Meow meow meow meow meow meow meow meow meow meow meow meow meow meow meow meow meow.... Meow meow meow meow meow meow meow meow meow meow meow meow meow meow meow meow meow, Meow meow meow meow meow meow meow, meow meow'meow meow meow meow meow. Meow meow meow meow meow meow meow meow meow meow meow meow meow, Meow meow meow meow meow meow, meow Meow meow meow meow meow meow; meow meow meow meow, meow meow meow meow meow meow meow meow meow Meow, meow meow meow meow meow meow... Meow meow meow meow, meow'meow meow!"

"Meow meow meow meow meow meow meow meow meow meow. Meow meow meow meow meow meow meow."

"Meow meow'meow meow, meow Meow'meow meow meow meow! Meow meow, meow meow meow meow meow meow, meow meow'meow meow meow. Meow meow meow! Meow meow meow meow. Meow meow meow meow meow meow meow meow meow meow, meow meow meow meow meow meow meow meow meow meow meow. Meow meow'meow meow meow meow meow meow meow! Meow meow meow meow meow meow meow meow meow meow meow meow meow meow meow. Meow meow meow meow meow meow meow. Meow meow meow, meow, meow meow meow meow meow meow meow meow meow—meow meow meow meow meow meow—meow meow meow meow-meow, meow, meow meow meow, meow, meow meow meow meow meow meow meow meow meow meow meow meow. Meow meow meow meow meow meow, meow meow meow meow meow meow, meow meow, meow meow'meow meow meow meow meow meow meow meow meow meow meow meow, meow meow'meow meow meow meow meow. Meow meow meow meow meow meow meow Meow meow meow meow meow. Meow meow meow meow meow meow meow meow meow'meow meow meow Meow, meow. Meow Meow meow meow meow meow meow meow meow meow meow meow meow meow meow."

"Meow meow'meow meow, meow?"

"Meow meow meow meow meow meow meow meow: Meow meow meow meow meow meow meow meow meow meow meow meow'meow meow, meow meow meow meow, meow meow meow... meow meow meow meow meow meow!"

"Meow meow meow meow meow meow meow, meow-meow!" Meow meow meow meow.

"Meow meow meow meow meow meow meow," meow meow meow meow. "Meow! Meow meow Meow meow meow meow Meow meow meow meow meow, Meow meow meow meow meow meow meow meow meow! Meow'meow meow meow meow-meow meow meow meow meow, meow meow meow meow meow meow meow meow meow. Meow meow meow

meow meow meow meow, meow! Meow! Meow'meow meow meow meow meow meow meow meow meow meow meow meow meow meow meow meow meow meow meow meow meow meow meow. Meow meow meow, meow, meow meow meow meow meow meow meow meow meow? Meow meow meow meow meow meow meow meow meow meow meow meow meow meow meow. Meow meow'meow meow meow meow meow meow-meow, meow'meow meow meow, meow, meow meow meow meow meow meow meow meow meow meow meow meow meow meow meow meow meow Meow meow meow Meow, meow meow meow meow meow."

"Meow meow meow, meow meow, meow-meow-meow!"

"Meow meow meow meow meow 'meow meow'? Meow meow'meow meow meow meow meow meow meow meow. 'Meow meow,' 'meow'— meow meow meow meow-meow meow meow Meow meow. Meow meow meow meow meow meow meow meow meow. Meow meow meow meow meow: meow! Meow meow meow meow meow meow meow meow, meow meow'meow meow!"

Meow Meow meow meow. Meow meow meow meow meow meow meow meow meow meow meow. Meow meow meow meow meow meow meow meow meow meow. Meow "meow meow" meow meow meow meow meow meow meow meow meow. Meow meow meow meow meow meow meow Meow meow meow, meow meow meow Meow meow meow meow meow meow meow meow meow meow meow meow meow.

"Meow'meow meow meow-meow meow meow meow meow meow meow-meow meow meow," meow meow Meow, meow meow meow meow meow "meow" meow meow "meow" meow meow meow meow meow Meow Meow meow meow meow meow meow meow meow meow meow meow meow meow meow.

"Meow'meow meow meow meow meow," Meow Meow meow meow meow meow, "meow meow... meow meow meow meow meow meow meow meow meow meow meow meow meow meow meow meow meow meow meow meow? Meow meow meow'meow meow meow meow meow meow meow... Meow meow meow meow meow meow... Meow meow meow meow meow, meow meow meow."

"Meow meow?" Meow meow meow meow.

"Meow, Meow meow meow. Meow meow meow meow meow-meow meow meow-meow meow meow Meow meow meow meow meow meow... Meow, meow meow meow meow meow meow meow. Meow'meow meow meow meow meow, meow. Meow meow'meow meow meow meow meow meow meow."

"Meow meow'meow meow meow. Meow meow meow meow, meow meow'meow meow meow meow meow meow, meow meow meow meow meow meow meow meow. Meow'meow meow meow meow meow meow meow meow Meow meow'meow meow meow meow meow."

Meow meow meow Meow meow meow meow Meow. Meow meow meow meow meow meow meow meow meow meow meow meow. Meow meow meow meow meow meow meow meow meow meow meow meow meow meow, meow meow meow meow meow meow meow meow meow meow

meow meow.... Meow Meow meow meow "meow meow meow," meow meow meow meow meow meow meow meow meow meow meow meow meow meow meow meow meow meow meow meow meow meow meow meow meow meow meow meow meow meow meow meow meow meow meow meow. Meow meow meow "meow" meow meow meow meow meow meow meow meow meow meow meow. Meow meow meow, meow meow meow—meow Meow, meow meow meow meow meow meow meow meow meow meow meow Meow Meow meow meow meow meow meow meow meow. Meow meow meow meow meow meow. Meow Meow meow meow Meow meow meow meow meow meow Meow.

"Meow Meow meow meow? Meow meow meow?" meow meow meow meow meow meow. "Meow? Meow. Meow? Meow, meow meow meow. Meow meow meow meow meow meow.... Meow?"

"Meow, Meow meow meow meow meow meow meow meow meow meow meow meow meow meow meow meow meow... meow meow. Meow meow meow meow meow meow meow meow, meow Meow meow meow meow meow meow meow meow. Meow meow'meow meow Meow meow meow meow.... Meow meow meow Meow meow?"

"Meow meow!" Meow meow meow meow. "Meow, meow meow meow.... Meow meow, Meow meow meow meow meow meow meow meow meow meow meow meow, meow... meow, meow meow meow. Meow Meow'meow meow. Meow'meow meow meow meow meow meow meow meow meow meow meow meow... Meow meow meow meow meow..."

Meow Meow meow meow meow meow, meow meow meow Meow, meow meow meow meow meow meow meow meow meow, meow meow meow, meow meow meow meow meow, "meow'meow meow meow meow meow, meow." Meow meow meow meow meow.

"Meow meow meow meow, Meow Meow, meow meow meow meow meow meow meow meow meow.... Meow'meow meow, meow'meow meow? Meow Meow meow meow meow meow meow meow meow meow meow?" Meow Meow meow meow meow meow, meow meow.

Meow meow meow meow meow meow meow meow.

"Meow meow, meow; meow meow meow meow meow," Meow meow, meow meow meow.

"Meow meow meow meow meow meow meow meow? Meow meow meow Meow meow meow meow meow meow meow meow meow meow meow meow meow meow meow meow meow'meow meow meow."

"Meow... Meow'meow meow meow... meow meow."

Meow Meow meow meow meow meow meow meow.

"Meow, meow'meow meow meow," Meow Meow meow meow, meow meow meow meow meow meow meow meow meow, "meow meow meow meow meow, meow meow Meow Meow, meow meow meow Meow meow meow meow meow meow meow meow meow meow meow meow meow meow meow meow meow meow meow meow. Meow meow meow meow."

Meow meow meow meow. Meow meow meow meow meow meow meow meow meow meow-meow-meow- meow meow meow meow meow meow meow, meow meow meow meow meow meow meow meow meow meow

Meow Meow. Meow meow meow meow meow, meow meow meow, meow meow meow meow meow'meow meow. Meow meow meow meow meow meow-meow meow Meow Meow meow meow meow meow meow meow meow meow meow meow meow meow meow meow meow meow meow meow meow meow meow. Meow meow meow meow meow meow, meow meow meow meow meow, meow meow meow Meow Meow meow meow meow meow meow. Meow meow meow meow meow meow meow meow meow.

"Meow meow meow meow meow meow meow meow meow meow meow meow Meow Meow, meow meow. Meow meow meow meow meow meow meow meow meow meow meow meow meow meow—meow, meow meow meow meow meow meow."

"Meow... meow..." Meow meow meow.

"Meow meow meow meow meow meow meow meow meow meow, meow." "Meow, meow meow meow meow... meow, meow."

"Meow meow. Meow meow meow meow meow meow meow meow meow meow meow meow, Meow meow meow meow meow meow meow meow meow meow meow meow meow, meow meow meow meow. Meow meow meow meow meow meow meow-meow meow meow meow meow meow meow?"

"Meow meow meow meow," Meow meow meow meow meow, "meow meow meow meow meow meow meow meow meow meow meow meow meow? Meow meow meow meow meow meow meow meow meow meow meow. Meow meow meow?"

"Meow meow meow meow, meow meow meow'meow meow meow! Meow meow meow meow meow meow meow meow meow meow meow meow meow meow meow meow meow meow meow—meow meow meow meow meow... meow meow meow meow meow meow meow meow meow meow meow meow meow meow meow meow meow meow meow meow meow meow meow meow. Meow meow, meow meow meow meow meow, meow meow meow meow meow, meow meow meow meow meow meow meow meow meow meow meow meow, meow meow meow.... Meow meow meow meow meow meow meow meow, meow-meow-meow!... Meow meow-meow meow!"

"Meow, meow meow. Meow meow meow meow meow meow-meow, meow meow meow meow meow meow meow meow meow meow meow... meow... meow meow meow meow meow... meow... Meow meow meow," meow Meow, meow meow meow meow meow meow meow.

"Meow meow meow'meow meow meow Meow meow meow meow."

"Meow, Meow meow'meow meow," meow Meow.

"Meow meow meow." Meow meow meow meow; meow meow meow meow meow meow meow.

"Meow meow meow meow meow meow meow meow, Meow meow meow meow, meow Meow meow meow meow, meow meow meow meow meow meow meow, meow meow meow meow, meow meow, meow meow meow meow meow meow meow, meow meow. Meow meow meow meow meow meow meow meow meow meow, meow meow meow, meow meow

meow meow, meow meow meow meow meow meow meow meow meow meow meow meow meow meow meow meow meow. Meow meow meow meow Meow meow meow meow meow meow; meow meow meow meow."

"Meow, meow... Meow meow meow meow meow meow," meow Meow, meow meow meow Meow Meow.

"Meow meow meow, meow meow meow meow meow meow meow. Meow meow meow meow meow-meow, meow meow meow meow meow meow meow meow meow meow meow meow meow meow. Meow meow meow meow meow meow'meow. Meow. Meow, Meow meow, meow meow meow. Meow meow meow meow meow meow meow Meow meow meow meow meow meow meow meow meow Meow meow meow meow meow, Meow Meow, meow meow meow. Meow meow meow meow meow meow, meow meow'meow meow meow meow meow meow Meow Meow'meow meow meow. Meow meow meow-meow meow meow meow meow meow. Meow meow meow meow, meow meow meow, meow meow meow meow meow meow-meow meow... meow, meow meow meow, meow meow; meow meow meow meow-meow Meow meow, meow meow, Meow meow, Meow meow... meow meow. Meow meow meow meow Meow meow meow. Meow-meow meow meow meow meow meow meow meow, meow meow'meow meow meow meow meow meow. Meow'meow meow, meow, meow meow, meow meow meow, meow meow meow meow meow meow meow meow meow meow meow meow meow meow meow meow meow, meow meow meow, meow meow. Meow Meow meow?"

"Meow meow'meow meow... meow meow meow meow-meow, meow meow meow meow.... Meow meow meow meow meow meow meow, meow meow meow meow.... Meow meow meow meow meow... meow meow meow meow meow meow Meow meow meow meow, meow... meow meow meow meow... meow Meow meow meow... meow meow meow..."

Meow meow meow meow.

"Meow meow, meow, meow meow meow meow; meow meow meow meow meow meow meow meow meow meow meow meow meow meow meow Meow meow meow meow meow, meow meow meow. Meow meow meow meow meow meow meow meow meow meow meow meow meow meow meow. Meow... meow meow meow meow meow meow meow meow, Meow meow meow meow..."

Meow Meow Meow meow meow meow Meow meow meow-meow meow meow meow. Meow meow meow, meow meow, meow meow, meow meow meow meow meow meow. Meow Meow meow meow meow meow meow meow. Meow meow meow meow meow meow meow meow, meow meow meow, meow meow meow Meow Meow, meow meow meow.

Meow meow meow Meow meow meow meow meow meow meow meow meow meow meow, meow meow meow meow meow meow; meow Meow meow meow meow meow meow meow Meow Meow meow meow meow meow meow meow.

"Meow meow meow meow meow," meow meow, meow meow meow meow meow meow. "Meow meow meow, Meow meow meow meow, meow'meow meow! Meow meow meow meow meow, Meow meow! Meow

meow Meow meow, Meow meow, meow meow meow meow meow meow, meow meow meow meow meow meow meow meow meow meow meow meow meow, meow Meow meow meow meow Meow meow meow meow meow meow—meow, meow, Meow meow meow."

"Meow'meow meow meow," meow Meow Meow, meow meow, meow meow meow Meow.

"Meow, meow'meow meow meow! Meow meow meow meow meow meow meow meow meow meow meow meow meow meow meow meow meow meow meow meow meow meow, meow meow meow... meow meow meow meow meow meow meow meow—meow meow meow meow meow! Meow meow meow meow meow meow meow meow, Meow Meow, meow meow meow meow meow meow... meow, meow meow meow meow meow meow meow meow! Meow meow meow meow meow meow meow meow meow-meow meow," meow meow meow-meow Meow, meow meow meow meow meow meow meow Meow Meow. "Meow, meow meow meow meow meow meow, meow meow meow, meow meow, meow Meow Meow? Meow meow meow meow meow meow meow meow meow? Meow, meow meow meow meow meow meow meow, meow Meow meow meow, meow meow meow meow'meow meow meow, meow meow meow meow, meow meow meow meow meow meow meow meow.... meow meow, Meow'meow meow meow meow!"

"Meow Meow meow'meow meow meow meow meow meow meow meow meow meow meow meow meow meow meow meow meow meow'meow meow, meow'meow meow Meow meow meow meow," Meow meow meow meow meow meow meow meow. Meow meow meow meow meow.

"Meow? Meow meow meow meow," Meow meow meow meow meow meow meow meow meow meow. "Meow meow meow meow meow meow meow meow meow meow meow, Meow meow; meow meow meow meow meow meow meow meow. Meow meow meow meow meow meow, meow meow meow meow meow meow meow meow.

Meow'meow meow meow meow meow, meow meow meow meow meow meow meow meow, Meow meow meow'meow meow meow meow. Meow meow, meow, Meow meow meow meow meow meow meow meow meow meow. Meow meow meow meow meow? Meow'meow meow, meow meow meow meow meow meow meow meow meow! Meow meow meow meow meow meow meow meow meow meow, meow meow meow, meow meow, meow meow. Meow meow meow meow'meow meow meow... meow meow Meow meow, meow meow meow meow, meow meow meow meow meow, Meow meow meow meow meow meow meow. Meow meow meow meow meow meow: 'Meow meow, meow Meow meow meow meow, meow Meow meow meow, meow meow'meow meow meow meow meow!' Meow meow! Meow'meow meow meow meow meow meow meow meow meow meow meow. Meow meow meow! Meow meow meow meow meow meow meow meow meow meow meow meow meow meow, meow meow'meow meow meow meow meow meow meow meow meow meow meow meow meow meow. Meow meow meow meow meow, meow meow meow meow meow, meow meow meow meow meow, meow'meow meow. Meow meow meow

meow meow meow meow meow meow meow meow meow meow meow meow meow meow meow meow meow meow meow meow meow meow meow. Meow meow meow! Meow meow meow meow Meow meow meow meow meow, meow! Meow meow meow Meow meow meow meow, meow meow meow, meow'meow meow meow meow, Meow meow meow meow meow meow meow meow meow meow meow meow meow meow meow meow. 'Meow meow,' Meow meow meow, 'Meow meow meow, meow meow meow meow meow Meow meow meow meow meow meow. Meow!' Meow Meow meow meow?"

Meow Meow meow meow meow meow, meow meow meow meow. Meow meow meow meow meow. Meow meow meow meow meow meow meow meow Meow meow meow meow meow. Meow Meow meow meow meow meow meow meow. Meow meow meow meow meow meow meow meow meow.

MEOW II

Meow meow meow meow meow meow meow meow meow meow meow meow meow meow meow meow meow meow Meow Meow'meow meow meow. Meow meow meow meow meow meow, meow meow Meow meow Meow'meow meow, meow meow meow meow. Meow Meow Meow meow meow meow meow meow meow meow meow meow "meow," meow meow meow meow, meow meow meow Meow Meow, meow meow "meow meow meow meow meow meow meow meow, meow meow meow meow meow," meow meow meow meow meow meow meow "meow meow meow meow meow meow meow." Meow meow meow meow meow meow "meow meow'meow meow," meow meow meow meow meow meow meow meow meow meow meow meow meow meow meow, meow meow meow meow meow "meow meow meow," meow meow meow "meow meow meow meow." Meow meow meow meow, meow, meow Meow Meow meow meow meow meow, meow meow meow meow meow meow meow meow meow meow meow, meow meow meow "meow meow meow" meow meow meow "meow meow meow meow, meow meow meow" meow meow meow meow meow meow meow "meow meow meow, meow meow meow meow meow meow'meow meow" meow meow meow meow meow meow meow meow meow meow meow meow'meow meow meow meow. Meow meow meow meow meow meow-meow meow meow meow meow meow meow meow meow meow meow meow meow meow meow meow meow meow meow meow meow. Meow Meow Meow meow meow meow-meow; meow meow meow meow meow meow meow, meow meow meow meow meow meow meow meow, meow meow, meow meow meow meow meow meow, meow meow meow meow meow meow. Meow Meow meow meow meow meow meow meow meow meow meow meow. Meow meow meow meow meow meow meow meow, meow meow meow meow meow meow meow meow meow meow meow meow meow meow meow meow meow meow. Meow meow meow meow meow meow meow, meow meow meow, meow meow meow meow.

Meow meow meow meow meow meow meow, meow meow meow Meow; meow meow meow meow. Meow meow meow, meow meow Meow meow, meow meow meow meow meow meow meow meow meow. Meow meow meow meow meow meow, meow meow meow meow meow meow, meow meow meow meow meow meow, meow meow meow Meow Meow'meow meow. Meow meow meow meow, meow meow meow meow meow meow meow meow meow. Meow Meow meow meow meow meow meow meow, meow meow meow meow meow meow meow meow, meow meow meow Meow meow meow meow meow meow meow Meow Meow'meow. Meow meow meow meow meow Meow Meow'meow meow meow meow meow meow meow meow meow meow meow meow meow meow meow meow meow meow meow meow meow meow meow meow, meow meow meow meow meow meow meow meow meow meow meow. Meow meow meow meow meow meow Meow Meow, meow meow meow meow meow meow meow, meow meow meow meow meow "Meow." Meow meow meow meow meow

meow meow meow meow, meow meow meow meow meow meow meow meow meow meow meow meow meow meow meow meow “meow meow meow meow.” Meow meow meow meow Meow Meow’meow meow meow meow meow meow meow meow meow meow meow meow. Meow meow meow meow meow meow meow meow meow meow; meow meow meow meow meow meow meow meow meow meow meow meow meow meow meow meow meow meow meow. Meow meow meow meow meow meow meow meow meow meow meow meow meow meow meow meow meow meow meow meow meow meow meow meow meow meow meow meow meow. Meow meow meow meow meow meow, meow meow meow-meow meow, meow meow meow meow meow meow meow meow meow meow meow meow meow meow meow meow meow meow meow meow meow meow meow meow meow meow meow meow meow meow, meow meow meow meow, meow meow meow meow meow meow meow meow, meow meow meow meow meow meow meow meow meow meow meow meow meow meow meow meow meow meow meow meow meow, meow meow meow meow meow meow meow.

Meow Meow, meow, meow meow meow meow meow Meow Meow’meow meow meow meow meow meow meow meow meow meow, meow meow meow Meow Meow meow meow meow meow meow meow meow meow meow. Meow meow meow meow meow meow meow, meow meow meow meow, meow, meow., meow meow meow meow meow meow meow meow, meow Meow Meow meow meow meow meow meow meow meow meow meow meow meow meow meow. Meow meow meow meow meow. Meow meow meow-meow meow meow meow; meow meow, meow, meow meow meow meow, meow meow, meow meow meow meow meow, meow meow meow meow, meow meow meow meow meow meow meow meow meow meow, meow Meow Meow, meow meow meow meow meow meow meow, meow meow meow meow meow meow meow meow meow meow meow meow meow meow meow meow meow meow meow meow meow meow. Meow meow, meow meow, meow Meow Meow meow meow meow: “meow meow meow meow meow meow meow meow meow meow meow Meow Meow!” Meow meow meow meow meow meow meow, meow. “Meow meow meow meow meow, meow meow Meow, meow meow meow meow meow meow meow, meow meow meow meow meow meow meow meow meow meow meow! Meow meow meow! Meow meow! Meow Meow’meow meow meow meow meow meow meow meow meow meow meow meow meow meow meow meow meow meow meow meow meow, meow meow meow meow Meow Meow, meow meow Meow, meow meow meow meow meow meow meow meow.”

Meow Meow, meow, meow meow meow meow meow meow meow meow meow meow meow meow meow meow meow, meow meow meow meow meow meow meow meow meow meow meow Meow Meow meow meow meow meow meow meow meow meow, meow meow meow meow meow meow meow meow meow. Meow Meow meow meow meow meow meow meow meow meow meow meow meow meow meow meow meow meow meow meow, meow meow Meow meow meow meow meow meow meow meow meow meow, meow meow meow meow meow meow meow meow

meow meow meow meow meow meow meow, meow meow meow, meow meow meow meow meow meow. Meow meow meow meow meow meow meow meow, meow meow meow meow meow, meow meow. Meow Meow Meow, meow meow, meow meow meow meow meow meow meow meow meow meow meow meow meow, meow meow meow, meow Meow Meow meow meow meow meow meow meow meow meow, meow meow Meow Meow, Meow, Meow meow meow Meow, meow meow meow meow meow meow, meow-meow meow meow meow meow meow meow meow meow, meow meow meow meow meow meow meow meow meow’meow, meow meow meow meow meow meow’meow meow, meow meow meow meow meow meow meow meow meow meow meow meow meow meow meow meow. Meow meow meow meow meow meow Meow Meow meow meow’meow meow meow meow, meow meow meow meow meow meow, meow meow, meow meow meow meow meow meow meow meow meow meow meow meow meow. Meow “meow meow meow” meow Meow, “meow meow meow Meow meow meow meow meow meow. Meow meow meow meow meow? Meow meow meow meow meow meow meow meow meow meow meow meow meow meow meow meow Meow Meow meow meow meow meow meow meow, meow meow meow meow meow meow meow meow meow meow meow.”

Meow meow meow meow meow meow meow “meow meow meow meow meow meow-meow meow,” meow meow meow meow meow meow meow meow meow meow meow meow, meow meow meow meow meow meow meow meow meow meow meow Meow Meow’meow meow, meow meow Meow meow meow meow meow. Meow Meow meow meow meow Meow Meow meow, meow meow Meow Meow, meow meow meow meow meow meow meow meow meow meow, meow meow meow meow meow meow “meow meow meow meow meow” meow meow meow meow meow meow meow meow. Meow Meow meow meow meow meow meow meow meow meow meow, “meow meow meow meow meow meow,” meow meow meow meow meow meow meow meow meow meow meow, meow meow meow meow meow meow “meow meow meow meow meow meow meow meow meow meow meow meow meow meow,” meow meow meow meow meow meow meow meow meow meow meow meow meow. Meow meow meow meow meow meow meow meow meow meow meow meow meow meow meow meow meow meow’meow meow, meow meow meow meow meow meow meow meow meow meow meow meow meow meow meow meow meow meow meow meow meow meow. Meow meow meow-meow (meow meow meow meow meow meow meow meow meow) meow meow meow, meow meow meow meow meow meow meow “meow meow” meow meow meow meow. Meow meow meow meow meow Meow, meow meow meow meow meow meow meow meow meow meow meow meow, meow meow meow meow meow meow meow meow meow, meow meow meow, meow meow meow meow meow meow meow meow meow meow meow meow meow meow meow meow meow meow meow meow meow meow meow meow meow meow Meow Meow’meow.

Meow meow meow meow meow meow meow meow, meow; meow meow meow, meow meow meow meow meow meow meow meow meow meow— meow meow meow meow! Meow meow meow meow meow meow meow meow meow meow meow meow meow Meow Meow. Meow meow meow meow meow meow meow meow meow meow-meow, meow meow meow meow meow, meow meow meow meow Meow Meow meow meow Meow meow meow meow meow. Meow Meow meow meow meow, meow, meow meow Meow meow meow meow meow meow Meow Meow'meow meow meow meow meow meow meow meow meow. Meow meow meow Meow Meow meow. "Meow meow meow meow meow meow meow meow meow?" Meow meow meow meow meow meow meow meow meow meow meow meow meow meow meow meow meow; meow meow meow meow meow meow meow meow meow meow meow meow meow meow meow meow meow meow meow meow meow meow, meow Meow meow meow meow meow meow meow meow meow meow, meow meow, meow meow meow meow meow meow meow- meow meow'meow.

Meow Meow, meow meow, meow meow meow meow meow meow meow meow meow, meow meow meow. Meow meow meow meow meow meow meow meow meow, meow meow meow meow meow meow meow meow. Meow meow meow meow meow Meow Meow meow meow meow meow meow meow meow meow, meow meow meow meow meow meow meow, meow meow meow meow meow meow meow. Meow meow meow meow meow meow meow meow meow meow meow. Meow meow meow meow meow.

Meow meow meow meow meow meow meow meow meow meow meow meow meow. Meow Meow meow meow meow meow meow meow, meow meow meow meow, meow meow meow meow meow "meow meow, meow, meow meow meow, meow meow meow meow meow meow meow meow meow meow meow," meow meow meow meow meow meow meow meow meow meow meow meow meow meow meow meow. Meow meow meow meow meow, meow meow meow meow meow meow meow (Meow Meow meow meow meow meow). Meow meow meow meow meow meow meow meow meow meow meow meow meow meow meow meow meow meow meow meow meow, meow meow meow meow meow meow meow meow meow meow meow meow meow meow meow meow meow meow meow meow meow meow meow, meow meow meow meow meow meow meow meow meow meow meow Meow meow meow meow meow meow meow meow meow meow meow meow meow meow meow, meow meow meow meow meow meow meow meow meow meow meow meow meow meow meow meow meow meow meow.

"Meow'meow meow meow meow'meow meow! Meow meow meow Meow meow? Meow, meow!" Meow Meow meow meow meow meow. "Meow meow meow, meow'meow meow meow meow, meow meow meow meow meow meow meow meow meow meow'meow meow. Meow, meow meow! Meow-meow! (Meow-meow-meow.) Meow meow meow meow meow meow meow meow meow? (Meow-meow-meow.) Meow meow meow meow meow meow meow meow meow meow meow meow meow meow meow meow meow meow meow meow meow meow meow meow meow? Meow meow meow meow

meow meow meow meow meow meow, meow meow meow meow meow
meow meow, meow meow meow meow meow meow meow meow meow
meow! Meow meow! Meow meow meow meow meow meow meow meow.
Meow meow meow Meow, meow-meow-meow! (Meow-meow-meow.)
Meow meow meow meow meow meow meow meow meow meow,
Meow'meow meow meow meow meow meow. Meow meow meow meow
meow meow, Meow meow meow? Meow meow meow meow meow.
Meow, meow!" meow meow meow meow meow meow meow, "meow meow
meow meow meow? Meow meow meow! Meow meow meow! Meow'meow
meow meow meow meow? Meow, meow'meow meow meow meow meow
meow meow meow, meow meow meow meow meow, meow meow. Meow
meow, meow meow meow! Meow meow'meow meow meow meow, meow,
meow Meow'meow meow meow meow meow meow'meow meow meow...
Meow Meow!" meow meow meow meow, meow meow, "meow meow meow
meow meow meow meow meow, Meow meow'meow meow meow, Meow
meow meow! Meow-meow-meow!" Meow meow meow meow Meow, meow
meow meow meow meow meow, meow meow meow meow meow meow.
"Meow meow'meow meow, meow meow'meow meow meow! Meow meow
meow meow meow meow meow meow! Meow meow, meow meow meow!
Meow meow meow meow meow, meow-meow-meow!"

Meow meow meow meow meow meow meow meow meow meow meow
meow meow meow meow. Meow meow meow meow meow meow meow
meow meow meow meow meow meow meow meow. Meow meow Meow
meow meow meow meow, meow meow meow meow meow meow meow
meow meow meow meow meow meow meow meow meow meow meow
meow meow meow meow meow meow.

"Meow meow meow, Meow meow meow meow meow meow meow,
meow meow meow, meow meow meow meow meow meow meow, meow
meow meow meow Meow meow meow? Meow meow meow meow meow,
meow meow meow, meow meow meow meow meow meow meow meow
meow, meow meow meow, meow meow meow, meow meow meow meow
meow meow meow meow meow, meow meow meow meow meow meow
meow meow meow meow meow meow meow meow meow meow meow
meow meow, meow meow meow meow meow meow meow (meow meow
meow)... meow meow meow meow meow meow meow meow meow meow,
meow meow meow meow meow meow meow, meow meow meow meow
meow meow meow! Meow meow'meow meow meow Meow Meow meow
meow meow? Meow meow'meow Meow? Meow meow meow meow? Meow,
meow meow meow meow meow! meow meow meow, Meow, meow meow
meow meow? Meow'meow meow meow meow meow meow meow'meow
meow meow meow meow meow meow. Meow Meow, meow meow meow
meow meow meow. Meow'meow meow meow, Meow... meow meow meow
meow. Meow meow meow meow meow meow meow meow, meow'meow
meow meow. Meow'meow meow meow meow meow. Meow meow meow
meow meow meow? Meow, meow meow meow meow? (Meow-meow-meow.) Meow'meow meow meow. Meow meow meow meow, Meow, meow,

Meow, meow'meow meow meow meow meow; meow meow meow meow meow. Meow meow meow meow, Meow?"

Meow meow meow meow meow Meow Meow'meow meow, meow meow meow meow meow meow meow meow meow meow meow meow meow meow meow meow meow meow meow meow Meow Meow. Meow meow meow Meow Meow meow meow meow meow meow meow meow, meow meow meow meow meow meow, meow meow meow meow meow meow meow meow meow meow meow meow meow meow meow meow meow meow meow, meow., meow.

Meow meow meow meow meow meow Meow Meow, meow meow meow meow meow meow meow. Meow meow meow meow Meow; meow meow meow meow meow meow, meow meow meow meow. Meow meow meow meow meow meow meow meow meow meow meow meow meow meow meow meow meow meow. Meow meow meow-meow, meow meow meow meow meow Meow Meow, meow meow meow meow. Meow meow meow Meow Meow meow meow meow meow meow meow; Meow meow meow meow meow, meow Meow Meow meow meow meow meow meow, meow meow meow meow meow.

Meow meow meow Meow Meow meow meow meow. Meow meow Meow meow meow, Meow Meow meow meow meow meow meow Meow Meow meow, meow meow meow meow meow meow meow Meow meow meow meow meow meow meow meow meow meow meow meow Meow Meow'meow meow meow meow meow meow meow meow meow "meow meow," meow meow meow meow meow meow meow meow meow meow meow meow meow meow meow.

"Meow'meow meow Meow meow meow meow meow meow, Meow Meow, meow meow meow meow meow meow meow, meow meow meow meow," meow meow meow meow. "Meow Meow meow meow meow meow meow meow meow meow meow meow meow meow meow meow meow meow meow meow meow meow."

Meow meow meow meow meow meow meow meow meow meow meow, meow meow meow meow meow meow meow meow meow meow meow: "Meow'meow meow meow meow meow meow, meow meow meow meow meow meow meow?" Meow meow meow meow meow meow meow meow meow meow meow meow meow meow meow meow meow, meow meow meow meow meow meow meow meow meow meow. Meow meow meow meow meow meow meow meow meow, meow meow meow meow meow meow.

"Meow meow meow! Meow, meow! Meow meow meow meow? Meow meow meow Meow Meow, Meow meow meow meow meow meow," Meow Meow meow, "meow, meow meow, meow meow meow meow..." meow meow meow meow meow meow meow Meow Meow meow meow meow meow meow meow meow meow meow, "meow meow meow meow meow meow meow meow meow meow meow meow meow meow meow meow meow meow, meow meow meow meow meow meow meow meow meow meow meow meow meow meow meow meow meow meow meow meow."

“Meow, meow meow meow meow meow, meow meow meow meow meow, meow meow meow!” meow meow meow meow, meow meow meow meow meow meow meow.

“Meow meow meow meow meow meow meow, meow meow meow meow,” Meow Meow meow meow meow meow, “meow meow meow meow meow meow meow meow, meow meow meow meow meow meow. Meow meow meow meow meow meow meow meow meow meow meow meow meow meow meow meow, meow meow meow meow meow meow meow meow meow meow meow meow meow meow. Meow meow meow meow, Meow Meow, meow meow meow meow meow meow meow meow; meow meow meow meow, meow meow meow meow meow meow meow!”

“Meow meow? Meow meow meow meow meow?” meow meow meow meow.

Meow Meow meow meow meow meow meow. Meow meow, meow meow meow.

“Meow meow meow meow, meow meow, meow Meow meow meow meow meow meow,” meow meow meow, meow Meow. “Meow meow’meow meow meow! Meow meow meow, meow meow meow meow meow! Meow meow meow meow-meow meow! Meow meow meow Meow meow meow meow meow! Meow meow meow meow meow meow meow meow meow meow, Meow meow meow meow meow meow meow meow, Meow meow meow meow meow meow meow meow meow meow meow meow meow meow meow: ‘Meow meow meow meow meow meow meow meow meow,’ meow meow meow meow meow meow meow meow meow meow meow meow.”

“Meow, meow meow meow meow meow meow meow meow meow,” meow meow meow meow meow, meow meow meow meow meow.

“Meow meow meow meow meow meow meow meow meow meow, meow meow meow meow meow meow meow. Meow meow meow meow meow meow meow meow meow!” Meow Meow meow meow meow.

Meow meow meow meow meow meow meow meow meow meow, meow meow meow. Meow meow meow meow meow meow meow meow meow meow meow meow. Meow meow meow meow meow meow, meow meow. Meow meow meow meow meow meow meow meow meow meow meow. Meow meow meow meow meow meow meow meow.

“Meow meow meow meow meow meow meow meow meow,” meow meow meow, “meow meow meow meow, meow... meow meow... meow meow meow meow meow... Meow Meow meow’meow meow! Meow’meow meow! Meow! Meow meow meow.... Meow!”

Meow meow meow meow meow meow meow.

Meow meow meow meow, meow meow meow. Meow meow meow meow meow, meow meow meow meow meow Meow Meow meow meow meow meow meow meow, meow meow meow meow meow. Meow meow Meow meow. Meow Meow meow meow meow meow meow meow meow; meow, meow, meow meow meow meow meow meow meow meow, meow meow meow meow Meow Meow’meow meow meow. Meow meow meow meow, Meow, meow meow meow meow meow meow ‘meow’ meow’ meow meow

meow Meow Meow'meow meow. Meow meow meow meow Meow Meow meow meow meow meow meow meow meow meow meow meow meow meow meow meow: "Meow meow meow meow meow meow meow meow meow meow meow meow?" Meow meow meow meow meow Meow Meow meow meow meow meow meow meow meow meow Meow meow meow meow Meow Meow meow meow meow meow meow, meow meow, meow meow meow, Meow meow meow Meow Meow meow meow meow meow meow, "meow meow meow meow meow meow meow meow meow meow..." Meow meow meow meow meow meow Meow, meow meow meow meow meow meow meow, meow meow meow meow meow meow meow meow meow, meow meow meow meow meow.

Meow Meow meow meow meow meow meow meow meow meow meow meow meow meow meow meow meow meow meow "meow meow meow!"

Meow Meow meow meow meow meow, meow meow meow meow meow meow meow meow Meow Meow'meow meow, meow meow meow meow meow-meow meow meow meow meow meow meow meow meow meow meow meow, meow meow meow, meow meow meow meow meow meow meow meow "Meow meow meow meow'meow," meow meow meow meow meow meow meow meow, meow meow "meow meow meow meow meow meow, meow Meow meow meow meow meow meow meow meow, meow meow meow meow meow, meow meow meow meow meow meow meow meow." Meow Meow Meow meow, meow meow meow meow meow Meow Meow meow meow meow meow meow meow Meow; meow meow meow meow meow meow, meow meow meow meow meow "Meow meow Meow meow meow meow meow meow, meow meow meow meow meow meow meow meow." Meow Meow meow meow meow meow meow meow meow meow meow Meow Meow meow meow meow meow meow meow meow.

"Meow meow meow meow!" Meow Meow meow meow meow, meow meow-meow meow meow, "meow meow meow meow meow meow meow meow meow meow meow, meow meow meow meow meow meow meow meow meow'meow meow. (Meow-meow.) Meow meow meow meow, Meow Meow, meow meow meow Meow meow, meow Meow meow, meow meow meow meow meow! Meow meow meow meow meow meow meow meow 'Meow meow meow meow'meow' 'meow meow meow meow meow' meow meow meow meow, meow meow meow meow meow, 'meow meow meow meow meow, meow meow meow.' Meow, meow meow! Meow meow meow meow meow meow'meow meow meow meow meow meow meow meow meow meow meow! Meow meow meow meow meow meow meow meow meow meow meow, meow meow meow meow meow meow meow meow meow meow meow meow, meow meow meow, meow meow meow meow meow meow meow meow meow.... Meow meow meow meow meow! Meow meow meow, meow-meow! (Meow-meow- meow.)"

Meow meow meow-meow, Meow Meow meow meow meow meow Meow meow meow meow meow meow meow meow, meow meow meow meow meow meow meow meow meow meow meow meow meow meow meow—. Meow meow meow meow meow meow meow meow meow meow meow meow meow meow, meow meow meow meow meow meow meow meow meow.

Meow meow meow meow Meow Meow meow meow meow meow meow meow meow meow meow meow meow Meow meow meow meow Meow meow meow meow, meow meow meow meow meow Meow Meow, meow meow, meow meow meow meow meow meow meow meow meow meow meow meow meow meow meow. Meow meow meow meow meow meow meow meow meow meow Meow Meow'meow meow meow meow meow meow-meow; meow meow meow meow meow meow meow meow meow meow meow meow meow "meow meow meow- meow meow" meow meow meow meow meow meow, meow meow meow meow Meow Meow meow meow meow meow meow, "meow meow meow meow meow meow, meow meow'meow meow meow meow meow meow meow meow meow meow meow meow meow meow meow meow meow meow meow." Meow meow meow meow meow meow meow meow meow meow meow meow meow, meow Meow Meow meow meow meow meow meow meow, meow meow meow meow meow meow meow meow meow, meow meow meow meow meow meow meow meow meow meow, meow meow meow meow meow meow meow, meow meow meow meow meow meow meow meow meow meow meow.

Meow meow, Meow Meow meow meow meow meow meow meow meow meow meow meow meow meow meow Meow, meow meow meow meow meow meow meow meow meow meow meow meow meow meow-meow, meow meow meow meow meow Meow, meow Meow, meow meow meow Meow Meow meow meow meow meow meow meow meow meow meow Meow meow meow meow meow meow meow meow meow meow meow meow. Meow meow meow meow Meow meow meow meow meow meow meow Meow meow meow meow meow meow meow meow. Meow meow meow meow meow meow meow meow meow meow meow meow meow meow.

Meow Meow Meow meow meow meow meow meow meow meow meow meow, meow meow meow meow meow meow meow meow meow meow meow meow Meow'meow meow meow meow meow meow, meow "meow meow, meow, meow, meow meow meow meow," meow Meow meow meow meow meow meow meow meow meow. Meow meow meow, meow Meow Meow meow meow meow meow, meow meow meow meow "meow meow meow, meow meow meow meow meow meow, meow meow meow meow meow meow, meow meow meow meow meow meow, meow meow meow meow meow meow meow meow."

Meow meow meow, Meow Meow, meow meow meow meow meow meow meow meow meow, meow meow meow meow meow, meow meow meow meow, meow meow meow meow meow meow meow meow meow meow meow, meow "meow meow meow meow-meow meow meow meow meow meow meow meow meow meow Meow, meow meow meow meow meow meow meow meow meow meow meow meow meow meow meow, meow meow meow meow meow meow meow meow meow meow meow meow meow."

Meow Meow, meow meow meow meow meow meow meow, meow meow meow meow meow meow meow meow, meow meow meow meow Meow Meow, meow "meow meow meow meow meow meow meow meow meow,

meow meow meow meow meow meow meow meow meow, meow meow meow meow meow meow meow meow- meow meow-meow meow meow meow meow Meow, meow meow meow meow-meow, meow meow meow meow, meow meow meow meow meow meow meow." Meow Meow meow meow meow meow meow meow meow meow meow "meow meow meow," meow meow "meow meow meow meow meow meow," meow meow "meow meow meow meow meow meow meow meow meow meow meow meow."

Meow Meow meow meow "meow meow meow," meow meow meow meow meow meow meow meow meow meow meow meow, meow meow meow meow meow meow meow meow meow meow meow meow, meow meow meow meow meow meow meow. Meow meow Meow Meow meow meow meow meow meow meow meow meow meow, meow "meow meow meow meow meow, meow meow meow meow meow meow meow meow meow meow meow meow meow meow meow meow." Meow Meow meow meow meow meow meow meow, meow meow meow meow meow meow meow meow meow meow meow meow meow meow meow meow. Meow Meow meow meow meow meow meow "Meow meow Meow meow meow meow, meow meow meow, meow meow meow meow meow meow, meow meow meow meow meow: 'Meow! meow!'" meow meow meow meow meow meow meow meow meow meow meow, meow meow meow meow meow meow, meow meow meow, meow meow meow meow meow "meow! meow!" meow meow meow meow meow meow meow, meow meow meow Meow Meow, meow meow meow meow.

Meow meow meow meow meow meow Meow Meow, meow meow meow meow meow, meow meow meow meow meow, meow Meow Meow meow meow meow meow meow, meow meow meow meow meow Meow Meow, meow meow meow meow meow meow meow meow meow meow meow. Meow Meow meow meow meow meow meow meow meow meow meow meow Meow Meow meow meow meow meow, "meow meow meow meow Meow meow Meow meow meow meow meow meow meow meow meow meow meow meow-meow-meow!"

Meow Meow meow meow meow meow meow meow meow meow meow meow meow meow meow meow meow meow meow meow meow meow meow meow meow meow meow meow meow meow meow, meow Meow Meow'meow meow—meow meow meow meow meow—meow meow meow Meow meow, meow meow meow meow meow meow meow meow meow meow, meow meow meow meow meow meow meow meow meow Meow Meow meow Meow Meow.

Meow meow Meow Meow, meow meow meow, meow meow meow meow meow meow, meow meow meow meow meow Meow Meow, meow meow Meow, "meow meow Meow meow meow Meow meow meow meow meow meow meow, meow meow Meow Meow'meow Meow meow meow meow meow meow." Meow Meow meow meow meow meow, meow meow meow meow meow meow meow meow (meow meow meow meow meow meow meow meow meow) meow meow "meow meow meow meow meow meow meow meow meow meow meow meow meow meow meow meow meow meow meow meow meow, meow, Meow Meow, meow meow meow meow meow

meow meow meow meow meow meow meow." Meow Meow meow meow meow meow, meow meow meow meow meow meow meow, meow meow meow meow meow meow meow meow meow Meow Meow meow meow meow meow meow meow; meow meow meow meow meow meow meow meow meow meow meow meow meow meow. Meow meow meow meow meow meow meow, meow meow meow meow. Meow meow meow meow Meow Meow, meow meow Meow Meow meow meow meow "meow meow meow," Meow Meow meow Meow meow, meow meow meow meow meow meow meow meow meow meow.

Meow meow meow meow meow meow, meow Meow Meow Meow meow meow meow meow. Meow meow meow meow meow meow meow meow meow meow. Meow Meow meow meow meow.

MEOW III

"Meow Meow," meow meow, "meow meow... meow meow meow! Meow meow meow meow meow meow meow meow'meow meow meow meow meow meow meow meow meow... meow meow meow meow meow meow meow meow.... Meow'meow meow meow meow meow-meow meow.... Meow meow meow meow meow.... Meow meow meow'meow meow meow meow meow."

"Meow meow, meow.... Meow meow." Meow Meow meow meow meow. "Meow meow meow meow meow meow meow Meow meow meow meow meow meow meow" (meow meow meow) "meow Meow meow meow meow meow meow meow meow meow meow meow meow Meow Meow.... Meow meow meow meow meow meow meow meow meow meow... meow Meow meow meow meow meow meow meow meow meow, Meow... Meow, Meow meow meow meow? Meow meow meow meow."

Meow Meow, meow meow meow, meow meow meow meow meow meow Meow meow.

Meow Meow meow meow meow meow meow, meow meow meow. Meow meow meow meow meow Meow Meow meow meow meow meow meow meow'meow meow. Meow meow meow meow meow meow, meow meow meow meow meow meow meow meow. Meow meow meow meow meow meow meow, meow meow meow meow meow meow meow Meow Meow. Meow meow meow meow meow meow meow meow meow. Meow meow meow meow "meow meow meow" meow meow meow meow meow meow meow meow, meow meow meow meow, meow, meow meow meow meow meow meow meow meow meow, meow meow meow meow meow meow meow meow meow meow meow meow meow meow meow meow. Meow, meow meow Meow, meow meow meow meow meow meow; Meow Meow meow meow meow meow meow meow. Meow meow meow Meow, meow, meow meow meow meow; meow meow meow meow meow, meow meow meow, meow meow meow meow, meow meow, meow meow meow meow meow meow.

"Meow meow meow meow meow meow, meow meow'meow meow meow meow meow meow," Meow Meow meow, meow meow meow meow. "Meow meow meow meow meow meow meow meow meow. Meow Meow, Meow meow meow meow meow meow meow meow meow meow meow meow meow meow meow Meow meow meow meow meow Meow Meow. Meow Meow," meow meow meow, meow Meow, meow meow meow meow meow meow meow meow, "meow meow meow meow Meow meow meow meow meow-meow meow meow meow meow meow meow, meow meow meow meow meow meow Meow. Meow. Meow meow meow meow meow meow meow meow meow meow meow meow meow meow meow, Meow meow meow meow meow meow meow meow meow meow meow meow meow meow meow meow meow meow meow meow. Meow meow meow meow Meow meow meow meow meow meow meow meow meow meow meow meow meow... meow meow meow meow."

Meow meow meow meow meow meow. Meow meow meow meow meow meow. Meow meow meow meow, meow meow Meow meow meow meow meow meow meow. Meow meow meow meow meow. Meow meow meow.

"Meow, meow meow meow meow meow meow?" meow Meow, meow meow meow meow.

"Meow meow'meow meow.... Meow meow meow meow meow," Meow meow meow meow meow.

"Meow, meow meow meow?" Meow meow meow meow meow meow meow meow meow. "Meow meow meow, meow," meow meow meow, meow meow, meow meow meow, meow meow. "Meow, Meow meow meow meow meow meow meow meow meow. Meow meow meow: meow Meow meow meow meow meow meow Meow meow meow, meow meow meow meow, meow meow meow meow meow meow meow meow meow. Meow meow meow meow meow meow meow meow, meow meow meow meow meow, Meow meow meow meow meow meow meow meow meow meow, Meow meow meow meow meow. Meow meow Meow meow meow meow meow meow meow meow-meow-meow meow meow meow meow meow meow meow meow meow. Meow meow meow meow meow meow meow meow-meow. Meow meow meow meow Meow meow meow meow meow meow—meow Meow. Meow meow meow meow—meow meow meow meow meow meow meow meow Meow meow meow meow meow meow meow-meow meow meow meow meow. Meow meow meow meow meow meow meow meow meow meow meow meow meow meow meow meow meow meow. Meow meow meow meow meow (meow meow meow)—meow meow meow meow meow meow meow meow meow meow meow; meow meow meow meow meow meow meow meow meow meow meow meow meow meow meow meow meow meow meow. Meow. Meow meow meow meow meow meow. Meow meow, meow, meow meow meow meow meow meow meow meow meow Meow meow meow meow Meow. Meow, meow meow meow meow meow meow meow meow meow meow meow meow meow meow meow, Meow Meow (meow meow Meow meow meow meow meow), meow meow meow meow meow meow meow meow meow meow meow meow meow, meow meow meow meow, meow meow meow. Meow meow meow meow meow meow meow. Meow meow meow meow meow meow meow meow, meow meow meow meow meow meow meow meow meow meow meow meow meow meow meow meow meow meow meow meow meow meow. Meow Meow meow meow meow-meow meow meow meow meow meow meow meow meow meow meow meow meow meow meow meow meow meow meow meow meow meow meow meow meow. Meow. Meow meow meow meow. Meow Meow meow meow meow meow meow—meow meow meow meow meow meow meow meow meow—meow meow, meow meow meow meow Meow. Meow Meow meow meow meow meow meow meow—meow Meow. Meow meow meow meow Meow meow meow meow meow meow meow meow meow meow meow, meow meow meow meow meow meow meow meow meow, meow Meow meow meow meow. Meow meow meow meow meow-meow meow meow meow. Meow meow meow meow. Meow. Meow Meow meow meow. Meow meow meow meow meow meow meow meow

meow. Meow meow meow meow meow meow meow meow meow, meow meow meow meow meow meow Meow meow meow meow meow meow meow meow meow meow. Meow meow meow meow meow meow meow, meow meow meow meow meow meow meow meow meow meow meow meow meow meow meow meow meow meow meow, meow meow meow meow meow meow meow meow meow meow meow meow meow meow, Meow meow, meow meow meow, meow meow meow meow meow meow meow, meow meow meow meow meow—meow meow, meow meow meow! Meow meow meow meow meow meow meow meow meow meow meow meow meow, Meow meow meow Meow meow meow meow meow meow meow meow meow, meow meow meow meow, Meow meow meow meow meow meow. Meow meow meow meow meow Meow meow meow meow meow: meow, meow, meow, meow meow meow meow meow! Meow! Meow meow meow meow meow meow meow meow meow meow, Meow meow meow meow meow meow meow meow meow meow meow, meow meow meow, meow meow meow meow meow meow meow meow meow. Meow meow meow meow! Meow meow meow meow. Meow! Meow, meow meow meow meow Meow meow meow—meow meow meow meow meow meow meow meow meow meow—meow meow meow meow meow, meow Meow meow meow meow! Meow, meow meow meow meow?"

"Meow meow meow meow," Meow meow meow meow, "meow meow meow meow meow, meow meow meow, meow meow."

Meow meow meow meow meow meow meow meow, meow meow meow meow meow, meow meow meow meow-meow meow meow meow meow meow Meow.

"Meow meow meow meow meow meow meow meow meow meow?" meow meow meow, meow meow meow meow.

Meow meow meow meow. Meow meow meow meow meow meow meow meow, meow, meow, meow meow. Meow meow meow Meow... meow meow meow meow meow, meow meow meow meow, meow meow meow meow meow meow.

"Meow Meow!" meow meow Meow.

"Meow Meow, meow meow meow meow meow meow meow meow meow meow meow Meow meow meow meow meow meow meow meow meow meow meow," Meow meow meow meow meow meow.

"Meow meow Meow! Meow meow meow meow meow meow," meow Meow Meow, meow meow meow meow.

"Meow meow meow?" Meow meow meow meow, "meow Meow meow meow meow meow meow meow meow meow meow meow. Meow meow meow, meow Meow Meow, meow meow meow meow meow meow meow meow meow meow."

Meow meow meow meow meow meow meow meow meow meow. Meow meow meow meow.

"Meow!" meow Meow Meow, meow meow meow meow, meow meow meow meow Meow. "Meow! Meow meow meow meow meow? Meow? Meow, meow meow, meow meow!"

Meow meow meow Meow meow meow meow meow meow meow meow meow meow meow meow meow meow meow.

"Meow! meow meow meow meow meow meow meow meow? Meow meow! Meow meow meow meow! Meow meow meow meow meow meow meow—meow!"

Meow meow meow meow meow Meow, Meow Meow meow meow meow meow meow meow meow meow Meow'meow meow. Meow meow meow meow meow meow meow meow meow meow meow. Meow Meow meow meow meow meow meow. Meow Meow meow meow meow.

"Meow meow meow meow!" meow meow.

Meow meow meow meow meow meow, meow Meow, meow meow meow meow, meow meow meow meow meow.

"Meow! Meow? Meow Meow meow? Meow!" meow Meow Meow. "Meow meow meow meow meow, meow meow, meow meow! Meow, Meow meow meow meow! Meow meow meow! Meow, meow'meow meow meow meow meow meow!" meow Meow Meow meow meow meow meow. "Meow meow meow meow meow meow meow?" meow meow meow meow meow meow. "Meow meow meow?" meow meow meow meow meow, "meow meow meow, meow meow, meow meow meow meow meow meow meow, meow meow Meow meow'meow meow meow meow meow! Meow meow'meow meow meow meow meow meow: meow meow meow meow meow, meow meow, meow meow meow meow meow, meow meow meow. Meow meow meow, meow Meow Meow. Meow meow! Meow meow'meow meow meow meow meow, meow meow meow meow meow meow meow meow! Meow meow, meow meow! Meow meow meow meow'meow meow meow, meow meow meow, meow meow meow, meow'meow meow meow meow! Meow'meow meow meow meow Meow, meow meow Meow, meow meow meow Meow meow, meow meow meow meow meow meow, meow-meow, meow meow! Meow meow meow meow meow meow! Meow meow meow meow meow! Meow meow meow meow meow'meow? Meow'meow meow, Meow meow meow meow! Meow meow meow meow! Meow meow meow meow meow! Meow meow meow meow! Meow Meow meow meow meow meow, meow meow meow meow! Meow'meow meow meow meow meow. Meow meow, meow meow!"

Meow Meow Meow meow meow meow meow Meow meow meow meow meow Meow.

"Meow meow meow, Meow'meow meow meow... meow meow meow, meow, meow meow. Meow meow meow meow meow meow meow meow!... Meow, meow, meow meow meow meow..." Meow meow, "meow meow meow meow meow meow meow... meow meow meow meow meow meow meow meow meow.... Meow meow meow.... Meow meow meow meow meow'meow meow meow meow meow... meow meow meow meow meow.... Meow meow meow meow meow Meow Meow... meow, meow meow, meow'meow meow meow meow meow meow meow.... Meow meow meow meow meow meow?"

"Meow meow meow! Meow meow meow meow meow meow!" meow Meow Meow. "Meow, meow meow meow meow! Meow! Meow, meow,

meow meow meow meow, meow meow meow meow! Meow meow meow meow meow, meow! Meow'meow meow, meow'meow meow?"

Meow Meow Meow meow—meow meow meow—meow meow meow meow. Meow meow meow meow meow meow meow meow meow meow meow meow meow meow meow meow meow meow meow meow Meow'meow meow. Meow meow meow, meow meow meow. Meow Meow meow meow, meow meow meow meow meow meow meow, meow meow meow meow meow meow meow meow meow meow. Meow meow meow meow-meow meow meow meow meow. Meow Meow meow meow meow meow meow meow meow meow.

"Meow! Meow meow meow meow. Meow, meow!" meow Meow Meow. "Meow meow meow Meow meow meow! Meow!"

Meow meow meow meow meow. Meow meow meow, meow meow meow meow meow Meow, meow meow meow meow meow meow meow Meow. Meow meow meow, meow meow meow. Meow meow meow meow meow meow meow. Meow meow meow meow meow meow meow; meow meow meow meow meow meow meow meow meow meow meow.

"Meow, meow meow'meow Meow! Meow meow'meow meow meow! Meow meow meow meow meow," meow meow meow meow meow meow, meow meow meow meow Meow Meow, meow meow meow meow meow meow meow, meow meow meow meow meow meow meow meow meow meow.

"Meow! Meow! Meow meow'meow meow meow! Meow meow, Meow meow'meow meow meow!" meow meow meow meow meow meow meow meow meow, meow meow meow meow meow meow meow meow meow meow meow, meow meow meow meow, meow meow meow meow meow meow meow meow, meow, "meow meow meow! Meow meow meow meow meow! Meow meow! Meow meow meow, meow," meow meow, meow meow meow meow, "meow meow'meow meow, meow meow'meow meow meow meow meow meow meow, meow meow meow meow meow! Meow meow meow, meow? Meow'meow meow meow meow meow, meow'meow meow meow meow meow meow meow meow meow meow, meow'meow meow meow meow! Meow meow meow meow meow meow meow meow meow meow, meow meow meow meow meow! Meow, meow, meow! Meow meow meow? Meow meow meow? Meow meow meow meow meow meow! Meow meow! Meow meow, meow meow meow meow meow meow? Meow Meow, meow meow'meow meow meow meow meow meow? Meow meow meow meow, meow? Meow meow meow meow meow meow meow, meow meow meow meow! Meow Meow! Meow meow meow, meow meow!"

Meow meow meow meow meow, meow, meow meow meow meow meow meow meow meow meow meow meow. Meow meow, meow, meow meow, meow meow meow-meow meow, meow meow meow, meow meow meow meow meow meow'meow, meow meow, meow meow meow meow meow meow meow meow meow meow meow meow meow meow meow meow meow. Meow Meow meow meow meow meow meow meow meow meow meow.

"Meow, meow, meow meow meow meow meow meow meow!" meow meow meow, "meow meow meow meow meow meow meow meow meow meow meow meow meow meow meow meow meow meow meow, meow meow meow meow meow meow meow meow meow meow meow meow, meow meow meow meow meow meow meow meow meow. Meow meow meow meow, meow meow meow meow meow, meow meow, meow meow meow, meow Meow Meow meow meow, meow meow meow meow meow meow meow, meow? Meow meow meow meow meow meow? Meow meow meow? Meow meow meow meow, meow? Meow meow meow meow meow.... Meow meow meow meow meow meow meow meow meow meow meow? Meow," meow meow meow meow meow, "meow! Meow meow, meow meow meow, meow meow meow, Meow meow meow meow meow meow meow meow meow meow meow meow meow meow meow meow meow! Meow meow meow meow meow meow meow meow meow meow meow meow," meow meow, meow Meow, "meow Meow meow meow meow meow meow meow. Meow!"

Meow Meow meow meow meow meow Meow. Meow meow meow, meow meow meow meow Meow'meow meow meow meow meow meow meow meow. Meow Meow Meow meow meow meow. Meow meow meow meow meow Meow meow meow meow. Meow meow, meow, meow meow Meow meow meow meow, meow Meow—meow meow meow meow meow meow meow meow meow—meow meow meow meow meow meow meow meow, meow meow meow meow meow meow meow, meow meow meow, meow Meow'meow meow.

"Meow meow!" meow meow meow meow meow meow meow meow. Meow Meow meow meow meow.

"Meow meow!" Meow meow, meow meow meow meow meow meow.

Meow Meow meow meow meow meow—meow meow meow meow meow meow meow. Meow meow meow meow meow.

"Meow meow meow meow meow meow meow meow?" meow meow, meow meow meow Meow Meow. "Meow meow meow meow? Meow meow meow meow meow?" meow Meow.

"Meow meow meow meow... meow meow meow, meow'meow meow meow meow meow!" Meow meow meow, meow meow meow meow meow meow meow-meow meow.

Meow meow meow meow. Meow meow meow meow meow, meow meow meow meow meow meow meow. Meow meow meow meow meow. Meow Meow meow meow meow meow meow meow meow meow.

"Meow meow meow meow meow meow,..." meow meow, meow. "Meow meow'meow meow meow meow meow? Meow meow meow meow meow meow?"

"Meow'meow meow meow meow, meow meow meow meow meow! Meow, meow meow! Meow meow meow meow. Meow meow meow meow meow meow meow meow, meow Meow meow meow meow meow meow meow meow meow meow.... Meow meow meow meow meow meow meow Meow meow'meow meow."

"Meow, meow meow Meow meow meow? Meow meow meow meow meow meow meow! Meow meow meow meow meow!"

"Meow meow meow meow meow, meow, meow meow, meow Meow meow meow! Meow meow meow meow, meow meow'meow meow meow meow. Meow meow meow meow, meow, meow meow, meow meow meow meow meow Meow Meow meow meow-meow meow—Meow meow meow, Meow meow meow meow, Meow'meow meow meow meow! Meow meow meow, meow!" meow Meow, meow meow.

"Meow meow meow, meow?" meow Meow. "Meow meow meow meow meow—meow meow meow meow meow meow meow meow meow Meow meow meow meow meow meow. Meow meow Meow meow meow meow meow meow?"

"Meow meow meow, Meow meow meow," Meow meow, "meow meow meow meow meow meow meow, Meow meow meow meow meow meow meow meow meow meow meow meow meow meow meow, meow Meow meow meow meow meow meow meow meow meow. Meow meow meow meow Meow meow meow meow meow meow meow meow! Meow meow meow meow meow-meow meow meow meow meow meow, meow meow meow meow meow meow meow meow, meow meow meow, meow meow, meow meow meow meow meow meow meow. Meow meow meow, Meow meow meow!"

Meow meow meow.

"Meow meow!" meow meow meow, "meow, meow meow meow, meow meow meow meow, meow meow meow? Meow meow meow meow meow meow-meow meow. Meow meow meow!"

"Meow, Meow meow'meow meow meow. Meow meow Meow meow meow meow meow meow, Meow meow meow meow. Meow meow meow meow meow meow meow meow meow meow meow meow meow meow—meow'meow meow—Meow meow meow meow meow meow meow meow meow-meow meow, meow, meow meow meow meow meow meow Meow Meow meow meow, meow meow meow meow meow meow meow meow-meow meow (Meow meow meow meow Meow meow meow meow meow, meow meow meow meow meow meow meow, meow meow Meow meow meow meow meow meow meow meow meow meow). Meow meow meow meow meow meow meow meow meow meow meow meow. Meow meow'meow meow meow meow meow meow, meow meow meow meow meow, meow meow meow meow meow meow meow meow meow meow meow meow meow meow! Meow meow meow meow meow meow meow meow meow meow, meow meow meow meow meow meow meow meow meow meow meow. Meow meow meow meow Meow meow meow meow Meow meow meow meow meow meow meow meow meow meow meow. Meow meow meow, Meow meow meow, Meow'meow meow meow meow."

Meow meow meow meow. Meow meow meow meow meow meow meow meow meow, meow meow meow meow meow meow. Meow meow meow meow Meow Meow. Meow Meow meow meow Meow.

"Meow meow meow meow meow! Meow meow! Meow meow meow meow meow meow meow meow meow! Meow meow meow meow. Meow meow meow meow!"

Meow Meow, meow meow meow meow meow meow, meow meow meow meow meow meow.

"Meow meow meow meow!" meow Meow, meow meow meow, "meow'meow meow meow meow'meow meow meow! 'Meow meow meow meow, meow meow'meow meow, meow meow'—meow meow meow meow meow? Meow Meow meow meow meow meow meow meow meow meow meow? Meow meow? Meow meow meow? Meow meow Meow meow meow meow meow...?"

"Meow meow? Meow'meow meow Meow meow'meow meow, meow meow meow Meow meow meow meow meow meow meow, meow'meow meow! Meow meow meow meow meow meow, meow meow meow meow, Meow meow meow, meow meow meow meow, meow meow meow meow meow meow meow, meow meow Meow meow meow meow meow meow meow meow. Meow meow meow meow meow meow meow meow meow? Meow meow meow meow meow, Meow meow? Meow meow meow meow meow meow meow meow, meow meow meow meow meow meow meow meow meow meow Meow meow meow meow meow meow meow, meow meow meow meow meow? Meow, Meow meow meow meow meow meow meow meow meow meow meow meow meow meow meow. Meow, meow, Meow meow, meow meow meow meow meow meow meow, meow meow meow meow meow meow-meow meow meow meow meow. (Meow Meow meow, meow meow meow meow meow meow meow meow meow meow meow meow meow meow meow.) Meow meow meow meow meow, meow, meow meow meow meow meow meow, meow meow meow, meow meow meow meow, meow meow meow meow meow meow. Meow, meow, meow meow meow meow meow meow meow meow, meow meow meow meow, meow meow meow meow meow meow... meow meow meow meow, meow meow. Meow meow meow meow meow meow meow Meow meow meow meow meow, meow meow meow meow meow meow meow meow meow Meow meow meow meow. Meow meow meow meow meow meow meow Meow Meow meow meow meow meow meow meow meow meow, meow meow meow Meow meow meow meow meow meow meow meow meow meow meow meow meow meow meow meow meow meow meow meow meow meow meow meow meow meow meow. Meow meow meow meow Meow meow meow meow Meow Meow'meow meow meow meow meow 'Meow Meow meow meow Meow Meow' meow meow meow meow Meow'meow meow (meow meow Meow'meow); meow Meow meow meow meow meow meow meow meow meow meow Meow meow! Meow meow Meow, meow Meow, meow meow meow meow meow meow meow Meow meow meow meow meow meow meow meow-meow meow meow meow meow?"

Meow Meow meow meow meow-meow meow meow meow meow meow meow meow meow, meow meow meow meow, meow meow meow meow meow meow meow. Meow meow meow, meow, meow meow meow meow

meow Meow, meow meow meow meow meow meow, meow meow meow meow meow meow, meow meow meow meow meow meow. Meow meow meow meow meow meow meow. Meow meow meow meow meow meow, meow meow meow meow meow meow meow meow. Meow Meow meow meow meow meow meow meow meow meow.

"Meow meow meow meow meow meow meow meow meow meow meow meow meow meow?" meow meow, "meow'meow meow meow. Meow meow meow meow meow, meow'meow meow! Meow Meow meow meow, meow meow meow, meow. Meow meow meow meow meow meow meow meow meow meow, meow meow meow, meow Meow meow meow meow meow meow meow-meow, meow, meow meow!"

Meow meow meow meow meow meow Meow Meow. Meow meow meow meow meow meow meow meow.

"Meow, meow'meow meow meow meow, meow meow!" meow Meow, "meow'meow meow! Meow meow meow meow Meow'meow meow meow meow! Meow'meow meow meow meow Meow meow'meow meow: meow meow meow meow meow meow meow meow. Meow, meow, meow meow!"

"Meow meow meow meow meow meow meow meow meow, meow meow meow, Meow, meow, meow meow meow meow," Meow meow meow meow meow meow meow meow, meow meow meow meow.

Meow meow meow meow meow meow meow. Meow meow meow, meow meow meow meow meow meow meow meow meow meow meow meow meow meow meow meow meow meow meow meow.

"Meow Meow meow meow meow meow meow meow," meow Meow, meow Meow. "Meow meow meow meow meow meow meow, Meow meow meow meow meow meow meow meow meow meow meow meow meow. Meow meow meow meow meow meow meow meow meow meow meow meow meow, meow Meow meow meow meow meow meow meow: meow meow meow meow. Meow meow meow meow meow meow meow meow meow meow. Meow meow meow, meow meow meow. Meow meow (meow meow meow Meow) meow meow meow meow meow meow meow meow meow meow—meow meow, Meow Meow Meow. Meow meow meow Meow meow meow meow meow, meow meow meow meow, meow meow meow meow meow Meow meow meow meow meow meow meow—Meow meow meow meow meow meow meow. Meow meow meow meow meow meow.... Meow meow meow meow Meow meow meow meow meow meow meow meow meow, meow meow meow, meow meow meow meow meow meow meow meow meow—meow meow meow meow—meow meow meow meow Meow Meow meow meow meow meow meow, meow meow meow meow meow meow Meow. Meow. Meow meow meow meow meow meow meow meow meow meow meow meow meow Meow meow meow meow meow meow meow, meow meow Meow Meow meow meow Meow Meow, meow meow meow meow meow meow meow meow meow... meow meow Meow Meow, meow meow, meow meow meow meow meow meow meow meow Meow Meow. Meow meow meow meow meow meow meow meow meow meow meow meow meow meow meow meow, meow meow meow Meow meow meow meow meow meow meow meow meow meow meow meow

meow meow meow meow meow meow meow. Meow meow, meow meow meow meow meow meow meow meow meow, Meow meow meow Meow meow meow meow meow meow Meow Meow meow meow meow meow meow meow Meow Meow meow meow Meow meow meow meow meow Meow Meow meow meow meow meow meow meow, meow. Meow meow meow meow Meow meow meow meow, Meow Meow Meow, meow meow meow meow, meow meow meow Meow Meow'meow meow meow, meow meow meow meow meow meow meow. Meow meow meow – meow Meow meow Meow Meow meow meow meow meow meow, Meow meow meow Meow meow meow meow meow meow meow. Meow meow meow meow meow meow meow meow meow meow meow meow meow meow meow, meow meow meow meow meow meow meow meow. Meow meow meow meow meow meow meow meow meow meow meow meow meow. Meow meow meow meow meow. Meow Meow meow meow meow meow: meow: meow meow meow meow meow meow meow meow Meow Meow meow meow meow, meow meow meow meow meow meow meow meow meow meow meow meow meow meow meow meow meow, meow meow meow meow meow meow meow meow meow meow meow meow meow meow meow meow meow Meow Meow, meow, meow meow meow, meow meow meow meow meow meow meow meow meow meow, meow meow. Meow meow meow meow meow, meow meow meow, meow meow meow meow meow meow meow meow meow, meow meow meow meow meow meow meow meow meow meow meow meow meow; meow meow meow meow meow meow meow meow meow, meow meow meow meow meow meow meow meow meow meow meow meow Meow Meow meow meow meow meow meow. Meow meow meow meow meow meow meow! Meow'meow meow Meow meow meow. Meow'meow meow meow meow meow meow meow meow meow meow meow meow!"

Meow meow meow meow, meow meow meow meow, meow Meow meow meow meow meow meow meow meow meow meow, meow meow meow meow meow meow meow meow. Meow meow meow meow meow meow meow meow, meow, meow, meow. Meow meow meow, meow meow meow meow meow meow meow meow meow meow meow meow meow meow.

"Meow, meow, meow'meow meow," Meow meow meow, "meow meow meow meow, meow meow meow meow, meow meow meow Meow Meow meow meow meow meow, meow meow meow meow, meow Meow meow meow meow meow Meow Meow'meow meow. Meow meow meow meow meow meow meow meow meow meow meow. Meow meow meow meow meow meow meow meow meow meow! Meow'meow meow, meow'meow meow!"

Meow meow meow meow meow meow meow. Meow meow meow meow meow. Meow meow meow meow meow meow meow meow meow meow. Meow meow meow meow meow meow meow meow meow meow meow meow meow, meow meow meow meow meow meow meow meow. Meow meow meow meow meow meow meow meow meow meow meow meow. Meow, meow meow, meow meow meow meow meow meow meow, meow meow meow meow meow meow meow meow. Meow meow meow,

meow meow meow meow meow meow meow meow meow, meow meow meow meow meow meow meow meow meow meow meow meow meow Meow. Meow meow meow meow meow meow meow; meow meow meow meow meow meow meow. Meow meow Meow meow meow meow meow meow meow meow meow meow: "Meow meow meow meow meow!" meow meow meow meow Meow. Meow meow meow meow meow meow meow, meow meow meow meow meow meow meow meow meow; meow meow meow meow meow meow meow meow meow meow. Meow meow meow meow meow meow meow Meow, meow meow meow meow meow meow meow meow. Meow Meow meow meow meow meow meow meow meow meow. Meow Meow meow meow meow meow meow meow, meow meow meow meow meow, meow meow meow meow meow meow meow. Meow meow meow meow Meow Meow meow meow meow meow meow.

Meow meow meow meow meow meow, meow meow meow meow meow meow. Meow meow meow meow Meow meow meow meow meow meow meow. Meow Meow Meow meow meow meow. Meow meow meow meow meow Meow meow meow meow, meow meow meow meow meow:

"Meow meow, meow, meow meow! Meow'meow meow, meow meow meow!" meow meow, meow meow meow meow meow meow. "Meow meow meow, meow meow meow! Meow meow meow meow meow meow meow, meow meow meow meow meow meow. Meow meow meow, meow'meow meow meow meow, meow, meow meow meow meow meow meow. Meow meow meow meow meow meow meow, meow Meow meow meow. Meow meow meow meow meow meow meow... meow meow meow, meow meow meow meow meow meow meow meow meow meow, meow, meow meow, meow meow meow meow meow meow meow meow meow meow meow meow meow meow meow.... Meow, meow meow meow meow!"

"Meow'meow meow meow meow meow meow meow meow meow meow meow! Meow meow meow meow, meow meow meow meow meow meow meow meow! Meow Meow meow meow meow meow Meow'meow meow meow, meow meow Meow'meow meow meow... meow meow meow!"

"Meow meow meow meow meow-meow meow Meow meow meow, meow meow meow meow meow meow; meow Meow meow meow meow meow meow meow meow meow. Meow meow meow meow meow meow meow meow meow meow meow meow meow meow. Meow meow meow, meow!"

Meow meow meow meow meow. Meow meow meow meow meow meow meow meow meow meow meow meow: meow meow meow meow meow meow meow meow, meow meow meow meow meow meow meow meow meow Meow Meow; meow meow meow meow meow meow Meow Meow. Meow meow, meow meow meow, meow, meow meow meow meow meow. Meow Meow meow meow meow meow meow meow meow meow meow meow meow meow meow meow meow. Meow, meow meow meow, meow meow meow meow meow meow meow meow meow meow-meow meow meow meow meow, meow meow meow meow meow meow meow meow. Meow meow meow meow meow meow meow meow meow meow meow meow meow meow, meow meow meow meow meow. Meow meow meow

meow meow. Meow meow, meow meow, meow meow meow meow meow meow meow meow, meow meow. Meow meow meow meow meow meow meow meow meow meow. Meow meow meow meow meow meow meow meow—meow meow meow meow meow meow meow meow meow meow meow meow meow meow meow—meow meow meow meow meow meow meow meow meow meow meow meow meow meow meow meow meow meow meow meow meow meow meow meow meow meow. Meow meow, meow meow meow meow meow, meow meow meow meow meow meow meow meow meow, meow meow meow Meow'meow meow. Meow meow meow meow meow meow meow meow Meow Meow, meow meow meow meow meow meow meow meow. Meow meow meow meow meow meow meow meow meow Meow Meow, meow meow meow meow meow meow.

"Meow meow meow meow! Meow meow! Meow meow!"

Meow meow meow meow meow meow meow meow meow meow meow meow meow meow meow meow meow meow Meow Meow, meow meow meow meow meow meow. Meow Meow, meow, meow meow, meow meow meow meow, meow meow meow meow meow meow meow meow meow meow meow meow meow meow Meow Meow. Meow meow meow meow meow meow: meow meow meow meow meow meow meow meow.

"Meow! Meow meow meow meow meow meow meow—meow meow meow meow meow! Meow! Meow meow meow meow meow meow'meow meow Meow meow meow meow meow meow! Meow meow meow meow meow meow meow meow meow meow meow meow, meow meow meow! Meow meow Meow meow meow?" meow meow meow meow, meow meow meow. "Meow Meow!" meow meow meow meow meow, "meow meow meow meow meow meow? Meow meow meow meow meow meow meow meow? Meow meow meow! Meow meow meow meow meow meow meow, meow meow, Meow meow meow meow! Meow meow meow, meow meow! Meow, meow meow meow meow, Meow'meow meow meow. Meow meow meow, meow meow meow meow meow meow meow meow. Meow meow meow meow meow meow meow meow meow!"

Meow meow meow meow meow meow meow meow meow Meow meow meow meow Meow, Meow Meow meow meow meow meow meow meow meow meow meow meow meow meow meow meow meow meow, meow, meow meow meow, meow meow meow meow meow—meow meow meow meow meow meow meow meow meow meow meow meow. Meow meow meow meow meow meow meow meow meow meow, meow, meow meow meow meow meow meow meow meow meow, meow meow meow meow meow meow meow meow meow meow. Meow Meow meow meow meow meow, meow, meow meow meow meow meow meow meow meow meow meow. Meow meow meow meow, meow meow meow meow meow meow meow meow meow meow meow meow, meow meow meow meow meow meow meow, meow meow meow meow meow meow....

"Meow meow'meow meow meow meow meow meow," meow Meow. "Meow, Meow Meow, meow meow meow meow meow'meow meow meow!"

Meow meow meow meow meow meow meow meow Meow'meow meow.

MEOW IV

Meow meow meow meow meow meow meow meow meow Meow meow Meow, meow meow meow meow meow meow meow meow meow meow meow meow meow meow. Meow meow meow meow meow meow meow meow meow, meow meow meow meow meow meow meow meow meow meow meow, meow meow meow meow meow meow meow meow meow meow meow Meow. Meow meow meow meow, meow meow meow meow, meow meow meow meow meow meow meow meow Meow: meow meow meow meow meow meow meow meow Meow. Meow meow meow meow meow meow meow meow meow meow meow, meow meow meow, meow meow meow meow meow meow. Meow meow meow meow meow meow meow Meow Meow’meow, “Meow, Meow Meow, meow meow meow meow meow’meow meow meow!” meow meow meow meow meow, meow meow meow meow meow meow meow meow Meow. Meow, meow meow meow, meow meow meow meow meow Meow’meow meow, meow meow meow meow meow meow meow. Meow meow meow meow meow meow meow meow, meow meow meow meow meow: “Meow meow meow meow meow meow Meow?” Meow meow meow meow meow meow meow meow meow meow meow meow meow meow meow meow meow meow meow meow meow, meow meow meow meow meow meow meow meow meow meow. Meow meow meow meow meow meow meow meow meow meow, meow meow meow meow, meow meow meow meow meow meow meow meow meow meow meow meow meow. Meow meow meow meow meow meow, meow meow meow meow meow meow meow meow Meow meow meow meow. Meow meow meow meow meow meow meow meow meow meow meow meow meow meow meow, meow meow Meow meow meow meow meow meow meow meow meow meow meow meow meow meow meow meow meow.

“Meow meow meow meow meow meow meow meow meow?” meow meow meow, meow meow meow meow meow meow meow meow.

Meow meow meow meow meow meow meow meow meow meow. Meow meow meow meow meow meow meow meow.

Meow meow meow meow meow meow meow meow meow meow meow meow meow meow meow meow meow meow. Meow meow meow meow, meow meow meow, meow meow meow meow meow meow meow meow.

“Meow, Meow?” meow meow, meow meow meow meow meow meow meow, “meow meow meow meow meow ‘meow meow meow meow meow meow meow meow meow.’ Meow meow meow meow meow meow?”

Meow meow meow meow meow.

“Meow meow’meow meow meow meow meow meow meow meow,” meow meow meow. “Meow meow’meow meow meow. Meow meow meow meow meow meow.”

Meow meow meow meow meow, meow meow meow meow meow meow meow meow.

"Meow meow meow meow meow meow meow meow. Meow meow meow meow meow? Meow meow meow meow meow meow, meow Meow meow meow meow... meow meow meow."

Meow meow meow meow Meow Meow meow meow meow meow meow meow meow meow meow Meow Meow meow meow meow meow "meow meow meow."

"Meow Meow!" meow Meow, "meow'meow meow meow meow...." Meow meow meow meow meow meow.

"Meow'meow meow meow meow meow!" meow Meow, meow. "Meow'meow meow meow meow meow meow! Meow meow meow meow meow."

"Meow... Meow Meow?"

"Meow meow'meow meow Meow Meow, meow meow meow meow, meow'meow meow meow meow meow meow meow meow meow meow," meow meow meow. "Meow meow meow'meow meow meow meow, meow'meow meow meow meow meow...."

Meow meow meow meow meow meow. Meow meow meow, meow meow meow meow meow meow.

"Meow meow Meow meow meow meow meow meow meow," meow meow, meow meow meow Meow, "meow meow meow meow meow meow, meow meow meow meow meow meow, meow meow meow meow meow meow meow meow meow meow meow meow meow Meow meow meow. Meow?"

"Meow," meow meow meow meow meow meow. "Meow," meow meow, meow meow meow.

"Meow Meow meow meow meow meow meow meow. Meow meow meow meow meow meow Meow'meow meow meow."

Meow meow meow.

"Meow meow meow'meow meow meow meow, meow meow? Meow meow meow meow Meow meow meow?" Meow meow meow meow meow. Meow meow.

"Meow meow meow meow meow meow meow 'meow'meow meow meow meow, meow meow.'" Meow meow meow meow, meow meow meow meow meow. "Meow, meow meow?" meow meow meow meow meow. "Meow meow meow meow meow, meow meow. Meow meow meow meow meow meow meow meow meow meow meow meow meow meow 'meow' meow Meow meow meow." (Meow meow meow meow meow meow meow.) "Meow, meow, Meow meow meow. Meow, Meow, meow meow meow meow meow Meow'meow meow meow. Meow, meow meow, meow meow meow, meow meow meow meow meow meow meow Meow Meow meow meow meow meow meow meow meow—meow meow meow'meow meow meow meow meow—Meow meow... meow meow'meow meow meow meow meow. Meow, meow meow meow meow meow meow meow meow meow meow meow meow meow meow meow meow, meow meow meow Meow meow meow meow meow meow meow meow meow, meow Meow Meow meow meow? Meow meow meow meow meow meow meow meow meow meow? Meow meow meow?"

Meow meow meow meow meow. Meow meow meow meow meow meow meow meow, meow meow meow meow meow meow meow meow.

"Meow meow meow meow meow meow meow meow meow meow meow meow," meow meow, meow meow meow meow.

"Meow meow meow meow meow. Meow meow meow meow meow meow meow?"

"Meow meow meow meow meow meow meow meow meow?" meow Meow meow.

"Meow meow meow meow meow meow Meow meow meow meow meow meow meow meow meow? Meow meow'meow meow meow meow meow meow!"

"Meow Meow meow'meow meow meow Meow Meow.... Meow meow meow meow meow meow meow'meow meow meow? Meow'meow meow meow meow meow meow meow? Meow meow meow meow meow meow meow meow meow meow meow—meow meow meow meow meow meow meow meow meow meow meow meow meow meow meow meow meow meow?"

"Meow, meow meow Meow Meow meow meow meow meow meow meow meow, meow meow meow meow meow," Meow meow meow.

"Meow'meow meow meow meow meow meow meow meow!" Meow meow meow meow. "Meow meow meow meow meow meow meow.... Meow meow meow meow meow meow meow meow?"

Meow meow meow meow meow meow meow meow meow. Meow meow meow meow meow meow meow. Meow meow meow.

"Meow meow meow'meow meow, Meow," meow meow meow meow meow. Meow meow meow meow. Meow meow meow meow meow meow meow meow meow. Meow meow meow meow meow meow. "Meow meow meow meow meow Meow meow meow meow meow meow meow meow meow meow meow Meow'meow meow meow meow meow meow.... Meow meow meow meow Meow meow Meow meow meow meow meow. Meow meow meow meow, Meow...."

Meow meow meow meow, meow meow meow meow meow meow meow meow meow meow meow. Meow meow meow meow meow meow meow meow meow meow meow.

Meow meow meow meow, meow meow meow meow meow meow meow meow meow Meow meow meow meow meow. Meow meow meow meow meow meow meow meow meow, meow meow meow meow meow meow meow meow meow; meow meow meow meow meow meow meow meow meow meow meow meow; meow meow meow meow meow; meow meow meow meow meow meow. Meow meow meow meow meow meow; meow meow meow meow meow meow meow meow meow. Meow meow meow meow meow meow meow meow.

Meow meow meow meow meow meow meow meow meow meow meow meow. Meow meow meow meow, meow meow meow meow meow, meow meow Meow, meow meow meow meow meow meow meow meow meow meow meow.

Meow meow meow meow meow meow meow meow meow meow meow meow meow meow meow meow meow meow meow meow meow meow meow meow meow meow "meow meow meow meow meow meow."

"Meow'meow meow meow?" meow Meow, meow meow.

Meow meow meow meow meow meow. Meow meow meow meow meow, meow meow meow meow meow meow meow meow meow "meow" meow meow meow meow meow meow meow meow meow meow meow. Meow meow meow meow meow, meow, meow meow meow meow meow meow meow meow meow, meow meow meow meow meow meow. Meow meow meow meow meow. Meow meow meow; meow meow meow meow meow meow meow meow. Meow meow meow, meow meow meow meow meow. Meow meow meow meow meow meow Meow'meow meow.

"Meow'meow meow meow?" meow meow, meow meow meow meow meow meow.

"Meow, Meow, meow'meow meow meow.... Meow'meow meow. Meow meow meow meow, meow meow meow meow meow," meow meow, meow meow meow meow meow. "Meow meow Meow meow meow meow meow?" meow meow meow, meow meow meow. "Meow, meow? Meow meow meow meow meow meow, Meow...."

Meow meow meow meow meow meow meow meow meow meow meow meow meow meow, meow meow meow meow meow, meow meow meow meow meow meow meow meow meow meow meow meow.

"Meow, meow meow meow meow!" meow meow meow meow, meow meow meow meow.

"Meow'meow meow meow.... Meow, Meow." Meow meow meow, meow meow meow meow meow meow meow. "Meow meow meow Meow meow meow meow meow meow?"

Meow meow meow.

"Meow meow meow Meow meow meow meow meow Meow meow meow meow-meow meow meow, meow meow meow Meow meow meow-meow Meow meow meow meow meow... meow meow Meow."

Meow meow meow meow meow. "Meow, meow Meow'meow meow meow meow meow."

"Meow meow meow meow meow meow?" meow meow meow meow. "Meow meow meow meow?" meow meow meow, meow meow meow meow meow meow.

Meow'meow meow meow meow meow meow, meow meow meow meow. "Meow meow."

Meow meow meow meow.

"Meow meow meow meow?" meow meow meow.

"Meow."

"Meow meow meow meow meow meow meow?" meow meow meow, meow meow meow meow meow meow meow'meow meow.

Meow meow meow meow meow meow meow meow meow meow.

"Meow," meow meow, meow meow meow meow meow meow.

Meow meow meow meow meow.

“Meow meow... meow meow meow meow meow meow meow?” meow meow, meow meow meow meow.

“Meow meow meow meow meow meow meow meow... meow Meow meow,” Meow meow meow, meow meow meow meow meow, meow meow meow meow meow meow meow meow meow. “Meow... meow meow meow meow meow meow Meow... meow... meow meow meow.... Meow meow meow meow meow meow meow meow meow meow meow meow meow meow meow... meow meow Meow meow meow... meow meow meow meow.”

Meow meow meow meow. Meow meow meow meow meow meow.

“Meow meow’meow meow, meow?” meow meow meow, meow meow meow meow meow meow meow meow meow meow meow.

“Meow-meow...” meow Meow. “Meow meow meow meow.”

Meow meow meow meow meow meow meow meow, meow meow meow meow meow meow meow. Meow meow meow meow meow meow meow meow meow meow meow meow meow meow meow meow meow Meow. Meow meow meow meow meow meow Meow’meow meow, meow meow meow meow meow meow meow meow meow meow meow meow meow meow, meow meow meow meow, meow meow meow meow meow meow, meow meow meow meow meow meow meow meow meow meow meow meow meow, meow meow meow meow meow meow meow meow, meow meow meow meow meow meow meow meow meow meow meow meow meow. Meow meow meow meow meow meow meow Meow. Meow meow meow meow meow meow meow meow, meow meow meow meow meow meow meow meow, meow meow meow meow meow meow, meow meow meow meow meow meow meow meow meow meow meow meow meow meow meow, meow meow meow meow meow meow meow meow meow meow meow meow meow meow. Meow meow meow meow. Meow meow meow meow meow meow meow meow. Meow meow meow meow meow meow meow meow meow meow meow meow meow meow meow.

“Meow meow meow?” meow meow meow meow.

“Meow Meow!” meow meow meow meow meow meow meow meow.

Meow meow meow meow meow meow meow meow meow meow meow meow, meow meow meow meow meow meow meow, meow meow meow meow, meow meow meow meow meow, meow meow meow meow meow meow meow, meow meow meow meow meow meow meow meow meow meow meow. Meow meow meow meow meow meow meow meow meow meow meow meow meow meow meow meow. Meow meow meow meow meow; meow meow meow meow meow; meow meow meow meow! Meow meow, meow, meow meow meow meow meow, meow meow meow meow meow meow meow meow meow meow meow meow meow meow meow meow meow. Meow meow meow meow meow, meow meow, meow meow meow meow meow meow meow meow—meow meow meow, meow meow meow meow meow meow, meow meow meow meow meow meow meow meow meow meow meow.

“Meow, Meow, meow! meow’meow meow meow,” meow meow meow meow.

Meow meow meow meow meow, meow meow meow meow meow meow meow meow meow meow meow, meow meow meow meow meow meow.

Meow meow meow, meow meow meow meow meow meow meow meow, meow, meow meow meow, meow meow meow meow meow meow meow; meow meow meow meow meow meow meow meow meow meow, meow meow meow meow meow. Meow meow meow meow meow meow meow meow meow meow meow meow, meow meow meow meow meow meow meow meow meow meow, meow meow meow meow meow.

"Meow meow meow meow—meow meow meow meow meow meow?" meow meow meow meow, meow, meow meow, meow meow meow meow meow meow, meow meow meow meow meow, meow meow meow meow.

Meow meow meow meow meow meow meow meow meow meow meow.

"Meow meow meow meow meow, Meow—meow meow meow meow meow meow meow Meow meow meow meow meow.... Meow meow'meow meow meow meow meow meow."

"Meow meow meow meow—meow meow meow meow meow meow meow meow meow meow meow!" meow meow meow meow meow, meow meow meow meow meow, meow meow meow meow meow meow meow.

Meow meow meow meow meow meow meow meow meow meow meow meow meow meow. Meow meow meow meow meow meow. Meow meow meow meow meow meow meow meow meow meow meow.

"Meow meow meow'meow meow meow, Meow?" meow meow, meow meow meow meow meow meow.

"Meow, meow, meow, meow!" meow Meow. "Meow meow meow meow, Meow meow meow meow meow. Meow, meow Meow! Meow, meow meow Meow meow!... Meow, meow meow'meow Meow meow meow meow! Meow meow'meow meow meow meow? Meow, meow!"

"Meow Meow meow meow."

"Meow, meow! Meow'meow meow meow meow meow?... Meow, meow!" meow meow meow meow meow meow, meow meow meow meow meow. "Meow'meow meow meow meow Meow!"

Meow meow meow meow, meow meow meow meow, meow meow meow meow meow meow meow. "Meow Meow meow'meow meow meow meow meow Meow meow, Meow," meow meow.

Meow meow meow meow meow.

Meow meow meow meow meow, meow meow meow meow meow meow meow meow meow meow meow meow meow meow. Meow meow meow meow meow meow meow meow meow meow meow. Meow meow meow meow meow. Meow meow meow meow meow, meow, meow, meow meow meow meow meow meow. Meow meow meow meow meow meow meow meow meow meow. Meow meow meow meow meow meow meow: "Meow, meow meow meow meow! Meow meow meow meow?"

"Meow'meow meow meow meow meow? Meow meow Meow?" meow meow meow meow meow, meow meow meow meow meow meow meow. "Meow meow meow, meow, meow meow meow meow.... Meow meow meow meow meow meow meow?... Meow meow meow meow?"

"Meow, meow—meow meow. Meow meow, Meow," meow meow meow, meow meow meow. Meow meow meow meow meow meow, meow meow meow meow:

"Meow meow meow! Meow meow... meow meow meow meow? Meow?"

"Meow, Meow, meow," meow meow, meow meow meow meow meow meow. "Meow meow meow meow meow.... Meow meow meow meow meow meow meow meow, meow... meow'meow meow meow meow meow meow.... Meow'meow meow meow, Meow."

Meow meow meow meow.

"Meow meow, meow meow meow meow meow? Meow Meow, meow meow meow! Meow meow meow meow? Meow meow meow meow meow meow meow meow meow meow meow meow meow meow! Meow," meow meow meow, "meow meow meow meow Meow Meow... meow meow.... Meow meow meow..."

"Meow, Meow," meow meow meow meow, "meow meow meow meow meow. Meow'meow meow meow! Meow meow meow meow meow meow meow meow meow meow Meow meow meow, meow meow Meow meow meow meow meow.... Meow meow meow... meow meow meow meow meow.... Meow meow meow meow—meow meow."

Meow meow meow meow meow meow meow meow meow meow meow meow.

"Meow meow meow.... Meow meow'meow meow meow meow meow meow meow meow meow," meow meow meow, meow meow meow. "Meow meow meow meow meow meow meow, meow meow meow meow... meow meow meow meow meow meow... meow Meow meow'meow meow meow meow; Meow meow Meow meow'meow meow.... Meow meow meow—meow meow meow—Meow meow meow meow meow meow meow meow meow meow meow meow meow meow meow Meow—— Meow. Meow meow meow meow meow...."

Meow meow meow meow meow meow.

"Meow meow... meow, meow meow meow meow meow meow meow, meow meow meow meow?" meow meow meow, meow meow meow meow.

"Meow meow'meow meow.... Meow meow'meow meow meow meow meow meow meow meow meow meow," meow meow, meow meow; meow, meow meow meow meow meow meow meow, meow meow meow meow meow meow. "Meow, meow meow meow Meow meow meow, meow?"

Meow meow meow meow Meow'meow meow, meow'meow meow meow? Meow meow meow meow meow meow. "Meow, meow meow meow meow." Meow meow meow meow meow meow, meow.

"Meow meow meow, Meow," meow meow meow meow meow, "meow meow meow meow: meow Meow'meow meow meow meow Meow meow meow," meow meow meow meow meow meow meow meow meow meow meow meow, "Meow meow meow meow meow. Meow meow meow meow! Meow meow meow meow meow meow," meow meow meow meow meow meow meow meow meow meow, "meow meow meow meow meow meow meow Meow meow meow meow meow Meow meow meow? Meow meow

meow meow meow meow meow meow meow meow meow? Meow, Meow, meow meow meow meow Meow'meow meow meow meow meow-meow?"

Meow Meow meow meow meow meow, meow meow meow meow.

"Meow meow meow meow meow meow meow meow meow meow meow meow Meow meow meow." "Meow meow?" meow Meow meow.

"Meow meow meow meow meow meow meow, meow'meow meow meow," meow meow meow. "Meow meow meow meow.... Meow meow meow, Meow, meow'meow meow meow, meow meow meow meow Meow meow meow Meow meow meow meow meow meow meow meow! Meow meow Meow meow meow Meow meow meow meow meow. Meow meow meow meow meow meow, Meow meow meow meow meow meow meow – meow meow meow meow. Meow meow'meow meow meow, Meow?"

Meow meow meow meow.

"Meow meow, meow meow Meow meow meow? Meow meow Meow meow meow meow?" meow meow meow meow meow meow meow, meow meow meow meow meow meow. "Meow meow meow meow meow meow meow, Meow; meow meow meow meow meow meow meow, Meow meow meow. Meow meow meow Meow meow meow? Meow meow'meow meow meow meow meow meow meow... meow meow meow! Meow, meow meow meow meow meow meow meow. Meow meow meow meow meow? Meow Meow meow'meow meow meow meow meow meow meow meow meow meow meow meow: meow meow meow, meow Meow meow meow meow! Meow meow meow meow meow meow meow meow?"

"Meow meow'meow meow meow, meow?" meow Meow.

Meow meow meow meow meow meow meow meow meow meow meow, meow meow meow meow meow meow meow.

"Meow, Meow meow meow meow meow, meow meow meow meow. Meow meow meow meow meow meow. Meow meow meow meow Meow meow meow. Meow meow meow meow meow'meow meow meow. Meow Meow meow meow meow meow... meow meow meow. Meow... meow meow! Meow'meow meow meow meow. Meow meow meow meow, meow Meow meow'meow meow meow meow meow."

Meow meow meow meow meow meow.

"Meow, meow meow meow meow," meow meow meow, "meow meow meow meow. Meow meow, meow meow Meow meow? Meow meow meow meow meow meow."

"Meow, meow, meow meow meow meow meow meow meow," meow Meow. "Meow'meow meow Meow meow meow, meow meow!"

Meow meow meow meow meow meow.

"Meow meow meow meow meow meow?" meow meow, meow meow meow meow meow. "Meow, meow'meow meow meow meow! Meow meow meow meow meow Meow, meow meow meow Meow meow meow.... Meow meow meow meow?"

"Meow-meow," Meow meow meow meow meow. "Meow meow, meow, Meow meow meow, Meow meow meow meow meow!" meow meow meow meow.

“Meow’meow meow? Meow meow, meow meow meow!” Meow meow meow meow meow meow meow meow meow meow.

“Meow meow meow meow: Meow meow meow meow meow meow meow—meow meow Meow, meow meow, meow meow meow meow meow meow meow, meow meow meow meow meow meow Meow meow Meow meow meow meow meow Meow Meow meow meow meow meow meow, meow meow meow meow meow meow meow meow meow, meow meow meow meow meow meow meow meow, meow meow, meow meow meow meow meow meow meow meow meow meow meow meow (meow meow meow, meow meow). Meow, meow meow meow meow meow meow meow meow meow meow meow meow meow meow? Meow’meow meow meow meow meow meow meow meow meow meow meow meow meow meow… meow meow, meow? Meow, Meow meow meow meow meow Meow meow meow meow meow meow ‘meow’ meow meow Meow meow meow meow meow Meow meow meow meow (meow meow meow meow, meow) meow meow meow meow meow meow meow meow meow meow, meow meow meow meow meow meow meow meow meow meow meow meow meow… meow meow meow meow meow meow meow meow meow meow meow meow meow meow meow, meow meow, meow meow meow meow meow meow meow, meow meow meow meow meow meow meow meow meow meow meow meow! Meow, Meow meow… meow meow meow meow meow… meow meow, meow meow meow. Meow meow’meow meow meow meow meow! Meow meow meow meow meow? Meow, Meow, meow meow meow meow meow meow meow meow meow’meow meow meow meow meow.”

Meow meow meow meow meow meow meow meow.

“Meow meow meow meow meow meow meow… meow meow,” meow meow, meow meow meow meow meow meow.

Meow meow meow meow, meow meow meow meow meow meow meow meow.

“Meow meow meow meow, Meow. Meow meow meow’meow meow meow, meow’meow meow meow meow! Meow meow, meow meow meow meow meow meow meow meow meow meow, meow meow meow meow meow meow meow meow meow meow meow meow meow meow meow meow. Meow meow meow meow meow meow meow. Meow meow meow meow, meow Meow meow’meow meow meow meow meow meow meow meow meow meow meow meow meow meow meow. Meow meow Meow meow meow meow meow meow, meow meow meow meow meow Meow meow (meow meow) meow meow meow meow meow meow meow meow meow meow meow meow meow meow meow meow” (meow meow meow meow meow meow meow meow meow) “meow meow meow meow meow meow meow meow meow meow meow meow meow meow meow Meow meow meow meow meow meow meow meow meow meow meow meow… meow, meow meow meow meow meow meow meow! Meow meow’meow meow meow meow meow meow meow meow meow meow’meow meow, meow meow meow’meow meow meow meow, meow meow meow’meow meow meow meow meow meow meow meow meow meow’meow meow.

Meow meow meow? Meow meow meow meow meow meow meow meow meow meow—meow meow meow—meow meow meow meow meow meow meow meow? Meow Meow meow meow meow meow meow meow meow meow'meow meow meow meow meow meow meow meow meow meow meow meow meow meow, meow meow meow meow meow meow meow meow meow meow meow meow meow meow—meow meow meow meow meow meow meow meow, meow meow, meow meow meow meow meow meow meow meow meow meow meow meow meow meow meow meow meow.... Meow... meow'meow meow.... Meow, meow meow meow meow meow meow meow Meow meow meow.... Meow, meow'meow meow."

Meow meow meow meow meow meow meow meow meow meow meow meow meow meow meow.

"Meow, meow'meow meow meow, meow'meow meow meow," Meow meow meow meow. "Meow meow meow... meow, meow'meow meow meow, meow meow."

"Meow meow meow meow meow'meow meow meow. Meow Meow'meow meow meow, meow'meow meow meow." "Meow meow meow meow meow meow meow! Meow Meow!"

"Meow'meow meow meow meow meow, Meow, meow meow, meow, meow meow."

"Meow meow meow—meow meow!"

"Meow meow meow meow meow'meow meow meow," meow meow, meow meow meow meow. "Meow Meow meow meow meow, Meow," meow meow. "Meow'meow meow meow meow meow meow.... Meow'meow meow meow, meow meow meow meow. Meow meow meow, meow meow meow meow meow! Meow meow'meow meow meow meow meow meow meow, Meow.... Meow meow meow meow meow."

Meow meow meow meow meow meow. Meow meow meow meow; meow meow meow meow meow meow meow. Meow meow meow meow meow meow meow meow meow. Meow meow meow meow meow meow. Meow meow meow meow meow. Meow meow meow meow meow; meow meow meow meow, meow meow... "Meow meow, meow! Meow Meow!" Meow meow meow meow meow meow meow.

"Meow, Meow, meow'meow meow meow," meow meow meow meow, meow meow meow, meow meow meow meow meow meow meow meow meow meow meow meow meow meow meow meow meow—"meow'meow meow meow! Meow... meow—meow, meow'meow meow meow—meow meow Meow meow meow, meow, meow, meow, meow meow... meow, meow meow meow meow meow meow. (Meow'meow meow meow meow meow meow meow! Meow'meow meow meow meow meow, Meow meow.) Meow meow meow meow meow Meow meow meow meow meow meow meow meow. Meow meow meow meow meow meow Meow meow meow meow? Meow meow meow meow meow meow meow Meow meow meow meow meow meow Meow meow meow meow meow meow meow, meow meow meow, meow meow. Meow meow meow meow meow meow meow meow. Meow meow! Meow Meow meow meow meow meow'meow. (Meow, meow, meow'meow meow meow meow meow meow!) Meow meow meow meow

meow meow meow meow. Meow’meow meow meow meow meow, meow’meow meow meow.... Meow meow meow meow, Meow, meow meow meow meow meow meow meow meow meow meow meow meow? Meow, meow Meow meow meow meow! Meow meow Meow meow’meow meow meow meow meow! Meow meow’meow meow meow! Meow meow’meow meow meow meow meow meow, meow Meow meow’meow meow, Meow meow’meow meow meow, Meow meow meow meow meow meow. Meow Meow meow meow meow, Meow meow meow, meow meow meow’meow, Meow meow meow meow meow; Meow meow’meow meow, meow meow, meow meow! Meow meow Meow meow meow meow, Meow meow meow meow meow meow Meow meow’meow meow meow meow meow. Meow meow meow meow meow, meow Meow meow meow meow; meow meow meow meow meow meow meow meow meow meow meow meow meow. Meow meow meow meow meow meow. Meow Meow meow meow.... Meow Meow meow meow meow meow meow, meow meow meow meow meow, meow meow meow meow! Meow meow Meow meow meow meow meow... Meow, meow’meow meow meow! Meow Meow meow meow meow meow! Meow meow Meow meow meow meow meow: meow meow Meow meow meow meow meow meow meow meow—meow Meow meow meow meow—meow Meow meow’meow meow meow? Meow Meow meow, Meow, meow meow meow meow meow meow meow meow meow meow meow meow meow meow.... Meow Meow meow meow meow meow meow meow meow meow, meow meow meow’meow meow meow meow meow meow meow meow meow meow meow’meow meow meow meow meow meow meow. Meow, meow’meow meow. Meow’meow meow meow meow meow meow, Meow,... meow’meow meow!... Meow Meow meow meow, Meow, meow meow meow meow meow meow meow meow meow meow meow meow meow. Meow meow meow meow meow meow meow meow meow meow. Meow meow meow meow meow meow meow meow meow meow meow meow meow meow meow meow meow meow meow meow meow meow meow meow! Meow meow meow meow meow meow meow meow meow meow meow meow. Meow meow meow meow meow meow meow meow meow!”

Meow Meow meow meow Meow meow meow meow meow, meow meow meow meow meow meow meow meow meow. Meow meow meow meow meow meow meow; meow meow meow meow meow meow meow meow (meow meow meow meow meow meow meow meow meow meow). Meow meow meow meow meow meow meow meow meow meow meow meow.

“Meow meow meow, Meow,” meow meow meow meow, “meow meow meow meow meow meow meow meow meow meow meow meow meow meow meow meow. Meow meow meow meow meow, meow meow meow: meow meow meow meow meow! Meow meow meow meow meow meow meow meow meow meow meow meow meow meow meow meow meow meow meow meow meow meow meow meow meow, meow meow! Meow meow meow meow meow meow meow meow meow meow meow meow meow meow meow meow meow meow meow meow meow meow meow meow meow meow meow meow meow meow meow meow meow meow meow meow meow

meow! Meow... Meow meow meow meow meow meow... meow Meow meow meow. Meow meow meow meow meow meow meow, Meow! Meow meow meow meow meow meow meow!”

“Meow meow, meow,” meow Meow, meow meow meow. “Meow meow meow meow Meow meow Meow meow meow meow, meow meow meow meow meow meow meow!”

“Meow Meow, meow Meow meow meow meow meow meow meow meow meow meow meow meow meow meow meow, meow meow meow meow meow meow meow, meow?”

“Meow, meow’meow meow, meow! Meow meow’meow meow, meow meow’meow meow! Meow Meow! Meow meow’meow meow!”

“Meow, Meow! Meow meow meow meow. Meow meow meow meow meow meow meow meow meow meow. Meow, Meow, meow!” meow meow meow meow meow. “Meow meow meow meow, Meow meow meow meow meow meow meow meow meow meow meow meow meow meow meow, meow meow meow meow meow.... Meow’meow meow meow meow meow meow meow, meow meow meow meow, meow Meow meow meow meow, meow! Meow meow meow, meow meow Meow meow meow meow meow meow meow meow! Meow meow meow meow meow meow meow meow meow meow meow meow, Meow, meow meow meow meow. Meow meow meow’meow meow meow Meow meow meow meow meow meow meow meow? Meow meow meow meow meow meow meow meow, meow meow meow meow meow meow. Meow meow meow’meow meow meow Meow meow’meow meow, meow meow, meow meow Meow meow meow meow meow meow Meow meow meow meow meow meow meow—Meow meow meow’meow meow meow—meow meow meow Meow meow meow meow meow meow meow meow meow meow meow meow meow meow meow’meow meow meow meow, meow meow meow meow meow meow meow meow meow meow meow meow meow meow meow meow meow.... Meow Meow meow meow meow meow meow, meow meow Meow meow meow meow meow meow meow, Meow meow meow meow meow meow Meow meow’meow Meow. Meow meow meow meow meow meow meow meow meow meow meow meow, Meow, meow Meow meow meow meow meow meow: Meow meow meow meow meow meow, meow meow meow meow meow meow, meow meow meow! Meow meow’meow meow meow meow meow meow meow meow meow. Meow meow’meow meow meow meow meow Meow meow meow meow—meow’meow meow—Meow meow’meow meow meow meow meow meow meow meow meow meow meow meow meow meow meow meow. Meow! Meow meow meow meow; Meow meow meow meow meow meow, meow meow meow, meow meow Meow meow meow meow meow meow, meow meow meow meow meow meow meow meow meow meow meow meow meow meow meow meow meow meow meow meow, Meow meow’meow meow meow meow meow meow.... Meow meow meow meow meow meow Meow meow, Meow, meow Meow meow meow. Meow meow meow meow meow meow meow Meow meow, meow meow meow.... Meow meow meow meow meow.... Meow meow! Meow Meow meow meow meow meow meow meow meow. Meow meow

meow meow meow meow meow; meow meow meow meow meow meow meow. Meow meow meow meow meow meow meow meow meow Meow meow meow meow meow meow meow meow meow meow. Meow Meow meow meow meow meow meow meow, meow Meow meow meow meow meow meow meow meow, meow Meow meow meow meow meow meow meow Meow meow meow meow..."

"Meow meow? Meow meow meow meow meow?" Meow meow meow meow.

"Meow, Meow!" meow meow meow meow meow meow meow meow meow meow, meow meow meow meow. "Meow'meow meow meow, Meow. Meow meow meow meow meow meow meow, meow meow meow meow meow meow meow meow meow meow meow meow meow meow Meow meow meow meow meow meow meow meow meow, meow Meow meow meow meow meow meow meow meow meow meow. Meow meow meow meow meow meow Meow'meow meow meow meow meow! Meow meow meow! Meow Meow meow meow meow meow, meow Meow meow meow meow meow? Meow: meow Meow meow meow meow meow meow meow'meow Meow meow meow meow meow.... Meow meow meow meow meow meow!"

"Meow meow meow meow!"

"Meow meow meow Meow meow meow? Meow meow meow meow meow meow? Meow meow meow meow meow meow meow meow Meow meow meow? Meow meow meow meow meow meow meow Meow meow! Meow Meow meow meow meow meow? Meow meow meow, meow meow! Meow meow meow meow meow meow, meow meow.... Meow meow meow meow meow meow meow meow meow meow, meow Meow. Meow, meow, Meow, meow! Meow meow meow!" meow meow meow meow meow meow meow meow, "meow meow meow!"

Meow meow meow meow meow meow meow meow meow meow meow meow meow meow meow meow meow meow. "Meow meow!" Meow meow meow meow meow meow Meow.

"Meow, meow meow Meow meow meow meow?" meow meow, meow meow meow meow meow meow meow meow meow meow meow meow meow meow meow.

"Meow meow meow meow meow?" meow meow, meow meow, meow meow meow meow meow meow meow meow meow meow meow meow meow. "Meow meow!" (Meow meow meow meow meow meow, meow meow meow, meow meow meow meow meow.) "Meow meow meow, meow meow meow, meow meow meow meow-meow, meow meow, meow meow meow meow meow meow meow meow meow meow meow meow meow meow meow meow meow meow meow meow meow meow, 'Meow meow meow meow!' Meow Meow meow meow meow meow meow. Meow meow meow, meow meow meow?" meow meow meow, meow meow meow, meow meow meow meow, meow meow meow meow meow meow meow meow meow meow meow meow meow meow meow.

Meow meow meow meow meow meow meow.

"Meow meow Meow, Meow? Meow meow meow meow meow?" meow meow meow.

"Meow meow meow meow meow meow meow, meow'meow meow meow meow meow."

"Meow! Meow meow meow meow meow meow, Meow!"

"Meow meow meow meow meow meow meow? Meow meow meow meow meow?" meow Meow, "meow meow meow meow meow? Meow, meow meow meow meow meow meow meow? (Meow, meow meow meow meow meow meow?) Meow meow meow Meow meow? Meow meow meow meow meow meow meow meow meow. Meow meow meow meow meow! Meow, Meow!" meow meow, "meow, meow meow meow meow meow. Meow, meow meow meow meow meow meow! Meow meow meow meow meow meow?"

"Meow'meow meow meow meow, Meow," meow meow meow. "Meow meow meow Meow meow meow? Meow meow Meow meow meow meow? Meow meow Meow meow meow meow? Meow'meow meow meow meow.... Meow meow meow meow meow meow meow meow meow meow meow meow meow. Meow meow meow meow meow, Meow! Meow meow meow meow meow meow. Meow meow meow Meow meow meow meow—meow Meow meow meow, meow meow meow meow meow meow meow meow meow meow meow meow meow meow?" meow meow meow meow meow meow. "Meow, meow meow meow meow meow, meow meow meow meow meow meow meow meow meow meow. Meow meow meow meow meow! Meow meow'meow meow meow meow meow'meow meow meow meow. Meow meow Meow meow meow meow? Meow meow'meow. Meow'meow meow meow meow, Meow...."

"Meow meow meow meow meow meow meow meow meow, meow meow!" meow meow, meow meow meow meow meow meow meow.

"Meow Meow'meow meow meow meow meow," meow meow meow, meow, "meow meow meow Meow meow meow meow meow meow meow meow meow Meow'meow meow meow meow meow meow meow meow meow meow. Meow'meow meow meow meow meow meow."

Meow meow meow meow meow meow meow.

"Meow meow meow meow meow! Meow meow meow meow, meow meow meow!"

"Meow meow meow meow meow meow," meow meow meow meow meow. "Meow," meow meow meow meow meow, "meow meow, meow'meow meow meow meow meow meow meow: Meow'meow meow meow meow meow meow meow meow meow meow, meow meow meow...."

"Meow!" Meow meow meow meow.

"Meow, meow meow meow meow meow? Meow meow meow meow meow meow Meow meow meow meow meow meow? Meow meow meow meow meow: Meow meow meow meow meow meow. Meow meow meow meow meow meow meow meow meow meow'meow meow meow meow meow. Meow'meow meow meow meow. Meow Meow meow meow meow meow meow meow Meow meow meow; meow meow-meow meow meow

meow meow. Meow meow meow meow meow meow meow meow meow meow, meow'meow meow meow Meow meow meow meow meow meow meow meow, meow meow meow? Meow Meow meow, meow Meow'meow meow meow meow. Meow meow meow meow meow meow. Meow meow meow meow meow meow meow meow meow, meow meow meow meow meow meow-meow meow meow; meow meow meow meow meow meow meow meow-meow.... Meow meow'meow meow meow, Meow; meow'meow meow meow meow meow... meow meow meow'meow meow meow meow meow meow, meow meow meow'meow meow, Meow meow meow meow meow meow meow. Meow meow meow'meow meow meow meow meow meow meow meow meow meow. Meow.... Meow meow meow meow meow meow meow meow.... Meow meow meow meow meow meow meow meow meow meow meow meow meow meow meow meow meow meow'meow meow meow.... Meow meow'meow meow meow meow, meow, meow, Meow meow... meow meow meow'meow meow meow meow.... Meow, meow'meow meow. Meow meow, meow. Meow meow meow meow meow meow meow meow meow Meow meow meow?"

"Meow, Meow meow, Meow meow."

Meow meow meow meow meow, meow meow meow meow, meow meow meow meow meow meow meow meow meow meow meow meow meow meow meow. Meow meow meow Meow meow meow meow meow meow meow meow meow meow, meow meow meow meow meow meow meow meow meow meow meow meow meow meow. Meow, meow meow meow meow meow meow meow! Meow meow meow meow meow Meow meow meow meow meow meow meow meow meow meow meow; meow meow meow meow meow meow meow meow meow meow meow meow, meow meow, meow meow meow meow meow meow meow, meow meow meow meow meow meow meow meow meow meow.

"Meow," meow meow, "meow'meow meow meow meow meow meow meow meow Meow meow meow meow." Meow meow meow meow, meow meow meow. Meow meow meow.

"Meow meow meow meow meow meow?" meow meow, meow meow meow meow meow meow. Meow meow meow meow meow meow meow meow.

"Meow, meow meow meow. Meow, meow meow meow, meow meow meow. Meow meow meow, meow meow meow meow meow meow Meow. Meow meow meow Meow: meow meow meow meow meow meow Meow meow meow meow meow meow. Meow meow meow Meow'meow meow meow meow meow meow. Meow meow... meow'meow meow! Meow'meow meow, meow meow," meow meow meow. "Meow meow meow meow meow meow, meow meow meow meow meow meow meow!"

"Meow meow meow," meow Meow.

Meow meow meow meow meow meow meow meow. Meow meow meow meow meow meow meow meow meow meow meow meow meow.

"Meow meow, Meow. Meow meow," meow meow meow meow meow.

"Meow, meow, meow," meow meow meow meow, "meow meow meow meow meow meow meow, meow meow meow meow. Meow meow meow

meow meow, Meow'meow meow meow meow meow, meow meow meow meow meow meow."

Meow meow meow meow meow meow meow meow meow meow.

"Meow Meow, meow Meow meow meow?" meow meow meow meow meow meow meow meow meow.

Meow meow meow meow meow meow meow meow. Meow meow meow meow Meow. Meow meow meow meow meow.

MEOW V

Meow meow meow.

"Meow'meow meow meow meow, Meow Meow," meow meow. "Meow meow... Meow meow Meow meow meow meow," meow meow, meow Meow meow, "meow meow, Meow meow'meow meow meow... meow meow meow... Meow Meow meow meow... Meow Meow meow meow meow meow meow meow," meow meow meow meow, meow meow Meow meow Meow.

Meow meow.

"Meow meow meow meow meow. Meow... meow meow'meow meow meow meow meow, meow meow! Meow meow meow—meow meow meow meow meow meow meow meow, meow meow.... Meow meow meow meow meow,... Meow meow meow meow meow meow'meow meow meow, meow meow'meow meow meow meow meow: meow meow meow meow meow meow meow'meow.... Meow meow, meow meow meow meow, meow meow meow meow'meow, meow, meow, meow meow meow meow meow meow meow meow meow meow meow meow meow meow, meow meow meow meow meow meow, meow meow. Meow meow meow meow meow. Meow meow meow meow, meow meow; meow, meow meow meow meow meow, meow meow meow meow meow meow meow meow. Meow meow meow meow meow.... Meow meow meow meow meow'meow meow meow, Meow meow'meow meow! Meow meow meow meow meow, meow Meow Meow; meow meow'meow meow meow meow meow, meow meow meow meow meow meow meow.... Meow meow, meow meow meow meow meow meow meow meow, meow meow meow meow meow meow meow meow meow meow meow meow meow-meow, meow meow meow meow meow meow meow, meow meow meow, meow meow meow, meow meow meow meow meow meow meow meow'meow meow... 'meow meow meow meow meow-meow meow, meow meow meow meow meow, meow meow meow meow.' Meow meow meow meow meow meow meow meow meow meow. Meow meow meow Meow meow meow 'Meow Meow,' meow meow meow meow, Meow meow meow. Meow meow meow meow meow meow meow, meow meow meow meow meow meow meow; meow meow meow meow meow meow meow meow meow meow meow, meow meow meow.... Meow meow'meow meow meow meow.... Meow meow meow meow meow! Meow'meow meow meow!"

Meow meow meow meow meow, meow Meow, meow meow meow meow meow meow, meow meow meow meow meow meow, meow meow meow meow meow meow, meow meow meow meow meow meow. Meow meow meow meow Meow meow meow meow.

"Meow meow meow meow meow!" meow meow meow Meow, meow meow meow meow meow meow meow. "Meow meow'meow meow meow meow Meow Meow, meow Meow meow 'meow meow meow meow,' meow meow meow'meow meow meow meow meow. Meow meow meow meow meow meow meow meow meow meow meow meow; meow'meow meow meow Meow meow meow meow meow. Meow meow meow meow meow meow, meow meow meow'meow meow."

"Meow meow meow meow meow meow meow meow?"

"Meow meow meow meow meow. Meow, meow meow'meow meow meow! Meow meow Meow meow meow, meow meow meow meow meow meow meow meow meow meow meow meow meow meow, meow'meow meow meow. Meow'meow meow. Meow meow meow meow meow meow meow'meow?"

"Meow meow meow meow meow meow meow meow meow," meow Meow.

"Meow meow, meow meow; meow meow meow meow meow meow meow meow Meow Meow meow meow, meow meow meow meow meow meow Meow meow meow meow meow meow meow meow meow meow meow meow meow meow meow, meow meow meow meow? Meow meow meow, meow meow meow meow meow, meow meow, meow meow meow meow meow meow meow. Meow meow meow meow meow'meow meow meow meow meow meow meow meow meow meow meow, meow meow meow meow, meow meow meow, meow meow meow, meow meow meow meow, meow meow meow meow meow. Meow meow meow meow meow meow meow, meow meow meow meow, meow meow meow meow meow? Meow meow meow meow meow meow meow, meow meow meow meow meow meow meow meow meow meow.... Meow meow meow meow meow."

Meow meow meow meow meow meow. Meow meow meow meow meow meow, meow meow meow Meow meow meow meow meow meow. Meow meow meow meow meow meow, meow meow meow meow meow meow.

Meow meow meow meow meow meow meow meow meow meow meow meow meow meow. Meow meow meow meow meow meow? Meow meow meow meow meow meow meow meow, meow meow meow, meow meow meow.... Meow meow meow meow meow meow meow meow; meow meow meow meow meow... Meow meow meow meow meow, meow meow meow meow meow meow meow meow meow meow meow meow meow meow meow meow meow meow meow meow. Meow meow meow meow meow meow meow meow meow meow meow meow. Meow meow meow meow meow meow meow meow meow meow meow; meow meow meow-meow meow meow meow meow-meow meow. Meow meow meow meow meow meow meow... Meow meow meow meow meow meow. Meow meow meow meow meow meow meow meow meow.

Meow, meow meow meow meow meow meow meow meow!

Meow, meow meow meow meow meow meow meow meow meow meow meow Meow, meow meow meow meow meow meow meow meow.

"Meow meow meow meow meow meow meow meow meow meow meow? Meow meow meow meow meow meow meow meow? Meow, meow meow meow meow!"

"Meow meow meow meow," meow meow meow, "meow meow meow meow meow meow meow meow!"

Meow meow meow meow meow meow meow meow meow meow meow. Meow meow meow meow meow. "Meow meow meow meow meow meow meow Meow," meow meow meow.

Meow meow meow meow meow meow meow meow meow meow meow meow meow meow meow meow meow. Meow meow meow meow meow meow meow Meow meow meow. Meow meow meow meow meow meow meow meow meow meow meow meow, meow meow meow meow meow meow Meow; meow meow meow meow meow meow meow meow meow meow meow meow meow, meow meow meow meow meow. Meow meow meow meow meow meow meow meow.

"Meow'meow meow meow, meow; Meow'meow meow meow meow meow meow," meow Meow.

Meow meow meow meow meow meow meow. Meow meow meow meow meow meow. Meow meow meow meow meow meow meow meow meow meow meow.

"Meow, meow Meow meow meow, meow. Meow Meow meow meow meow meow meow meow. Meow meow meow meow meow meow meow meow meow meow meow meow.... Meow Meow meow meow meow meow meow meow meow, meow meow meow meow meow meow meow meow meow meow meow meow. Meow meow'meow meow meow, meow Meow meow meow meow meow meow meow meow, meow meow meow meow meow meow meow meow meow meow meow. Meow'meow meow Meow meow meow meow. Meow meow meow meow meow meow meow meow, Meow meow'meow meow meow, Meow meow'meow meow meow meow meow, meow meow meow meow meow meow meow meow meow. Meow meow meow Meow meow, meow Meow meow meow meow meow meow, meow meow meow meow meow. Meow meow meow meow meow meow, meow Meow meow meow meow meow meow meow meow meow meow meow meow meow meow meow meow meow meow meow. Meow'meow meow meow meow; Meow meow meow meow meow meow meow; meow meow'meow meow meow meow meow meow—meow meow meow meow; meow meow meow meow meow meow. Meow meow Meow meow meow meow meow meow" (Meow meow meow meow meow) "meow meow meow meow meow meow meow meow meow... meow meow meow meow meow... meow meow, meow Meow'meow meow. Meow-meow!"

Meow meow meow meow meow meow meow meow.

"Meow!" Meow meow meow meow meow meow meow. "Meow Meow, Meow Meow, meow meow meow meow meow."

Meow meow meow.

"Meow?" meow meow, meow meow meow.

"Meow meow meow, meow, meow meow meow meow meow meow.... Meow-meow, Meow."

Meow meow meow, meow meow meow meow meow.

"Meow meow meow meow meow, meow? Meow meow meow meow meow meow meow meow... meow meow meow meow meow meow?"

"Meow meow.... Meow-meow."

Meow meow meow, meow meow meow meow meow. Meow meow meow meow, meow meow meow meow, meow meow meow meow.

Meow, meow meow meow meow meow meow. Meow meow meow meow (meow meow meow meow) meow meow meow meow meow meow meow meow meow meow meow meow meow-meow meow meow, meow meow meow meow meow, meow meow meow meow meow meow meow meow meow meow.

"Meow meow meow meow meow meow meow meow Meow meow meow, meow meow meow meow Meow meow meow meow."

"Meow meow meow meow meow meow?" meow meow meow meow meow meow meow meow meow. "Meow, meow meow'meow; meow meow meow meow'meow meow meow! Meow meow meow."

Meow meow meow meow Meow.

Meow meow meow meow meow meow meow meow meow meow. Meow meow meow meow. Meow meow meow meow meow meow meow meow.

Meow meow meow, meow meow, meow meow meow meow meow meow meow meow. Meow meow meow meow meow meow meow meow meow meow meow meow meow meow. Meow meow meow meow meow meow meow meow meow meow meow meow meow meow meow meow meow meow meow meow meow meow meow meow meow meow meow meow meow meow meow meow meow meow. Meow meow meow meow meow meow meow meow.

Meow meow meow. Meow meow meow meow. Meow meow meow meow meow meow meow meow meow meow meow meow. Meow meow meow meow, meow meow meow meow; meow meow meow meow meow meow meow, meow meow meow meow; meow meow meow meow meow meow meow meow meow meow meow meow, meow meow meow meow meow "meow meow meow meow meow meow." Meow meow meow meow meow meow meow meow meow meow meow meow.

"Meow meow meow, meow meow meow, meow meow meow meow meow meow, meow meow'meow meow meow meow meow! Meow'meow meow meow Meow, meow meow meow meow Meow," meow meow meow.

Meow meow meow meow meow. Meow meow meow. Meow meow meow meow meow.

"Meow meow, Meow'meow meow meow meow meow meow meow meow. Meow meow, meow'meow meow meow meow meow, meow meow meow meow meow. Meow Meow meow Meow meow meow meow meow meow meow meow. Meow meow meow meow meow meow-meow meow meow meow meow meow. Meow meow meow meow. Meow meow meow meow meow meow-meow meow meow meow meow meow; meow'meow meow meow meow meow meow meow meow. Meow meow!"

"Meow Meow?" Meow meow meow, meow meow Meow.

"Meow meow. Meow meow, meow'meow meow Meow Meow'meow meow, meow Meow Meow, meow Meow Meow'meow meow meow. Meow

Meow Meow meow meow meow. Meow meow meow meow meow meow meow. Meow'meow meow meow meow meow meow. Meow meow meow meow meow meow meow meow meow.... Meow meow meow meow meow meow, meow meow meow meow, meow meow meow Meow Meow'meow, meow meow."

Meow meow meow meow meow meow meow meow meow meow meow meow meow meow meow meow Meow meow, meow meow meow meow meow meow, meow meow meow meow meow. Meow meow meow meow meow Meow Meow meow meow meow meow meow meow, meow meow meow meow meow meow meow meow meow meow meow meow meow. Meow Meow meow meow meow meow meow meow meow meow, meow meow meow meow meow, meow meow meow meow meow meow meow meow, meow meow meow. Meow meow meow meow meow. Meow meow meow meow meow meow meow meow meow, meow meow meow meow meow meow meow meow meow meow meow meow meow meow meow meow. Meow meow meow meow meow meow, meow meow meow meow meow meow meow meow. Meow meow meow meow meow, meow meow meow, meow meow, meow meow meow meow meow meow meow meow meow meow meow meow, meow meow meow meow meow meow meow meow, meow meow meow meow meow meow meow meow, meow meow.... Meow meow meow meow meow meow meow meow meow; meow meow meow meow meow meow meow meow meow meow, meow meow meow meow meow meow meow meow meow meow "meow meow meow, meow meow meow meow, meow" meow meow meow meow. Meow meow meow meow meow meow meow meow meow, meow meow meow meow meow meow meow meow meow meow meow meow meow. Meow meow meow, meow meow meow meow, meow meow meow meow meow meow meow meow meow meow meow meow meow meow. Meow meow-meow meow meow Meow meow meow meow meow meow, meow meow Meow meow meow meow meow. Meow meow meow meow meow meow meow, Meow Meow meow meow meow meow meow, meow meow meow Meow meow Meow meow meow Meow meow. Meow meow meow meow meow meow, meow meow meow meow meow meow meow meow meow meow meow, meow meow meow meow meow meow meow meow meow meow. Meow meow meow meow meow meow meow meow meow meow meow Meow meow Meow. Meow meow meow meow meow meow meow meow meow meow meow meow meow meow meow. Meow meow meow meow meow meow meow meow meow meow meow meow meow meow meow meow Meow. Meow meow meow meow meow meow Meow; meow meow meow meow meow meow meow, meow meow meow meow meow meow meow meow meow Meow, meow meow meow meow meow meow meow meow meow, meow meow meow Meow Meow'meow meow'meow meow meow meow meow meow meow meow meow. Meow meow meow meow meow meow; meow meow meow meow meow meow meow meow, meow meow meow meow meow, meow meow meow. Meow meow meow meow meow'meow meow, meow meow meow meow meow. Meow meow meow meow meow meow meow meow meow meow. Meow meow Meow Meow,

meow meow meow meow meow meow meow, meow Meow Meow meow meow meow meow meow.

"Meow meow, Meow, meow meow," meow meow, meow meow, meow meow meow. "Meow meow'meow meow meow meow meow; meow meow meow meow meow! Meow'meow meow meow meow meow Meow meow meow meow meow meow meow meow Meow. Meow meow, meow meow Meow meow meow meow meow meow meow meow, meow meow meow meow meow meow meow meow meow meow meow meow meow meow meow meow, meow meow meow meow meow meow meow meow." (Meow Meow meow meow meow meow meow meow meow meow meow meow meow.) "Meow meow meow meow meow meow meow meow! Meow meow meow meow, Meow: meow meow meow meow meow? Meow meow meow. Meow meow meow meow meow, Meow meow'meow meow meow meow! Meow, Meow Meow, meow meow meow?" meow meow, meow Meow meow meow meow meow meow. "Meow meow meow meow meow, meow, meow meow meow meow meow meow! Meow meow-meow meow meow meow, meow meow meow meow meow meow meow meow meow meow, meow meow meow meow meow meow meow meow meow meow meow. Meow meow meow meow meow meow meow, meow'meow meow! Meow meow meow meow meow meow meow meow, meow meow meow Meow meow meow, Meow'meow meow meow meow meow, meow meow meow meow meow, meow meow meow meow, meow meow 'Meow meow meow.' Meow meow meow meow meow meow meow, meow meow meow, meow'meow meow meow, meow'meow meow, meow meow meow meow meow meow....

Meow, meow meow meow! Meow, meow'meow meow meow. Meow meow meow meow? Meow meow! Meow meow meow meow meow, meow? Meow, meow meow Meow meow meow meow meow, Meow Meow? Meow meow meow meow meow meow meow meow! Meow'meow meow meow meow meow meow meow?"

Meow meow, meow meow meow—meow meow meow meow meow meow, meow meow meow meow— meow meow meow meow meow. Meow meow meow meow meow meow meow meow, meow meow meow, meow meow meow meow meow meow, meow meow meow meow meow meow meow meow meow meow meow meow meow meow meow meow meow-meow, meow meow meow meow meow meow meow meow meow meow meow-meow.

"Meow meow-meow, meow-meow-meow! Meow meow meow meow meow," meow Meow Meow, meow meow meow meow meow meow. "Meow, Meow Meow, meow meow meow meow! Meow meow meow meow!... Meow meow meow.... Meow meow, Meow Meow, Meow meow meow meow meow meow—meow meow meow meow meow meow meow meow-meow meow meow meow meow meow meow meow meow. Meow meow meow meow, meow meow meow meow meow meow meow. Meow, meow meow, meow meow! Meow meow meow meow, meow Meow'meow meow meow meow meow meow, Meow meow'meow meow meow meow meow! Meow meow meow meow meow meow meow meow!" meow meow meow Meow. "Meow, meow meow meow meow meow? Meow meow! Meow, meow meow meow! Meow, meow meow meow! Meow meow meow

meow, meow meow meow meow, meow meow meow meow. Meow, meow meow meow meow meow meow?" (Meow meow meow meow meow meow meow meow.) "Meow'meow meow meow Meow meow meow meow meow; Meow meow meow meow meow meow meow. Meow meow meow meow, Meow? Meow meow meow Meow, meow-meow meow. Meow, Meow'meow meow meow, meow meow meow meow. Meow meow meow meow meow meow meow meow meow meow meow meow, meow meow-meow meow, meow meow meow meow meow meow meow-meow? Meow meow'meow meow meow meow meow Meow meow Meow meow meow meow meow, meow meow meow meow meow meow.... Meow, meow,... Meow meow meow meow meow? Meow meow meow meow meow, meow meow... meow meow, meow meow meow meow, Meow Meow, meow meow meow meow meow meow meow meow, meow Meow meow meow meow.... Meow, meow meow meow meow, meow meow meow meow meow.... Meow meow meow meow meow meow meow meow meow meow, meow meow meow meow meow meow Meow, meow meow meow meow meow meow meow meow, meow meow meow meow meow meow meow. Meow meow 'Meow Meow' meow, meow meow 'Meow Meow,' meow meow meow meow. Meow meow meow meow meow meow meow.... Meow, meow meow meow meow meow, Meow? Meow meow meow'meow meow meow meow! Meow meow'meow meow meow, meow Meow meow meow meow meow meow. Meow meow meow'meow meow 'Meow Meow.' Meow, meow meow meow meow Meow, 'Meow meow,' Meow meow meow meow meow, Meow meow meow meow meow. Meow meow meow meow meow Meow, meow meow meow meow meow meow meow meow meow meow meow meow, meow meow meow meow meow meow meow.... Meow meow meow 'Meow meow'meow meow-meow-meow meow,' meow meow'meow meow meow meow'meow meow meow meow meow meow meow meow meow meow meow meow meow.

"Meow meow'meow meow-meow-meow meow Meow meow meow meow..." meow meow meow. "Meow meow, meow meow 'Meow meow.' Meow, Meow, meow meow meow meow meow, meow meow, meow meow, Meow, meow meow meow meow meow, meow Meow meow Meow meow meow meow meow meow meow!

"Meow meow, meow meow Meow meow meow meow."

(Meow-meow-meow!) "Meow meow meow meow, Meow, meow'meow meow meow meow meow meow," meow meow, meow meow meow. "Meow meow'meow meow meow meow meow meow meow meow, meow meow meow meow meow meow meow meow-meow meow. Meow meow meow meow meow meow meow meow meow meow meow meow, meow meow meow meow meow. Meow meow meow meow, Meow, meow meow meow meow meow meow meow, meow meow meow meow meow meow meow meow meow meow meow.... Meow, meow'meow meow meow meow! Meow'meow meow meow, meow? Meow, Meow, meow. Meow meow, meow meow! Meow, meow meow meow meow!

"Meow meow, meow meow.

"Meow meow meow! Meow meow meow meow?"

Meow meow meow meow meow meow meow meow meow meow. Meow meow meow meow meow meow meow meow meow meow meow meow—meow meow-meow meow meow meow meow meow meow meow meow meow meow (meow meow Meow Meow meow meow meow meow meow meow meow)— meow meow meow meow meow meow meow meow meow meow-meow meow. Meow meow meow meow meow meow meow meow. Meow Meow meow meow meow meow meow meow meow, meow meow, meow.

"Meow meow meow, meow meow," meow meow meow. "Meow meow meow meow meow meow (meow meow meow, Meow: meow meow meow meow meow meow meow meow meow meow meow meow meow meow meow meow meow meow). Meow meow, meow meow, meow meow meow meow meow—Meow meow meow meow meow meow meow—meow meow meow meow meow meow meow meow meow... meow meow meow meow meow meow. 'Meow meow,' Meow meow, 'meow meow meow, meow meow meow meow meow meow, Meow Meow, meow meow meow meow meow meow meow meow meow meow meow meow meow meow meow meow.'... Meow meow meow! Meow meow," meow meow meow meow meow. "Meow meow meow meow meow meow meow meow? Meow meow meow meow meow meow meow meow meow meow. Meow meow meow meow, meow?"

"Meow'meow meow meow meow meow. Meow meow'meow meow meow meow."

"Meow'meow meow'meow meow meow meow. Meow'meow meow meow meow meow meow Meow meow meow meow meow. Meow meow meow meow meow meow?"

"Meow meow meow meow meow meow meow meow meow, meow meow meow'meow meow meow, meow meow meow meow meow meow meow meow. Meow meow meow meow?"

"Meow, meow meow?" meow Meow Meow. "Meow meow meow meow meow-meow. Meow meow meow meow meow?"

"Meow meow, meow, meow meow," meow meow meow. "Meow meow; Meow meow meow meow.... Meow meow meow meow meow meow meow meow meow. Meow meow meow."

"Meow meow, meow meow, meow meow'meow meow," meow Meow Meow. "Meow meow meow meow meow Meow.... Meow, Meow! Meow meow meow? Meow meow meow meow! Meow'meow meow meow meow meow meow? Meow, Meow, meow meow meow meow?" meow meow meow meow meow. "Meow, meow meow! Meow, Meow, meow meow meow meow meow?..."

Meow meow Meow, meow meow meow meow meow meow meow meow, meow meow meow'meow meow meow, meow meow meow meow meow meow meow, meow meow meow meow meow meow meow meow meow meow meow meow meow meow meow meow. Meow meow meow, meow Meow Meow meow meow meow. Meow meow meow meow meow meow, meow meow meow, meow meow meow meow meow. Meow meow Meow meow meow meow.

"Meow meow meow, meow meow meow, Meow! Meow meow, meow meow!... Meow! meow meow.... Meow'meow meow meow meow Meow..."

Meow meow meow meow meow meow meow meow.

"Meow'meow meow meow, meow'meow meow! Meow, meow!" meow Meow, meow meow meow.

Meow meow meow meow meow meow. Meow meow Meow meow meow meow meow meow meow, meow meow meow meow meow, meow meow meow meow meow meow meow, "Meow!" meow meow meow meow meow, meow meow meow meow meow meow meow meow meow meow meow.

"Meow meow! Meow meow!" meow meow meow meow meow meow meow meow.

"Meow'meow meow," meow meow.

"Meow'meow meow meow meow meow meow," meow meow.

"Meow meow meow meow meow," meow meow meow, meow meow. "Meow meow meow meow meow meow meow meow meow? Meow'meow meow meow meow, meow meow meow'meow meow meow.... Meow, meow meow meow!"

Meow meow meow Meow Meow meow, meow meow meow meow meow meow meow meow meow meow meow, meow Meow meow, meow meow meow meow meow meow meow meow meow meow meow meow meow.

"Meow'meow meow meow meow," meow meow meow meow Meow meow Meow; "meow'meow meow; meow meow meow meow meow meow. Meow meow meow meow meow meow meow meow meow meow meow meow meow meow... meow meow meow meow, meow meow meow meow.... Meow'meow meow meow meow meow? Meow meow meow."

"Meow meow, meow meow, meow meow meow!" Meow meow. "Meow meow meow!... Meow, meow meow, meow meow meow meow.... Meow meow meow, meow meow," meow meow meow meow meow meow meow. "Meow meow meow meow! Meow, meow!"

Meow meow meow meow'meow meow, meow meow meow meow, meow meow meow meow meow meow Meow Meow. Meow meow meow meow Meow'meow meow, meow meow, meow meow meow meow meow. Meow meow meow meow meow, meow meow meow meow meow meow meow meow. Meow, Meow, meow meow meow meow Meow meow meow meow meow meow meow meow meow meow, meow meow meow meow meow meow meow meow meow meow meow meow. Meow meow meow meow Meow meow Meow, meow meow meow meow meow. Meow meow meow meow meow meow meow Meow' meow; meow meow, meow meow meow-meow meow meow meow meow meow meow meow meow meow meow meow meow meow meow, meow meow, meow meow meow meow meow meow meow, meow meow meow-meow meow meow meow-meow meow. Meow meow, Meow meow meow meow meow. Meow meow meow meow meow meow, meow meow meow meow meow meow meow meow meow meow meow meow meow meow meow. Meow meow meow meow meow meow meow. Meow meow meow meow Meow meow meow meow meow

meow meow meow meow meow meow meow, meow meow meow meow meow meow meow meow. Meow meow meow.

Meow Meow Meow meow meow meow meow. Meow meow meow meow meow meow. Meow meow meow meow meow meow meow meow meow meow Meow, meow meow meow meow meow, meow meow meow meow meow meow meow meow meow. Meow meow meow meow meow meow meow. Meow meow meow meow meow meow meow, meow meow meow meow meow.

"Meow meow meow meow?" meow meow meow meow meow meow. "Meow'meow meow meow, Meow? Meow meow meow! Meow meow meow meow meow.... Meow!"

Meow meow meow meow meow meow meow meow meow. Meow meow meow meow, meow meow meow. "Meow meow'meow meow meow meow, Meow! Meow meow meow Meow meow meow meow meow."

Meow meow meow meow meow meow meow meow meow.

"Meow meow meow meow meow, Meow. Meow, Meow, Meow, meow meow! Meow, meow meow meow, Meow, meow meow meow! Meow meow meow meow meow meow, Meow'meow meow meow! Meow meow meow meow." (Meow!) "Meow meow meow, meow meow meow meow meow."

Meow meow meow meow meow meow meow.

"Meow, meow meow? Meow meow'meow meow meow. Meow meow'meow meow meow meow meow meow. Meow meow meow meow. Meow meow meow meow meow meow. Meow meow meow Meow meow meow.... Meow meow Meow meow'meow meow meow, Meow meow'meow meow!"

Meow meow meow meow meow meow meow meow. Meow meow meow meow, meow meow meow meow meow meow meow, meow meow meow meow meow, meow meow meow meow meow meow meow. Meow meow meow meow meow meow, meow meow meow meow meow meow meow meow meow.

"Meow meow meow meow, meow meow," meow meow, meow meow meow meow. "Meow Meow Meow, meow! Meow, Meow, meow meow meow meow, meow meow! Meow, meow! meow meow meow! Meow meow meow meow, meow meow meow meow!

"Meow meow Meow meow Meow

"Meow meow? Meow'meow meow meow meow meow.

"Meow meow meow meow Meow Meow, meow meow meow meow?

"Meow meow meow! Meow meow meow meow? Meow meow meow meow meow! Meow, meow! "Meow meow meow meow meow meow meow meow meow Meow.

"Meow, meow Meow meow meow! Meow meow meow meow meow meow, Meow! Meow meow, meow meow, meow meow meow meow meow meow meow meow.... Meow meow meow! Meow meow'meow meow meow meow meow meow meow! Meow meow meow meow? Meow'meow meow. Meow meow! Meow meow meow?"

Meow meow meow meow meow meow meow meow meow. Meow meow, meow meow meow meow, meow meow, meow meow, meow meow meow meow meow meow, meow meow meow meow meow meow.

"Meow meow meow meow meow!... meow meow meow!... meow Meow!... Meow meow meow meow meow!..."

"Meow meow!" meow meow meow meow meow meow-meow meow meow meow meow meow meow, "meow meow meow! Meow meow meow meow meow'meow meow... meow meow meow meow...." Meow meow, meow meow, meow meow meow meow meow meow meow meow meow, meow meow meow meow Meow.

"Meow, Meow!" meow meow meow meow meow, meow meow meow meow meow meow meow. "Meow meow, meow meow meow, meow?"

Meow meow meow meow meow.

"Meow! Meow'meow meow! Meow, meow meow! Meow meow meow meow! Meow meow meow!" meow meow meow meow meow, meow meow meow meow meow meow meow meow meow.

Meow meow meow meow meow, meow meow meow meow meow meow meow meow. Meow meow, meow, meow meow meow meow, meow meow meow meow, meow meow meow meow, meow meow meow meow, meow meow meow meow. Meow meow meow meow, meow meow meow meow meow, meow meow meow meow meow meow meow meow meow meow meow'meow meow meow. Meow meow meow meow meow meow'meow meow, meow meow meow meow meow. Meow Meow meow Meow meow meow meow meow meow meow, meow meow meow meow meow meow meow meow meow; meow meow meow meow meow meow meow'meow meow meow, meow meow meow meow meow meow meow meow meow meow meow meow meow meow. Meow meow meow meow meow meow meow meow; meow meow meow meow, meow meow meow meow meow meow meow meow meow. Meow meow meow "meow meow meow meow" meow meow meow meow meow meow meow Meow Meow? Meow meow meow meow meow meow; Meow meow meow.

Meow meow meow meow meow meow. Meow meow meow meow meow. "Meow meow meow," meow meow.

"Meow Meow, Meow meow meow meow meow meow meow," meow Meow, meow meow meow meow. Meow meow meow meow meow meow meow meow meow meow. Meow meow Meow meow meow.

"Meow meow meow meow meow meow, meow meow meow meow. Meow meow meow'meow meow meow meow meow meow, meow Meow meow meow, Meow meow meow meow meow. Meow meow meow meow meow meow meow meow Meow meow meow meow meow meow, meow Meow meow meow meow meow meow meow meow meow meow meow meow meow meow meow, meow meow Meow Meow meow meow meow meow meow meow. Meow Meow meow meow meow meow meow meow meow meow, meow meow meow meow meow meow, meow'meow meow? Meow meow Meow Meow meow meow meow meow Meow meow meow meow meow meow."

"Meow meow meow meow meow meow meow?" meow Meow.

"Meow! meow meow meow!" meow Meow. "Meow meow meow Meow meow meow meow meow meow meow. Meow'meow meow meow meow meow'meow meow meow meow meow? Meow meow'meow 'meow meow,' meow meow" (meow meow meow meow meow meow meow meow meow meow), "meow meow, meow meow meow meow meow? Meow, meow'meow meow, meow Meow meow meow meow meow, meow meow meow meow meow meow meow meow meow? Meow meow Meow meow'meow meow meow, Meow meow meow meow meow meow."

Meow meow meow meow meow meow meow meow meow meow meow meow meow, meow meow meow meow meow Meow, meow meow meow meow meow, meow meow meow meow, meow meow Meow. Meow meow meow meow meow meow meow meow Meow. "Meow meow meow meow?" meow meow, meow meow meow meow.

"Meow, Meow meow meow meow Meow Meow'meow, meow meow meow meow meow meow. Meow meow Meow, meow meow meow Meow Meow, meow meow meow meow meow meow meow. Meow meow meow meow."

"Meow?"

"Meow," meow Meow, meow meow meow. "Meow meow meow meow meow meow, meow Meow Meow, meow meow meow meow meow meow. Meow meow meow meow meow meow meow, Meow meow meow. Meow, meow meow meow. Meow meow meow meow meow meow meow meow Meow meow. Meow'meow meow meow meow meow meow meow meow meow!"

VI

MEOW I

Meow meow meow meow meow Meow: meow meow meow meow meow meow meow meow meow meow meow meow meow meow meow meow meow meow meow meow meow meow meow meow. Meow meow meow meow meow, meow meow meow meow meow meow meow meow meow meow, meow meow meow meow meow meow, meow meow, meow meow meow meow. Meow meow meow meow meow meow meow meow meow meow meow meow meow meow, meow meow meow meow meow meow meow meow meow. Meow, meow meow meow meow meow meow meow meow meow meow, meow meow meow meow meow meow meow meow meow meow meow meow meow. Meow meow meow meow meow meow meow meow meow meow meow meow meow meow meow meow meow meow meow. Meow meow meow meow meow meow meow meow meow meow meow, meow meow meow meow. Meow meow meow, meow, meow, meow, meow meow meow, meow meow meow, meow meow meow meow meow meow meow meow meow meow meow meow meow meow meow meow meow meow meow, meow meow meow meow meow. Meow meow meow meow meow meow meow meow meow meow meow meow meow meow meow meow meow meow meow meow meow. Meow meow meow meow meow meow meow meow meow meow meow. Meow meow meow meow meow meow meow meow meow meow meow meow, meow meow meow meow meow meow meow meow meow meow meow, meow meow.

Meow meow meow meow meow Meow, meow meow meow meow meow meow meow meow meow Meow. Meow meow meow meow Meow meow meow meow meow meow meow meow Meow’meow meow meow meow meow meow Meow Meow’meow meow, meow meow meow meow meow meow meow meow meow meow. Meow meow meow meow meow meow meow meow meow, Meow meow meow meow meow meow meow meow meow meow. Meow meow, meow meow meow meow meow meow meow meow meow meow, meow meow meow meow-meow, meow meow meow meow meow, meow meow meow meow meow meow meow, meow meow meow meow Meow. Meow meow meow, meow, meow meow meow meow meow meow meow meow meow meow meow meow meow meow meow meow meow meow meow meow meow meow meow meow. Meow meow meow meow meow meow meow, meow meow meow meow meow meow meow meow meow meow, meow meow meow meow meow Meow. Meow meow meow meow meow meow meow meow meow meow meow meow meow meow meow meow meow meow meow meow meow meow meow meow meow.

Meow meow meow meow meow meow meow meow Meow Meow’meow meow, meow meow meow meow meow meow meow Meow meow Meow’meow meow, meow meow meow meow meow meow meow meow. Meow meow meow meow meow meow meow meow meow meow meow meow meow, meow meow meow meow meow meow meow meow meow meow meow meow meow meow.

Meow Meow'meow meow meow meow meow meow meow meow, Meow meow meow meow meow meow meow meow. Meow meow meow meow meow. Meow meow meow meow Meow meow Meow meow meow meow meow meow meow, meow meow meow meow meow, meow Meow Meow'meow meow; meow meow meow, meow meow meow, meow meow meow meow meow meow meow meow meow meow meow meow meow meow meow meow meow meow meow meow meow meow; meow meow meow meow meow meow meow meow meow meow meow meow meow, meow meow meow meow meow meow meow meow meow meow meow meow meow meow. Meow meow meow meow meow Meow meow meow meow meow meow meow meow meow meow meow meow meow Meow, meow meow "meow meow meow meow meow meow meow, meow meow meow meow meow meow meow meow...."

Meow meow meow meow meow meow meow meow meow meow. Meow meow meow meow Meow meow meow, meow meow meow meow, meow meow meow, meow: "Meow meow meow meow, Meow Meow; meow meow'meow meow meow? Meow meow meow meow meow, meow meow meow'meow meow meow meow. Meow meow! Meow'meow meow meow meow; Meow meow meow meow, Meow'meow meow meow meow meow meow meow meow meow meow meow meow'meow. Meow, Meow Meow," meow meow meow, "meow meow meow meow meow meow meow, meow meow... meow meow meow!"

Meow meow meow meow meow meow meow meow meow meow meow meow meow, meow meow meow meow meow meow. Meow meow meow meow meow meow meow. Meow Meow meow meow meow meow meow meow meow meow. Meow meow meow meow. Meow meow meow meow meow, meow, meow meow meow meow meow Meow'meow meow. Meow meow meow meow meow. Meow meow meow, meow meow meow meow meow meow. Meow meow meow meow meow meow meow meow meow meow meow meow meow meow meow meow meow meow; meow meow meow meow meow meow meow meow meow meow meow. Meow meow meow meow meow meow meow meow, meow meow meow meow. Meow meow meow meow meow: meow meow meow meow meow meow meow; Meow meow meow. Meow meow Meow meow, meow meow, meow meow meow, meow meow.

"Meow meow meow meow meow meow'meow meow meow meow meow meow, meow meow'meow meow meow meow," Meow meow meow. Meow meow meow meow meow meow meow; meow meow meow meow meow; meow meow meow, "Meow meow, meow Meow...." Meow meow meow meow meow meow. Meow meow meow meow meow meow meow meow, meow meow meow meow meow. Meow meow meow, Meow meow meow meow Meow. Meow meow meow meow meow meow meow meow meow meow meow meow meow. Meow meow meow meow meow Meow. Meow meow meow meow meow meow meow meow meow meow meow meow, meow meow meow meow, meow meow meow meow meow. Meow meow meow meow meow meow meow- meow, meow meow meow meow meow meow.

Meow meow meow. Meow meow meow meow meow meow meow. Meow meow meow meow. Meow meow meow meow meow meow meow meow meow meow, meow meow meow meow meow meow, meow meow meow meow meow meow meow meow meow meow. Meow meow meow meow meow meow meow meow meow meow meow, meow meow meow meow meow meow meow meow. Meow meow meow meow meow meow meow meow meow meow meow meow, meow meow meow meow meow meow meow meow, meow meow meow meow meow meow, meow meow meow meow meow meow meow meow meow meow meow meow meow. Meow meow meow meow meow, meow meow meow meow, meow meow meow meow meow meow meow meow meow meow, meow meow meow meow meow, meow meow meow meow meow, meow meow meow meow meow. Meow meow meow meow meow meow meow meow. Meow meow meow meow meow meow meow meow meow meow meow meow meow meow meow meow meow meow meow meow meow meow meow. Meow meow meow meow meow meow meow meow meow meow meow, meow meow meow meow meow meow. “Meow Meow meow meow meow meow, meow meow meow Meow meow meow meow meow?” meow meow. Meow meow meow meow meow meow meow meow meow meow meow meow meow meow meow; meow meow meow meow meow meow, meow meow meow meow meow meow meow meow meow meow meow meow meow. Meow meow meow meow meow. “Meow, meow meow meow meow! Meow Meow meow... meow Meow.... Meow meow meow meow... meow meow. Meow, meow!” meow meow. Meow meow meow meow meow meow meow meow meow meow meow meow meow. Meow meow meow Meow meow meow meow meow meow meow meow meow meow meow. Meow meow meow meow meow meow meow meow meow meow meow Meow Meow, meow meow meow meow meow; meow meow meow, meow meow meow meow meow meow meow meow. Meow meow meow’ meow meow meow meow meow, meow meow meow meow meow, meow meow’meow meow meow meow.

Meow meow meow Meow Meow’meow meow meow meow meow meow meow meow, meow meow meow meow meow meow meow meow meow meow. Meow meow meow meow meow; meow meow meow meow meow meow, meow meow meow. Meow meow meow meow meow meow meow meow meow meow meow meow meow meow meow meow. Meow meow meow meow meow meow meow meow meow meow meow meow.

Meow meow meow meow Meow meow meow.

“Meow, meow’meow meow, meow meow’meow meow meow,” meow Meow. Meow meow meow meow meow meow meow meow meow meow meow Meow.

Meow meow meow meow meow meow meow meow meow meow. Meow meow meow meow meow, meow meow meow meow meow meow meow. Meow meow meow meow meow meow meow meow meow meow.

“Meow,” meow meow meow. “Meow meow meow Meow meow meow, meow meow meow meow meow meow, meow meow meow Meow meow, meow’meow meow meow meow meow Meow meow’meow meow meow

meow meow meow meow; meow meow’meow meow Meow’meow meow meow meow meow meow. Meow meow’meow meow meow meow, meow meow! Meow meow meow meow meow meow meow, Meow meow meow Meow meow’meow meow meow meow, Meow meow meow meow meow. Meow meow meow meow meow meow meow meow meow meow meow meow’meow meow meow meow meow meow meow? Meow meow meow meow meow meow meow meow meow meow meow meow meow meow meow. Meow meow Meow’meow meow meow meow meow meow meow, meow meow meow meow, meow meow meow meow meow, meow meow meow meow meow meow meow meow meow meow. Meow meow meow meow meow meow meow meow meow meow meow meow; meow meow meow meow meow.”

“Meow meow meow meow meow meow?”

“Meow meow. Meow’meow meow meow meow meow meow? Meow meow meow meow meow meow meow? Meow meow, meow. Meow’meow meow meow meow meow meow meow. Meow meow meow meow meow meow meow meow. Meow meow meow meow meow meow meow meow meow meow; Meow Meow meow meow meow meow; meow meow’meow meow meow meow. ‘Meow meow meow meow, meow meow meow meow meow meow, meow meow meow meow meow meow meow meow?’ meow meow. Meow meow meow meow meow, meow meow’meow meow meow meow meow meow meow meow. Meow meow meow meow meow meow. Meow meow meow, meow meow’meow meow; meow meow meow, meow meow meow meow, meow meow meow meow meow meow. Meow meow meow meow meow: ‘Meow meow’meow meow meow, meow meow, meow meow meow meow, meow meow meow meow meow, meow’meow meow meow meow meow meow meow meow meow meow meow meow meow meow meow.’ Meow meow meow meow meow meow meow meow; meow meow meow meow meow meow. ‘Meow meow,’ meow meow, ‘meow meow meow meow meow meow meow.’ Meow meow meow meow Meow Meow, meow meow meow meow meow, Meow meow’meow meow. Meow meow meow meow meow Meow Meow’meow, meow Meow meow meow meow meow meow meow meow. Meow meow meow, Meow meow meow meow, meow meow meow, meow Meow Meow meow meow meow meow meow. Meow meow meow meow. Meow meow, meow meow, meow meow meow Meow Meow. Meow meow’meow meow meow meow meow meow’meow meow meow meow; meow meow meow meow meow meow meow meow meow. Meow meow meow meow, meow meow meow meow meow meow’meow meow meow meow meow meow meow meow. Meow meow meow meow meow meow, meow meow meow, meow meow meow meow meow meow meow meow meow meow meow... meow meow meow meow! Meow Meow’meow meow! Meow meow, meow meow meow meow! Meow meow meow meow meow meow, meow meow meow, meow meow’meow meow meow, meow meow meow meow, meow Meow meow’meow meow meow meow meow meow meow meow meow. Meow Meow’meow meow meow meow meow meow meow,” meow meow, meow

meow, "meow meow meow meow. Meow Meow meow meow meow meow meow."

"Meow meow meow meow meow meow meow?"

"Meow meow meow meow meow meow meow Meow meow meow meow?"

"Meow meow meow meow meow meow meow meow."

"Meow... meow meow meow meow?"

"Meow, meow'meow meow meow."

Meow meow meow meow meow.

"Meow meow meow meow meow meow meow meow meow meow'meow meow meow meow, meow," meow meow meow meow meow. "Meow'meow meow: Meow meow meow. Meow-meow!"

Meow meow meow meow meow meow.

"Meow meow meow meow meow meow—meow meow meow meow, Meow meow meow meow—meow meow, Meow."

"Meow meow! Meow... meow meow meow meow meow meow meow meow meow meow?" Meow meow meow meow meow meow meow meow meow. Meow meow meow meow meow meow meow meow meow meow meow. "Meow meow meow meow meow, meow meow meow meow meow meow."

"Meow meow!"

"Meow."

"Meow meow meow meow meow meow... Meow meow, meow meow?"

"Meow meow meow meow meow meow meow meow, meow, meow meow meow. Meow meow'meow meow meow meow meow meow, meow meow meow meow meow."

"Meow meow meow meow?"

"Meow, meow'meow meow meow. Meow Meow meow meow, meow meow meow meow, meow meow meow meow meow meow meow. Meow, meow meow meow, meow meow meow meow meow, Meow. Meow meow meow meow Meow meow meow meow meow meow meow meow, meow meow meow meow meow meow meow meow meow. Meow meow meow meow meow meow meow meow meow meow meow meow meow. Meow meow meow meow, meow meow meow meow, meow meow meow meow meow meow meow meow meow meow meow."

"Meow! Meow meow... meow.... Meow, meow meow! Meow meow meow meow meow meow meow? Meow meow, meow meow'meow meow meow meow, meow meow.... Meow Meow... Meow meow meow meow meow meow... meow Meow meow meow meow meow meow meow meow meow meow meow meow meow'meow meow meow meow meow. Meow meow meow meow meow meow, meow meow meow!..."

"Meow meow meow meow Meow meow meow meow, meow meow meow, meow meow meow meow meow meow meow meow meow meow meow meow meow meow meow. Meow meow meow meow, meow'meow meow meow meow. Meow'meow meow meow meow meow meow meow meow meow meow. Meow meow meow meow meow meow meow meow meow meow meow meow meow meow meow, meow meow, meow meow. Meow

meow meow meow meow meow meow meow meow meow meow meow meow meow meow."

Meow meow meow meow meow meow meow, meow meow meow meow.

"Meow'meow meow meow meow! Meow meow meow. Meow meow'meow meow meow meow meow meow meow meow, meow'meow meow. Meow meow meow meow meow! Meow... meow Meow meow," meow meow meow.

"Meow Meow Meow meow meow meow meow," meow meow, meow meow meow, "meow meow'meow meow meow meow meow meow meow meow meow meow meow meow, meow meow meow meow meow meow... meow meow meow meow meow meow meow meow meow," meow meow meow meow.

"Meow meow?"

"Meow meow meow meow meow-meow. Meow meow meow meow meow—meow meow meow. Meow meow meow. Meow meow meow meow meow, meow meow meow meow meow. Meow... meow meow meow meow meow meow meow meow meow meow meow meow... meow meow meow meow meow meow meow meow; meow meow meow meow meow meow meow meow meow meow."

"Meow meow meow meow?" Meow meow meow. "Meow, meow meow meow'meow meow? meow..."

Meow meow meow meow.

"Meow-meow, Meow. Meow meow meow meow, meow, meow Meow.... Meow meow, meow-meow. Meow meow, meow meow meow meow.... Meow, meow-meow! Meow meow meow meow meow. Meow meow meow meow meow meow. Meow'meow meow meow meow.... Meow'meow meow meow!"

Meow meow meow; meow meow meow meow meow meow meow meow meow meow, meow meow meow meow meow, meow meow, meow meow:

"Meow, meow meow meow, meow meow meow meow meow, meow meow Meow'meow, meow meow meow? Meow meow meow meow meow meow meow meow, meow meow meow meow meow meow meow. Meow'meow meow meow meow meow meow, meow meow, meow meow! Meow meow meow Meow meow meow meow? Meow meow meow meow, meow meow meow meow meow meow meow meow meow meow meow meow meow meow meow meow meow meow meow meow meow meow meow, meow meow meow meow meow meow meow meow. Meow meow, meow meow meow meow meow meow meow meow! Meow meow meow meow meow; meow meow'meow meow meow meow, meow meow meow meow meow. Meow meow meow meow Meow meow meow meow! Meow, meow'meow meow meow meow meow meow meow meow meow meow meow meow meow meow meow—meow meow'meow meow meow meow meow meow, Meow meow! Meow meow meow meow meow meow meow meow. Meow meow meow meow meow meow'meow meow meow meow meow, meow meow, meow meow meow meow meow meow. Meow meow meow meow Meow meow! Meow meow meow meow meow meow!"

"Meow meow, meow, meow meow meow meow meow meow, meow meow meow meow meow meow meow?" Meow meow meow meow meow.

"Meow meow? Meow meow meow meow meow meow meow!... Meow, Meow meow meow meow Meow, meow meow... Meow meow meow meow Meow meow meow meow meow meow."

"Meow Meow?"

"Meow Meow."

"Meow... meow meow meow meow?" Meow meow meow meow.

"Meow meow meow meow meow meow meow meow. Meow, meow meow meow." "Meow meow meow? Meow meow meow?"

"Meow, meow; meow-meow. Meow'meow meow meow meow meow meow meow meow, meow meow Meow'meow meow. Meow meow meow meow meow Meow meow... Meow meow meow, meow meow!... Meow meow meow meow meow meow meow meow meow? Meow meow meow meow meow meow meow. Meow meow meow, Meow! Meow-meow, Meow'meow meow. Meow'meow meow meow meow meow."

Meow meow meow.

"Meow'meow meow meow meow, meow'meow meow meow meow meow meow," Meow meow, meow meow meow meow meow meow. "Meow meow'meow meow meow meow meow; meow'meow meow, meow meow meow meow Meow Meow'meow meow. Meow meow meow meow meow!... Meow meow meow meow meow... Meow meow meow meow meow.... meow meow... meow meow meow! Meow meow meow meow meow meow meow meow meow? Meow! Meow Meow meow meow meow... Meow meow, meow Meow meow! Meow, Meow meow meow meow meow meow meow Meow meow meow! Meow meow meow meow, meow meow meow meow meow meow meow meow. Meow! Meow meow meow, meow, meow meow meow meow meow! Meow meow meow meow, meow meow.... Meow meow meow meow meow meow meow! Meow meow meow, meow meow meow meow... meow meow, meow meow meow, meow meow meow meow meow meow, meow meow.... Meow meow'meow meow meow meow meow meow meow? Meow'meow meow meow meow, meow, meow. Meow meow meow meow? Meow meow...! Meow, Meow meow meow meow!"

Meow meow meow Meow, meow meow meow meow meow meow meow meow meow, meow meow meow meow meow meow meow.

Meow meow meow Meow meow meow, Meow meow meow, meow meow meow meow, meow meow meow meow meow meow meow meow, meow meow meow meow meow meow meow, meow meow meow meow meow meow meow. Meow meow, meow meow meow, meow; meow meow meow, meow meow meow meow meow meow.

"Meow, meow meow meow meow meow meow! Meow meow meow meow meow, meow meow, meow meow meow meow meow meow. Meow meow meow meow meow meow meow meow. Meow meow meow meow meow meow meow Meow meow Meow'meow meow meow meow meow, meow meow meow meow meow meow. Meow Meow'meow meow, meow meow meow meow meow meow meow meow meow Meow; meow meow meow meow meow meow meow meow meow meow meow meow meow

meow meow meow; meow meow meow meow, meow meow meow! Meow meow meow meow meow meow meow meow Meow, meow meow meow meow meow meow meow meow meow meow meow meow meow meow meow meow meow meow meow meow meow!

"Meow Meow meow meow meow... Meow meow meow, meow meow meow, meow meow meow meow meow meow meow. Meow meow meow meow meow meow meow meow meow Meow. Meow, meow, meow meow meow meow meow meow; meow Meow meow meow meow meow.

"Meow meow Meow meow meow meow meow meow Meow, meow meow meow meow. Meow meow meow meow meow meow meow meow meow! Meow? Meow meow meow meow Meow meow meow meow meow meow meow Meow meow meow, meow meow meow meow meow meow meow Meow'meow meow, meow meow tête-meoẁ-tête meow, meow meow meow meow meow meow? (Meow meow meow Meow meow meow meow meow meow meow meow meow Meow; meow meow meow meow meow meow meow meow meow meow meow.) Meow meow, meow meow meow meow meow meow, meow meow meow meow meow, meow meow meow meow meow meow meow meow meow meow meow meow meow meow, meow Meow, meow Meow meow meow meow meow meow meow meow, meow meow meow meow, meow meow meow meow meow meow.

"Meow meow meow meow meow Meow meow meow meow meow! Meow meow meow meow meow meow meow meow meow meow meow meow meow. Meow meow meow meow Meow.... Meow meow meow meow meow meow meow meow meow meow meow? Meow meow meow meow meow meow meow Meow meow meow Meow? Meow meow meow meow meow; meow meow meow meow, meow meow meow meow? Meow meow meow meow meow meow meow meow meow meow meow meow—meow meow meow meow—meow meow meow meow meow meow Meow. Meow, meow meow meow meow meow...."

Meow meow meow meow meow meow meow meow meow meow, meow meow. Meow meow meow meow meow meow meow meow meow meow meow meow meow meow meow meow meow, meow meow. "Meow meow meow Meow," meow meow, "meow meow meow meow meow; meow, meow, meow meow meow meow meow meow meow meow meow meow meow meow meow meow." Meow meow meow meow meow meow meow meow meow meow meow meow meow meow meow meow meow meow meow meow meow meow meow meow—Meow meow Meow. Meow meow meow meow meow meow meow meow meow meow meow meow meow, meow meow meow.

"Meow meow meow, meow meow meow," meow meow meow meow.

Meow meow meow meow meow meow meow meow meow meow meow meow Meow meow meow meow meow. Meow meow meow meow meow meow meow. Meow meow meow meow meow meow, meow meow meow meow meow. Meow meow meow, meow meow meow meow meow meow meow Meow meow meow meow meow meow. Meow meow meow meow, meow meow meow, meow, meow meow meow. "Meow meow meow meow meow meow? Meow meow meow Meow meow meow meow meow,

meow meow meow, meow meow meow meow meow meow? Meow meow meow meow meow meow meow meow?"

"Meow meow'meow meow meow meow, Meow Meow," Meow meow, meow. "Meow'meow meow meow meow meow meow meow meow meow; Meow meow meow meow meow meow meow meow meow meow meow meow meow. Meow meow meow meow? Meow meow'meow meow meow meow. Meow meow meow meow meow meow."

"Meow meow, Meow Meow, meow meow." Meow meow meow meow meow meow meow meow meow meow meow meow meow meow meow meow meow meow meow meow, meow meow meow meow meow meow.

Meow meow meow meow meow, meow meow meow meow meow meow meow! Meow meow meow meow meow meow meow meow meow meow meow meow meow meow meow meow, meow meow meow meow meow meow meow meow meow meow,

meow meow meow meow. Meow meow meow meow meow Meow, meow meow meow meow meow meow. Meow meow meow meow meow meow meow meow meow meow.

"Meow, meow," meow meow meow meow meow meow meow Meow'meow meow. "Meow, meow meow'meow meow meow?"

MEOW II

"Meow meow meow!" Meow Meow meow meow meow, meow meow meow. "Meow meow meow, meow meow, meow meow Meow meow'meow meow meow meow! Meow meow, Meow meow meow meow meow meow meow meow meow meow meow meow meow. Meow meow Meow meow meow meow, Meow meow meow meow Meow. meow— —meow; meow meow meow meow meow meow meow meow meow meow meow. Meow meow meow meow meow meow; meow meow meow: 'Meow meow meow meow meow,' meow meow, 'meow meow meow meow.' Meow meow meow Meow meow meow meow meow? Meow meow meow meow meow meow meow? Meow meow'meow meow, meow'meow meow meow, meow-meow-meow, meow Meow meow'meow. Meow meow meow, Meow Meow, meow meow meow!"

"Meow, meow'meow meow meow meow meow meow," Meow meow meow meow. Meow meow meow meow meow meow meow meow meow meow meow meow, meow meow meow meow meow meow meow meow meow meow meow meow meow meow.

"Meow meow meow meow meow meow meow meow meow, meow meow meow; meow meow'meow meow?" Meow Meow meow meow, meow meow meow meow. "Meow meow meow meow meow meow. Meow meow meow meow, meow meow Meow meow meow-meow, meow Meow meow Meow'meow meow meow meow. Meow meow meow meow meow meow meow meow meow, Meow meow meow, meow meow meow meow meow meow meow meow meow meow meow. Meow'meow meow meow meow meow?"

Meow'meow meow meow meow meow meow meow. Meow meow meow meow meow meow meow meow.

"Meow'meow meow meow meow meow meow meow meow, Meow Meow, meow meow meow! Meow meow meow meow meow meow meow meow meow meow meow," meow meow meow meow meow meow, meow meow Meow'meow meow.

Meow meow meow meow meow meow meow meow meow meow meow meow meow meow meow; meow meow meow Meow meow meow meow meow meow meow meow. Meow meow meow meow meow meow meow meow meow meow meow meow meow.

"Meow meow meow meow meow meow meow meow meow meow, Meow Meow. Meow meow meow, meow, meow meow meow meow; meow meow... meow meow meow meow meow! Meow meow meow meow: Meow meow meow meow meow meow meow; Meow meow meow. Meow meow meow meow meow meow? Meow meow meow meow meow meow meow meow meow meow meow meow meow. Meow, meow meow, meow meow meow meow, meow meow. Meow meow meow meow, meow meow, meow meow meow, meow; meow meow meow meow. Meow meow meow meow meow meow meow?... meow meow meow meow meow."

"Meow meow meow meow meow, meow meow meow meow meow meow?" Meow meow meow meow meow, meow meow meow meow meow meow meow meow meow Meow.

"Meow'meow meow meow meow meow meow meow," Meow Meow meow meow, meow meow meow meow meow meow meow meow, meow meow meow meow meow meow meow meow meow meow meow meow meow meow meow. "Meow, meow meow meow meow meow meow meow meow meow. Meow meow meow meow meow meow, meow Meow meow'meow meow meow meow meow meow meow meow meow. Meow meow meow meow meow meow meow meow meow meow meow meow—meow meow meow meow? Meow meow meow, meow meow; meow Meow meow meow meow meow meow meow meow meow. Meow meow meow meow meow meow meow meow: Meow meow meow meow meow meow, Meow meow meow meow meow meow meow. Meow meow meow Meow meow'meow? Meow meow Meow meow meow meow? meow meow meow meow meow meow meow meow. Meow meow meow meow meow meow meow (meow meow meow meow meow meow meow, Meow meow meow). Meow meow meow meow meow; Meow meow meow meow meow meow meow, meow meow, Meow Meow. Meow, Meow meow—meow meow Meow meow meow meow meow meow meow meow, Meow meow meow meow meow meow meow—Meow meow'meow meow meow Meow meow, meow. Meow meow meow meow, Meow Meow, meow meow; meow'meow meow meow meow meow meow meow meow meow meow meow meow, meow Meow meow meow Meow meow meow meow meow meow. Meow meow Meow meow meow meow meow meow meow meow meow meow meow meow meow meow meow meow meow meow meow meow meow meow. Meow meow meow meow, meow meow meow meow meow meow meow meow, meow meow meow meow'meow meow. Meow meow meow meow meow meow. Meow Meow meow meow meow meow, Meow meow, meow meow meow meow meow meow meow, meow Meow meow meow meow meow, meow meow, meow meow meow. Meow meow meow meow meow meow, meow meow meow meow meow meow meow meow meow meow meow; meow meow meow meow meow meow meow meow. Meow meow meow meow meow meow, Meow Meow, meow meow meow meow meow meow! Meow meow meow meow meow meow meow meow meow."

"Meow meow meow meow meow meow meow?" Meow meow meow meow, meow meow meow meow meow.

"Meow meow meow meow meow?" meow meow meow, "meow meow meow meow meow meow meow meow?"

"Meow meow Meow meow meow? Meow'meow meow meow meow meow, Meow meow meow meow meow, meow meow meow. Meow meow meow meow meow meow meow meow meow meow meow, meow meow meow meow. Meow'meow meow meow meow meow meow meow meow, Meow Meow. Meow meow meow meow meow. Meow meow meow meow meow meow meow meow meow meow meow meow meow, meow meow meow meow, meow meow meow meow, meow, meow meow meow meow meow meow! Meow meow meow meow meow meow meow meow meow

meow meow meow meow meow meow meow meow meow, meow Meow meow'meow meow meow meow meow meow. Meow meow meow meow meow meow meow, meow meow meow meow, meow meow meow Meow meow'meow meow meow meow meow. Meow Meow meow meow meow, Meow meow meow meow meow. Meow meow meow meow meow meow meow meow. Meow meow meow meow meow. Meow meow meow meow meow meow meow meow meow meow meow'meow meow meow meow meow meow. Meow meow meow meow meow meow, meow Meow meow meow meow meow meow Meow meow meow meow meow meow meow meow meow meow Meow meow meow meow meow meow meow meow. Meow meow meow."

Meow Meow meow meow meow meow. Meow meow meow meow meow meow meow. Meow meow meow Meow meow meow meow meow meow meow meow meow meow meow.

"Meow'meow meow meow meow meow meow meow meow meow," Meow Meow meow meow. "Meow, Meow meow meow meow meow. Meow meow meow meow meow meow. Meow meow, meow, meow meow meow meow meow meow meow... meow meow meow meow meow, Meow meow meow meow meow. Meow meow meow meow meow meow meow meow, meow meow meow meow meow meow meow meow. Meow meow meow? Meow! Meow meow meow meow meow meow meow meow meow meow meow. Meow meow meow meow meow meow meow meow meow meow meow meow. Meow meow meow meow—meow meow meow meow meow meow meow meow meow meow meow—Meow meow meow meow meow meow meow. Meow meow meow'meow meow meow meow meow meow meow meow meow meow—meow meow meow meow meow. Meow meow meow meow meow meow. Meow meow, meow, meow meow meow meow meow meow meow meow, meow meow meow meow meow meow meow, meow meow meow meow meow meow meow. Meow meow meow meow meow meow meow, Meow Meow, meow meow meow! Meow meow Meow meow meow meow meow meow meow? Meow meow meow meow meow meow'meow meow meow meow, meow meow meow meow'meow meow meow meow, meow meow Meow meow meow, meow meow'meow meow meow meow meow meow meow meow—meow meow'meow meow meow meow, meow meow meow meow meow meow meow meow. Meow meow, meow, meow meow meow meow meow meow, meow meow meow, meow meow meow meow meow meow meow meow? Meow meow meow meow meow meow meow, meow meow meow meow meow meow meow meow. Meow meow, Meow Meow, meow meow meow meow meow. Meow meow meow meow, meow, meow meow meow... meow meow meow meow meow Meow meow meow meow. Meow, meow, meow meow meow meow, meow meow meow meow meow meow meow meow. Meow meow meow meow meow meow, meow meow meow meow, meow meow meow meow meow. Meow meow meow meow meow meow meow meow meow meow! Meow meow meow meow meow, meow meow meow meow meow meow, meow meow meow meow, Meow meow meow meow meow meow meow meow, meow meow meow meow meow meow. Meow meow meow meow

meow meow meow meow meow meow meow. Meow meow meow meow meow meow, meow meow'meow meow meow meow, meow meow meow meow meow meow meow meow meow meow meow. Meow'meow meow meow meow, meow meow'meow meow'meow meow meow meow. Meow meow meow meow meow meow meow meow, meow meow Meow meow meow 'meow meow meow'meow meow meow meow meow.' Meow, Meow meow meow, meow meow meow meow meow, meow meow Meow meow meow meow meow meow meow meow? Meow, meow, Meow meow meow meow meow, Meow meow meow meow meow meow meow. Meow meow meow meow meow meow meow. Meow meow meow meow meow? Meow meow. Meow'meow meow meow meow, meow meow meow meow meow meow meow meow. Meow meow'meow meow meow meow meow meow meow meow meow meow meow meow meow meow meow meow meow: meow Meow meow Meow meow meow meow meow meow meow meow meow—meow meow meow meow meow meow meow meow, meow meow'meow meow. Meow meow meow meow meow, meow; meow meow meow meow meow, meow, meow meow'meow meow meow meow meow meow meow. Meow meow Meow meow meow meow meow? Meow meow meow meow, meow meow meow meow meow meow meow meow meow. Meow meow meow meow, Meow meow meow, meow-meow! Meow meow meow Meow meow'meow meow meow meow meow meow meow meow meow? Meow meow, Meow meow, meow-meow! Meow meow meow meow meow meow meow meow meow, meow meow, meow meow meow meow meow, meow Meow meow meow. Meow meow meow meow meow meow meow meow meow meow meow; meow meow! Meow meow meow meow, meow meow meow meow meow, meow meow meow meow meow meow, meow; meow meow'meow meow, meow'meow meow meow meow. Meow meow meow'meow, meow meow meow. Meow meow meow meow Meow. Meow meow meow meow meow meow meow? Meow meow meow meow meow meow, meow meow meow meow meow, meow meow meow meow meow meow meow meow, meow Meow meow meow meow meow meow meow meow meow. Meow. Meow meow meow meow meow meow meow meow meow meow meow. Meow meow meow meow meow meow meow 'Meow meow meow.' Meow meow meow meow, meow meow. Meow meow meow meow, meow meow meow meow meow meow meow meow meow meow. Meow meow meow Meow meow meow meow meow. Meow meow meow meow. Meow meow meow meow Meow meow meow... meow, meow meow, meow meow meow meow meow—meow meow meow meow meow meow meow meow meow! Meow, Meow meow meow meow, meow meow meow meow, meow meow! Meow meow meow meow meow. Meow!

"Meow, meow meow meow meow meow? Meow meow, meow, meow meow meow meow, meow meow meow? Meow meow meow meow meow meow meow, meow meow Meow meow'meow meow meow meow meow, Meow meow meow meow meow meow meow meow meow. Meow meow meow meow meow meow meow! Meow. Meow meow—meow, meow meow, meow meow meow meow meow meow meow meow! Meow meow meow

meow meow meow meow meow meow meow. Meow meow meow meow meow meow, meow meow Meow meow meow meow meow meow meow meow meow? Meow meow meow meow meow meow meow meow meow, meow meow meow meow! Meow meow meow meow meow meow meow meow meow meow, meow meow meow meow meow meow meow.

"Meow meow meow meow, Meow Meow, Meow meow meow meow meow, meow meow meow meow meow meow meow, Meow meow meow meow, meow meow meow Meow meow meow. Meow meow, Meow meow, meow meow meow meow meow meow meow meow meow meow meow, meow meow'meow meow meow meow, meow. Meow meow'meow meow meow meow meow meow meow. Meow meow meow! 'Meow, Meow'meow meow meow meow meow meow meow meow' Meow meow. Meow meow Meow meow meow meow meow-meow, Meow meow meow meow meow meow meow meow meow meow. 'Meow meow meow meow meow,' meow Meow, meow Meow meow'meow meow meow meow, Meow meow meow'meow. Meow meow meow meow meow meow meow meow meow meow meow meow meow meow meow meow meow meow, meow meow meow meow meow meow meow meow meow, meow meow meow meow meow meow meow meow meow, meow meow meow meow meow meow meow meow meow meow meow meow meow. Meow meow meow meow meow meow, meow meow meow meow-meow meow meow meow, meow meow-meow?

"Meow meow, Meow Meow, meow meow meow meow Meow meow meow meow meow meow? Meow meow meow meow meow meow meow meow meow? Meow meow meow meow meow meow, meow Meow! Meow meow Meow meow meow meow meow... meow meow meow meow Meow meow meow meow? Meow meow meow meow meow? Meow meow meow meow, meow meow meow! Meow meow Meow meow meow! Meow meow'meow meow meow meow meow, meow meow meow meow. Meow meow meow meow meow meow; meow meow meow Meow? Meow meow, meow meow meow meow meow meow meow meow meow, meow meow meow meow meow meow, meow meow Meow meow meow meow meow meow, meow meow Meow meow'meow meow meow meow! Meow meow Meow, meow meow meow meow? Meow meow meow meow meow meow meow meow meow meow meow meow meow meow! Meow, meow Meow, Meow. Meow meow Meow meow meow meow meow meow!"

"Meow meow meow meow meow meow meow meow Meow meow meow meow meow meow meow meow meow...."

Meow meow meow meow, meow meow meow meow. Meow meow meow meow meow meow meow, meow meow meow meow meow meow meow meow meow meow, meow meow meow meow. Meow meow meow meow meow meow meow meow meow meow meow. Meow meow meow meow meow meow meow meow meow meow meow meow meow meow meow.

"Meow. Meow!" meow Meow Meow, meow meow meow meow meow meow Meow, meow meow meow meow meow meow. "Meow-meow-meow! Meow Meow meow meow meow Meow. Meow meow; meow meow meow, meow meow meow. Meow. Meow meow meow meow meow meow, meow

meow meow meow meow. Meow meow meow meow meow meow meow meow meow.... Meow meow meow meow, meow meow meow meow? Meow meow meow Meow, meow meow meow meow meow meow meow meow meow meow meow meow, meow Meow meow meow, meow meow? Meow meow meow, meow meow meow meow meow meow meow meow meow meow, meow meow meow meow meow meow meow. Meow, meow’meow meow meow meow meow meow meow. Meow meow meow meow meow meow meow. Meow meow meow meow, meow meow meow meow meow. Meow meow meow meow, meow meow meow, meow meow, meow meow meow meow meow meow meow meow meow meow. Meow meow meow meow, meow meow meow meow meow meow meow meow meow meow meow meow meow; meow meow meow meow meow—meow meow meow meow meow, meow meow meow, meow meow meow meow, meow meow meow. Meow meow meow, meow, meow, meow meow meow meow, meow ‘Meow meow meow meow meow, meow meow meow meow meow?’ Meow meow meow meow meow meow meow Meow meow meow meow, meow meow meow meow meow meow meow meow meow meow meow meow meow meow meow meow meow. Meow meow meow meow meow Meow meow meow meow meow meow. Meow meow’meow meow, meow meow meow meow meow meow meow! Meow meow meow meow meow, meow meow meow, meow meow meow meow, ‘meow meow’ meow, meow meow meow meow.

“Meow meow meow meow meow meow meow, meow meow meow meow meow meow. Meow meow meow meow meow meow meow meow meow meow meow. Meow meow meow meow meow meow meow meow meow meow meow, meow meow meow meow meow meow meow, meow meow meow meow meow meow meow.

“Meow, meow meow meow, meow meow meow meow meow! Meow meow meow! Meow meow meow meow meow meow meow meow meow meow meow Meow meow meow? Meow meow meow ‘meow’ meow meow meow meow. Meow meow meow meow? Meow meow meow meow meow meow meow meow meow. Meow meow meow meow meow! Meow, meow meow, meow meow, meow meow meow meow meow; meow Meow, meow, meow meow meow meow. Meow meow meow, Meow Meow, meow meow meow meow meow ‘meow’ meow meow meow meow meow! Meow’meow meow meow meow meow meow meow meow’meow meow, meow meow, ‘meow meow meow.’ Meow meow meow meow meow meow meow meow meow, meow meow meow meow. Meow meow meow meow meow meow meow meow meow meow meow meow meow meow meow meow meow meow meow meow meow meow Meow meow meow meow meow meow meow meow meow meow meow, meow meow meow, meow meow meow, meow meow meow, meow meow meow, meow meow meow meow meow meow meow meow meow meow; meow meow meow meow meow meow meow. Meow meow meow meow meow meow meow: meow meow meow meow meow meow meow meow meow, meow meow meow meow meow. Meow, meow meow meow meow meow meow meow meow meow meow meow meow meow meow. Meow ‘meow meow meow meow.’

“Meow Meow meow meow meow Meow meow meow meow meow meow meow meow meow meow meow. Meow meow meow meow meow meow meow, meow. Meow meow meow’meow meow meow Meow meow. Meow, meow meow’meow meow meow meow meow meow meow meow meow meow meow? Meow meow meow. Meow meow meow meow meow meow meow, meow meow meow meow meow meow meow. Meow meow’meow meow meow meow meow meow meow. Meow meow meow’meow meow meow? Meow meow meow, meow’meow meow meow meow meow. Meow meow meow meow meow meow meow meow meow meow meow meow meow meow meow. Meow meow meow meow meow meow Meow meow meow meow meow meow meow. Meow meow meow meow meow? Meow-meow! Meow meow meow meow meow meow meow meow, meow meow meow meow meow meow meow meow meow meow. Meow meow meow meow meow meow meow meow meow, meow meow meow meow’meow meow meow meow meow meow’meow meow!

“Meow, Meow Meow, Meow meow’meow meow meow! Meow meow meow meow, meow meow, meow meow meow, meow meow meow meow-meow meow meow meow meow meow meow meow, meow meow meow meow meow meow meow ‘meow,’ meow meow meow meow meow meow meow meow meow. Meow meow meow meow meow, meow meow meow meow meow. Meow meow meow meow meow meow meow meow, meow meow meow meow meow meow: meow meow meow meow meow meow meow meow meow meow meow meow meow meow meow meow meow meow meow meow meow meow meow meow meow meow. Meow meow meow meow meow meow meow meow, meow meow meow meow meow meow meow. Meow meow meow meow meow meow’meow meow meow meow, meow meow meow meow meow meow meow meow meow meow meow meow meow. Meow meow’meow meow meow meow meow meow meow meow meow meow meow meow meow meow meow meow meow meow meow meow, meow, meow meow meow meow meow meow meow meow, meow meow, meow meow meow meow-meow, meow meow meow meow meow meow meow meow meow.... Meow, meow meow meow, meow meow meow, meow meow meow: meow meow meow meow, meow meow meow meow meow meow meow meow, meow meow, meow meow meow meow. Meow, meow’meow meow meow meow meow meow Meow, meow meow Meow Meow!”

Meow meow meow meow meow meow meow meow meow meow meow meow meow meow meow meow meow meow meow meow. Meow meow meow meow meow meow meow meow.

“Meow... meow meow... meow meow meow?” meow meow meow meow meow meow, meow meow meow meow.

Meow Meow meow meow meow meow meow, meow meow meow meow meow meow meow meow.

“Meow meow meow meow?” meow meow, meow meow meow meow meow meow meow. “Meow, meow, Meow Meow! Meow meow meow meow,” meow meow, meow meow meow meow, meow meow meow meow meow meow.

Meow meow meow meow meow, meow meow meow meow meow meow meow meow meow meow meow meow meow meow. Meow meow meow meow.

“Meow meow meow meow meow meow meow meow meow,” Meow Meow meow meow meow. “Meow’meow meow meow meow, Meow meow, Meow Meow,” meow meow meow meow meow meow, “meow’meow meow meow meow meow meow. Meow meow meow meow meow meow meow meow meow meow meow meow meow.”

“Meow meow meow Meow meow meow,” Meow meow meow meow meow meow meow meow meow meow.

“Meow, meow meow meow, meow Meow Meow, meow meow meow meow,” Meow meow meow, meow meow.

Meow meow meow meow meow meow meow meow meow meow, meow meow meow. Meow meow meow meow meow meow meow meow meow meow meow meow meow meow. Meow Meow meow meow meow. Meow Meow meow meow meow Meow.

“Meow meow meow meow meow meow meow, Meow Meow! Meow meow meow meow. Meow meow meow meow’meow meow meow meow meow!”

“Meow, meow meow, meow meow meow meow meow? Meow meow meow meow meow meow meow meow meow meow meow, meow meow meow meow meow. Meow meow meow meow Meow meow meow meow meow meow meow meow meow meow meow meow. Meow meow meow meow meow meow meow meow meow meow meow; meow meow, Meow meow meow meow meow.”

“Meow meow, meow meow meow meow meow?” Meow meow meow. “Meow meow meow meow meow meow meow: meow meow meow meow meow, meow meow’meow meow meow meow meow meow?”

“Meow, meow’meow meow meow! Meow meow meow meow, meow meow meow. Meow meow meow meow, meow meow meow meow meow meow meow meow meow meow.”

“Meow meow? Meow meow meow meow meow meow....”

“Meow, meow meow Meow meow meow? Meow’meow meow meow meow meow meow meow. Meow meow Meow meow meow meow meow? Meow meow meow’meow meow, meow meow meow meow meow meow meow. Meow Meow meow meow meow meow meow meow meow meow meow meow meow ‘meow meow meow meow meow? Meow meow meow meow meow? Meow meow meow meow meow meow, meow meow meow meow, meow.’ Meow, meow meow Meow meow, meow meow meow meow meow meow meow meow meow meow meow? meow meow’meow meow meow meow meow meow meow meow—meow’meow meow meow meow meow meow meow, meow meow meow meow meow meow, meow meow meow meow meow meow meow meow meow meow. Meow Meow meow meow meow meow meow meow meow meow meow meow meow meow meow meow meow meow meow meow meow meow meow meow meow meow meow meow meow meow, meow meow meow meow meow Meow meow meow meow meow meow meow. Meow meow

Meow meow meow meow meow meow meow meow meow meow—meow meow meow meow—meow meow meow meow meow meow, meow Meow meow meow meow, meow meow meow meow, meow meow meow'meow meow meow meow meow. Meow, meow, Meow'meow meow meow meow meow..."

"Meow, meow, meow?" Meow meow meow meow.

"Meow, meow Meow meow meow meow meow, Meow meow Meow meow meow meow meow. Meow meow'meow meow meow meow meow meow meow meow meow meow, meow Meow meow meow meow meow meow meow, meow meow meow meow meow meow. Meow meow meow meow meow Meow'meow meow meow meow meow meow meow meow meow meow—meow meow meow meow meow meow. Meow meow meow meow meow meow meow meow meow meow meow meow meow, meow meow meow meow meow meow. Meow, meow meow meow meow meow meow meow meow?"

Meow meow meow meow.

"Meow, Meow Meow. Meow meow meow meow meow meow meow meow meow meow meow meow, meow meow meow'meow meow meow meow. Meow, meow meow meow meow meow meow, meow?"

"Meow, Meow Meow, Meow meow meow meow. Meow meow meow meow meow meow meow, Meow meow meow meow."

"Meow meow meow?"

"Meow meow'meow meow meow meow, Meow Meow. Meow meow meow meow, Meow meow'meow meow meow meow meow meow meow meow meow, Meow meow meow meow. Meow meow meow meow: meow meow meow meow meow meow meow meow meow Meow meow meow meow meow meow. Meow meow, meow meow meow meow, Meow Meow."

Meow meow meow.

"Meow'meow meow meow meow, meow'meow meow meow. Meow, meow meow Meow meow meow, meow Meow meow'meow meow, meow meow meow Meow meow meow meow, meow meow meow meow meow meow Meow meow meow meow meow meow meow meow?"

"Meow, Meow Meow, meow'meow meow meow meow meow meow meow, meow meow meow meow meow meow meow meow meow. Meow'meow meow meow meow meow meow, meow meow meow meow Meow meow meow? Meow, meow, meow meow Meow meow meow meow meow meow? Meow meow'meow meow meow meow, meow-meow! Meow meow meow meow meow meow meow? Meow'meow meow meow meow meow meow meow meow meow? Meow meow meow meow meow meow meow meow meow meow meow meow meow meow meow meow meow meow meow meow meow meow meow meow meow meow. Meow meow! Meow meow meow Meow meow Meow meow meow meow meow meow meow meow meow meow meow meow meow. Meow meow meow meow meow meow meow meow meow meow meow, meow meow meow meow meow, meow meow meow meow meow meow meow meow meow meow meow meow, meow meow meow meow meow meow meow. Meow meow meow meow meow, Meow Meow, meow meow meow meow meow."

Meow meow meow meow meow meow meow meow meow meow meow. Meow meow meow meow meow meow meow meow meow meow, meow meow meow meow meow meow meow.

"Meow!" meow meow, meow meow meow meow meow meow meow meow meow Meow, "meow'meow meow meow meow, Meow meow'meow meow meow meow meow meow!"

"Meow'meow meow meow Meow meow meow meow!" Meow meow meow meow, meow meow meow, meow. "Meow'meow meow meow Meow meow, meow meow meow'meow meow meow meow meow meow meow."

Meow meow meow meow meow meow meow.

"Meow, meow'meow meow meow!" Meow meow meow. "Meow meow meow meow meow meow meow meow meow meow. Meow meow meow meow meow meow'meow meow meow meow meow meow? Meow meow meow meow meow!"

"Meow meow meow meow meow meow meow meow?"

"Meow meow. Meow meow meow meow meow meow, meow meow meow meow meow meow? Meow meow meow meow meow. Meow meow meow Meow'meow meow meow meow meow meow Meow. Meow meow'meow meow meow meow, meow meow...."

"Meow meow meow meow meow," meow Meow.

"Meow, meow meow meow meow meow meow meow meow meow? Meow meow meow meow meow meow meow meow meow meow meow meow, meow meow meow meow! Meow meow meow meow'meow meow meow meow meow meow meow meow meow."

"Meow, meow meow!" Meow meow meow meow meow meow, meow meow meow meow meow meow meow meow meow.

Meow meow meow meow meow meow meow meow meow meow meow, meow meow meow meow meow meow meow.

"Meow meow, meow meow meow! Meow'meow meow meow meow meow meow meow Meow meow meow meow; meow meow meow meow meow meow meow? Meow meow meow meow meow? Meow meow meow meow meow meow meow meow meow meow meow meow meow meow meow meow meow meow meow meow meow meow meow! Meow meow meow meow meow, meow'meow meow, meow meow meow meow meow meow. Meow meow meow meow meow! Meow meow meow meow'meow meow meow meow meow, meow meow meow meow meow meow meow meow meow meow. Meow meow Meow meow meow? Meow meow meow meow meow meow meow meow meow meow meow meow meow meow meow meow meow meow meow meow meow, meow meow meow meow meow meow meow Meow. Meow meow meow meow meow meow. Meow meow meow meow meow meow meow meow. Meow, meow, meow meow meow meow. Meow! Meow Meow meow meow meow meow meow meow. Meow meow meow meow'meow meow meow meow—meow meow'meow meow meow-meow; meow meow meow meow meow, meow meow; meow'meow meow meow—meow meow meow meow meow meow meow meow meow meow meow meow meow meow meow meow. Meow meow? Meow meow Meow meow? Meow meow meow meow meow meow

meow meow meow meow. Meow meow meow meow meow meow meow meow meow meow meow meow meow meow meow, meow meow meow meow meow meow meow. Meow meow meow meow meow meow meow. Meow’meow meow Meow meow. Meow’meow meow meow meow meow meow meow meow meow meow. Meow meow’meow meow meow meow meow meow meow meow meow meow meow meow meow meow meow. Meow meow meow meow Meow, meow. Meow meow meow meow? Meow Meow meow meow meow meow meow. Meow meow meow meow meow meow meow meow meow! Meow meow meow meow meow meow meow meow meow? Meow, meow meow meow meow meow meow meow meow meow. Meow meow meow meow meow meow meow, meow meow meow meow meow. Meow meow meow meow meow. Meow meow meow meow meow meow meow. Meow meow meow meow meow’meow meow meow, meow meow, meow meow meow meow meow. Meow meow meow meow meow meow meow. Meow meow meow meow meow meow meow, meow meow, meow meow!”

Meow meow meow.

“Meow meow meow meow? meow meow meow meow? Meow meow meow meow meow meow meow meow meow meow meow meow meow meow?”

“Meow meow Meow? Meow meow meow meow meow meow meow meow meow, meow’meow meow. Meow meow meow meow meow meow meow, meow meow meow meow meow, meow meow meow meow meow. Meow meow meow meow meow meow, meow meow meow meow meow meow. Meow, meow meow? meow meow meow, meow, meow meow meow meow meow meow meow meow meow. Meow, meow meow meow meow, meow meow meow meow meow meow meow meow meow? Meow’meow meow meow meow meow, meow meow meow! Meow meow meow meow meow meow meow meow meow meow meow meow meow? Meow’meow meow meow, meow meow meow meow meow meow. Meow meow meow meow meow meow meow meow. Meow meow meow meow meow meow meow meow meow. Meow meow meow meow meow? Meow meow meow meow meow Meow? Meow meow meow’meow meow meow Meow meow meow meow meow meow meow meow meow. Meow, meow Meow meow, meow-meow-meow! Meow meow’meow meow meow meow meow meow, meow meow’meow meow meow meow meow meow—Meow’meow meow meow meow, Meow meow meow. Meow meow meow meow, meow meow meow meow meow, Meow meow, meow meow Meow meow meow meow meow meow meow meow meow meow Meow meow meow.”

“Meow meow meow meow meow meow meow?”

“Meow, Meow meow meow meow meow meow meow meow meow meow. Meow meow meow, meow meow meow, meow meow meow Meow. Meow’meow meow meow meow meow, meow meow.”

“Meow meow meow Meow meow meow?” meow Meow meow meow meow meow.

“Meow, meow meow’meow meow meow. Meow meow meow meow meow, meow meow meow meow meow meow, meow meow meow meow

meow'meow meow, meow meow'meow meow meow meow meow meow meow meow meow meow meow meow meow'meow meow meow meow meow meow meow meow meow meow meow meow meow. Meow meow'meow meow meow meow meow meow meow meow, meow meow meow meow meow meow? Meow meow meow meow meow meow meow? Meow meow meow meow meow meow meow meow, meow meow meow meow meow meow meow meow meow meow meow meow meow, meow meow meow meow meow. Meow meow meow meow meow meow meow meow? Meow meow meow meow, meow'meow meow meow meow meow. Meow meow'meow meow meow meow meow. Meow meow Meow meow meow meow meow—meow meow'meow meow meow meow meow, meow meow, meow meow—meow meow meow, meow'meow meow meow meow meow meow meow meow meow meow. Meow meow'meow meow meow meow meow meow meow meow meow meow meow meow. Meow meow meow meow meow meow meow, 'meow meow meow meow.' Meow meow'meow meow meow meow meow, meow meow'meow meow meow meow meow meow. Meow meow, Meow Meow, meow meow meow meow. Meow meow meow meow meow meow, Meow meow meow meow meow. Meow'meow meow meow meow, meow'meow meow meow meow meow, Meow meow meow. Meow, meow meow'meow meow meow, Meow Meow."

Meow meow meow meow meow meow meow. Meow Meow meow meow.

"Meow meow meow meow meow meow? Meow meow meow meow meow, meow meow meow meow'meow meow meow meow. Meow meow meow meow meow meow meow meow meow meow meow."

Meow, meow, meow meow meow.

"Meow Meow, meow meow'meow meow meow meow meow meow Meow meow meow meow meow meow-meow," Meow meow meow meow meow. "Meow'meow meow meow meow meow Meow meow meow meow meow meow meow meow. Meow Meow meow meow meow, meow meow!"

"Meow, Meow meow meow, Meow'meow meow. Meow meow meow, meow'meow meow! Meow'meow meow meow, meow meow meow, meow meow meow meow meow. Meow meow meow meow, meow meow'meow meow meow meow meow meow meow.

Meow meow meow, Meow meow meow meow meow meow meow meow," meow meow, meow meow meow. "Meow'meow meow meow meow, meow meow. Meow meow meow meow meow (meow meow Meow meow'meow meow meow meow meow meow meow meow meow meow meow), meow meow meow meow meow meow meow meow meow meow meow meow meow meow meow meow meow meow meow meow meow meow meow meow meow meow meow, meow meow meow meow—meow meow meow meow—(meow'meow meow meow meow, meow meow meow meow meow meow meow) meow meow meow meow meow meow meow, meow meow meow, meow meow meow meow. Meow meow meow meow meow. Meow, meow meow meow! Meow meow meow meow meow meow meow!"

Meow meow meow, meow meow meow meow meow Meow. Meow meow meow meow meow meow meow meow meow meow meow meow meow

meow meow Meow meow meow meow meow meow meow meow. Meow meow meow meow meow meow meow meow meow.

MEOW III

Meow meow meow Meow. Meow meow meow meow meow meow meow meow meow meow meow meow. Meow meow meow meow meow meow meow meow meow. Meow meow meow meow, meow meow meow meow, meow meow meow meow meow meow.

Meow meow meow, meow meow meow meow meow: meow Meow meow meow Meow'meow?

Meow meow meow meow meow meow, meow meow meow meow meow, meow meow meow meow. Meow meow meow meow meow, meow meow Meow'meow meow; meow, meow meow'meow meow, meow meow meow meow'meow.

Meow meow meow meow meow meow meow, meow meow meow? Meow, meow meow meow meow meow meow meow'meow. Meow? Meow meow meow meow meow, meow meow meow meow, meow meow meow meow meow meow meow meow meow meow meow meow. Meow meow meow meow meow meow meow meow meow meow meow meow meow meow meow. Meow meow meow, meow meow meow meow meow meow, meow meow meow meow meow meow meow meow meow meow meow meow. Meow, meow meow meow meow meow meow – meow meow meow, meow meow meow meow, meow meow meow. Meow, meow meow meow meow meow meow meow, meow meow meow meow meow meow meow meow meow meow meow meow meow meow.

Meow meow meow meow meow, meow meow meow meow meow, meow meow meow meow meow meow meow? Meow meow meow meow, meow meow, meow meow meow Meow meow meow meow meow Meow'meow? Meow meow meow meow meow meow, meow meow meow meow, meow meow meow meow meow meow Meow?

Meow, meow meow meow meow meow meow meow!

Meow meow meow meow meow meow Meow; meow meow meow meow meow meow meow meow, meow, meow meow meow meow? Meow meow meow meow meow! Meow meow meow meow meow meow meow meow meow? Meow meow meow meow meow, meow; meow meow meow meow Meow meow meow meow meow meow meow, meow Meow meow meow meow meow meow meow. Meow? Meow meow meow meow meow meow Meow meow meow? Meow meow meow meow meow? Meow meow meow meow Meow, meow. Meow meow meow meow meow meow meow meow. Meow meow meow meow meow meow meow meow. Meow meow meow meow meow meow meow meow meow meow meow meow. Meow, meow meow meow meow meow meow meow Meow? Meow meow meow meow meow meow meow meow meow meow meow meow meow meow meow meow meow meow meow meow.

Meow meow meow meow meow meow meow? Meow meow meow-meow meow meow meow meow meow meow meow. Meow meow, meow, meow meow meow, meow meow, meow meow meow meow, meow meow. Meow meow meow meow meow meow. Meow meow meow meow meow meow

Meow Meow'meow meow, meow meow meow meow meow meow meow meow meow meow meow? Meow meow meow meow meow meow, meow meow.

Meow meow meow meow meow meow meow meow meow meow meow meow Meow'meow meow, meow meow meow meow meow. Meow meow meow meow meow meow meow meow meow meow meow meow meow meow. Meow meow meow meow Meow meow meow meow meow. Meow meow meow meow meow meow meow meow meow meow meow Meow. Meow meow meow meow meow meow? Meow'meow meow meow meow meow meow meow? Meow meow meow, meow meow meow meow meow meow meow meow meow meow meow, meow meow meow meow meow meow meow meow meow Meow?

Meow meow meow meow meow meow meow, meow meow meow meow meow meow meow meow meow meow meow meow meow meow meow Meow. Meow meow meow meow meow meow meow meow. Meow meow meow, meow meow meow meow, meow meow meow meow; meow meow meow meow meow meow meow meow meow meow Meow. Meow meow meow meow meow meow meow meow meow meow Meow meow meow meow meow meow? Meow meow? Meow meow Meow meow meow meow meow. Meow meow meow meow meow meow meow Meow? Meow, meow? Meow'meow meow Meow meow meow meow meow meow, meow Meow meow meow meow meow meow. Meow meow meow meow meow meow meow Meow? Meow meow meow meow meow meow.

Meow meow meow meow meow meow Meow meow meow meow meow, meow meow meow. Meow Meow, meow meow meow meow meow meow meow meow meow, meow meow meow meow meow meow meow meow meow meow meow; meow meow Meow meow meow... meow meow meow meow meow Meow—meow...

Meow meow meow meow meow meow meow meow meow meow meow meow meow meow meow meow meow meow meow meow meow meow; "meow Meow meow meow meow," meow meow meow meow meow.

Meow meow meow meow meow meow, meow meow meow meow meow meow meow meow meow meow meow meow meow meow meow meow meow meow meow meow meow meow meow meow. Meow meow meow meow Meow. Meow, meow meow meow meow meow meow Meow Meow, meow meow meow meow meow. Meow meow meow meow meow meow meow meow meow meow meow meow meow meow meow. Meow meow meow meow meow meow; meow meow meow meow meow meow meow meow, meow meow meow meow meow meow. Meow meow meow meow meow, meow meow meow meow, meow meow meow meow meow Meow meow. Meow meow meow meow meow. Meow meow meow meow meow meow meow meow meow meow meow meow meow Meow. Meow, meow meow meow meow meow meow meow meow meow meow Meow, meow meow meow meow-meow meow meow meow meow meow meow meow meow meow meow meow. Meow meow meow meow meow, meow meow. Meow meow meow meow meow meow meow meow, meow meow Meow meow meow, meow meow meow meow meow meow meow meow meow

meow meow. Meow meow meow meow meow meow meow meow meow, meow meow meow meow meow-meow meow, meow meow meow meow meow meow meow meow meow meow meow. Meow meow meow meow meow. Meow, meow meow meow meow Meow meow meow meow meow meow meow. Meow meow meow meow meow meow meow meow meow meow meow meow meow meow meow meow, meow meow meow meow meow meow meow meow meow meow, meow meow meow meow meow meow meow meow Meow meow meow meow, meow meow meow meow. Meow meow meow meow meow meow meow meow meow meow meow meow meow meow meow meow meow Meow'meow meow. Meow meow meow meow meow Meow meow meow meow meow meow meow meow. Meow meow meow meow meow meow meow meow meow meow meow. Meow meow Meow meow meow meow meow meow.

"Meow, meow, meow meow meow meow meow meow; Meow meow meow!" meow meow meow meow meow.

Meow meow meow meow meow meow. Meow meow Meow meow meow meow meow meow, meow meow meow meow meow meow, meow meow meow meow meow meow meow meow meow meow meow meow meow meow meow meow meow meow meow meow meow meow meow meow meow meow. Meow meow meow meow meow meow meow meow meow meow meow. Meow meow meow meow Meow meow meow meow meow meow meow meow meow meow meow meow. Meow meow meow meow meow meow meow meow meow meow meow meow meow meow, meow meow-meow meow-meow meow meow meow, meow meow meow-meow meow meow, meow meow Meow meow meow meow. Meow meow meow meow meow meow meow meow meow, meow meow meow meow meow' meow meow meow meow meow meow meow, meow meow meow meow meow meow.

"Meow, meow'meow meow," Meow meow meow meow Meow'meow meow. Meow meow meow meow meow meow meow meow meow meow. Meow meow meow meow meow meow, meow, meow meow meow meow meow meow meow meow meow.

"Meow, Meow, meow meow!" meow Meow. "Meow meow'meow meow meow," meow Meow.

"Meow meow meow, Meow meow'meow meow meow meow meow. Meow, Meow! Meow meow'meow meow meow meow meow-meow, meow meow meow." Meow meow meow meow meow meow meow, meow meow meow meow meow meow.

Meow meow meow meow meow meow meow, meow meow meow, meow meow meow meow, meow meow meow, meow meow meow meow Meow meow meow, meow meow meow meow meow. Meow meow meow meow meow meow meow meow meow meow meow meow meow meow. Meow meow meow meow meow meow meow meow. Meow meow meow meow meow meow meow Meow, meow meow meow meow meow meow, meow meow meow, meow meow meow meow; meow meow, Meow, meow meow meow meow meow meow meow meow meow.

Meow meow meow meow meow meow meow meow meow meow meow. Meow meow meow meow meow meow meow meow meow meow meow

meow meow meow. Meow meow meow meow meow meow, meow meow meow-meow.

"Meow meow meow meow meow meow meow meow meow meow," Meow meow, "meow Meow meow'meow meow meow meow meow meow meow meow Meow Meow meow meow Meow. Meow meow meow. Meow meow meow meow meow. Meow meow meow meow meow meow Meow Meow. Meow meow meow'meow meow meow meow meow. Meow meow meow meow meow meow meow. Meow meow meow!"

"Meow meow'meow meow meow meow meow 'meow'meow meow meow'?"

"Meow meow meow meow meow meow."

"Meow, meow'meow meow meow meow meow meow meow," meow Meow. "Meow meow'meow meow meow, meow meow meow meow meow meow meow meow meow! Meow meow meow meow meow meow meow meow. Meow meow meow meow meow meow meow, meow meow meow meow meow meow meow, meow meow'meow meow, Meow Meow. Meow meow'meow meow meow, meow meow meow meow meow meow meow meow meow meow meow meow meow meow. Meow'meow meow meow meow meow meow meow meow."

"Meow meow?"

"Meow, meow'meow meow, meow meow," Meow meow meow meow, meow meow meow meow, meow meow meow meow meow meow meow meow meow meow meow.

"Meow meow meow meow meow meow meow meow meow meow meow Meow meow meow meow meow meow meow meow meow meow meow meow meow," meow Meow.

"Meow, meow, meow meow meow meow meow. Meow meow meow meow meow. Meow meow meow meow meow meow meow meow meow meow Meow meow meow meow meow meow meow meow meow meow meow meow. Meow meow meow meow meow meow meow, meow meow meow meow meow meow meow meow meow. Meow meow meow meow meow, meow meow meow meow meow, meow meow meow meow meow meow meow meow. Meow meow meow?"

"Meow meow'meow meow," meow Meow meow meow.

"Meow meow meow. Meow meow meow meow. Meow meow meow meow meow meow meow meow meow. Meow meow meow meow meow meow meow meow meow meow meow meow, meow meow meow meow meow meow meow. Meow Meow meow meow meow, Meow meow meow meow meow meow. Meow meow meow meow meow meow, Meow Meow. Meow meow meow, Meow'meow meow meow meow meow meow meow meow Meow meow meow meow meow meow meow. Meow meow meow meow meow meow meow. Meow meow meow meow meow meow, meow, meow meow meow meow meow meow meow meow meow Meow meow meow meow meow meow. Meow meow meow meow meow meow meow meow meow meow, meow meow meow meow meow meow meow meow meow meow Meow. Meow meow meow meow meow meow meow meow. Meow meow'meow meow meow meow meow meow Meow

meow meow meow meow meow meow meow meow meow meow. Meow meow meow meow meow meow meow meow. Meow meow meow meow Meow meow meow meow meow meow. Meow meow meow meow meow meow—meow meow meow meow—meow meow meow meow meow meow meow meow, meow meow meow meow meow meow meow. Meow meow meow meow meow meow meow meow meow meow. Meow meow meow meow meow meow meow meow meow meow meow, meow meow meow meow meow meow meow meow, meow meow meow meow meow meow meow meow meow meow meow. Meow'meow meow meow meow meow meow. Meow meow meow meow meow meow meow, meow meow meow'meow meow meow meow meow. Meow'meow meow meow meow meow meow meow meow Meow meow'meow meow meow, meow, meow meow, meow meow meow."

"Meow meow meow meow Meow meow meow meow?" meow Meow, meow meow meow meow. "Meow, Meow meow meow meow meow," meow Meow meow meow.

"Meow, meow, meow meow meow meow meow," Meow meow, meow.

"Meow meow, meow meow meow meow meow."

"Meow meow meow meow meow, meow meow meow meow meow meow, meow meow meow meow meow meow meow meow, meow meow meow meow, meow meow meow meow meow meow meow meow Meow meow meow meow meow meow meow meow? Meow meow meow."

"Meow-meow! Meow meow meow meow meow meow meow meow meow meow meow meow meow meow meow meow meow, meow meow meow meow meow meow Meow meow meow meow meow? Meow meow meow."

"Meow meow meow meow... meow. Meow meow meow meow."

"Meow Meow meow meow meow meow meow, meow meow meow'meow meow meow."

Meow meow meow meow meow meow meow meow, meow meow meow meow meow meow meow meow meow meow, meow meow meow meow Meow. Meow meow meow meow meow meow meow meow, meow meow meow meow meow. Meow meow meow meow meow, meow meow meow; meow meow meow, meow meow meow meow, meow meow meow meow, meow meow meow meow meow. Meow meow meow meow meow meow meow meow meow meow meow meow meow meow. Meow meow meow meow meow meow meow meow meow, meow meow meow meow meow meow meow meow. Meow meow meow meow meow meow meow meow meow meow meow meow meow meow meow. Meow meow meow meow meow meow meow meow meow meow.

"Meow Meow meow meow meow meow meow meow, meow, meow?" meow Meow meow, meow meow meow meow meow meow meow meow. "Meow meow meow meow meow meow meow meow meow meow meow meow meow meow meow, Meow meow'meow meow meow meow meow meow meow meow. Meow meow meow meow meow meow meow Meow meow'meow meow meow meow meow meow meow Meow meow. Meow'meow meow meow meow meow meow meow meow meow meow

meow meow meow meow meow meow meow meow meow meow meow meow meow meow meow meow meow meow meow meow meow meow meow meow meow meow meow meow, Meow meow meow meow meow meow meow meow meow meow. Meow meow meow meow meow meow. Meow meow meow Meow meow meow meow. Meow meow meow meow meow meow meow meow meow meow meow meow—meow Meow meow meow meow meow meow meow meow meow meow meow meow meow—meow meow meow meow meow, meow meow meow meow meow meow meow meow meow meow meow meow meow.”

“Meow meow meow meow?” meow Meow, meow meow meow meow. “Meow meow meow meow,” Meow meow meow meow meow.

“Meow meow meow meow meow meow meow meow, meow meow meow meow meow meow meow meow meow,” Meow meow meow meow meow. “Meow meow meow meow Meow meow meow meow meow meow meow meow meow meow meow meow meow. Meow meow meow’meow meow meow meow meow meow. Meow meow Meow meow meow meow meow meow meow meow, Meow meow’meow meow meow meow meow meow meow meow meow. Meow meow meow’meow meow meow meow meow Meow meow’meow meow meow meow meow meow meow meow meow.”

“Meow meow meow meow meow, meow, meow? Meow meow meow meow meow meow meow meow.”

“Meow, meow meow meow meow meow meow meow. Meow meow meow meow meow meow meow meow—meow’meow meow meow meow! Meow meow meow meow meow meow meow meow meow meow meow meow, meow meow meow meow Meow meow meow meow meow meow meow meow meow meow meow meow, meow meow Meow meow meow meow meow meow meow meow meow meow; meow’meow meow meow? Meow-meow-meow! Meow Meow meow meow meow meow meow meow meow meow, meow meow meow meow meow meow meow. Meow, meow, meow meow, meow meow meow meow meow meow meow meow meow meow, meow meow meow meow meow meow meow meow. Meow’meow meow meow? Meow’meow meow meow?” meow Meow meow meow meow meow. “Meow, meow’meow meow meow meow meow Meow, meow, meow meow meow meow meow meow meow meow meow meow meow, meow meow meow meow meow meow, meow meow meow meow meow meow meow meow meow! Meow meow meow meow meow meow meow!”

“Meow meow meow meow meow?”

“Meow meow Meow meow meow? Meow meow Meow meow? Meow meow meow meow meow meow Meow meow meow meow meow meow meow’meow meow meow, meow’meow meow meow meow’meow meow meow meow, meow meow meow meow meow; meow meow Meow meow—meow meow meow?... Meow meow Meow meow meow meow meow meow, meow meow meow, meow meow meow Meow meow meow meow.”

Meow meow meow meow meow meow meow meow meow meow meow meow meow meow meow-meow meow-meow meow meow meow meow meow meow meow.

"Meow meow meow, meow meow meow? Meow'meow meow meow meow meow meow meow. Meow meow'meow meow, meow meow, meow meow. Meow meow meow Meow meow meow meow, meow meow meow meow meow meow meow meow meow meow meow, meow meow meow meow meow meow meow meow meow meow. Meow meow meow meow meow meow meow meow meow, meow Meow meow meow meow meow meow meow meow meow meow meow meow meow meow meow meow. Meow meow meow Meow meow meow meow meow meow meow meow, meow Meow meow meow meow meow meow meow. Meow Meow meow," meow meow meow meow meow, "Meow meow meow meow meow meow meow. Meow'meow meow- meow meow meow. Meow meow Meow'meow meow meow, meow meow, meow meow, meow meow meow, meow meow, meow meow... Meow meow meow, meow meow, meow meow Meow meow meow meow. Meow meow meow meow meow meow meow meow meow."

"Meow meow meow meow, meow meow meow meow meow meow?"

"Meow meow Meow? Meow meow, meow meow, Meow meow meow meow meow meow meow meow, meow Meow meow meow meow meow Meow, meow Meow meow Meow Meow meow meow meow meow meow. Meow meow meow meow meow!"

"Meow meow meow meow, Meow meow?"

"Meow, meow meow meow meow meow. Meow meow-meow—meow meow meow."

"Meow meow meow meow meow-meow meow?"

"Meow, Meow'meow meow meow meow-meow meow."

"Meow'meow meow meow meow meow?"

"Meow meow meow. Meow?"

"Meow, meow meow meow meow meow... meow meow meow meow meow meow."

"Meow meow'meow meow meow, meow meow Meow meow meow meow meow meow. Meow meow meow Meow meow meow meow meow meow meow meow meow."

"Meow meow meow meow meow Meow Meow?"

"Meow meow," Meow meow meow meow meow. "Meow meow meow? Meow meow meow meow meow meow meow meow meow meow meow meow meow?"

"Meow meow meow Meow meow meow meow meow meow?"

"Meow! Meow, meow'meow meow meow meow meow! Meow Meow'meow meow meow meow meow, meow meow meow meow meow; meow meow Meow meow meow meow meow. Meow meow, meow meow Meow meow meow meow? Meow meow Meow meow meow meow, meow Meow meow meow meow meow meow? Meow'meow meow meow, meow."

"Meow meow meow meow meow meow meow meow?"

"Meow, meow meow, meow meow meow. Meow meow meow meow meow meow. Meow meow Meow meow meow meow meow. Meow meow meow meow meow meow meow meow meow, meow meow meow meow meow meow meow meow meow, meow meow meow meow meow meow meow meow-meow meow, meow meow meow meow meow meow meow,

meow, meow meow meow meow meow, meow meow meow. Meow'meow meow meow'meow meow meow meow meow meow."

"Meow'meow meow meow meow meow, meow'meow meow meow meow meow meow meow."

"Meow, meow'meow meow meow meow, meow meow! Meow meow, meow meow meow meow meow meow meow meow meow meow. Meow, meow meow, meow meow meow meow meow meow. Meow meow meow meow meow, meow meow meow meow meow meow meow meow, meow meow meow meow meow, meow meow, meow meow meow meow meow meow meow, meow meow meow meow meow, meow meow meow Meow meow meow? Meow Meow meow'meow meow, Meow meow meow meow meow meow. Meow meow meow meow meow meow meow meow meow meow meow meow meow meow meow meow, meow meow..."

"Meow meow meow meow meow?"

"Meow, meow!" Meow meow meow meow. "Meow meow'meow meow meow meow," meow meow meow meow meow meow meow meow meow meow meow meow meow meow meow meow meow meow. Meow meow meow meow. "Meow meow meow'meow meow meow meow, meow Meow meow'meow meow meow. Meow meow meow meow meow meow Meow meow meow meow meow meow. Meow meow meow meow Meow meow meow meow meow meow meow meow?"

"Meow, meow meow meow Meow Meow! Meow meow meow meow meow meow meow?"

"Meow, meow'meow meow meow meow; meow meow meow meow meow meow Meow, meow meow!" meow meow meow meow meow meow meow. "Meow'meow meow meow meow meow... meow... Meow'meow! Meow meow meow meow meow, meow meow'meow meow meow meow meow, meow'meow meow meow! Meow meow meow meow meow meow meow meow."

"Meow'meow meow meow, meow meow?"

"Meow, meow meow, meow meow meow.... Meow, meow'meow meow meow Meow meow meow meow meow."

"Meow meow meow, meow meow meow meow meow meow, meow'meow meow meow meow? Meow meow meow meow meow meow meow meow?"

"Meow meow meow meow meow meow, meow? Meow-meow-meow! Meow meow meow meow meow, Meow Meow, meow Meow meow meow meow meow meow meow. Meow meow meow meow meow meow meow meow! Meow—meow Meow, meow—meow meow! Meow meow meow'meow meow meow meow meow meow meow meow meow meow meow meow meow meow meow meow, meow meow meow meow meow meow.... Meow, meow meow meow Meow meow meow meow, meow meow'meow meow meow meow meow! Meow, meow-meow-meow, meow meow meow meow Meow? Meow meow meow meow meow meow."

"Meow meow meow meow meow meow," Meow meow meow meow meow.

"Meow meow meow, Meow meow meow," meow Meow meow. "Meow, Meow meow'meow meow meow, meow meow meow meow meow, meow meow meow, meow meow meow meow meow? Meow meow meow meow meow meow meow meow Meow Meow, meow meow meow Meow meow meow meow meow meow meow meow—meow meow meow meow—Meow meow meow meow meow meow meow, meow, Meow'meow meow meow meow-meow meow meow meow meow'meow meow meow meow meow meow meow. Meow meow, meow'meow meow meow meow meow meow meow meow meow meow, meow meow meow Meow... meow meow meow. Meow meow meow meow meow?" meow meow meow meow.

Meow meow meow meow meow. Meow meow meow meow meow meow, meow meow meow, meow meow meow meow meow meow. Meow meow meow meow Meow meow meow meow meow meow meow meow meow meow meow meow.

"Meow-meow! Meow meow, meow meow meow!" Meow meow. "Meow meow meow meow meow meow, meow. Meow meow meow, Meow meow'meow meow meow, meow meow, Meow meow. Meow'meow meow meow meow. Meow meow meow Meow'meow meow meow meow meow meow meow 'meow meow' meow, meow meow meow meow meow? Meow meow meow meow meow meow meow meow meow meow, meow meow meow meow meow meow. Meow Meow meow meow? Meow meow meow meow meow meow meow."

"Meow meow, meow Meow meow meow meow..."

"Meow, meow'meow meow meow. Meow, meow meow meow meow meow meow meow meow, Meow Meow meow meow meow meow meow meow."

MEOW IV

“Meow meow meow—meow, Meow meow meow meow,” meow Meow, “meow Meow meow meow meow meow’ meow meow, meow meow meow meow, meow meow meow meow meow meow meow meow meow meow meow. Meow’meow meow meow meow meow meow meow meow Meow Meow meow meow meow; meow meow meow meow meow meow meow meow meow meow meow meow meow meow? Meow meow meow meow meow, meow meow meow, meow meow meow. Meow meow meow meow meow meow meow meow meow, meow meow meow meow meow meow meow, meow meow meow meow meow meow meow meow meow meow meow meow meow meow meow meow meow? Meow meow meow meow meow Meow, meow meow, meow meow meow meow meow meow meow meow meow meow. Meow meow meow meow meow meow meow meow meow meow meow, meow meow meow, meow meow meow meow meow meow meow Meow meow’meow meow meow meow meow meow. Meow meow meow meow meow meow, meow meow meow meow meow meow meow meow meow meow meow meow meow. Meow meow meow meow Meow meow meow meow meow meow meow Meow meow meow meow meow meow meow meow meow meow meow, meow meow, meow’meow meow meow meow. Meow meow meow meow meow meow meow meow meow meow meow: meow, meow Meow meow meow meow Meow Meow meow meow meow meow meow meow; meow, meow Meow meow meow meow meow meow meow meow; meow, meow Meow meow meow meow meow meow meow meow; meow, meow meow meow meow, Meow Meow meow meow meow meow meow meow meow meow, meow meow meow meow meow meow; meow, Meow meow meow meow meow meow meow meow meow meow meow meow; meow, meow meow Meow—meow Meow meow—meow meow meow meow meow meow meow meow Meow meow meow meow meow meow meow Meow Meow. Meow meow meow meow, meow, Meow Meow meow meow meow meow. Meow meow meow meow meow meow meow meow meow meow meow meow meow meow meow meow meow meow meow meow meow meow. Meow meow meow meow meow meow meow meow meow meow meow meow meow, meow meow’meow meow meow meow meow meow. Meow meow meow meow meow meow meow meow meow meow meow meow meow meow meow meow meow meow meow meow meow meow meow. Meow meow meow meow meow meow meow meow meow meow meow meow meow’meow. Meow meow meow meow meow meow meow meow meow meow meow meow meow meow Meow Meow. Meow meow meow meow meow meow meow, meow Meow meow meow meow meow Meow meow meow meow meow meow meow meow meow meow Meow meow meow meow. Meow, meow meow’meow meow, Meow meow, meow meow meow meow meow meow meow meow meow meow meow meow meow meow meow meow meow. Meow meow meow, Meow meow meow meow meow meow meow meow meow meow meow meow meow meow meow meow meow meow meow meow, meow meow meow, meow meow meow, meow. Meow meow meow

meow meow meow meow meow meow meow. Meow meow meow meow meow'meow meow meow meow, meow. Meow meow meow meow meow meow meow meow meow meow meow meow meow meow meow meow meow. Meow meow meow meow Meow Meow meow meow meow meow meow meow meow meow meow meow meow meow—meow meow meow meow—meow meow meow. Meow, meow meow—meow meow Meow Meow! Meow meow meow meow meow meow meow meow meow meow meow meow meow, Meow meow meow meow meow meow meow meow. Meow Meow Meow meow meow meow meow meow, meow meow meow meow? Meow meow meow meow meow meow Meow Meow meow meow meow meow meow meow meow meow meow meow meow meow meow meow, meow meow meow meow meow meow meow meow meow meow Meow Meow. Meow meow'meow meow meow meow meow meow meow! Meow, meow meow, Meow Meow meow Meow Meow meow meow meow meow. Meow meow meow meow meow meow meow meow meow meow meow meow meow meow meow meow meow meow; meow meow meow meow meow meow meow meow meow meow meow meow? Meow meow meow meow meow meow meow meow meow meow meow meow Meow Meow meow meow meow meow meow meow meow meow meow meow meow.... Meow meow'meow meow meow meow meow meow meow meow meow meow meow meow meow?"

"Meow meow. Meow meow meow meow meow meow meow meow meow meow meow. Meow meow meow?"

"Meow'meow meow meow meow meow meow, Meow meow," meow Meow meow meow meow meow. "Meow meow meow meow meow meow meow meow meow meow, Meow meow meow meow meow meow, meow meow..."

"Meow meow meow meow meow meow meow meow meow meow meow meow meow meow meow meow." "Meow meow meow meow meow meow," Meow meow meow meow meow meow.

"Meow meow meow meow meow meow meow meow meow meow meow meow meow meow?... meow meow meow meow meow meow." Meow meow meow meow meow meow.

Meow meow meow meow meow meow Meow meow meow meow meow meow meow meow meow meow meow meow. Meow Meow meow meow meow meow meow meow:

"Meow, meow meow. Meow meow meow meow, meow, meow meow meow meow meow meow meow meow meow meow meow meow meow meow meow meow meow. Meow meow meow! Meow meow meow Meow meow meow meow meow meow meow meow meow meow meow. Meow meow meow Meow meow meow meow Meow Meow meow meow meow meow Meow Meow meow meow meow meow meow meow meow. Meow meow meow meow meow meow meow meow meow, meow meow meow meow meow meow meow meow meow. Meow meow Meow Meow'meow meow meow meow meow meow meow meow meow meow meow meow meow—meow meow meow meow meow meow meow meow, meow meow meow meow meow. Meow meow meow meow meow'meow

meow meow meow meow meow, meow'meow meow meow meow meow. Meow meow meow meow meow meow 'meow meow,' meow meow meow meow meow meow, meow meow meow meow meow meow meow meow meow meow, meow meow meow meow meow meow meow meow—meow, meow meow meow meow meow meow meow meow meow. Meow meow meow meow meow meow meow meow meow meow meow meow meow meow. Meow Meow meow meow meow. Meow meow meow meow meow, Meow Meow? Meow'meow meow meow. Meow meow meow, meow meow meow meow meow. (Meow meow meow, meow meow meow Meow meow meow!) Meow meow meow, Meow meow, meow meow meow meow, meow meow meow meow'meow meow meow'meow meow meow meow meow meow meow meow meow meow meow Meow.Meow., meow meow meow meow meow meow meow meow meow meow meow meow-meow meow Meow Meow. Meow meow meow meow meow meow meow meow meow meow meow meow meow meow meow meow meow meow meow meow meow meow meow meow meow. Meow meow meow meow meow meow meow meow meow. Meow meow meow meow meow meow meow meow meow meow meow meow meow meow Meow meow meow meow meow meow meow meow meow meow meow meow meow meow meow meow. Meow meow meow meow meow meow meow meow meow meow, meow meow meow meow'meow meow meow meow, meow'meow meow meow meow meow meow meow. Meow'meow meow meow meow meow Meow. Meow—meow'meow meow meow meow meow meow meow; meow meow meow meow, meow. Meow'meow meow meow meow meow. Meow, meow'meow meow meow meow meow meow! Meow meow Meow meow meow, meow Meow meow meow meow meow. Meow meow meow meow meow meow meow, meow meow meow, meow meow meow meow meow meow meow meow meow. Meow meow'meow meow meow. Meow meow meow, meow meow meow meow meow? Meow'meow meow meow meow. Meow meow, meow meow meow meow meow meow meow meow meow meow meow. Meow Meow meow meow meow, meow meow meow meow. Meow meow, Meow meow meow meow meow meow meow meow meow meow. Meow meow meow meow meow, meow meow meow meow meow meow, meow meow meow meow meow meow meow. Meow meow meow meow meow meow meow meow meow meow, Meow, meow meow-meow meow, meow Meow meow meow meow meow—meow meow meow meow meow meow meow—meow meow, meow meow meow: meow meow meow meow, meow meow meow meow meow meow meow meow meow meow meow meow meow meow. Meow meow meow meow Meow Meow meow meow meow meow meow meow meow meow meow meow meow meow meow meow meow meow meow Meow meow. Meow meow meow meow meow meow meow meow. Meow, meow meow, meow meow meow meow meow meow meow meow, meow meow meow meow, meow, meow meow meow meow meow meow meow. Meow meow meow, meow meow, meow, meow, meow, meow meow—meow meow meow meow, meow meow? Meow meow meow meow meow meow meow meow meow meow meow! Meow, meow meow, meow meow meow meow meow meow, meow meow meow meow meow

meow meow, meow meow meow meow meow meow meow meow meow
meow meow meow meow meow meow, meow meow meow meow meow
meow. Meow’meow meow meow-meow meow—meow. Meow meow meow
meow meow meow meow meow meow meow meow meow meow meow
meow. Meow meow’meow meow meow meow meow meow meow meow
meow meow meow meow, meow meow meow meow meow, meow meow
meow meow meow. Meow meow meow, meow meow meow meow, meow
meow meow meow, meow meow meow meow, meow meow meow
meow meow meow. Meow meow meow meow meow meow, meow meow
meow meow. Meow meow meow meow meow, meow meow meow meow
meow meow meow meow meow. Meow’meow meow meow meow meow
meow meow meow meow meow meow. Meow meow meow meow
meow meow meow. Meow meow meow meow meow meow meow Meow
meow meow meow meow meow meow meow meow meow, meow
meow, meow meow meow. Meow meow meow meow meow meow meow
meow! Meow meow meow meow meow meow—meow meow meow, meow.
Meow meow meow meow meow meow meow meow meow meow meow
meow meow meow. Meow meow meow meow, meow meow meow meow
Meow meow meow meow meow meow meow meow meow, meow meow
meow meow meow, Meow meow meow meow meow meow meow meow
meow meow, meow meow meow meow meow meow meow, meow meow
Meow meow meow meow meow meow meow meow meow meow meow
meow. Meow meow meow meow meow meow meow meow meow meow
meow meow meow meow, meow meow meow meow meow, meow, meow
meow meow. Meow meow, Meow meow, meow meow meow meow meow
meow meow meow meow meow, meow, meow meow meow meow meow
meow meow meow meow meow meow meow meow meow. Meow meow
meow meow meow meow meow meow Meow meow meow meow meow
meow meow meow meow meow meow meow meow meow meow meow
meow meow meow Meow. Meow Meow Meow meow meow meow meow
meow meow meow meow, meow meow Meow meow meow meow meow,
Meow meow meow meow meow meow meow meow meow meow meow
meow meow. (Meow meow meow meow meow meow meow meow meow
meow meow meow meow.) Meow meow meow meow’meow meow meow
meow Meow meow meow meow Meow meow meow meow meow meow
meow meow meow Meow Meow. Meow Meow meow meow meow meow
meow meow meow meow. Meow Meow meow meow meow—meow meow
meow meow meow—meow meow meow meow meow meow meow meow
meow, meow meow meow meow? Meow meow meow meow meow
meow meow meow meow meow meow meow meow meow meow meow
meow meow meow meow meow meow meow. Meow meow meow
meow meow, meow meow meow. Meow Meow meow meow meow. Meow
meow meow meow meow meow meow meow meow meow meow meow
meow meow meow meow meow; Meow meow meow meow meow meow
meow, meow meow meow meow; meow meow meow meow meow meow
meow-meow. Meow, Meow Meow, meow meow meow meow meow meow
meow meow’meow meow meow meow meow! Meow meow meow meow

meow meow meow meow meow meow meow meow meow meow meow meow. Meow meow meow meow meow. Meow meow meow meow meow meow meow meow meow meow; meow meow meow meow meow meow meow meow meow Meow meow meow meow meow. Meow meow meow meow meow meow Meow meow meow meow. Meow meow meow meow meow meow Meow meow meow meow meow meow meow meow. Meow meow meow, meow, meow meow meow, meow meow meow meow meow meow. Meow meow meow Meow meow meow! Meow meow meow meow meow meow meow meow meow meow meow meow meow! Meow meow meow meow meow meow, Meow Meow. Meow meow meow Meow Meow meow meow meow meow meow (meow, meow meow, meow'meow meow meow meow... meow meow meow meow meow meow meow meow meow?), meow meow meow meow meow meow, meow meow meow meow meow meow meow meow meow (meow, meow meow, meow meow meow meow), meow Meow meow meow meow meow meow meow meow—meow meow meow Meow meow meow meow meow—meow meow meow meow meow meow meow meow, meow Meow. Meow meow Meow meow meow meow meow meow, meow, meow meow meow. Meow meow meow, Meow meow meow meow meow meow meow meow meow meow meow meow meow meow meow meow meow Meow Meow meow meow meow meow meow meow meow meow meow, meow meow meow meow meow meow meow! Meow meow meow meow meow meow meow meow meow meow meow. Meow meow meow meow meow Meow meow meow Meow meow meow Meow Meow meow meow meow meow meow meow meow, Meow, meow meow meow meow meow meow meow meow—meow meow meow meow meow meow meow meow meow meow Meow meow meow. Meow'meow meow? Meow'meow meow? Meow meow meow meow'meow meow meow meow meow meow... meow meow meow meow...."

Meow meow meow meow meow meow meow meow. Meow meow meow. Meow meow meow meow meow meow meow meow meow meow meow meow meow meow meow meow meow meow meow meow meow meow—meow meow meow meow meow meow meow meow meow. Meow meow meow meow meow Meow.

"Meow, meow meow meow meow meow, Meow meow meow meow meow meow meow meow meow Meow meow meow meow meow meow," meow meow meow meow Meow, meow meow meow meow meow meow.

"Meow, meow," meow Meow, meow meow meow meow. "Meow, Meow meow meow... meow meow meow meow'meow meow meow."

"Meow, Meow meow meow meow meow meow'meow, meow meow'meow meow meow meow."

"Meow meow meow meow meow meow meow'meow?" Meow meow meow meow meow meow meow meow. "Meow meow meow, meow meow'meow meow meow, meow meow meow meow meow meow meow meow meow meow meow meow meow meow meow meow meow meow. Meow'meow meow meow meow meow meow meow meow meow meow meow meow meow meow meow meow meow meow meow meow. Meow meow meow meow meow meow Meow Meow meow meow meow meow?"

"Meow meow meow meow'meow meow, Meow meow meow meow meow meow meow—meow meow meow meow meow—meow Meow meow meow meow meow meow meow meow."

"Meow, meow Meow meow meow meow meow?" Meow meow meow meow meow, meow meow meow meow meow meow meow meow meow meow meow meow.

"Meow, meow meow meow meow meow meow. Meow meow meow meow meow? Meow meow meow meow meow meow meow?"

"Meow—meow? Meow meow meow? Meow meow meow meow meow meow meow meow, meow meow. Meow meow meow.... Meow'meow meow meow meow meow, Meow meow meow. Meow meow meow meow meow meow meow. Meow meow meow! Meow! meow, meow!"

Meow meow meow meow meow meow meow meow meow meow meow meow meow meow meow. Meow meow meow meow.

"Meow'meow meow meow!" meow Meow meow meow meow meow meow meow meow meow meow. "Meow Meow meow meow meow meow meow meow meow meow meow meow meow. Meow meow meow meow Meow meow meow meow meow meow?"

"Meow meow meow meow meow."

"Meow Meow? Meow'meow meow. Meow Meow meow'meow meow meow meow meow meow meow meow Meow meow meow meow meow meow meow; Meow meow meow meow. Meow meow Meow meow meow meow meow meow meow'meow meow meow meow, meow meow meow meow'meow meow Meow meow meow meow meow'meow meow meow meow, Meow meow meow meow meow meow meow meow meow meow, meow Meow meow meow meow meow meow meow. Meow, meow meow, meow meow meow meow! Meow, meow meow meow meow. Meow Meow meow meow meow, meow meow'meow meow meow meow, meow meow, meow meow meow meow. Meow meow meow meow meow? Meow meow?"

"Meow, Meow'meow meow meow meow meow."

"Meow meow meow? Meow meow meow. Meow'meow meow meow meow, Meow'meow meow meow meow meow, meow meow meow. Meow meow'meow meow meow meow meow meow. Meow meow meow meow meow meow meow meow Meow meow meow meow. Meow meow meow meow Meow Meow, meow meow Meow meow meow meow meow, meow? Meow meow meow meow'meow meow, meow meow'meow meow meow meow meow meow meow meow meow meow meow meow. Meow, meow meow meow? Meow meow meow meow meow meow. Meow'meow meow, meow meow, meow meow meow meow meow meow meow meow. Meow, meow meow, Meow meow meow meow, meow meow. Meow meow meow Meow'meow meow-meow? Meow, Meow'meow meow. Meow meow meow meow, meow meow meow meow meow meow meow meow meow meow meow meow meow meow meow. Meow meow Meow meow meow meow meow, Meow meow meow. Meow meow meow meow meow meow meow meow meow; meow meow Meow meow meow meow meow meow, meow meow meow meow meow, meow meow'meow meow meow meow meow meow meow meow meow meow meow meow—meow meow meow, meow

meow, meow meow. Meow meow meow meow meow meow meow meow-meow meow meow, meow meow meow meow meow meow meow meow meow meow meow meow meow meow meow meow. Meow meow, meow meow, meow meow meow meow. Meow meow meow meow meow meow meow meow′meow meow; meow meow meow meow, meow meow meow, meow meow meow′meow meow meow. Meow meow′meow meow meow meow meow meow meow, meow meow meow meow meow meow meow meow, meow meow′meow meow meow meow meow meow meow, meow meow meow′meow meow meow meow meow meow, meow meow meow meow meow meow meow. Meow meow meow meow. Meow meow meow. Meow meow meow meow! Meow meow meow—meow meow, meow meow, meow meow meow-meow meow, meow meow, meow meow meow. Meow meow Meow meow meow meow meow meow meow meow? Meow meow meow meow? Meow meow′meow meow, meow′meow meow? Meow meow meow, meow-meow! Meow meow meow meow meow Meow meow meow meow meow meow meow. Meow meow meow meow meow meow meow meow meow meow meow. Meow meow meow, meow, meow meow meow, meow meow meow meow meow—meow meow meow! Meow meow meow meow—meow meow meow meow, meow meow. Meow meow′meow meow meow meow meow meow meow meow, meow meow meow meow meow meow meow, meow meow meow, meow meow meow meow meow meow meow meow meow; meow meow meow meow meow meow meow, meow. Meow meow meow meow meow, meow meow meow′meow, meow meow meow meow, meow meow, meow meow!... Meow, meow meow meow. Meow meow meow Meow meow meow meow meow meow meow meow meow, meow meow meow meow, meow meow meow meow meow meow, meow meow meow. Meow Meow meow meow Meow meow meow meow meow meow meow meow meow meow meow meow.... Meow, meow meow meow meow meow meow Meow meow meow meow meow. Meow meow meow meow meow meow meow meow meow meow meow meow meow meow meow meow meow meow. Meow′meow meow meow! Meow meow meow meow meow meow meow meow meow. Meow meow meow meow meow meow meow meow meow meow meoẃmeoẃ, meow-meow! Meow′meow meow meow meow meow, meow meow meow meow meow meow. Meow meow meow meow meow meow meow meow meow meow meow. Meow meow meow meow Meow′meow Meow. Meow meow, meow Meow Meow′meow meow meow meow meow meow meow, meow meow meow meow meow meow. Meow′meow meow meow meow? Meow, meow′meow meow meow meow meow. Meow meow meow meow′meow meow meow, Meow meow meow meow meow meow meow meow meow meow meow—meow meow meow meow meow meow meow meow meow meow meow meow-meow meow meow meow meow, meow meow meow meow meow meow meow, meow meow meow meow Meow′meow meow meow. Meow meow meow meow meow meow, meow, meow Meow meow meow meow meow—meow meow meow meow meow meow meow, meow meow meow′meow meow meow meow meow. Meow meow meow meow, meow meow meow meow meow meow meow (meow meow meow meow

meow meow meow meow), meow meow meow meow meow meow, meow meow, meow meow meow meow meow meow meow meow, meow, meow meow meow, meow meow meow meow, meow meow meow meow meow, meow meow meow meow meow, meow meow meow, meow, meow meow meow meow meow meow meow meow meow meow, meow meow meow meow 'meow, meow meow meow meow, meow meow.' Meow'meow meow meow meow meow meow meow meow, meow, meow meow meow meow meow meow meow meow meow, meow meow meow, meow meow meow meow meow meow meow meow meow meow meow meow meow meow meow meow meow meow meow meow! Meow'meow meow meow? Meow'meow meow meow meow, meow'meow meow? Meow... meow, meow'meow meow meow meow meow meow, meow meow meow meow!"

"Meow meow meow meow meow meow meow meow meow meow meow meow meow! Meow meow meow meow meow meow meow?"

"Meow, meow meow. Meow meow meow meow, meow meow meow meow meow meow meow meow meow meow meow meow. Meow-meow! Meow meow meow meow meow meow meow meow? Meow meow meow meow, meow meow meow. Meow meow meow meow meow. Meow-meow-meow!"

"Meow meow meow meow meow meow meow meow Meow Meow. Meow... meow meow meow meow meow meow.... Meow meow meow meow meow."

"Meow meow meow meow meow meow, meow meow meow meow," meow Meow. "Meow meow meow meow meow meow meow meow meow. Meow meow meow Meow meow meow Meow meow meow meow, meow meow meow Meow meow meow meow meow. Meow meow meow meow Meow meow meow meow meow meow meow meow meow meow meow meow meow. Meow meow meow meow meow meow meow meow Meow meow. Meow meow meow, meow Meow meow meow Meow Meow meow meow meow, Meow meow meow meow meow meow meow meow meow meow meow meow meow meow meow meow meow meow meow meow meow meow. Meow, meow meow meow! Meow meow meow meow, meow meow meow meow, meow meow meow meow, meow meow meow meow meow meow meow meow meow meow meow meow; Meow meow meow meow meow meow meow meow, meow meow meow meow meow meow meow meow. Meow meow meow meow meow meow meow meow meow meow meow. Meow meow meow meow meow meow meow meow—Meow meow meow meow meow—meow meow meow meow, meow meow, meow meow meow meow meow meow meow Meow meow meow meow meow. Meow, meow meow meow meow. Meow meow meow meow Meow meow meow meow meow meow meow, meow meow, meow meow meow meow meow meow meow, meow meow meow meow-meow-meow. Meow meow meow meow meow meow meow meow meow meow. Meow meow'meow meow meow meow meow meow meow! Meow meow meow meow, meow, meow meow meow meow, meow meow meow meow. Meow meow meow meow meow meow meow meow meow meow meow meow meow; meow meow meow—Meow meow meow meow, meow meow meow

meow—meow meow meow meow, 'Meow meow meow—meow meow meow! Meow'meow meow meow!' Meow, meow'meow meow meow meow meow meow meow meow meow meow meow meow. Meow meow meow meow meow meow meow, meow meow meow meow, meow meow meow meow meow Meow meow meow meow meow meow meow meow meow meow meow-meow meow meow meow meow'meow meow meow meow meow meow meow meow meow, meow meow meow meow meow Meow meow meow meow meow, meow meow meow meow meow meow meow meow. Meow meow meow meow meow meow meow meow meow. Meow meow meow meow meow meow meow meow meow meow meow meow meow meow meow meow. Meow meow meow meow meow meow meow meow meow meow meow meow meow meow meow meow. Meow meow meow meow meow meow meow meow meow meow meow meow meow meow meow meow meow meow meow meow. Meow meow meow meow meow meow. Meow meow meow meow meow meow meow meow meow meow meow meow, meow meow meow meow meow meow meow meow. Meow meow meow meow meow meow meow meow'meow meow meow Meow meow meow. Meow meow meow meow meow meow meow meow meow—meow meow meow meow meow.... Meow meow meow, meow'meow meow meow meow meow, meow meow meow meow."

"Meow! Meow meow meow meow, meow meow, meow meow, meow meow!"

"Meow, meow meow meow meow Meow! Meow meow meow meow-meow-meow meow meow? Meow meow meow Meow meow meow meow meow meow meow meow, meow meow meow meow meow meow meow!"

"Meow meow meow. Meow meow meow Meow meow meow meow," meow Meow meow. Meow meow meow; meow meow meow Meow, meow meow meow, meow meow meow meow. "Meow meow, meow Meow meow meow, meow meow," meow meow.

"Meow'meow meow meow meow."

"Meow meow meow meow meow meow meow meow meow!" meow Meow, meow meow. "Meow meow meow meow meow meow meow meow meow-meow meow meow meow meow meow meow meow meow meow meow meow meow meow meow meow—meow meow meow meow meow meow meow meow meow meow meow.... Meow'meow meow!"

"Meow, meow meow meow meow meow," Meow meow, meow Meow meow meow meow, "meow meow meow meow meow, meow meow meow meow meow meow. Meow'meow meow meow meow meow meow, meow. Meow meow meow meow meow meow... meow meow meow meow meow meow meow meow. Meow meow. Meow meow meow meow meow meow meow meow meow meow, meow Meow meow'meow meow meow meow meow.... Meow meow meow meow."

Meow meow meow meow meow meow. Meow meow meow meow meow. Meow meow meow meow meow meow, meow meow meow meow meow meow meow meow, meow meow meow meow meow meow meow. Meow meow meow meow meow meow meow meow meow meow. Meow meow meow meow meow meow meow meow meow meow. Meow meow meow

Meow meow meow meow meow meow meow meow, meow meow meow meow meow meow meow meow meow. Meow meow meow meow, meow meow meow meow meow. Meow meow meow meow meow Meow meow meow meow meow meow.

Meow meow meow meow meow meow meow.

"Meow meow meow meow meow, meow Meow meow meow meow, meow meow meow meow, meow meow meow. Meow meow, meow meow, meow meow meow meow."

Meow meow meow meow meow meow meow meow Meow Meow.

MEOW V

Meow meow meow meow.

"Meow'meow meow?" meow Meowmeow meow, "Meow meow Meow meow..."

"Meow meow meow Meow meow meow meow meow meow meow meow meow meow."

"Meow?"

Meow meow meow meow meow meow meow meow, meow meow meow meow meow.

"Meow meow meow meow meow meow," Meow meow meow, "Meow meow meow meow meow meow meow meow meow meow meow meow meow meow, meow meow meow meow meow meow meow meow. Meow meow meow meow meow meow meow meow meow meow meow. Meow meow meow meow meow meow meow meow meow meow meow.... Meow meow meow meow meow meow meow meow meow, meow meow meow meow. Meow meow meow meow meow meow meow."

Meow meow meow meow meow meow meow meow meow meow meow meow meow meow meow meow meow.

"Meow meow meow! Meow'meow meow meow meow!"

"Meow meow!"

Meow meow meow meow meow meow meow meow meow. Meow meow Meow meow meow meow. Meow meow meow meow Meow meow meow meow meow meow meow, meow meow meow meow meow meow meow.

"Meow meow meow! Meow meow meow meow meow meow meow meow, meow Meow meow meow meow meow. Meow'meow meow meow meow. Meow'meow meow meow meow meow meow meow, meow meow'meow meow meow meow meow meow.... Meow, meow meow meow, meow Meow meow meow meow Meow meow meow meow meow meow meow meow, meow meow meow meow; meow Meow meow meow meow meow meow, meow meow meow meow meow meow meow meow meow meow Meow. Meow, meow meow meow meow meow meow meow?"

"Meow'meow meow meow meow meow, meow meow meow meow meow Meow Meow, meow meow Meow'meow meow meow meow meow meow meow meow meow."

"Meow'meow meow meow meow, meow Meow Meow meow meow meow meow. Meow meow meow meow meow meow meow meow meow meow meow meow meow, meow meow meow meow meow meow, meow Meow meow meow meow meow meow. Meow meow meow meow meow

meow meow meow meow meow meow meow meow meow meow meow meow meow meow meow Meow Meow meow meow meow meow meow meow meow. Meow meow meow meow meow meow meow Meow Meow meow meow meow, meow meow. Meow meow meow meow meow meow meow. Meow’meow meow Meow Meow meow meow meow meow meow meow-meow meow meow Meow. Meow meow meow meow meow meow meow meow meow.”

“Meow meow, Meow’meow meow meow meow meow.”

“Meow meow meow, meow’meow meow meow meow, meow Meow meow’meow meow meow meow; meow meow meow meow meow. Meow meow meow, Meow meow meow meow meow meow meow meow meow meow meow Meow meow meow meow meow meow meow meow meow meow meow meow meow meow... meow meow? Meow meow meow meow meow; Meow meow’meow meow meow meow’meow meow. Meow, meow meow meow meow meow meow!”

“Meow meow meow meow meow!”

“Meow, meow’meow meow, meow meow?” meow Meow. “Meow, Meow meow meow meow meow meow meow meow meow meow meow meow meow meow meow meow. Meow meow! Meow Meow meow meow meow meow meow meow meow meow meow meow meow meow meow meow Meow Meow meow, meow meow meow meow meow meow? Meow Meow meow meow meow meow meow meow meow’meow meow. Meow meow’ meow, meow meow, meow meow meow. Meow meow meow meow!”

“Meow meow’meow meow meow meow. Meow’meow meow meow meow meow!”

“Meow Meow’meow meow meow meow meow (meow Meow meow meow meow). Meow, Meow’meow meow meow meow meow meow meow meow meow meow meow. Meow Meow meow meow meow meow meow meow meow, meow meow meow meow meow meow meow meow meow meow. Meow meow’meow meow meow meow, meow meow meow meow meow meow meow meow meow meow: meow meow meow meow meow meow meow meow. Meow meow meow meow meow meow meow meow’meow meow meow meow, meow meow meow meow meow meow meow’meow meow, meow’meow meow meow meow meow Meow meow meow meow. Meow, meow meow! Meow meow meow meow meow. Meow’meow meow meow. Meow’meow meow meow meow? Meow’meow meow meow meow meow.”

“Meow’meow meow meow meow meow meow meow,” Meow meow meow meow.

“Meow meow (meow meow’meow meow meow meow, meow’meow meow meow meow meow meow’meow meow meow). Meow meow meow meow meow meow meow meow—meow meow, meow’meow meow? Meow meow meow meow meow? Meow meow meow meow. Meow meow meow meow meow meow, meow-meow! Meow’meow meow meow meow meow meow meow meow meow meow. Meow meow meow meow meow meow meow meow meow meow meow. Meow’meow meow meow meow meow

meow meow meow meow meow meow meow. Meow, meow'meow meow meow meow, meow meow'meow meow meow meow?"

"Meow meow meow meow meow meow, meow meow meow meow meow."

"Meow meow meow meow! Meow meow meow meow. Meow meow meow meow. Meow meow, meow'meow meow meow meow Meow Meow. Meow, meow meow meow meow meow meow. Meow'meow meow meow meow? Meow Meow. Meow meow meow meow meow meow. Meow meow Meow meow Meow meow. Meow, meow? Meow meow meow meow. Meow meow meow meow? Meow? Meow meow meow? Meow meow meow meow meow meow'meow meow meow meow meow meow meow meow. Meow, meow meow meow meow; meow meow meow meow meow meow meow, meow'meow meow? Meow meow meow. Meow Meow'meow meow meow meow. Meow meow meow meow meow meow meow meow, meow meow meow Meow meow meow.... Meow meow meow meow meow meow meow meow meow meow meow meow meow meow meow meow. Meow, meow! Meow meow meow meow-meow-meow meow meow meow meow meow—meow meow meow meow Meow'meow meow meow meow meow—meow meow meow meow meow meow meow meow-meow. Meow meow'meow meow meow meow meow. Meow meow meow meow, meow meow meow meow, meow meow meow meow meow meow meow meow. Meow meow meow meow meow? Meow'meow meow meow meow Meow. Meow meow meow meow meow? Meow'meow meow meow meow. Meow, meow meow? Meow meow meow meow meow! Meow meow meow meow! Meow meow meow meow meow meow meow meow. Meow meow, meow'meow meow meow meow meow...."

Meow meow meow meow meow meow. Meow meow meow meow meow meow meow meow meow meow meow meow. Meow meow meow meow meow meow meow meow meow meow meow Meow Meow. Meow meow meow meow meow meow meow meow meow meow meow meow meow Meow meow meow meow meow meow meow meow, meow meow meow meow meow meow meow meow. Meow meow meow meow meow meow meow meow meow meow. Meow meow meow meow meow meow Meow.

"Meow meow meow Meow meow meow meow meow meow meow meow meow meow meow meow meow, meow meow meow meow meow!" meow meow.

Meow'meow meow meow meow meow meow meow meow: meow meow meow meow Meow meow meow meow meow meow meow, meow meow meow meow. Meow meow meow meow, Meow meow meow meow Meow meow meow meow meow meow meow. Meow meow meow meow meow meow meow meow meow meow meow meow meow meow.

Meow meow meow meow, meow meow meow meow meow meow meow meow meow, meow meow, meow meow meow. Meow meow meow meow meow meow meow meow meow meow meow meow meow meow. Meow meow meow meow meow meow meow meow.

Meow meow meow meow meow meow meow meow meow, meow meow meow meow meow meow. Meow meow meow meow meow meow meow

meow meow meow meow meow meow meow meow meow. Meow meow meow meow meow meow meow meow meow meow meow meow meow meow. Meow meow meow Meow meow meow meow meow meow meow meow Meow Meow.

Meow meow meow meow meow meow. Meow meow meow meow meow meow meow meow, meow meow meow meow meow meow, meow meow meow meow meow meow Meow'meow meow meow. Meow meow meow Meow meow meow meow meow meow meow meow meow meow meow. Meow meow meow meow meow meow meow meow meow meow meow meow meow meow, meow meow meow meow meow.

Meow meow meow Meow meow. Meow meow meow meow meow meow meow meow meow Meow.

"Meow meow meow meow meow," Meow meow meow meow, "Meow meow'meow meow Meow Meow meow meow meow meow meow. Meow meow meow meow Meow'meow meow meow meow meow meow meow meow meow meow, meow meow meow meow meow meow Meow meow meow meow meow meow meow meow meow. Meow meow meow meow meow meow meow meow meow meow meow meow. Meow meow'meow meow meow meow meow, meow meow, meow meow meow meow, meow meow?"

"Meow, meow'meow meow meow meow meow," Meow meow, "meow meow meow meow'meow meow meow. Meow meow meow meow meow meow Meow meow meow meow meow meow meow. Meow meow meow meow. Meow meow meow meow meow meow meow meow."

"Meow meow meow meow, Meow meow'meow meow meow meow meow meow; meow, meow meow meow Meow Meow meow; meow, meow, Meow meow meow meow meow meow.... Meow meow, meow meow meow'meow meow meow meow meow meow, Meow meow meow meow meow meow meow meow meow meow meow. Meow Meow meow meow meow meow meow meow meow meow meow meow meow meow meow meow'meow meow meow meow meow meow."

Meow meow meow, meow, meow meow meow Meow meow meow meow.

"Meow meow meow meow meow?" meow meow meow. "Meow meow meow meow meow meow. Meow meow meow meow meow meow meow meow meow meow meow Meow meow meow."

"Meow meow meow Meow Meow?"

"Meow, Meow meow meow meow meow meow meow meow meow meow meow meow meow meow meow meow meow meow meow. Meow meow meow meow meow. Meow meow meow meow meow meow-meow: meow meow meow meow meow meow meow meow meow meow meow. Meow meow meow Meow meow'meow meow meow meow meow meow meow meow meow Meow meow meow meow meow meow meow. Meow meow meow meow meow meow meow meow meow meow meow meow meow. Meow meow meow meow meow meow, meow meow meow meow meow. Meow'meow meow meow meow meow meow—meow meow meow meow meow; meow meow, meow'meow meow; meow meow Meow'meow

meow meow meow meow meow meow meow meow meow meow meow meow meow meow meow meow meow meow meow meow meow meow meow meow meow meow meow meow. Meow meow meow meow meow meow. Meow meow'meow meow meow meow meow; Meow Meow'meow meow meow meow meow meow—meow meow meow meow meow meow. Meow meow meow meow meow meow meow meow. Meow meow meow meow meow meow meow? Meow Meow meow meow meow?"

Meow meow meow meow meow meow meow meow meow; meow meow meow meow meow meow meow. Meow meow meow meow meow meow meow meow meow. Meow meow meow meow meow meow meow meow meow. Meow Meow meow meow meow meow meow meow, meow meow meow meow meow meow meow meow meow meow meow meow meow meow meow meow meow meow meow meow meow meow meow meow.

"Meow Meow meow meow meow meow meow meow meow... meow meow, Meow meow meow meow meow meow meow meow meow. Meow meow meow," meow meow meow meow meow, meow meow meow meow meow meow.

Meow meow meow Meow'meow meow.

"Meow meow meow meow meow meow meow meow meow.... Meow meow meow. Meow meow! Meow Meow meow meow meow meow meow meow. Meow meow'meow meow meow, meow meow meow meow meow meow meow meow meow meow meow.

Meow meow meow meow.... Meow'meow meow meow meow meow meow meow meow. Meow Meow Meow meow meow meow meow meow meow meow, Meow meow meow meow meow meow, meow-meow meow meow meow. Meow meow meow meow. Meow meow meow meow meow. Meow Meow, meow meow, meow meow meow meow. Meow, meow meow meow. Meow meow meow meow meow meow meow meow meow: meow meow meow meow meow meow meow meow meow meow meow, meow meow meow meow. Meow meow meow... Meow meow meow meow meow meow meow meow."

Meow meow meow meow meow meow meow. Meow meow meow meow meow meow, meow meow meow meow meow meow meow meow meow meow meow meow. Meow meow meow meow meow meow, meow meow, meow Meow meow meow meow meow meow meow meow meow meow meow. Meow meow meow meow meow meow meow meow meow, meow meow meow meow'meow meow meow meow meow. Meow meow meow meow meow meow meow meow, Meow meow Meow meow meow meow meow meow meow meow meow. Meow meow meow meow, meow meow meow meow meow meow meow meow meow, meow Meow meow meow meow.

"Meow meow, meow meow meow meow meow. Meow meow meow, meow'meow meow. Meow meow meow meow meow meow, meow meow meow meow meow meow meow. Meow meow meow meow meow meow meow meow meow meow meow meow. Meow meow meow meow meow meow meow meow Meow Meow'meow meow; meow meow meow meow meow Meow Meow. Meow Meow meow meow meow meow meow meow

meow, meow meow meow meow meow—meow meow meow Meow meow meow meow meow meow, meow meow meow meow?”

“Meow meow?”

“Meow, Meow meow. Meow meow meow meow meow meow; meow meow’meow meow meow meow.”

Meow meow Meow Meow meow meow meow meow-meow meow meow meow meow meow. Meow meow meow meow meow meow meow meow meow meow, meow meow meow meow meow meow, meow meow meow meow meow meow meow meow meow meow meow meow meow meow Meow meow meow. Meow meow meow meow meow meow meow meow meow. Meow meow meow meow meow; meow meow meow meow meow meow meow meow meow. Meow meow meow meow meow Meow meow meow meow meow meow. Meow meow meow meow meow meow meow meow meow meow meow meow, meow meow meow meow meow meow. Meow, meow meow meow meow meow meow meow meow meow meow meow meow meow. Meow meow meow meow meow.

“Meow meow meow meow,” meow meow, meow meow meow meow meow. “Meow meow meow meow meow meow meow? Meow meow meow meow meow meow, meow meow, meow meow meow. Meow meow meow meow meow meow; meow meow’meow meow meow meow. Meow meow meow meow meow Meow’meow meow meow meow meow meow meow meow meow meow meow’meow meow meow meow meow meow. Meow’meow meow meow meow meow meow. Meow meow meow meow meow meow meow meow meow meow meow. Meow meow meow meow meow. Meow meow meow meow meow. Meow! Meow meow meow meow meow meow Meow meow’meow meow meow! Meow meow’meow meow meow!”

Meow meow meow, meow meow, meow meow meow meow meow meow meow meow meow meow.

“Meow meow meow’meow meow meow, meow meow meow meow meow meow meow meow meow? Meow meow meow meow? Meow meow meow?”

“Meow’meow meow meow. Meow, meow!”

“Meow’meow meow meow meow meow meow meow meow meow. Meow meow meow, Meow meow meow meow meow meow Meow. Meow meow meow meow meow. Meow meow meow meow meow meow meow meow meow. Meow meow meow meow meow-meow. Meow’meow meow meow meow, meow meow meow meow meow meow Meow Meow. Meow meow meow meow meow meow.... Meow meow meow, meow meow Meow meow meow meow meow? Meow’meow meow meow meow meow. Meow meow meow meow meow meow?”

“Meow meow’meow meow meow meow meow meow meow meow meow?”

“Meow, meow meow meow, meow meow meow meow meow. Meow meow meow meow meow meow meow meow meow Meow Meow. Meow’meow meow meow meow meow meow. Meow meow meow meow meow meow meow. Meow meow meow meow. Meow meow meow meow

meow, meow meow, meow meow meow meow meow meow meow. Meow meow meow meow meow, meow meow meow meow Meow, meow meow meow meow meow meow meow meow meow meow meow. Meow meow meow meow meow meow meow meow meow meow. Meow meow meow meow meow meow meow meow meow meow meow. Meow meow meow meow meow meow.... Meow meow meow meow, meow meow meow, meow Meow Meow, meow meow meow meow meow meow meow. Meow meow meow meow meow meow meow meow meow meow meow meow meow; meow meow meow meow meow meow meow meow meow meow. Meow'meow meow meow, meow meow'meow meow meow."

"Meow meow meow," meow Meow, meow meow meow. Meow meow meow meow.

"Meow meow meow. Meow meow meow meow meow meow, meow meow meow meow.... Meow'meow meow meow, meow meow!"

"Meow meow meow, meow meow meow meow, meow meow meow meow meow. Meow'meow meow meow meow meow meow meow meow meow meow meow meow meow meow meow meow, meow meow meow meow meow meow, meow meow meow meow. Meow meow meow meow meow meow meow meow meow meow meow."

"Meow meow meow meow meow, meow? Meow meow meow meow meow meow?" meow Meow, meow meow meow meow meow meow meow. "Meow, meow meow meow, meow meow'meow meow meow, meow meow meow meow meow?"

Meow meow meow meow meow Meow meow meow meow meow meow meow.

"Meow meow meow meow meow meow meow meow meow, Meow Meow. Meow meow meow meow meow meow meow meow, meow Meow'meow meow meow meow meow meow meow meow meow meow. Meow meow, meow meow meow meow meow meow meow meow meow! Meow meow Meow meow meow meow meow meow meow meow Meow'meow meow meow meow meow meow meow meow, meow Meow meow meow meow meow. Meow meow meow meow meow meow meow meow Meow Meow meow, meow meow meow meow meow meow meow meow meow, meow meow meow meow meow meow meow meow."

"Meow... meow meow meow?"

"Meow'meow meow meow meow, Meow Meow. Meow'meow... meow meow Meow meow meow?—Meow meow meow meow meow, meow meow meow meow meow Meow meow meow meow meow meow meow meow meow meow meow meow meow meow meow meow, meow meow meow meow meow meow meow meow! Meow'meow meow meow, meow meow, meow meow meow meow meow meow meow meow meow meow meow meow meow meow meow, meow meow, meow meow meow meow, meow meow meow, meow meow meow meow meow meow meow meow meow meow meow meow meow meow meow. Meow meow meow, meow meow meow meow, meow meow meow meow meow, meow meow, meow meow meow meow meow meow meow meow meow meow meow meow meow meow'meow meow meow'meow meow meow. Meow meow, meow, meow

meow meow, meow meow meow meow meow meow meow meow meow.... Meow meow meow meow meow, meow meow'meow meow meow; meow, meow'meow meow meow meow. Meow meow meow meow meow meow meow—meow meow meow meow meow—meow meow, meow meow, meow meow meow meow meow, meow meow meow meow meow meow meow meow meow meow meow meow meow meow, meow meow meow meow meow meow meow meow meow, meow meow, meow meow. Meow'meow meow meow meow meow meow, meow meow meow meow meow. Meow meow meow meow, meow meow, meow meow meow meow meow meow meow meow meow meow meow meow meow meow meow meow, meow meow meow meow meow meow meow meow meow. Meow meow meow meow meow meow meow meow meow meow meow—meow meow, meow meow meow meow meow meow meow meow. Meow meow meow meow meow meow meow meow meow meow meow meow meow meow meow meow meow meow meow meow, meow meow meow meow meow meow meow meow, meow meow meow meow meow meow meow meow meow. Meow meow'meow meow meow meow meow meow meow meow meow, meow meow meow meow...."

"Meow meow? Meow meow meow meow meow meow meow? Meow meow meow meow?"

"Meow, Meow Meow, meow meow meow meow meow meow; meow meow meow meow meow meow meow meow meow. Meow meow meow meow meow meow meow meow, Meow Meow, meow meow meow meow meow meow meow meow meow meow, meow meow. Meow meow'meow meow meow meow meow meow meow meow meow meow. Meow meow meow meow meow meow meow meow meow meow meow meow meow meow, meow meow meow meow meow meow meow meow meow? Meow, meow meow meow meow meow meow meow! Meow meow, meow meow meow meow meow meow meow meow meow meow meow meow meow meow meow meow meow. Meow meow meow meow meow meow meow, meow meow meow meow meow, Meow Meow. Meow meow meow meow meow meow meow meow meow meow meow meow meow meow meow meow meow meow meow. Meow meow meow meow meow meow meow meow meow meow meow meow meow, meow meow meow meow meow meow meow-meow meow meow meow meow meow. Meow meow meow meow meow meow, meow. Meow meow meow meow. Meow meow meow meow meow, Meow meow meow meow. Meow meow'meow meow meow meow meow meow meow meow. Meow meow meow meow meow meow meow meow meow meow meow meow.... Meow meow meow meow, Meow Meow."

"Meow meow meow meow. Meow meow meow meow meow meow meow meow meow meow meow meow meow. Meow meow meow meow meow."

"Meow. Meow? Meow meow'meow meow? Meow meow meow? Meow meow meow meow meow? Meow meow'meow meow. Meow meow meow meow. Meow meow meow meow meow, Meow Meow?"

"Meow meow meow meow Meow Meow," Meow meow meow. "Meow meow Meow meow meow meow? Meow meow meow meow, meow. Meow meow meow meow meow meow. Meow meow..."

Meow Meow meow meow meow. Meow meow meow meow meow.

"Meow Meow meow meow meow meow meow meow, meow meow Meow meow meow. Meow meow meow meow meow meow meow meow, meow meow meow, meow meow meow meow meow meow meow meow meow."

"Meow, meow meow meow meow! Meow meow... meow meow meow... meow meow meow meow.... Meow meow'meow meow meow! Meow meow'meow meow meow!" meow Meow, meow meow meow meow.

Meow meow, meow meow meow meow meow meow meow Meow meow meow meow meow meow. "Meow Meow, meow meow meow? Meow meow! Meow meow meow meow. Meow meow meow...." Meow meow meow meow meow meow. Meow meow meow meow meow meow.

"Meow meow meow meow," Meow meow meow meow, meow. "Meow Meow, meow meow! Meow meow, meow meow meow. Meow meow meow meow. Meow meow meow meow meow meow meow meow? Meow meow meow, Meow meow meow meow meow meow meow meow. Meow meow meow meow meow, meow meow meow meow meow meow meow meow meow, meow meow meow meow. Meow meow. Meow meow meow meow meow meow. Meow, meow meow meow? Meow meow meow meow?"

"Meow meow! Meow meow meow meow meow meow meow! Meow meow meow..." "Meow meow meow meow?"

"Meow meow. Meow meow meow? Meow meow meow? Meow meow meow meow meow? Meow meow meow meow meow meow meow meow meow meow meow. Meow meow meow meow meow meow meow?"

"Meow meow'meow meow meow meow meow meow meow meow meow meow meow. Meow meow meow meow meow; meow'meow meow meow Meow'meow meow meow meow meow meow. Meow meow meow meow meow meow meow meow meow? Meow meow meow meow meow meow? Meow meow meow meow meow meow, meow meow meow meow meow meow. Meow meow meow meow, meow meow meow meow meow; meow meow meow meow meow meow. Meow meow meow meow meow meow meow. Meow meow meow: Meow meow meow meow meow meow meow meow meow meow. Meow meow meow meow meow. Meow meow meow, meow meow; meow meow meow meow meow meow. Meow meow meow meow meow meow meow meow meow meow meow meow meow meow meow meow meow meow. Meow meow meow meow!"

"Meow meow meow meow meow? Meow meow meow meow meow?" Meow meow meow. Meow meow meow meow meow.

"Meow meow meow meow meow, meow meow, meow meow meow," meow meow meow meow meow, meow meow meow meow meow meow meow meow meow meow meow meow meow.

Meow meow meow meow meow meow meow. Meow meow meow meow meow meow.

"Meow... meow meow meow meow, meow meow meow meow. Meow... Meow'meow meow meow. Meow meow meow meow meow. Meow'meow meow meow meow meow meow. Meow'meow meow meow meow, meow meow, meow meow meow meow meow meow meow. Meow meow meow... meow meow.... Meow meow meow, Meow'meow meow meow meow meow meow... meow meow meow.... Meow meow meow meow meow Meow? Meow meow meow meow.... Meow meow meow meow meow.... Meow meow meow meow meow meow meow meow, meow meow, meow meow.... Meow meow meow meow meow meow meow meow meow meow. Meow meow, 'meow meow,' meow Meow'meow meow meow. Meow'meow meow meow. Meow meow meow meow meow. Meow meow meow, Meow meow meow. Meow'meow meow meow—meow! Meow'meow, meow'meow meow meow meow meow meow. Meow meow meow meow meow meow meow meow?..."

Meow meow meow meow meow meow.... Meow meow meow meow meow meow meow. Meow meow meow meow meow meow meow meow.

"Meow meow! Meow meow!" meow meow, meow meow meow. "Meow meow! Meow meow meow meow meow?"

Meow meow meow meow meow meow meow. Meow meow meow meow meow meow meow meow meow meow meow.

"Meow meow meow meow meow meow," meow meow meow meow meow. "Meow meow meow meow meow, meow meow'meow meow meow meow meow meow meow meow. Meow meow meow meow meow meow."

"Meow meow meow meow? Meow meow meow meow, meow meow, meow meow!" "Meow meow meow meow meow meow meow meow meow."

"Meow meow meow meow," meow Meow, meow meow meow meow. Meow meow meow meow meow meow, meow meow meow meow meow meow meow meow meow meow meow.

Meow meow meow meow, meow meow meow meow meow meow meow meow meow meow meow meow meow meow.

Meow meow meow meow meow meow meow meow meow meow meow meow. Meow meow meow meow, meow meow meow meow, meow meow meow meow meow meow meow. Meow meow meow meow meow meow meow meow.

"Meow meow meow meow meow meow, Meow Meow. Meow meow meow meow meow meow meow Meow'meow meow meow. Meow Meow meow meow meow meow. Meow Meow meow meow meow—meow meow meow meow meow meow. Meow meow meow meow meow meow meow meow meow meow meow Meow meow meow meow meow, meow. Meow meow meow meow meow meow. Meow meow meow meow meow meow meow meow meow meow meow? Meow, meow meow meow meow meow. Meow meow meow meow meow meow meow meow meow meow meow meow meow meow meow? Meow meow meow meow meow meow meow meow meow, meow meow meow meow. Meow meow meow meow meow meow meow, Meow Meow."

"Meow!" meow Meow meow.

"Meow meow meow, meow meow Meow meow meow meow meow meow meow meow meow meow. Meow'meow meow meow meow meow meow meow meow meow—meow meow meow. Meow meow meow meow meow meow meow meow meow meow meow meow meow meow... meow meow meow meow meow meow meow meow meow meow meow, meow Meow meow meow meow. Meow meow meow meow meow meow meow, meow meow, meow meow, meow meow meow meow meow meow. Meow meow meow. Meow meow'meow meow meow meow'meow meow meow meow meow meow. Meow meow meow meow meow... meow meow meow... Meow meow meow meow."

Meow meow meow meow meow meow meow meow meow meow Meow. Meow meow meow meow meow meow meow meow meow meow meow. Meow, meow meow meow. Meow meow meow meow meow meow meow meow meow, meow meow meow meow meow meow meow meow meow meow meow. Meow meow meow.

"Meow! Meow meow'meow meow, meow meow?" meow meow, meow meow meow meow. "Meow, meow meow meow meow meow meow meow. Meow'meow meow meow meow meow meow meow, Meow Meow. Meow meow meow meow meow meow meow? Meow meow Meow. Meow? Meow, meow'meow meow meow, meow meow meow! Meow meow Meow'meow meow meow meow! Meow meow meow Meow'meow meow meow meow meow meow meow meow meow meow meow."

"Meow'meow meow meow meow, meow meow meow Meow Meow, meow meow meow, meow! Meow meow meow meow meow meow meow meow. Meow meow meow meow Meow meow meow meow meow meow meow meow meow. Meow meow meow meow meow meow meow, Meow meow Meow'meow meow meow." Meow meow meow.

"Meow meow meow? Meow meow meow meow," meow Meow, meow meow meow meow meow.

"Meow, meow meow meow meow! Meow'meow meow! Meow'meow meow meow! Meow'meow meow! Meow meow meow meow, Meow meow; meow meow meow meow meow!" Meow meow meow meow meow.

"Meow meow meow meow Meow meow Meow Meow?"

"Meow meow! Meow meow meow meow; meow meow meow meow meow meow.... Meow meow meow meow meow meow meow... meow meow meow meow meow.... Meow meow meow meow.... Meow meow meow meow meow meow.... Meow!"

"Meow meow meow meow meow, meow meow meow meow meow meow meow... meow meow meow meow meow meow." "Meow meow meow! Meow meow meow meow, meow...."

"Meow, Meow Meow! Meow meow meow meow meow meow meow meow meow meow meow meow meow meow meow. Meow meow meow meow meow meow. Meow meow meow meow meow, meow meow meow meow meow?"

"Meow'meow meow meow," meow meow meow meow meow meow meow Meow'meow meow, "meow'meow meow meow meow meow meow!"

"Meow meow? Meow, meow meow meow, meow'meow meow meow. Meow meow meow meow. Meow meow meow meow meow meow meow meow meow," meow meow.

"Meow meow meow meow meow, meow meow meow meow. Meow, meow meow!"

Meow meow meow meow, meow meow meow, meow meow meow, meow meow meow meow meow meow meow meow meow meow meow. Meow meow meow meow meow meow meow meow meow meow meow meow meow meow meow. Meow meow meow meow meow meow meow. Meow meow meow meow meow meow meow meow meow meow meow meow meow meow meow meow meow meow meow meow meow meow meow meow meow meow meow. Meow meow meow meow meow meow meow meow meow meow. Meow meow meow meow meow meow meow meow meow meow. Meow meow meow meow meow meow.

"Meow meow meow meow meow. Meow meow meow meow meow meow. Meow'meow meow? Meow?" meow meow meow meow meow meow meow meow meow, meow meow meow meow meow meow meow meow meow meow. Meow meow meow meow meow meow meow meow meow.

Meow meow meow meow meow meow meow Meow meow meow meow meow meow meow meow meow meow meow meow meow. Meow meow meow meow meow meow meow meow meow meow meow meow meow.

"Meow, meow meow! Meow meow, Meow'meow meow," meow Meow meow, meow meow, meow meow. "Meow meow meow meow meow meow, Meow meow meow meow meow meow meow meow meow meow meow."

Meow meow, meow meow meow meow meow meow meow meow.

"Meow meow meow," meow meow meow meow. "Meow meow Meow'meow meow meow. Meow... Meow'meow meow meow."

"Meow... meow meow meow meow meow meow meow meow. Meow meow meow meow'meow... meow." Meow meow meow meow meow meow meow meow meow. Meow meow meow: meow meow meow.

"Meow meow'meow meow meow meow. Meow meow, meow meow meow meow meow. Meow meow meow, Meow'meow meow."

Meow meow meow meow, meow meow meow, meow meow meow meow meow meow meow meow, meow meow meow, meow, meow meow. Meow meow meow meow meow meow meow meow meow meow meow. "Meow... meow, meow meow meow meow meow meow, meow meow meow!" Meow meow meow meow meow meow.

"Meow'meow meow meow!" meow Meow meow meow, meow meow meow meow meow meow. Meow meow meow meow meow meow meow meow meow—meow meow meow meow meow meow meow; meow meow meow meow meow meow meow meow meow meow. Meow meow meow meow meow meow meow, meow meow meow meow, meow meow meow meow meow meow meow.

Meow meow meow Meow meow meow meow meow meow meow meow meow. Meow meow meow meow, meow, meow meow meow meow, meow

meow meow meow meow meow. Meow meow meow meow meow, meow meow meow meow meow meow meow meow meow meow meow.

"Meow meow meow," Meow meow. Meow meow. Meow meow meow meow meow meow. "Meow meow meow'meow meow meow?" meow meow meow. Meow meow meow meow.

"Meow... meow meow meow'meow? Meow?" meow meow meow meow.

"Meow!"

Meow meow meow meow meow meow, meow meow meow meow meow meow Meow. Meow meow meow meow meow meow meow meow. Meow meow meow meow meow, meow meow meow meow meow meow meow meow meow. Meow meow meow.

"Meow'meow meow meow."

Meow meow meow meow meow meow meow meow meow meow meow meow meow meow meow meow meow meow meow, meow meow meow meow meow Meow.

"Meow meow! Meow meow!"

Meow meow meow meow meow meow meow. Meow meow meow meow meow meow meow meow meow meow.

"Meow meow! Meow meow!" meow Meow, meow meow meow meow meow. Mcow meow meow meow meow meow meow meow meow meow meow "meow meow."

Meow meow meow, meow meow meow meow, meow meow meow meow, meow meow meow meow meow meow meow meow meow. Meow meow meow, meow meow, meow meow meow meow meow meow meow meow meow meow meow meow Meow. Meow.

Meow meow meow meow meow meow meow meow. Meow meow meow meow meow, meow meow meow meow meow meow meow meow meow meow. Meow meow meow meow meow meow, meow meow, meow, meow meow, meow meow meow meow. Meow meow, meow meow meow meow meow, meow meow meow. Meow meow meow meow meow, meow meow meow meow meow meow meow meow. Meow meow meow Meow meow meow meow meow meow meow meow meow meow meow meow meow. Meow meow meow meow meow meow meow. Meow meow meow meow meow meow-meow meow meow meow-meow meow. Meow meow meow meow meow meow meow meow meow meow meow. Meow meow meow meow meow. Meow meow meow meow, meow meow meow meow meow meow, meow meow meow meow meow meow.

MEOW VI

Meow meow meow meow meow meow meow'meow meow meow meow meow meow meow meow. Meow meow meow meow meow meow meow meow meow, meow meow meow "meow meow meow," "meow meow Meow."

Meow meow Meow meow meow meow-meow meow meow meow meow meow meow meow meow meow meow. Meow meow meow meow meow meow meow meow meow meow meow meow meow meow meow, meow meow meow meow meow meow meow meow meow meow meow. Meow meow meow meow meow meow meow meow, meow meow meow meow meow meow. Meow meow meow meow meow-meow-meow meow-meow meow meow meow meow meow meow, meow meow "Meow," meow meow meow meow meow meow-meow meow meow meow meow meow, meow meow meow meow meow meow meow meow meow meow meow meow. Meow meow meow meow meow meow meow meow meow meow meow Meow meow meow Meow meow meow meow meow meow meow meow. Meow meow meow meow meow meow meow meow meow meow meow meow. Meow meow meow meow meow meow meow. Meow meow meow meow meow meow meow meow meow meow, meow meow meow meow meow meow meow meow meow meow meow meow meow. Meow meow meow meow meow meow meow meow meow meow meow meow meow meow meow meow meow meow meow meow meow meow meow meow meow meow Meow, meow meow meow meow meow meow meow meow meow. Meow meow meow meow meow meow meow meow meow meow meow meow meow Meow. Meow meow meow meow meow meow meow meow meow meow. Meow meow meow meow meow, meow meow, meow meow meow meow meow meow. Meow meow meow meow meow'meow. Meow meow meow meow meow meow meow meow meow meow meow meow meow meow meow meow meow meow meow meow meow meow meow.

Meow meow meow meow meow meow meow. Meow meow-meow meow meow meow meow meow meow meow'meow. Meow meow meow meow meow meow, meow meow meow meow meow meow meow meow. Meow meow meow meow meow meow meow, meow meow meow meow meow meow meow. Meow meow meow meow meow meow meow meow meow meow meow meow meow meow meow meow.

Meow meow meow meow, meow meow meow, meow meow meow, meow meow meow, meow meow meow meow meow meow meow meow meow meow meow meow. Meow, meow meow meow meow meow meow, meow meow meow meow meow meow meow, meow, meow meow meow meow meow meow meow meow meow meow meow meow meow, meow meow meow meow meow, meow meow meow meow meow meow meow meow meow meow meow meow meow meow. Meow meow meow meow Meow. Meow meow meow meow.

Meow meow meow meow: meow meow Meow meow meow meow meow. Meow meow meow meow meow. Meow meow Meow meow meow meow,

meow meow meow meow meow meow. Meow meow meow meow meow meow meow meow meow meow.

Meow meow meow meow meow meow meow meow Meow meow meow meow meow. Meow meow meow meow meow.

"Meow meow meow meow meow Meow, Meow Meow," meow Meow, "meow meow Meow meow meow meow meow meow meow meow meow, Meow meow meow meow meow meow meow. Meow, meow meow meow meow meow meow-meow? Meow meow meow meow meow meow meow, meow meow meow meow meow." (Meow meow meow meow meow meow.) "Meow meow meow meow meow meow meow meow meow. Meow meow meow meow meow meow meow, meow meow meow meow meow meow meow meow meow meow meow Meow'meow meow meow meow meow meow meow meow meow. Meow meow meow meow meow meow meow meow, meow meow meow meow. Meow, meow meow! Meow meow, meow'meow meow. Meow meow meow 5-meow-meow meow meow meow meow meow meow meow meow. Meow meow meow meow, meow meow meow, meow meow meow meow meow meow meow, meow meow meow meow meow meow meow, meow meow meow. Meow meow meow meow meow, meow meow meow meow meow meow meow meow meow, Meow Meow, meow meow, meow meow meow meow meow meow meow meow meow."

"Meow meow meow meow meow meow meow, meow meow meow meow meow meow meow meow," meow Meow meow, "meow meow Meow'meow meow meow meow... meow meow'meow meow..."

"Meow'meow meow! meow'meow meow!"

"Meow meow meow meow meow, Meow Meow, Meow meow meow meow meow meow, meow Meow meow'meow meow meow meow. Meow meow meow meow meow meow meow. Meow'meow meow meow meow. Meow meow meow meow meow, meow meow...."

"Meow'meow meow meow, meow meow, Meow Meow, meow meow meow'meow meow meow meow meow. Meow meow'meow meow meow meow. Meow meow meow meow. Meow Meow meow meow meow: meow meow meow meow meow meow Meow." (Meow meow meow meow meow, meow meow.) "Meow'meow meow meow, Meow meow meow meow meow meow meow meow Meow meow meow meow meow; Meow meow'meow meow meow. Meow meow meow meow meow meow meow meow meow meow meow meow meow meow. Meow meow meow meow meow meow. Meow, meow meow meow meow meow meow Meow, meow meow meow meow meow meow meow meow. Meow'meow meow, meow'meow meow? Meow meow meow, meow'meow meow meow. Meow'meow meow meow meow meow, meow meow meow? Meow meow meow meow meow meow meow meow meow meow meow meow meow. Meow, meow meow Meow Meow meow meow meow'meow meow. Meow meow meow. Meow meow meow meow meow meow meow meow, Meow Meow? Meow meow Meow Meow'meow meow meow meow meow, meow meow meow meow meow meow meow meow meow meow meow Meow meow. Meow meow'meow meow meow meow meow meow meow. Meow meow meow

meow meow meow meow—meow- meow meow meow meow meow meow meow meow meow—meow'meow meow meow meow meow meow meow meow meow meow meow'meow meow meow meow meow meow meow meow meow meow meow meow. Meow, meow meow-meow." (Meow meow meow.) "Meow meow meow Meow Meow. Meow meow meow, meow'meow meow meow meow meow meow meow meow meow Meow. Meow'meow meow. Meow meow Meow. Meow? Meow meow meow meow. Meow'meow meow meow meow meow. Meow meow meow meow meow-meow meow... meow meow meow meow. Meow meow meow, meow meow meow."

Meow meow meow meow meow meow meow meow meow meow meow meow Meow. Meow meow meow meow, meow meow meow meow, meow meow meow meow meow meow meow meow meow meow meow meow meow meow meow meow.

"Meow meow meow... meow meow meow meow meow meow, meow meow meow?"

"Meow, meow meow meow Meow, meow meow meow meow meow! Meow, meow! Meow-meow, Meow Meow, meow meow! Meow meow meow meow, meow meow meow meow meow meow meow. Meow meow meow... meow Meow. Meow Meow meow meow meow meow meow. Meow meow Meow Meow Meow meow meow meow. Meow meow meow."

Meow meow meow, meow Meow meow meow meow meow meow meow meow meow meow.

Meow meow meow meow meow meow meow meow, meow meow meow meow, meow meow meow meow meow meow meow meow. Meow meow meow meow. Meow meow meow meow, meow meow meow meow meow meow meow meow meow meow meow meow meow, meow Meow Meow meow Meow Meow. Meow meow meow meow meow meow meow meow, meow meow meow meow meow meow meow meow; meow Meow meow meow meow meow meow meow meow, meow meow meow meow, meow meow meow meow meow meow meow meow meow meow Meow meow meow meow meow meow meow meow meow meow meow meow meow meow meow meow meow meow meow. Meow meow meow meow meow meow meow meow Meow meow meow meow meow meow meow, meow meow meow meow meow meow meow meow meow meow. Meow meow meow meow meow meow, meow meow meow meow meow meow meow meow meow meow, meow meow meow meow meow meow meow—meow meow, meow Meow meow meow meow meow meow meow—meow meow meow meow meow meow meow meow meow meow Meow meow meow meow meow meow, meow meow meow meow meow meow meow meow meow Meow Meow. Meow meow meow meow meow meow meow meow meow meow, meow meow meow Meow Meow meow meow meow, meow meow meow meow meow meow meow meow, meow meow meow meow meow, meow meow meow, meow meow meow meow meow meow meow. Meow meow meow meow meow.

Meow meow meow meow meow meow meow meow meow meow meow meow meow meow meow Meow meow meow meow, meow meow meow

meow meow meow meow meow meow meow meow meow meow meow meow meow meow, meow meow meow meow meow meow meow meow meow meow meow meow meow meow meow. Meow meow meow meow meow meow meow meow meow meow meow meow meow meow meow meow meow meow meow meow meow meow meow meow meow meow meow meow meow meow meow meow meow. Meow meow meow meow meow meow meow; meow meow meow meow meow meow meow meow, meow meow meow meow meow meow meow meow. Meow meow meow meow, meow meow meow meow meow meow meow meow meow meow meow meow meow meow meow meow meow meow. Meow meow meow, meow, meow meow meow, meow meow meow, meow meow meow meow meow meow, meow meow meow meow meow, meow meow meow meow, meow meow meow meow meow meow, meow meow meow meow meow, meow meow meow meow meow meow meow meow meow meow meow meow meow meow meow meow meow meow meow meow meow meow meow meow meow meow meow meow meow meow meow meow meow. Meow meow meow, meow meow meow meow meow meow meow meow meow, meow meow meow meow, meow meow meow meow meow meow, meow meow meow meow meow meow meow meow meow, meow meow Meow meow meow meow meow, meow meow meow meow meow meow meow meow meow meow meow—meow meow meow meow meow meow meow meow meow meow. Meow meow meow meow meow meow meow meow meow meow meow meow meow meow meow meow meow, meow meow meow meow meow meow meow meow. Meow meow meow meow meow meow meow meow meow meow, meow Meow, meow meow, meow meow meow meow, meow meow meow meow meow meow meow meow′meow meow meow meow meow meow meow meow meow meow′meow meow meow meow. Meow, meow, meow meow meow meow meow meow meow meow meow meow meow meow meow meow meow. Meow meow, meow meow meow meow meow meow meow meow, meow Meow meow meow meow meow meow meow, meow meow meow meow meow meow meow, meow meow meow meow meow meow Meow, meow meow, meow meow meow meow meow. Meow meow meow meow meow meow meow meow meow meow meow meow meow, Meow Meow, meow meow meow meow meow meow. Meow meow meow meow meow meow meow′meow, meow meow meow meow meow meow meow meow, meow meow meow meow.

Meow meow, meow meow meow, meow meow meow meow meow meow meow meow meow meow. Meow meow meow meow meow meow meow meow meow meow. Meow meow meow, meow meow meow meow meow meow meow meow meow meow meow meow Meow Meow meow meow meow meow meow meow, meow meow. Meow meow meow meow meow meow meow, meow meow meow meow; meow meow meow meow meow Meow. Meow. Meow meow meow meow meow meow meow meow meow meow, meow meow meow meow, meow meow meow meow meow meow meow meow meow meow meow, meow meow meow meow meow meow meow meow meow meow meow meow. Meow meow meow meow meow meow meow meow meow meow meow meow meow meow meow meow meow, meow meow meow, meow meow meow, meow meow meow meow

meow meow meow meow Meow. Meow meow meow meow: meow meow meow meow meow meow meow Meow-meow meow meow meow meow meow meow meow meow meow meow meow meow meow. Meow meow meow meow, meow meow meow, meow meow meow meow meow meow meow meow meow meow meow meow meow meow meow meow meow meow. Meow meow meow meow meow meow meow meow meow meow meow meow meow meow meow meow meow. Meow meow, meow Meow, meow meow meow meow meow meow meow meow meow meow meow meow meow meow meow meow meow, meow meow meow meow meow meow, meow meow meow. Meow meow meow meow, meow meow meow. Meow meow meow meow meow.

"Meow meow meow?" meow Meow. "Meow, meow."

"Meow meow meow meow?"

"Meow, meow, meow."

"Meow meow meow meow meow."

"Meow meow meow meow meow?" meow meow meow meow meow. "Meow, meow."

Meow meow meow meow meow, meow meow.

"Meow meow meow meow meow meow," meow Meow. "Meow meow meow Meow meow'meow meow meow? Meow meow Meow meow meow meow Meow meow meow meow meow meow meow meow meow meow meow meow meow meow. Meow meow meow meow meow meow meow meow meow?"

Meow meow meow meow meow meow meow meow meow meow meow. Meow meow meow meow meow meow-meow meow Meow meow meow meow meow meow meow meow; meow meow meow meow; meow meow, meow meow meow meow, meow meow meow-meow meow meow meow meow meow meow meow. Meow meow meow meow meow meow meow meow meow meow, meow meow meow meow, meow meow meow meow meow meow meow meow meow, meow meow meow meow—meow—meow meow meow meow meow. Meow meow meow meow meow meow meow meow meow meow meow, meow meow meow meow meow meow meow meow meow meow meow meow.

Meow meow meow meow meow, meow meow meow meow meow meow meow meow meow. Meow meow meow meow meow meow meow meow meow meow meow meow meow meow meow meow meow meow. Meow meow meow meow meow meow meow meow meow meow meow meow. Meow meow: meow meow meow meow meow meow meow, meow meow meow meow meow meow.

Meow meow meow, meow meow meow meow meow meow meow meow meow meow meow meow meow meow meow meow meow meow; meow meow meow meow meow meow. Meow meow, meow meow meow meow meow meow, meow meow meow. Meow meow meow, meow meow meow-meow meow meow meow meow meow meow, meow meow meow meow meow meow meow meow, meow meow meow, meow meow meow meow meow meow meow meow meow, meow meow meow meow meow meow. Meow meow meow meow meow meow meow meow, meow meow meow

meow meow. Meow meow meow meow meow meow meow meow meow meow meow meow meow meow meow meow meow meow meow meow meow, meow meow meow meow meow meow Meow meow meow meow. Meow meow meow meow meow meow meow meow meow, meow meow meow meow meow meow meow meow meow meow meow meow, meow meow'meow. Meow meow meow meow meow meow meow meow meow meow, meow meow meow meow meow meow meow meow meow meow meow meow meow meow meow meow. Meow meow meow meow meow meow meow meow; meow meow meow-meow, meow meow meow meow meow meow, meow meow meow, meow meow meow meow meow meow meow meow. Meow meow meow meow meow, Meow meow meow meow meow meow meow meow meow meow.

Meow meow meow, meow meow meow meow, meow meow meow meow meow meow meow meow meow'meow meow meow meow, meow meow meow meow meow meow, meow meow. Meow meow meow meow meow meow meow meow meow meow meow meow, meow meow meow meow meow. Meow meow meow meow meow. Meow meow meow meow meow, meow meow meow meow meow, meow meow meow meow meow. Meow meow meow. "Meow meow meow meow meow meow meow meow meow meow meow," meow meow meow meow meow. Meow meow meow meow, meow meow meow meow, meow meow meow meow meow, meow meow meow meow meow meow meow meow meow meow meow meow meow meow meow meow meow. Meow meow meow meow meow meow: meow meow meow meow. Meow meow meow meow meow meow meow meow meow meow. "Meow meow meow meow meow meow meow," meow meow. "Meow'meow meow meow meow meow. Meow Meow meow meow meow meow meow meow meow meow meow, meow meow meow! Meow meow meow meow meow meow." Meow meow meow meow meow meow meow meow meow Meow Meow meow meow. Meow meow meow meow meow meow meow meow Meow Meow meow meow meow meow meow meow meow meow meow meow meow. "Meow meow meow meow meow," meow meow, "meow meow meow meow," meow meow meow meow meow meow meow meow meow: "Meow meow meow meow meow meow meow meow meow meow meow meow meow, meow Meow'meow meow meow meow, meow meow meow meow meow meow meow meow meow... meow meow meow meow. Meow meow meow meow meow meow meow Meow Meow! Meow meow meow meow meow, meow, meow-meow! Meow meow Meow meow meow meow meow!... Meow meow meow, meow meow'meow Meow meow meow meow meow?" meow meow meow meow. "Meow'meow meow meow meow meow meow," meow meow, meow meow meow meow meow meow meow. "Meow, meow, Meow Meow, meow meow meow meow meow meow meow meow meow; meow'meow meow, meow meow meow meow meow meow meow meow. Meow meow meow meow'meow meow!"

Meow meow meow meow, meow meow meow meow meow meow meow meow Meow, meow meow meow Meow meow meow meow meow Meow'meow meow. "Meow meow Meow meow meow meow meow, meow

Meow meow, meow meow meow. Meow meow meow meow meow Meow meow! Meow'meow meow meow meow meow meow. Meow meow meow meow meow meow meow meow meow meow'meow meow meow meow meow. Meow meow meow'meow meow meow meow meow. Meow meow meow meow meow meow meow meow. Meow, meow meow meow! Meow meow meow meow, meow'meow meow meow meow meow meow."

Meow meow meow meow meow meow. Meow meow Meow'meow meow meow meow meow, meow meow meow meow meow meow. "Meow, Meow meow meow meow meow meow meow," meow meow, meow meow. "Meow meow meow meow meow meow. Meow'meow meow meow meow. Meow meow meow meow meow meow meow meow, Meow meow meow meow meow meow meow meow, meow meow'meow meow meow meow, meow meow meow, meow meow meow. Meow meow meow meow meow, meow meow meow meow meow—meow'meow meow meow meow meow. Meow meow meow Meow meow meow meow meow, meow—Meow! Meow—meow meow?—meow meow meow meow meow meow meow meow meow meow meow...."

Meow meow meow meow meow meow meow meow meow. Meow Meow'meow meow meow meow meow, meow meow meow meow meow, meow meow meow meow meow, meow meow meow meow meow meow meow meow meow meow meow meow, meow meow meow meow meow meow meow meow meow meow meow meow meow meow meow meow meow meow meow meow meow meow meow meow meow meow meow meow meow. Meow meow meow meow meow meow meow meow meow meow meow meow, meow meow meow meow meow meow meow meow meow...

"Meow, meow meow meow! Meow meow meow meow meow!"

Meow meow meow meow; meow meow meow meow meow, meow meow meow meow meow meow meow meow meow meow meow meow meow meow. Meow meow. "Meow! meow meow! Meow meow meow'meow meow meow," meow meow, "meow'meow meow meow Meow meow meow meow meow." Meow meow meow meow meow meow meow meow meow, meow meow, meow meow, meow meow meow meow meow meow meow meow meow meow meow. Meow meow meow meow meow meow meow meow meow. Meow meow meow meow meow meow meow meow meow meow meow: meow meow meow. Meow meow meow meow meow meow meow meow meow meow meow meow meow. Meow meow meow meow meow, meow meow meow meow meow meow meow meow meow meow meow meow, meow meow meow meow, meow meow meow meow meow meow meow meow meow meow. Meow meow meow meow, meow meow meow meow meow meow meow meow meow meow meow meow meow meow meow meow meow meow meow meow meow meow. Meow meow meow meow meow meow.

Meow meow meow meow. Meow meow meow meow meow meow meow meow meow meow meow meow meow meow. Meow meow meow meow meow meow meow.

"Meow meow," meow meow meow meow.

Meow meow meow meow meow meow meow meow meow meow meow meow meow meow meow meow meow. "Meow'meow meow meow meow meow meow meow," meow meow. Meow meow meow meow meow meow meow meow meow, meow; meow meow meow meow meow meow meow meow meow meow meow meow meow meow. Meow meow meow meow meow meow meow meow meow meow meow meow. Meow meow meow meow meow meow, meow meow meow meow meow meow meow meow meow meow meow meow. Meow meow meow meow. Meow meow meow, meow meow meow, meow meow meow, meow meow meow meow meow meow meow meow meow meow meow meow meow meow meow meow meow meow meow meow meow. Meow meow meow meow meow meow meow, meow meow meow meow meow meow, meow meow, meow, meow meow meow, meow meow— Meow meow. Meow meow, meow meow meow meow meow Meow meow meow meow meow meow, meow meow meow meow meow meow meow; meow meow, meow meow meow, meow meow meow meow meow meow. Meow meow, meow meow, meow meow meow meow, meow meow meow meow meow meow meow meow. Meow meow meow meow meow meow meow meow meow, meow, meow meow meow meow meow meow meow, meow, meow meow meow. Meow meow meow meow meow meow meow meow, meow meow meow meow meow meow meow meow meow meow meow, meow meow-meow meow meow meow—meow meow meow, meow meow meow meow meow meow, meow meow meow meow meow—meow meow. Meow meow meow meow meow meow-meow meow meow, meow meow meow meow, meow meow, meow, meow meow meow meow meow meow. Meow meow meow meow meow meow meow, meow meow meow meow meow meow meow, meow meow meow meow meow meow meow meow meow, meow meow meow. Meow meow meow meow meow meow meow meow meow meow meow meow meow meow; meow meow meow meow meow meow meow meow. Meow meow meow meow meow meow meow meow meow meow meow, meow meow meow meow meow meow meow meow meow meow, meow meow meow meow meow meow. Meow meow meow meow meow meow meow; meow meow meow meow meow meow meow meow meow. Meow meow meow meow meow meow meow meow meow meow meow meow meow meow meow, meow meow meow meow meow meow meow meow meow meow meow meow meow meow meow meow meow. Meow meow meow meow; meow meow meow meow meow, meow meow meow meow meow meow; meow meow meow meow: meow meow meow meow meow. Meow meow meow meow, meow meow meow meow meow. Meow meow meow meow meow, meow meow meow meow meow meow meow meow meow meow meow meow, meow meow meow meow meow meow meow meow meow meow meow meow meow meow meow meow meow meow, meow meow meow meow, meow meow meow meow meow meow meow meow meow meow meow meow meow....

Meow meow meow meow, meow meow meow meow meow meow meow meow meow meow. Meow meow meow meow meow meow meow meow. Meow meow meow meow meow meow meow meow meow meow meow

meow meow meow meow, meow meow meow meow meow, meow meow meow meow. Meow meow meow meow meow meow meow meow meow meow meow, meow meow meow meow meow. Meow, meow, meow meow meow meow-meow meow meow meow meow meow. Meow meow meow meow meow meow meow meow meow meow meow meow meow meow; meow meow meow meow meow meow meow, meow meow meow meow meow meow meow meow meow meow meow meow meow. Meow, meow meow meow meow meow meow meow-meow, meow meow meow meow meow meow meow; meow meow meow meow meow, meow meow meow meow meow, meow meow meow meow meow meow meow. "Meow, meow meow! Meow meow meow meow," meow meow. "Meow meow meow meow meow meow meow meow meow meow meow meow meow, meow meow meow meow meow. Meow meow meow meow meow meow, meow meow meow meow meow meow meow meow meow meow meow meow meow meow meow meow meow meow meow. Meow meow meow meow meow?" Meow meow meow meow meow meow meow, meow meow, meow meow meow meow meow, meow meow meow, meow meow.

"Meow! Meow meow meow meow meow meow meow! Meow meow? Meow'meow meow meow meow meow meow meow meow meow. Meow'meow meow meow meow meow meow meow meow meow, meow meow meow meow meow meow'meow meow meow meow, meow meow meow meow meow meow'meow meow."

Meow meow meow meow meow meow, meow meow, meow meow meow, meow meow meow meow, meow meow meow meow meow meow meow meow, meow meow meow, meow meow meow meow meow meow meow meow meow meow meow meow meow meow meow meow meow meow meow-meow meow meow meow meow meow, meow meow meow meow meow meow meow meow meow meow. "Meow'meow meow meow meow; Meow meow'meow meow meow meow."

Meow meow meow meow meow meow meow meow meow meow meow meow meow meow meow meow meow meow meow meow, meow meow meow meow meow meow meow meow meow meow meow meow meow meow meow meow meow meow meow meow meow meow meow meow meow meow meow. Meow meow meow meow meow meow meow meow meow meow meow, meow meow meow meow meow meow, meow meow meow, meow meow meow meow meow meow meow meow meow-meow. Meow meow meow meow meow meow Meow, meow meow meow meow meow meow meow meow meow meow meow meow meow. Meow meow meow meow meow meow meow meow meow meow meow meow meow meow meow, meow meow meow meow meow meow. Meow meow'meow meow meow meow meow meow, meow meow meow meow meow. "Meow meow meow meow meow meow? Meow meow meow meow meow meow meow meow meow meow." Meow meow meow meow. Meow meow meow meow meow, meow meow meow meow meow meow, meow meow "meow" meow meow "meow meow meow meow," meow meow meow meow meow meow meow "meow." Meow meow meow meow meow meow. Meow meow meow meow meow meow meow meow meow meow meow meow meow meow,

meow meow, meow meow meow meow, meow meow meow meow meow meow, meow meow meow meow; meow meow meow meow meow meow meow meow meow’meow meow meow meow meow meow meow meow meow meow meow meow meow, meow meow meow meow meow meow meow meow meow meow meow, meow meow meow meow meow meow meow meow, meow meow meow meow meow meow meow meow meow, meow meow meow meow meow meow, meow meow meow meow meow meow meow meow meow meow meow meow meow. Meow meow meow meow meow meow, meow meow meow meow meow, meow meow meow meow meow, meow meow meow meow. Meow meow meow meow meow meow meow meow meow meow meow meow meow meow meow meow meow meow meow meow meow meow meow meow meow. Meow meow meow meow meow, meow meow meow meow meow meow, meow meow meow meow meow meow meow meow meow meow meow meow meow. Meow meow meow meow meow. Meow meow meow meow meow meow meow.

“Meow meow meow meow meow,” meow meow meow meow meow meow meow meow meow. “Meow meow!” Meow meow meow meow meow meow meow meow meow meow meow meow meow meow meow meow meow meow meow meow meow meow. “Meow meow meow!” meow meow meow meow meow meow meow, meow meow meow meow meow meow meow meow meow meow. Meow meow meow meow meow. Meow meow meow meow meow, meow meow meow meow meow meow meow, meow meow meow meow meow meow. Meow meow meow meow meow meow meow meow meow meow meow meow meow meow meow meow. “Meow’meow meow meow meow meow,” meow Meow. Meow meow meow meow meow meow meow, meow meow meow meow meow meow meow meow meow meow. Meow meow meow meow meow meow meow; meow meow meow meow? Meow meow meow meow meow meow meow meow meow, meow meow meow meow meow meow meow meow meow meow meow meow meow meow meow meow meow, meow meow meow meow meow meow meow meow, meow meow. Meow, meow meow meow. Meow meow meow meow meow meow. Meow meow meow meow meow meow, meow meow meow meow meow meow meow meow. Meow meow meow meow meow meow meow meow, meow meow meow meow meow, meow meow meow; meow meow meow meow, meow meow meow meow meow meow; meow meow meow, meow meow meow meow meow meow meow, meow meow meow meow meow Meow meow. Meow meow meow meow meow; meow meow meow meow, meow meow meow meow; meow meow, meow meow.... Meow meow meow meow meow meow meow meow meow meow, meow meow meow, meow meow meow meow meow meow meow meow meow. “Meow, meow meow meow meow?” Meow meow meow meow meow. “Meow meow meow meow?” Meow meow meow meow meow meow, meow meow meow meow meow, meow meow meow meow.... “Meow meow!” Meow meow, meow meow meow meow meow meow, meow meow meow meow meow meow meow.

Meow meow meow meow meow meow, meow meow meow meow meow. Meow meow meow meow meow meow, meow meow meow meow meow meow meow meow.

"Meow'meow meow meow meow meow!" Meow meow meow meow, meow meow meow; meow meow meow. Meow meow meow meow meow meow meow meow meow meow meow. Meow meow meow meow. Meow meow meow meow! Meow meow meow, meow meow meow meow meow meow meow meow. Meow meow meow meow meow meow, meow meow meow meow meow meow meow meow meow, meow meow meow meow meow meow meow meow meow meow meow meow meow meow meow meow meow meow meow meow meow meow meow meow meow meow. Meow meow meow, meow meow meow meow meow meow meow meow meow meow. Meow meow meow meow meow meow meow meow. Meow meow meow meow meow meow meow meow meow meow, meow meow meow meow meow meow. Meow meow meow meow meow meow meow meow meow meow meow meow meow meow meow meow meow. Meow meow meow meow meow meow, meow meow meow meow meow. Meow meow, meow meow meow meow meow meow meow meow meow, meow meow, meow meow meow meow meow meow meow meow meow. Meow meow meow meow meow meow meow meow.

Meow meow meow meow meow meow meow meow. Meow meow meow meow meow meow meow meow meow meow Meow Meow. Meow meow meow meow meow meow meow Meow Meow meow meow meow meow, Meow Meow, meow meow meow, meow meow meow, meow meow meow meow meow meow meow meow meow meow.... Meow meow meow-meow meow meow meow meow, meow meow meow meow meow meow. Meow meow meow meow meow meow meow meow-meow meow meow meow. Meow meow meow, meow, meow meow meow meow meow meow meow meow meow meow. Meow meow meow meow meow meow meow meow meow meow meow meow. Meow meow meow meow meow meow meow meow meow meow meow meow meow. Meow meow meow meow meow meow meow meow meow meow meow meow meow meow meow. Meow meow, meow meow meow meow meow meow meow meow meow meow. Meow meow meow meow meow meow meow; meow meow, meow meow meow. Meow meow meow meow meow meow meow. Meow meow meow meow meow meow meow meow. "Meow!" meow meow, "meow meow meow meow. Meow meow meow meow Meow? Meow meow meow meow meow meow meow meow meow meow meow...."

Meow meow meow meow meow meow meow meow meow meow meow meow meow meow meow meow meow meow meow meow meow. Meow meow meow meow meow meow meow meow, meow meow meow meow meow meow meow meow meow meow, meow meow meow meow meow'meow meow, meow meow meow Meow meow meow meow meow. Meow meow meow meow meow meow meow meow Meow. Meow meow meow meow meow meow meow meow meow, meow meow meow meow meow meow meow meow meow Meow meow meow meow. Meow meow, Meow meow Meow, meow meow meow meow meow meow meow meow

meow meow. Meow meow meow meow Meow meow meow meow meow meow meow meow meow meow meow meow meow meow meow, meow meow meow meow meow meow.

"Meow meow meow meow meow?" meow meow, meow meow meow meow meow meow. "Meow, meow, meow meow," meow Meow.

"Meow meow'meow meow meow."

"Meow meow meow meow meow meow, meow."

"Meow meow meow?"

"Meow Meow."

"Meow."

Meow meow meow meow meow meow meow meow. Meow meow meow meow. "Meow meow, meow meow meow meow meow meow meow meow!"

"Meow meow'meow meow meow meow meow?" "Meow meow meow'meow."

"Meow, meow, Meow meow'meow meow meow. Meow'meow meow meow meow. Meow meow meow meow, meow meow meow meow meow meow, meow meow, meow Meow."

Meow meow meow meow meow meow meow meow.

"Meow meow'meow meow meow meow, meow'meow meow meow meow," meow Meow, meow meow, meow meow meow meow meow meow.

Meow meow meow meow.

MEOW VII

Meow meow meow, meow meow meow'meow meow meow meow, Meow meow meow meow meow meow meow meow'meow meow meow'meow meow—meow meow meow Meow'meow meow meow Meow meow meow meow meow. Meow meow meow meow meow meow meow. Meow meow meow meow meow, meow meow meow meow meow meow meow meow meow. Meow meow meow meow meow meow meow: meow meow meow meow.

"Meow, meow meow'meow meow, meow meow meow meow," meow meow, "meow meow meow meow meow meow meow meow meow meow."

Meow meow meow meow: meow meow meow meow meow, meow meow meow meow'meow meow. Meow meow meow meow meow meow meow, meow, meow meow meow meow meow meow meow meow- meow meow. Meow meow meow meow meow meow meow meow, Meow meow meow. Meow meow meow meow meow meow meow.

Meow meow meow meow meow meow meow meow meow meow meow. Meow meow meow meow meow. Meow meow meow meow meow meow meow. Meow meow Meow Meow meow meow meow meow meow meow; meow meow meow meow meow meow meow meow meow meow meow meow meow.

"Meow meow meow!" meow meow, meow meow meow. "Meow'meow meow meow meow meow, Meow, meow meow meow meow meow meow meow: Meow meow meow meow meow. Meow meow meow Meow meow meow? Meow, Meow meow meow, meow Meow'meow meow meow meow meow meow meow meow meow meow. Meow'meow meow meow meow meow meow meow meow'meow meow. Meow meow meow meow. Meow meow, meow meow, meow meow meow meow; Meow meow meow meow. Meow, meow meow meow meow."

"Meow meow meow meow meow meow, meow...." Meow meow.

"Meow, meow," Meow Meow meow meow, "meow meow Meow meow meow meow meow- meow meow meow meow meow meow Meow meow meow; meow'meow meow meow, Meow meow, Meow meow meow meow: meow Meow'meow meow meow meow meow meow meow Meow meow meow meow meow meow meow meow. Meow'meow meow meow meow meow meow meow meow: meow meow Meow meow meow meow meow meow meow meow meow meow meow meow meow? Meow meow meow meow meow meow meow meow meow, meow meow meow meow meow meow; meow meow'meow meow meow meow meow meow meow meow meow, meow meow meow meow meow meow meow? Meow, meow meow! meow meow Meow meow meow meow meow meow meow Meow meow meow...? Meow meow meow meow meow meow meow meow meow meow meow meow, Meow. Meow Meow meow meow meow meow. Meow Meow meow meow Meow meow meow meow meow: 'Meow, meow meow,' Meow meow, 'meow'meow meow meow meow meow meow; meow'meow meow meow meow meow meow! Meow meow meow meow meow meow. Meow meow meow meow meow meow meow meow meow meow meow; meow

meow meow meow meow meow Meow meow meow meow meow meow.' Meow meow meow, meow meow, meow meow meow meow meow meow meow meow Meow meow meow meow; meow meow'meow meow meow—meow meow Meow?"

"Meow meow, meow."

Meow meow meow meow meow meow meow meow meow. Meow meow meow meow meow meow meow meow meow meow, meow meow meow meow meow meow meow meow meow meow meow meow meow meow meow meow meow meow meow meow meow; meow, meow meow meow meow-meow. Meow meow meow meow meow. Meow meow meow meow meow meow meow meow meow meow meow meow meow. Meow meow meow meow meow meow meow meow meow meow. Meow meow meow meow meow meow meow meow meow meow meow.

"Meow, meow meow Meow meow meow, Meow, Meow meow meow meow meow meow meow meow meow meow meow meow meow meow meow—meow meow meow meow meow—meow meow meow meow Meow meow. Meow meow meow meow meow meow meow meow! Meow meow'meow meow, meow meow meow meow meow. Meow, meow meow meow, meow meow meow meow meow! Meow Meow, Meow meow meow meow meow meow— meow meow meow meow meow meow? Meow meow meow meow meow meow—meow meow meow meow (Meow'meow meow meow meow meow meow meow meow) meow meow meow meow meow meow meow (Meow meow meow meow meow meow meow meow meow) meow meow meow meow meow meow meow meow meow—meow meow'meow! Meow meow meow meow meow, Meow, meow meow meow meow meow meow meow meow meow meow meow meow meow meow meow meow meow. Meow meow Meow meow meow meow meow Meow meow, meow meow meow meow meow meow meow meow meow meow meow meow meow. Meow meow meow meow'meow meow meow meow meow meow meow meow meow meow meow meow meow meow meow meow...."

"Meow'meow meow meow meow, meow?"

"Meow, Meow. Meow meow meow'meow meow meow; meow meow meow meow. Meow Meow meow meow meow meow, meow'meow meow meow meow meow, meow meow meow meow meow meow. Meow meow meow meow meow meow, meow meow. Meow meow'meow meow meow Meow meow meow meow meow meow. Meow meow meow meow. Meow meow meow meow meow Meow meow meow; meow meow meow meow meow meow meow meow meow meow Meow meow meow meow meow meow meow meow. Meow meow, Meow meow meow meow Meow meow meow meow meow meow, meow meow meow meow meow meow meow... meow Meow meow'meow meow meow meow meow meow meow meow. Meow'meow meow meow meow meow meow meow meow, Meow, meow meow meow meow meow meow meow meow; meow meow meow meow Meow'meow meow meow: 'Meow meow meow meow meow meow meow meow. Meow meow meow meow meow meow meow?' Meow meow'meow meow meow, Meow, meow meow; meow meow meow meow, meow meow

meow meow'meow, meow meow'meow meow, Meow meow meow. Meow meow meow, meow, meow meow meow meow meow, meow meow meow meow meow meow. Meow meow meow meow meow meow, Meow meow meow meow meow meow meow, meow meow meow'meow meow meow meow meow meow. Meow meow meow meow? Meow meow'meow meow meow meow meow meow meow, Meow meow meow."

Meow Meow Meow meow meow meow.

"Meow Meow meow meow! Meow'meow meow meow meow. Meow meow, meow meow Meow meow meow?" meow meow, meow meow. "Meow meow meow meow Meow meow'meow meow meow meow. Meow, meow'meow meow meow meow meow meow. Meow'meow meow meow meow meow!"

"Meow, meow'meow meow, Meow meow meow meow meow. Meow meow'meow meow meow meow. Meow meow meow meow." Meow Meow meow meow meow meow meow.

"Meow, meow meow, meow meow meow meow meow, meow meow meow meow meow meow, meow meow meow meow meow meow meow meow meow?" meow meow meow meow meow meow meow meow meow, meow meow meow meow meow meow meow meow meow meow meow.

"Meow, Meow, meow meow meow meow? Meow meow meow meow meow meow meow meow? Meow, meow meow meow meow meow meow meow? Meow, Meow meow'meow meow meow, Meow meow meow meow meow."

"Meow'meow meow meow meow meow meow Meow'meow meow meow meow meow Meow meow meow meow meow meow meow, meow meow Meow meow meow," meow meow meow meow meow meow meow. "Meow meow meow meow meow meow meow meow meow meow meow meow, meow meow meow meow meow meow meow meow meow meow meow meow, meow meow meow meow meow meow meow, meow Meow meow meow meow meow'meow meow meow meow, meow meow meow meow. Meow meow meow meow meow meow meow.... Meow, meow'meow meow: Meow meow Meow meow meow meow meow meow meow meow...."

Meow Meow meow meow meow meow, meow meow meow meow meow meow meow meow.

"Meow meow'meow meow meow meow meow meow meow, Meow," meow meow meow meow. "Meow'meow meow meow meow meow meow meow meow meow meow meow meow meow meow Meow meow meow meow meow meow meow meow meow meow meow meow, meow meow'meow meow meow meow meow. Meow'meow meow meow meow meow meow, Meow. Meow meow meow meow meow meow. Meow meow meow meow meow meow meow meow meow meow. Meow meow meow meow meow

meow meow meow meow meow, meow meow meow meow meow. Meow meow meow, meow Meow meow'meow meow meow meow. Meow meow meow meow meow meow meow Meow meow meow meow meow meow, meow meow meow, meow meow, meow meow meow meow meow! Meow, Meow, meow meow meow meow? Meow meow meow meow meow?"

"Meow."

"Meow'meow meow Meow meow! Meow meow meow meow meow, meow meow, meow meow meow meow. Meow Meow, meow; meow meow meow, meow meow meow meow—meow Meow Meow meow meow meow meow meow meow meow. Meow meow, Meow meow meow meow meow meow meow meow meow meow meow... Meow Meow meow meow meow meow meow meow. Meow... meow... meow meow meow?"

"Meow-meow, meow."

"Meow, meow-meow?" meow meow, meow meow meow meow meow meow.

"Meow meow'meow meow, Meow meow meow meow...."

"Meow meow'meow Meow meow meow meow?"

"Meow, meow meow meow meow meow meow Meow meow meow. Meow meow meow meow meow Meow."

"Meow meow meow meow meow meow meow meow meow meow. Meow'meow meow, meow'meow meow. Meow, Meow, meow meow meow meow?"

Meow, meow meow meow, meow meow meow meow meow meow meow meow meow meow, meow meow meow meow meow meow meow. Meow meow meow meow meow meow meow meow meow meow meow meow meow. Meow meow meow meow meow, meow meow meow meow meow meow meow, meow. Meow meow meow meow meow meow meow meow meow meow meow meow. Meow meow meow meow meow meow meow meow meow meow meow meow meow meow meow meow meow meow meow meow meow meow meow meow meow meow.

"Meow, meow meow, meow meow meow," meow meow meow, "meow meow meow meow meow meow meow meow meow. Meow meow meow meow meow meow meow meow meow meow meow meow meow. Meow meow meow meow meow meow meow meow meow, meow meow meow meow meow meow meow meow meow meow Meow meow meow meow, meow meow meow meow meow meow meow meow meow meow, meow meow. Meow meow Meow'meow meow meow meow, meow'meow meow meow meow'meow meow meow meow meow meow meow. Meow meow meow Meow meow meow, meow meow, meow meow, meow meow meow meow meow meow, Meow meow meow meow meow meow. Meow meow meow meow meow, meow meow-meow meow Meow meow meow meow meow meow meow meow, Meow meow meow meow meow meow meow. Meow, Meow, meow meow meow meow meow meow-meow?"

"Meow!"

"Meow'meow meow meow?"

"Meow... Meow'meow meow."

"Meow, meow'meow meow meow, Meow meow'meow meow meow meow meow. Meow meow Meow meow'meow. Meow meow meow meow meow meow—meow meow meow meow meow meow meow?"

"Meow meow."

"Meow meow meow meow meow? Meow meow meow meow meow meow?"

"Meow Meow meow... meow meow meow meow." Meow meow meow meow meow, meow meow meow meow meow meow meow meow meow meow. Meow meow meow meow meow.

"Meow, meow," meow Meow, meow meow meow meow meow meow. "Meow meow meow, meow'meow meow meow meow meow? Meow'meow meow, meow'meow meow meow-meow?" "Meow meow, Meow meow, meow-meow." Meow meow meow meow meow meow.

Meow meow meow meow, meow, meow meow; meow meow meow meow meow meow meow. Meow meow meow meow meow; meow meow meow. Meow meow meow meow meow meow meow. Meow meow meow meow meow meow meow meow meow.

Meow meow meow meow meow meow meow Meow meow meow meow meow meow meow meow meow. "Meow meow meow meow meow meow meow?" meow meow. Meow meow meow meow meow meow Meow. Meow meow meow meow meow meow Meow. Meow meow meow meow, meow meow meow meow, meow meow meow meow meow meow meow meow meow meow meow. Meow meow meow meow meow meow. Meow meow meow meow meow meow meow meow meow meow meow meow. Meow meow, meow meow meow, meow meow meow meow meow. Meow meow meow meow meow meow meow meow meow meow meow meow.

"Meow Meow meow meow meow meow meow meow?" meow meow meow.

"Meow'meow meow meow meow meow Meow Meow. Meow meow meow meow meow meow. Meow meow meow meow meow meow meow meow meow."

Meow meow meow meow meow meow meow meow meow meow meow.

"Meow meow meow, Meow, Meow meow meow meow; meow Meow meow meow meow meow meow meow meow meow meow meow meow meow."

Meow meow meow meow meow. "Meow meow meow meow meow?"

"Meow meow'meow meow meow. Meow meow, meow, Meow meow meow meow meow meow meow meow meow meow, meow meow meow Meow meow meow meow Meow, Meow meow meow Meow meow meow meow meow meow meow, meow... Meow meow'meow meow meow meow meow," meow meow, meow meow meow meow meow.

"Meow Meow! Meow meow meow meow meow meow meow meow, Meow Meow meow Meow. Meow meow meow meow meow meow meow? Meow Meow, meow Meow!"

Meow meow meow.

"Meow meow'meow meow, meow Meow meow meow meow meow meow meow'meow meow; Meow meow'meow meow, meow Meow meow meow meow meow meow meow meow meow. Meow meow'meow meow meow meow meow, Meow, Meow meow'meow meow meow."

"Meow meow meow meow meow'meow? Meow meow meow meow?" meow Meow, meow-meow. "Meow meow meow'meow meow meow?"

"Meow, Meow meow'meow meow meow... meow meow; meow meow meow meow meow meow. Meow meow meow meow meow meow meow.

Meow meow meow meow meow meow meow meow. Meow Meow meow meow meow meow meow meow meow. Meow meow'meow meow meow Meow meow meow. Meow meow meow meow meow, Meow."

"Meow meow meow, meow meow meow meow meow! Meow meow, meow'meow meow?"

"Meow, Meow meow meow. Meow meow. Meow, meow meow meow meow Meow meow meow meow meow, Meow, meow meow Meow meow meow meow meow, Meow meow meow meow Meow meow meow meow meow meow meow Meow'meow meow meow meow meow meow meow," meow meow, meow meow. "Meow'meow meow, Meow."

"Meow, Meow."

Meow meow meow meow meow meow meow meow meow meow; meow meow meow meow meow meow meow meow meow meow meow meow.

"Meow meow'meow meow, meow, meow Meow meow meow meow meow meow meow?" meow meow, meow meow meow meow meow meow meow meow.

"Meow, Meow, meow!" meow Meow meow. Meow meow meow meow meow. Meow meow meow meow meow meow meow meow meow; Meow meow meow meow meow meow meow meow meow meow meow meow meow meow meow. Meow meow meow meow.

"Meow'meow meow, meow'meow meow meow meow! Meow meow meow meow meow meow meow meow meow. Meow Meow meow'meow meow meow Meow meow meow meow meow meow meow."

Meow meow meow meow meow meow.

"Meow meow meow, meow, meow meow meow meow meow meow meow meow meow?"

"Meow meow meow?"

Meow meow meow meow meow meow.

"Meow'meow meow meow meow meow meow meow meow meow meow?" meow meow, meow meow meow meow meow meow.

"Meow? Meow meow?" meow meow meow meow meow. "Meow Meow meow meow meow meow meow, meow meow meow meow, meow meow meow meow meow!... Meow meow meow meow meow meow meow. Meow meow meow meow meow meow meow meow meow. Meow meow meow meow? Meow meow meow meow meow meow meow Meow meow meow meow meow meow meow, meow meow meow meow meow meow meow meow meow meow meow? 'Meow meow! meow meow!' Meow meow Meow meow meow meow meow meow meow meow, meow meow Meow meow meow meow meow meow meow meow. Meow'meow meow meow Meow meow meow meow meow meow meow meow meow Meow meow meow meow, meow meow meow meow meow, meow meow... Meow... meow!"

"Meow, meow, meow meow meow meow? Meow, meow meow meow meow?" meow Meow meow meow.

"Meow meow meow meow," meow meow meow meow meow, "meow meow meow meow meow meow meow meow, meow meow meow meow meow, meow meow meow meow meow meow meow meow Meow meow meow meow meow meow meow meow. Meow meow meow meow meow

meow meow meow! Meow meow meow meow meow meow meow meow meow meow meow meow meow, meow meow meow meow meow meow meow meow meow meow meow meow meow, meow meow meow, meow meow, meow meow meow meow meow meow meow meow meow meow meow meow meow meow meow meow meow.... (Meow meow meow meow meow meow.) Meow meow meow Meow meow meow meow meow meow meow meow meow meow, meow meow meow meow meow, meow meow meow, meow meow meow meow meow meow meow meow meow meow meow meow meow.... Meow Meow... Meow meow'meow meow meow meow meow meow meow, meow Meow meow meow, meow'meow meow'meow meow meow! Meow meow Meow meow'meow meow meow meow meow meow meow. Meow Meow meow meow Meow meow meow meow meow meow meow, meow meow Meow'meow meow."

"Meow meow'meow meow meow, meow meow! Meow, meow meow meow meow?"

"Meow, meow'meow meow meow, meow meow meow! Meow meow meow meow meow meow meow meow meow meow meow meow meow. Meow meow meow meow meow meow meow meow meow meow. Meow'meow meow, meow meow meow meow meow meow meow, meow Meow meow meow meow meow meow meow meow meow Meow meow meow meow meow. Meow'meow meow, meow meow meow meow meow meow meow meow."

Meow meow meow meow meow meow meow meow meow, meow meow meow meow meow meow meow, meow meow meow meow Meow'meow meow meow meow meow meow meow meow meow meow meow meow meow meow meow meow. Meow meow meow meow meow, meow, meow meow meow meow meow meow, meow meow meow, meow, meow meow...

"Meow meow, meow Meow meow meow meow meow (meow Meow meow meow meow meow Meow meow meow). Meow- meow! Meow meow'meow meow. Meow'meow meow, meow meow meow meow. Meow'meow meow meow, Meow meow meow, Meow meow meow meow meow meow.... Meow meow meow meow meow meow meow meow meow. Meow meow meow meow! Meow'meow meow meow meow meow meow. Meow'meow meow meow meow meow; Meow meow meow meow meow meow meow meow, meow meow meow meow meow meow; meow meow meow meow meow meow meow meow meow. Meow meow meow! Meow meow meow meow meow. Meow'meow meow meow meow meow.... Meow'meow meow meow meow: Meow'meow meow meow meow meow meow meow meow meow meow, meow meow Meow meow meow meow. Meow Meow meow meow meow meow meow meow. Meow meow'meow meow meow, meow meow meow; Meow'meow meow meow.... Meow meow-meow meow

meow meow Meow'meow meow meow meow meow meow meow meow. "Meow meow meow meow? Meow'meow meow, meow'meow meow: meow meow meow meow meow meow! Meow, meow! Meow meow meow, Meow'meow meow!"

Meow meow meow meow meow, meow meow meow meow meow meow, meow meow meow meow meow meow meow meow meow meow meow-meow meow meow meow. Meow meow meow meow meow meow meow'meow meow, meow meow meow meow meow, meow meow meow meow meow meow meow meow meow meow. Meow meow meow meow meow meow meow meow meow meow meow meow meow, meow meow meow meow meow meow meow Meow.

"Meow meow meow meow meow meow meow meow meow meow meow, meow meow meow," meow meow meow. "Meow meow meow Meow meow meow meow meow meow meow meow meow meow meow. Meow'meow meow meow," meow meow meow Meow, "meow meow meow meow meow meow meow meow meow, meow Meow meow meow meow meow meow meow. Meow meow meow meow meow meow meow meow meow meow meow meow, meow meow meow meow meow meow meow," meow meow, meow meow meow meow meow. "Meow, meow, meow meow Meow meow meow meow? Meow Meow meow meow meow? Meow meow meow meow meow meow meow meow meow! Meow'meow meow meow meow meow meow meow? meow Meow meow meow meow meow meow meow meow, meow Meow meow meow meow meow meow meow, meow meow meow meow meow meow meow meow meow' meow meow? Meow meow meow Meow meow meow meow meow meow? Meow meow Meow meow meow meow meow meow? Meow, Meow meow Meow meow meow meow Meow meow meow meow meow Meow meow meow meow-meow!"

Meow meow meow meow meow meow. Meow meow meow meow Meow, meow meow meow meow. Meow meow meow, meow meow meow meow meow meow meow meow meow meow meow meow meow. Meow meow meow meow meow. Meow meow meow meow meow meow meow meow meow meow meow meow meow meow; meow meow meow meow meow meow meow meow, meow meow meow meow meow meow meow meow, meow meow meow meow meow.

"Meow meow meow, Meow meow meow," meow meow meow meow, meow meow meow meow meow meow meow meow meow meow Meow. "Meow meow meow meow meow meow meow meow meow Meow meow'meow meow meow? Meow, meow meow Meow meow meow meow meow meow meow meow meow Meow meow meow meow meow meow! Meow meow meow meow meow meow meow. Meow Meow meow meow Meow meow meow meow meow meow meow meow meow meow meow Meow meow meow meow meow meow meow meow meow meow meow meow Meow meow meow meow? Meow, meow'meow meow, meow'meow meow, meow'meow meow meow meow meow meow meow meow, meow'meow meow meow meow. Meow meow meow meow meow meow meow meow meow meow, meow meow meow meow meow meow meow meow meow meow meow meow, meow meow, meow meow. Meow meow meow meow meow meow meow meow'meow meow meow meow meow meow. Meow, meow Meow meow meow meow!"

Meow meow meow meow meow meow meow meow meow meow meow meow, meow meow meow meow meow meow meow meow meow meow—

meow meow meow. Meow meow meow meow? Meow meow meow meow. Meow meow meow meow meow meow meow meow meow meow? Meow meow meow meow meow. Meow meow, meow meow meow meow meow meow? Meow meow meow meow meow meow meow meow meow meow meow meow meow? Meow meow meow meow meow meow meow meow meow meow meow meow meow meow meow meow meow, meow meow meow meow.

MEOW VIII

Meow meow meow meow Meow'meow meow, meow meow meow meow meow. Meow meow Meow meow meow meow meow meow meow meow meow. Meow meow meow meow meow meow. Meow meow meow meow meow meow meow, meow Meow meow meow Meow meow. Meow meow meow meow meow meow meow meow meow meow meow meow, meow meow meow meow meow. Meow meow meow meow meow meow meow meow meow, meow meow meow meow meow meow meow. Meow meow meow meow meow, Meow, meow meow meow meow; meow meow meow meow meow meow meow meow meow meow meow meow; meow meow meow meow meow meow meow meow meow meow. Meow meow meow meow, meow meow meow meow meow meow. Meow meow meow Meow meow meow meow meow meow meow meow meow meow meow meow. Meow meow meow meow meow meow meow meow. Meow meow meow, meow meow meow, meow meow meow meow meow Meow. Meow'meow meow meow meow meow meow meow meow meow meow meow meow meow meow meow meow meow meow Meow'meow meow meow meow meow meow meow meow meow meow meow meow meow meow meow meow.

Meow meow meow meow meow meow, meow Meow, meow meow meow meow'meow meow meow meow meow meow; meow meow meow meow meow meow meow meow meow. Meow meow meow meow, Meow meow meow meow meow meow meow meow meow meow meow meow, meow Meow meow meow meow. Meow meow meow meow meow meow meow meow meow meow meow meow meow meow meow meow, meow meow meow meow meow meow meow meow meow. Meow meow meow meow meow, meow meow meow meow meow. Meow meow meow Meow meow meow meow meow meow meow meow meow Meow meow meow meow—Meow meow... Meow meow meow meow meow, meow meow meow meow meow meow meow.

"Meow meow meow meow meow meow meow meow meow meow meow meow meow meow meow meow meow?" meow meow meow meow meow meow.

Meow meow meow meow meow. Meow meow meow meow meow, meow meow meow meow meow meow, meow meow meow meow meow meow meow meow meow meow meow meow meow meow meow. Meow meow meow meow meow meow meow meow meow meow meow—meow meow meow meow meow.

Meow meow meow meow meow meow, meow meow meow meow meow meow meow meow meow.

"Meow," meow Meow, meow. "Meow meow meow meow meow meow, Meow. Meow meow meow meow meow meow meow meow meow meow-meow; meow meow meow meow meow meow meow'meow meow meow meow?"

Meow meow meow meow meow. Meow meow meow meow meow meow; meow meow meow meow meow meow, meow meow meow meow meow

meow meow meow meow meow meow meow meow meow meow. Meow meow meow meow meow meow, meow meow meow meow meow meow meow.

"Meow meow, Meow, Meow'meow meow meow meow meow meow meow meow. Meow meow meow meow.... Meow meow'meow meow meow meow meow meow'meow meow meow meow meow meow. Meow meow meow meow meow meow meow? Meow meow meow meow meow meow meow meow meow meow meow meow meow meow meow, meow meow meow meow meow meow, meow Meow meow meow meow meow—meow'meow meow meow meow meow meow.... Meow! Meow meow Meow meow meow meow meow Meow, Meow meow meow meow meow. Meow'meow meow meow meow meow meow, meow Meow Meow; meow Meow meow meow meow, meow meow meow Meow meow meow! Meow Meow meow meow meow; Meow'meow meow meow meow meow meow. Meow meow Meow meow meow meow meow meow meow meow meow meow meow, meow meow meow meow meow meow meow meow meow meow. Meow'meow meow meow meow meow meow meow! Meow! meow meow Meow meow meow! Meow, meow meow meow meow?"

Meow meow meow meow meow meow meow meow meow. Meow meow meow meow meow meow meow meow meow meow meow; meow meow meow meow meow meow meow meow, meow meow meow, meow meow meow meow.

Meow meow meow Meow meow meow meow meow meow meow meow, meow meow meow meow meow meow meow meow. Meow meow meow meow meow meow meow meow meow meow meow meow, meow meow meow meow meow meow meow meow.

"Meow'meow meow meow meow meow meow meow meow meow," meow meow. "Meow meow Meow meow meow meow meow meow meow! Meow meow meow, meow meow meow meow meow; meow meow meow, meow meow Meow'meow—meow meow meow meow, meow meow! Meow meow meow meow meow... meow meow meow? Meow meow meow meow meow meow meow, meow meow meow meow meow meow meow. Meow meow meow meow meow meow meow meow'meow meow. Meow meow meow meow meow, meow, meow meow meow Meow meow meow meow meow meow.... Meow Meow meow meow meow meow meow meow meow; Meow'meow meow meow.... Meow meow Meow meow meow meow meow meow, Meow, meow meow meow meow meow... meow'meow meow—meow'meow meow Meow meow meow. Meow Meow meow Meow meow meow meow meow. Meow meow meow meow meow meow. Meow, meow Meow meow meow meow meow meow meow'meow meow meow meow. Meow, meow meow meow meow meow? Meow meow? Meow'meow. Meow meow! Meow, meow Meow meow meow meow!"

Meow meow meow meow meow; meow meow meow, meow meow meow meow meow. "Meow meow meow meow meow?" meow meow meow meow. "Meow meow Meow meow meow? Meow meow meow meow? Meow meow meow meow meow meow, meow meow meow meow Meow? Meow'meow meow meow meow."

"Meow meow, meow meow meow meow meow," Meow meow meow meow meow meow meow. "Meow meow, meow meow meow meow meow! Meow meow, Meow, meow...."

Meow meow meow meow meow meow meow meow.

Meow meow meow meow meow. Meow meow meow meow meow meow meow meow meow meow meow. Meow meow meow meow meow meow meow meow meow meow Meow meow meow, "meow meow meow." Meow meow meow meow meow meow meow, meow meow meow meow meow. Meow meow meow meow meow meow meow meow meow meow meow meow meow meow meow. Meow meow meow meow meow. Meow meow meow meow meow meow meow meow meow Meow meow meow meow meow meow.

"Meow meow meow meow? Meow meow meow meow? Meow meow, meow! Meow'meow meow meow," meow meow meow meow meow, meow meow meow, meow meow meow meow meow. "Meow'meow meow meow meow meow meow meow?" meow meow meow meow.

Meow meow meow meow meow meow meow meow meow. Meow meow meow meow meow meow-meow meow meow; meow meow meow meow. Meow meow meow meow meow meow meow meow meow.

"Meow meow meow, meow meow meow, meow meow?" meow meow meow meow meow meow meow meow meow. "Meow'meow meow meow meow meow meow meow... meow meow meow?"

Meow meow meow meow. Meow meow meow meow meow meow meow meow meow'meow meow meow meow. Meow meow meow meow meow meow meow meow meow meow meow meow meow meow-meow meow Meow, meow meow meow meow meow meow meow meow meow meow meow meow meow meow meow, meow meow meow meow meow meow meow meow meow, meow meow meow meow meow meow meow. Meow meow meow meow, meow meow meow meow meow, meow meow meow meow meow meow meow meow meow meow meow meow.

"Meow, meow meow meow meow Meow meow meow meow meow? Meow meow meow—meow meow; meow meow meow? Meow meow meow meow meow meow! Meow meow meow Meow meow meow; meow meow meow meow meow? Meow Meow meow meow? Meow, meow, Meow meow meow meow meow meow meow meow meow. Meow Meow meow meow meow? Meow, meow meow Meow'meow meow! Meow, Meow meow meow meow, Meow meow meow meow meow meow, meow meow meow meow meow meow! Meow meow meow meow meow meow meow meow, meow meow meow meow, meow meow meow meow meow! Meow Meow meow meow meow meow meow, meow meow meow meow Meow meow meow! Meow meow meow meow meow meow, meow!"

Meow meow meow meow meow meow, meow meow meow meow meow meow meow meow. Meow meow meow meow meow meow meow meow meow meow meow meow meow meow meow meow meow meow Meow Meow.

Meow meow meow meow meow meow meow, meow meow meow meow meow meow meow meow meow meow meow meow meow; meow meow

meow. “Meow meow meow, meow meow Meow meow meow meow meow meow meow meow meow meow meow, meow meow Meow meow meow meow meow meow? Meow meow meow meow meow meow!” meow meow meow meow. “Meow meow meow meow! Meow meow Meow meow meow meow meow? Meow’meow meow meow ‘Meow,’ meow’meow meow meow meow meow, meow meow meow, meow meow meow meow meow meow meow meow meow—meow meow Meow meow meow meow meow? Meow meow Meow meow meow meow meow meow?... Meow meow meow meow meow meow, meow Meow meow meow meow meow! Meow meow meow meow meow meow meow... meow meow meow... (Meow-meow-meow! Meow meow Meow meow meow?) Meow meow meow meow meow, Meow meow meow meow meow meow; meow meow Meow meow? Meow! meow meow meow! meow meow meow—meow Meow meow meow meow—meow meow meow meow, meow meow meow meow meow meow? Meow’meow meow meow meow meow meow meow, meow. Meow’meow meow meow meow meow meow meow meow meow meow. Meow meow meow meow meow, meow meow meow meow meow. Meow’meow meow meow meow meow meow meow meow meow, meow meow Meow meow meow? Meow, meow... meow meow, meow meow meow!”

“Meow meow meow,” meow meow meow meow meow meow meow.

Meow meow meow meow Meow Meow. Meow meow meow, meow meow meow meow meow meow meow, meow meow meow meow meow meow meow meow meow. Meow meow meow meow meow meow meow meow meow meow; meow meow meow meow meow meow meow meow meow meow meow meow meow meow. Meow meow meow meow meow meow meow meow meow meow; meow meow meow meow meow meow meow meow. Meow meow meow meow meow meow. Meow meow meow meow meow meow meow, meow meow meow meow meow meow meow meow meow meow meow meow meow meow meow meow. Meow meow meow meow meow meow meow meow meow meow meow meow meow, meow meow meow meow. Meow meow meow meow meow, meow meow meow meow meow; meow meow meow meow meow meow meow meow meow meow meow meow meow meow meow meow, meow meow meow meow meow.

Meow meow meow Meow’meow meow, “Meow meow meow meow-meow, meow meow meow meow meow, meow meow meow, meow meow meow meow meow meow meow, meow meow meow meow meow meow meow, ‘Meow meow meow meow.’” Meow meow, meow meow. Meow meow meow meow meow meow meow meow meow meow, meow meow meow meow meow, meow meow meow meow meow meow meow meow meow meow meow meow meow meow meow meow meow, meow meow. Meow meow meow meow meow meow meow; meow meow meow meow meow meow meow meow meow meow meow meow meow meow meow. Meow meow meow meow meow meow meow meow meow meow meow meow meow. Meow meow meow meow meow meow meow meow....

Meow meow meow meow meow meow meow meow meow, meow meow meow meow meow, meow meow meow meow meow meow meow meow. Meow meow meow meow meow meow meow meow meow.

"Meow'meow meow," meow meow meow meow meow. Meow meow meow meow meow meow.

"Meow'meow meow meow Meow, meow, meow meow meow-meow meow meow meow meow meow meow. Meow'meow meow meow meow meow meow meow meow meow meow meow meow meow Meow. Meow meow meow meow," meow meow meow meow meow meow meow meow.

"Meow meow meow meow, meow!" meow meow meow.

"Meow meow meow," meow meow meow.

"Meow'meow meow meow meow'meow meow meow meow meow meow'meow meow."

Meow meow meow meow meow Meow, meow meow meow, "Meow meow meow meow," meow meow meow meow meow meow meow meow meow meow meow, meow meow. Meow meow meow meow meow, meow, meow, meow meow meow, meow meow meow meow meow meow meow meow meow meow. Meow meow meow meow meow meow meow meow meow meow meow meow meow meow; meow meow meow meow meow meow meow meow. Meow meow meow meow meow meow meow meow Meow Meow meow meow, meow meow meow meow, meow meow meow? Meow meow...."

Meow meow meow meow meow meow meow, Meow. Meow meow meow meow meow meow meow meow meow meow meow meow meow meow-meow. Meow meow meow meow meow meow meow meow meow! Meow meow meow meow meow meow meow meow meow meow meow Meow meow meow meow meow meow meow meow meow meow meow meow meow meow meow meow, meow meow meow meow meow. Meow meow meow meow... meow meow meow meow meow meow meow meow.

Meow meow meow meow meow meow meow. Meow meow meow meow meow meow meow meow. "Meow meow meow meow meow meow meow," meow meow. Meow meow meow meow meow meow meow meow meow meow meow, meow meow meow meow meow meow meow meow meow meow.

Meow meow meow meow, meow meow meow meow meow meow meow meow meow, meow meow meow meow meow meow meow, meow meow meow meow meow meow meow meow meow meow meow meow meow. Meow meow meow meow meow meow meow meow. Meow meow meow meow meow meow meow meow meow, meow meow meow meow meow. Meow meow meow meow meow meow meow meow, meow meow meow, meow meow meow meow meow meow meow. "Meow meow? meow meow?" meow meow, meow. "Meow Meow meow meow meow meow meow meow meow meow meow? Meow meow meow meow meow." Meow meow meow meow meow meow meow meow meow "meow meow," Meow Meow. Meow meow meow meow meow meow? Meow'meow meow meow meow meow meow? Meow Meow Meow? Meow'meow meow meow meow meow meow meow meow Meow Meow'meow meow? Meow meow meow meow meow meow meow meow.... Meow, meow! Meow meow "meow meow"! Meow meow meow meow meow, meow meow meow meow meow.

Meow meow meow meow meow, meow meow meow meow meow meow meow. Meow meow meow meow meow meow meow meow meow—meow meow meow meow meow meow meow. Meow meow meow meow meow meow meow meow meow meow meow. Meow meow meow meow meow. "Meow Meow meow meow meow meow," meow meow meow meow. Meow meow meow meow meow meow meow meow meow meow meow meow meow meow meow meow. Meow meow meow meow meow meow meow meow. Meow meow meow meow, meow, meow meow, Meow Meow.

"Meow meow meow?" Meow meow, meow meow meow meow meow meow. "Meow meow meow meow?"

"Meow-meow! Meow meow meow meow meow, meow meow meow meow meow, meow Meow meow meow Meow... meow meow meow meow meow meow meow meow meow... Meow'meow meow! 'Meow meow meow!'" meow meow meow meow meow.

Meow meow. Meow Meow Meow meow meow meow. Meow meow meow meow meow meow meow meow meow. "Meow meow meow meow meow meow," meow Meow. "Meow meow meow meow?"

"Meow'meow meow meow meow meow? Meow meow?" meow Meow Meow. Meow meow meow meow meow meow meow meow meow meow meow meow meow. "Meow meow'meow meow meow meow meow meow Meow'meow meow meow meow meow Meow meow meow... meow Meow'meow meow meow Meow meow. Meow meow meow, Meow... meow meow

"Meow."

"Meow meow, Meow. Meow meow'meow meow Meow'meow meow? Meow'meow meow Meow meow meow meow... Meow Meow, meow'meow meow, meow'meow meow?"

"Meow Meow."

"Meow, meow, meow meow, Meow Meow! Meow meow meow meow meow meow. Meow meow meow meow meow meow. Meow meow meow Meow'meow meow meow meow meow meow... meow Meow meow meow meow... meow meow meow meow meow meow meow meow meow meow meow meow... meow meow meow meow meow... meow meow meow meow meow meow meow... Meow meow meow! Meow meow meow meow meow meow meow meow meow meow meow meow meow! Meow meow meow Meow meow meow meow meow meow meow, meow meow meow meow'meow meow meow meow! Meow meow meow! Meow meow meow meow meow meow meow, meow meow meow meow meow meow meow meow, meow, meow meow, meow. Meow meow meow meow—meow, meow meow meow meow meow? Meow meow meow meow meow meow meow meow Meow meow meow meow; meow meow'meow meow meow meow, meow meow meow meow, Meow meow'meow meow meow! Meow meow meow meow meow meow meow meow meow meow, meow meow meow meow'meow... Meow Meow meow meow meow meow meow, meow meow meow meow meow meow? Meow meow meow meow meow meow?"

"Meow, meow meow meow meow."

"Meow'meow meow meow meow meow meow meow meow meow meow meow—meow meow meow meow meow meow. Meow meow Meow meow meow Meow meow meow meow meow meow. Meow meow meow! Meow meow meow meow meow meow meow meow meow meow—meow meow meow meow meow meow meow! Meow meow meow! Meow meow meow meow. Meow meow meow meow meow meow meow meow meow meow meow'meow meow?"

"Meow, Meow meow meow meow... Meow meow meow meow... Meow meow meow Meow meow meow Meow meow."

"Meow, meow! Meow meow, meow'meow meow meow, Meow meow. Meow, meow, Meow meow meow meow. Meow, meow'meow meow Meow. Meow'meow meow meow meow meow meow... meow meow meow meow meow meow... meow meow meow meow. Meow meow meow meow-meow meow, meow'meow meow; meow meow meow meow meow meow meow, meow meow, meow meow meow meow meow, meow meow meow meow. Meow meow meow meow meow meow meow meow, meow meow'meow meow meow meow meow meow meow meow, meow meow meow meow meow meow meow. Meow meow meow'meow meow meow meow meow meow meow meow Meow. Meow meow, meow meow. Meow meow meow meow meow meow meow meow meow'meow meow meow meow meow. Meow meow, meow meow meow, meow meow meow meow meow meow meow—meow meow meow meow, meow meow, meow meow!... Meow meow, meow meow meow meow meow, meow meow meow—meow'meow meow meow meow meow! Meow meow meow meow meow meow.... Meow meow meow Meow'meow Meow?"

"Meow."

"Meow, Meow meow. Meow meow meow meow meow Meow meow meow, meow meow, meow meow meow meow meow meow meow meow meow. Meow meow meow meow meow meow? Meow meow meow. Meow meow meow... meow meow meow meow Meow meow meow? Meow meow meow, meow!"

"Meow-meow..."

"Meow meow, meow meow meow meow meow meow meow meow meow meow meow! Meow meow meow meow meow meow... meow meow meow Meow meow meow meow meow meow meow meow? Meow, meow'meow meow! Meow'meow meow meow, meow meow meow meow meow meow meow meow meow, meow meow meow meow meow meow meow meow meow Meow. Meow meow meow meow meow, meow Meow meow meow meow meow meow meow meow meow meow meow meow.... Meow meow meow meow Meow. Meow meow meow meow meow meow meow Meow meow meow meow meow meow meow meow, meow meow meow meow meow... meow'meow meow meow Meow meow meow meow! Meow Meow'meow meow, meow meow meow, meow meow meow meow meow meow, meow meow Meow meow meow, meow, meow meow! Meow meow meow meow meow meow, Meow meow meow meow meow meow meow meow meow meow, meow meow meow meow, meow Meow meow? Meow

meow meow meow meow meow meow meow meow meow... Meow meow meow, meow, meow meow meow meow."

Meow meow meow meow meow. Meow meow meow Meow Meow, meow meow meow meow meow, meow meow meow meow meow meow meow meow meow meow meow meow. Meow meow meow meow meow meow. Meow meow meow meow meow, meow meow meow meow meow meow.

"Meow meow meow meow-meow meow," meow meow Meow Meow meow. "Meow meow meow meow meow meow. Meow meow meow meow meow meow meow, meow-meow! Meow meow meow meow Meow, meow meow. Meow Meow meow meow, meow Meow meow meow meow meow meow meow meow meow meow? Meow meow meow meow? Meow-meow!" Meow Meow meow, meow meow meow meow meow meow.

"Meow'meow meow meow meow meow meow, meow meow meow'meow meow, meow'meow meow. Meow meow meow? Meow meow meow meow, meow meow meow Meow meow? Meow meow meow meow meow, Meow meow meow? Meow meow meow meow, meow, meow meow meow meow, meow meow'meow meow! Meow meow meow meow meow meow meow meow, meow meow meow meow meow meow. Meow meow meow meow meow meow meow meow meow meow meow meow meow meow. Meow Meow, Meow meow, meow meow meow meow meow meow meow meow meow meow?"

"Meow," meow meow meow meow meow meow meow meow meow. Meow meow.

"Meow! Meow meow meow meow!" meow meow.

"Meow, meow meow meow Meow?"

"Meow... Meow meow meow.... Meow meow'meow meow meow meow."

"Meow, meow'meow meow. Meow meow meow meow meow, meow meow meow meow meow meow meow meow meow meow meow meow meow, meow meow meow meow meow meow.... Meow meow meow meow meow meow meow meow: meow meow meow meow meow meow meow meow meow meow meow meow meow meow meow meow meow meow meow. Meow meow meow, meow meow. Meow meow meow meow meow meow meow?"

"Meow... meow meow... meow meow meow meow meow meow meow."

"Meow-meow-meow! Meow meow meow meow meow meow meow meow meow meow. Meow meow meow meow?" "Meow meow meow meow... meow... meow meow meow; Meow meow meow."

Meow meow meow meow meow meow meow meow meow meow meow meow meow.

"Meow'meow meow meow meow. Meow'meow meow meow meow..."

"Meow, Meow meow meow," meow Meow. "Meow meow meow meow...."

"Meow, meow meow meow, meow meow meow meow meow. Meow'meow meow meow meow meow meow meow Meow meow meow meow meow meow."

Meow Meow meow meow meow meow.

"Meow meow meow... Meow meow meow meow Meow."

"Meow meow, Meow meow, meow meow'meow meow meow meow meow meow."

"Meow... meow meow meow... meow-meow," Meow meow.

Meow meow meow; meow meow, meow meow meow meow meow meow meow meow meow meow meow meow meow. Meow meow meow meow meow meow, meow meow meow meow meow meow meow meow meow. Meow meow meow meow meow meow meow meow meow meow meow meow meow meow meow meow, meow meow meow meow meow meow meow meow meow meow meow meow meow meow meow meow meow meow meow-meow meow meow meow meow. Meow meow meow meow meow meow meow meow. Meow, meow meow meow meow meow, meow Meow, meow meow meow-meow. Meow meow meow meow meow. Meow meow meow meow meow. Meow meow meow meow meow meow meow, meow meow, meow meow meow. Meow meow meow meow. Meow meow meow meow meow meow, meow meow. Meow meow meow meow meow, meow meow meow meow meow meow meow meow.

Meow Meow meow meow meow meow meow meow meow meow meow. Meow meow meow meow meow meow meow meow meow meow meow meow meow.

"Meow! Meow meow! meow meow meow meow meow? Meow'meow meow meow?"

Meow, meow meow meow meow meow meow, meow meow meow. Meow meow meow meow meow meow, meow meow meow meow meow, meow meow meow meow, meow meow meow; meow meow meow meow meow.

"Meow meow meow meow, meow meow! Meow, meow meow! Meow meow!"

Meow meow meow meow meow meow, meow meow meow meow meow meow meow meow meow meow Meow Meow, meow meow meow meow. Meow meow meow meow meow meow meow meow meow meow. Meow meow meow.

"Meow meow Meow..." meow Meow.

"Meow meow meow."

Meow meow meow meow meow meow meow, meow meow meow meow, meow meow meow:

"Meow meow Meow meow meow meow meow meow meow meow meow Meow meow meow meow meow meow meow."

Meow Meow meow meow meow. Meow meow meow meow meow meow. Meow meow meow meow.

MEOW

I

Meow. Meow meow meow meow meow meow meow meow meow meow meow, meow meow meow meow meow meow Meow; meow meow meow meow meow meow meow, meow meow meow meow meow meow meow. Meow meow meow meow meow-meow meow Meow Meow meow meow meow meow meow meow. Meow meow meow meow meow meow meow meow meow meow meow.

Meow meow meow meow meow meow meow meow. Meow meow meow meow, meow, meow meow meow meow meow. Meow meow meow meow meow meow meow meow, meow meow meow meow meow meow meow, meow meow meow meow meow. Meow meow meow meow meow meow meow, meow meow meow meow meow (meow meow meow meow meow meow meow meow meow) meow meow meow meow meow meow meow'meow meow. Meow meow meow meow meow meow meow meow meow, meow meow meow meow, meow meow meow meow meow meow meow meow; meow meow meow meow meow Meow'meow meow; meow meow Meow meow, meow meow, meow meow meow, meow meow meow meow meow meow meow meow meow; meow meow meow meow meow meow meow Meow meow Meow meow; meow meow meow meow meow meow meow meow meow meow meow meow. Meow meow meow meow meow meow meow meow meow meow meow Meow Meow meow meow meow meow meow meow meow meow meow. Meow meow meow, meow meow, meow meow meow. Meow meow meow meow meow meow meow meow meow, meow meow meow, meow meow meow meow meow meow meow meow meow meow meow meow meow meow meow, meow meow meow meow meow, meow meow, meow meow meow, meow meow meow meow meow meow meow meow meow meow, meow meow meow meow meow meow. Meow meow meow meow meow meow meow meow meow meow meow meow meow meow meow meow meow meow meow meow meow. Meow meow meow meow meow meow meow meow meow meow meow meow meow meow meow meow. Meow meow meow meow meow meow meow, meow meow meow meow meow meow meow meow meow meow meow meow meow. Meow meow meow meow meow meow meow meow meow meow meow meow meow meow meow meow meow meow, meow meow meow meow meow meow meow meow meow meow meow meow. Meow meow meow meow meow meow meow meow meow meow meow meow meow meow meow meow meow meow meow meow meow, meow meow meow'meow meow meow meow meow meow meow meow meow meow meow meow. Meow meow meow meow meow meow meow meow meow meow meow meow meow meow meow meow meow, meow meow meow, meow meow meow meow meow meow meow. Meow meow meow meow meow meow meow meow meow meow meow meow, meow meow meow meow meow meow meow meow meow. Meow Meow'meow meow meow meow meow meow meow meow, meow Meow. Meow, meow meow meow meow, meow meow meow meow meow. Meow meow meow meow meow meow meow meow Meow meow

meow meow meow meow meow meow meow meow, meow meow meow meow meow meow meow meow meow.

Meow meow meow meow meow meow meow meow meow meow, meow meow meow meow meow meow meow. Meow meow meow meow meow meow meow meow meow meow meow meow meow meow meow meow, meow meow meow meow meow meow meow meow meow meow meow meow meow meow meow, meow meow meow meow, meow meow meow meow meow meow meow meow meow meow meow meow meow meow meow meow meow meow meow meow meow meow meow meow meow meow meow. Meow meow meow meow meow meow meow meow meow meow meow meow meow, meow meow meow meow meow meow. Meow meow meow meow meow meow meow meow, meow meow meow meow meow meow meow meow. Meow meow meow meow meow....

Meow meow meow meow meow meow meow meow meow meow meow, meow meow meow meow meow meow meow meow meow meow meow, meow meow meow meow meow meow meow meow meow meow. Meow meow meow meow meow meow meow meow meow meow meow meow meow. Meow meow meow meow meow meow meow meow meow meow-meow meow meow meow meow meow meow meow. Meow meow meow meow meow meow meow meow meow meow meow meow meow meow meow meow meow meow meow meow meow meow meow meow, meow meow meow meow meow meow meow meow meow meow meow meow. Meow meow meow meow Meow meow meow meow meow meow meow meow: meow meow meow meow meow meow meow meow meow meow meow meow! Meow, meow meow, meow meow meow meow meow meow meow meow meow meow meow meow meow meow meow meow Meow meow meow meow meow, meow meow, meow, meow meow meow meow meow meow meow meow, meow meow meow (Meow Meow meow meow meow meow)—meow meow meow meow meow meow meow meow. Meow meow, meow, meow meow meow'meow meow meow meow meow meow. Meow meow meow meow meow meow meow Meow meow meow meow meow meow meow meow meow meow meow meow meow meow meow meow meow meow meow meow meow meow meow meow meow meow, meow meow meow meow meow, meow meow meow meow meow meow meow meow meow meow meow meow meow meow, Meow meow meow meow meow meow meow meow meow meow meow meow meow meow meow meow meow. Meow'meow meow meow meow, meow, meow meow meow meow meow meow meow meow meow Meow Meow, Meow meow meow meow meow meow meow meow meow meow meow meow meow meow meow meow meow. Meow meow meow meow meow meow meow meow meow meow. Meow meow meow meow meow meow meow meow.

Meow meow meow meow meow meow meow, meow meow meow meow meow, meow meow meow meow meow meow meow meow meow meow meow meow meow meow.

Meow meow meow meow meow meow meow Meow'meow meow meow meow. Meow meow Meow meow meow meow meow meow meow meow meow Meow meow meow meow. Meow meow meow meow meow meow

meow meow meow meow Meow, meow meow meow meow meow meow meow meow meow meow meow meow meow meow meow meow meow meow meow Meow Meow meow meow meow meow. Meow Meow'meow meow meow meow meow meow meow meow meow meow meow meow meow meow meow meow meow.

Meow Meow meow meow meow meow meow meow meow meow, meow meow meow meow meow meow meow, meow meow meow. Meow meow Meow meow meow meow meow meow meow meow meow meow meow meow'meow meow meow Meow meow meow meow meow meow meow meow meow meow'meow meow meow meow meow meow meow meow meow meow meow meow meow Meow meow meow meow meow, meow meow meow meow meow meow meow meow meow meow.

Meow meow meow meow meow meow meow meow Meow Meow meow meow meow meow meow meow meow, meow meow meow meow. Meow meow meow, meow meow meow meow meow meow meow meow'meow meow meow; meow meow meow meow meow meow meow meow meow meow meow meow-meow meow meow, meow meow meow meow meow meow meow meow meow meow, meow meow Meow meow meow meow meow meow, meow meow meow meow meow meow meow meow meow meow meow. Meow meow meow meow meow, meow meow meow meow meow meow meow meow meow meow meow meow meow meow meow meow. Meow meow Meow meow meow meow meow meow meow meow meow meow, meow meow meow meow meow meow meow meow meow. Meow meow meow meow meow meow, meow meow meow meow meow, meow meow meow meow meow meow meow, meow meow meow meow Meow meow, meow meow meow meow meow meow meow meow meow, meow meow meow meow meow meow meow meow meow.

Meow meow meow meow meow meow meow meow Meow Meow'meow meow meow meow meow meow. Meow meow meow, meow meow, meow meow meow meow meow meow meow, meow meow meow meow meow meow meow meow meow meow meow meow meow meow meow meow Meow. Meow meow meow meow meow meow meow meow Meow; meow meow meow meow meow meow meow meow meow meow meow meow meow meow meow meow meow'meow meow meow meow meow meow meow, meow meow meow meow meow meow meow meow. Meow meow meow, Meow meow meow meow meow meow meow meow meow meow meow meow meow meow.

Meow meow meow meow meow, meow, meow Meow Meow meow meow meow meow meow meow meow meow meow meow meow meow meow meow meow meow meow Meow meow, meow meow meow meow meow meow meow meow meow meow meow meow meow meow, meow meow meow meow meow meow meow meow. Meow meow meow meow meow meow meow meow meow meow meow meow meow meow meow meow meow meow meow meow meow meow meow meow meow meow meow meow meow meow; meow meow meow meow meow meow meow meow meow meow meow meow meow. Meow meow meow meow'meow meow meow meow meow meow meow meow meow meow meow meow meow meow meow

meow meow meow meow meow Meow meow meow meow meow meow meow meow meow: meow meow meow meow meow meow meow meow? Meow meow meow meow meow meow meow meow meow meow meow meow meow meow meow meow meow meow meow, meow meow meow meow meow meow meow meow meow meow meow meow, meow meow meow meow meow meow.... Meow meow meow meow meow meow. Meow meow meow, meow meow meow meow meow (meow meow meow meow meow meow meow), meow meow meow meow meow meow.

Meow meow meow Meow’meow meow, meow meow meow. Meow meow Meow meow meow meow meow meow meow meow meow meow meow. Meow meow meow meow meow meow meow. Meow meow meow meow meow meow meow meow meow meow meow meow meow, Meow meow meow meow. Meow, meow meow meow meow, meow meow meow meow meow meow meow meow meow meow meow meow meow meow meow meow meow meow meow meow meow, meow meow meow meow meow meow, meow meow meow Meow, meow meow meow meow meow meow meow meow meow meow meow meow, meow meow meow meow. Meow meow meow meow meow meow meow meow Meow meow meow meow meow meow meow meow meow meow. Meow meow meow meow meow.

Meow meow meow meow meow meow meow meow meow meow. Meow meow meow meow meow meow meow meow meow meow meow meow meow meow. Meow meow meow meow meow meow meow meow meow Meow. Meow meow meow meow meow meow’meow meow meow meow meow meow. Meow Meow meow meow meow meow meow meow meow. Meow meow meow meow meow meow meow meow meow meow Meow, Meow meow meow meow meow meow meow meow meow meow meow meow meow meow meow meow meow meow meow Meow. Meow meow meow meow meow Meow meow meow meow meow meow, meow meow meow meow meow meow meow. Meow meow meow meow-meow meow meow meow meow meow meow’meow meow Meow’meow meow meow meow meow meow meow meow meow meow meow meow meow meow meow. Meow meow meow meow meow’meow meow meow meow meow meow meow meow. Meow meow meow meow meow meow meow.

Meow meow meow Meow meow meow meow Meow. Meow meow meow meow meow meow meow; Meow Meow meow Meow meow meow meow. Meow meow meow meow Meow meow meow meow meow meow meow. Meow meow meow meow meow meow meow meow meow meow meow meow meow meow meow meow meow meow meow. Meow meow meow meow meow meow meow. Meow meow meow meow meow meow meow meow meow meow meow meow meow meow. Meow meow meow meow meow meow meow meow; meow meow meow meow meow Meow meow meow meow meow meow. Meow meow meow meow meow meow meow Meow.

Meow Meow meow meow meow meow meow meow meow Meow’meow meow meow Meow; meow meow meow meow meow meow meow meow meow meow meow. Meow meow meow meow Meow meow meow meow Meow meow meow meow meow meow meow meow meow meow meow

meow meow meow meow meow meow meow meow meow meow meow meow meow meow meow meow meow meow meow. Meow meow meow meow meow meow Meow Meow'meow meow meow meow meow meow. Meow meow meow meow meow meow, meow meow meow meow meow meow meow meow meow, meow Meow meow meow meow. Meow meow meow meow meow, meow meow meow meow meow meow, meow meow meow meow meow meow meow meow, meow meow, meow meow meow meow meow meow, meow meow meow meow meow meow meow meow, meow meow meow! Meow meow meow meow meow meow meow meow. Meow meow meow meow meow meow meow meow, meow meow meow meow meow meow'meow meow Meow'meow meow meow meow meow meow meow meow. Meow Meow meow meow meow meow meow meow meow meow meow meow meow meow meow meow meow meow meow meow meow meow meow meow.

Meow meow meow meow meow meow meow meow. Meow meow meow meow meow meow meow meow meow meow meow meow meow meow. Meow meow meow meow meow meow meow meow Meow meow meow meow meow meow, meow meow meow meow meow meow meow-meow meow meow meow meow meow meow meow meow meow meow meow meow meow. Meow meow meow meow meow meow meow, meow meow meow meow meow meow meow meow meow, meow meow meow meow, meow meow meow meow meow meow meow meow meow meow. Meow meow meow, meow meow meow meow meow meow meow meow meow meow. Meow meow meow meow meow meow meow meow, meow meow meow-meow meow meow, Meow Meow meow meow meow meow meow meow meow meow meow meow meow meow meow meow. Meow meow meow meow. Meow meow meow meow meow. Meow meow meow meow meow meow meow meow meow meow meow meow meow meow meow meow meow'meow meow meow meow meow meow meow.

Meow meow meow meow Meow meow meow meow meow meow meow'meow meow, meow meow meow meow meow meow meow meow meow meow meow meow Meow. Meow meow meow meow meow meow meow Meow, meow meow meow meow meow meow Meow meow meow meow meow meow meow meow. Meow meow meow meow Meow'meow meow meow meow meow, meow meow meow meow meow meow meow meow meow meow meow meow meow meow, meow meow meow meow meow meow meow meow meow meow meow meow meow meow'meow meow. Meow'meow meow meow meow meow meow meow meow-meow-meow meow, meow meow meow meow meow meow meow Meow'meow meow meow meow meow. Meow meow meow meow meow meow meow meow, meow meow meow meow meow meow, meow meow meow meow meow. Meow meow meow meow meow meow meow meow meow meow meow meow meow, meow meow meow meow meow—meow meow, meow meow meow, meow meow meow meow meow meow, meow meow meow meow meow meow meow, meow meow meow meow meow meow meow meow. Meow meow meow meow meow meow meow meow. Meow meow meow meow meow meow meow meow meow meow meow meow meow

meow meow. Meow meow meow meow meow, meow meow meow meow meow meow.

Meow meow meow meow meow meow meow meow meow meow meow meow meow meow, meow meow meow meow meow meow meow meow meow, meow meow meow meow meow meow meow. Meow meow meow meow meow meow meow

meow meow meow meow meow meow meow meow meow meow, meow meow meow meow meow meow meow meow meow meow meow meow meow meow meow meow meow meow meow. Meow meow meow meow meow meow meow meow meow meow meow meow meow meow-meow, meow meow meow meow meow meow meow meow meow meow meow meow. Meow meow meow meow meow meow meow meow meow meow meow meow meow meow meow meow meow meow meow meow, meow meow meow meow meow meow meow meow meow Meow.

Meow meow, Meow meow meow meow meow meow meow meow meow meow meow meow meow, meow meow meow meow, meow, meow meow meow meow meow meow meow meow meow, meow meow meow meow meow meow meow meow meow meow meow. Meow meow meow meow meow meow meow meow meow, meow meow, meow meow Meow; meow meow meow meow meow meow meow meow.

Meow meow meow meow meow (Meow meow meow meow meow meow meow meow meow meow meow meow meow) meow meow meow meow meow meow, meow meow meow meow meow meow meow meow, meow meow meow meow meow meow meow meow meow meow meow meow meow. Meow meow meow meow Meow meow meow meow meow meow meow meow meow meow meow meow meow meow meow meow meow meow meow.

"Meow meow, Meow'meow meow meow meow meow meow meow Meow'meow meow meow meow meow, meow meow meow meow meow meow meow meow meow..." Meow meow, "meow meow meow meow meow meow meow meow meow? Meow meow meow meow meow, meow meow meow meow meow meow meow meow, meow meow meow meow meow, meow meow Meow meow meow meow meow meow meow meow meow meow meow meow meow... meow... Meow meow meow meow? Meow meow Meow meow meow meow meow meow Meow meow? Meow'meow meow meow Meow meow meow. Meow'meow meow meow meow meow meow meow meow Meow...."

Meow meow meow meow meow meow meow meow Meow meow meow meow meow meow meow meow meow meow; meow meow meow meow meow meow meow meow meow meow meow meow meow.

"Meow Meow meow meow meow meow meow meow meow meow meow meow meow meow meow meow meow meow Meow meow?" meow meow meow meow meow.

Meow meow meow meow meow meow, meow, meow meow meow, meow meow meow, meow, meow meow meow meow meow meow meow meow, meow meow meow meow meow meow meow.

“Meow... meow Meow’meow,” meow meow meow meow meow, meow, meow meow meow meow meow meow meow meow. “Meow meow meow meow Meow’meow meow meow, meow... meow meow. Meow meow meow meow meow... meow meow meow meow meow Meow, meow Meow meow meow meow meow meow meow meow meow....”

Meow meow meow meow meow meow meow meow.

“Meow Meow,” meow meow, meow meow meow meow meow, “meow meow Meow meow meow meow meow? Meow meow meow meow meow meow meow?” Meow meow meow meow, meow meow meow meow meow meow meow; meow meow meow meow meow, meow, meow meow meow meow meow meow meow meow meow meow meow meow; meow meow meow, meow meow meow meow meow meow, meow meow meow meow meow meow meow meow meow meow meow meow; meow meow meow meow meow meow.

Meow meow meow meow meow meow meow, meow meow meow meow meow meow, meow, meow meow meow meow meow. Meow meow meow meow meow meow, meow meow meow meow meow meow meow meow meow meow-meow meow meow meow meow meow meow, meow meow, meow meow meow meow, meow meow meow, meow meow meow meow meow Meow meow Meow meow, meow meow meow meow meow meow meow meow meow. Meow meow meow meow meow meow meow meow meow meow meow meow meow meow meow meow meow meow meow meow meow.

Meow meow meow meow meow. Meow meow meow meow meow meow meow meow meow meow meow meow meow meow meow. Meow meow meow meow meow meow meow meow, meow meow meow meow meow meow meow meow meow meow meow meow meow. Meow meow meow meow meow meow meow, meow meow meow meow meow meow meow meow; meow meow meow meow meow meow meow meow meow meow meow meow meow meow meow meow. Meow meow meow meow meow meow meow meow meow meow meow meow meow, meow meow meow meow meow meow; meow meow meow meow meow, meow meow meow, meow meow meow meow meow meow meow meow meow meow. Meow meow meow meow meow meow meow meow meow meow meow, meow meow meow, meow meow meow meow meow meow meow meow meow meow, meow meow meow, meow meow meow meow meow meow meow meow. Meow meow meow meow meow, meow meow, meow meow meow, meow meow meow meow meow meow. Meow meow meow-meow meow meow meow meow meow meow. Meow meow meow meow meow meow meow meow, meow meow meow meow meow meow meow. Meow meow meow meow meow meow meow meow meow, meow meow meow meow meow meow meow. Meow meow meow meow meow, meow meow meow meow meow meow meow, meow meow meow meow meow meow meow meow. Meow meow meow meow meow meow meow meow meow meow meow meow meow meow meow meow meow meow meow meow meow meow meow meow meow meow meow meow meow meow meow meow, meow meow meow meow meow meow meow meow meow meow,

meow meow meow meow meow, meow meow meow meow meow meow. Meow meow meow meow meow meow meow meow meow meow meow meow meow meow meow meow meow meow meow meow meow meow meow meow meow meow meow meow meow meow meow meow meow meow. Meow meow meow meow, meow meow-meow, meow meow meow meow meow meow meow meow meow meow. Meow meow meow'meow meow, meow meow meow meow meow meow, meow meow meow meow meow meow meow meow meow meow meow meow meow meow meow. Meow meow meow meow meow meow meow, meow meow meow meow meow meow meow meow meow, meow meow meow meow meow meow meow meow meow meow meow meow meow meow meow meow meow meow meow meow meow meow meow meow. Meow meow meow meow meow meow meow meow meow meow meow meow meow meow meow meow meow meow meow meow meow; meow meow meow meow meow'meow meow meow meow meow meow meow meow meow. Meow meow meow meow meow meow: meow meow meow meow meow meow meow meow meow meow, meow meow meow meow meow meow meow, meow meow, meow meow, meow meow-meow meow meow meow, meow meow meow meow meow meow meow meow. Meow meow meow meow meow meow meow meow meow, meow meow meow meow. Meow meow meow meow meow meow meow meow meow meow meow meow-meow meow meow meow meow meow meow meow meow meow meow. Meow meow meow meow meow meow meow meow-meow, meow meow meow meow, meow meow, meow meow meow meow, meow meow meow meow meow meow meow meow meow meow, meow meow meow meow meow meow meow meow meow meow meow meow. Meow meow, meow meow meow, meow meow meow meow meow meow meow meow meow meow meow meow meow, meow meow meow meow' meow meow meow meow meow meow meow meow meow meow meow meow meow meow meow meow meow, meow meow meow meow meow meow meow meow meow meow meow meow meow. Meow meow meow meow meow meow meow meow, meow meow meow meow meow meow meow, meow meow meow meow meow, meow meow meow meow meow meow meow meow, meow meow meow meow meow meow meow meow meow meow meow meow. Meow meow meow meow meow meow meow meow meow meow meow, meow meow meow meow, meow meow meow meow meow meow meow meow meow meow meow meow meow meow, meow meow meow meow meow meow meow meow meow meow meow meow meow.

"Meow meow, meow meow!" meow meow meow meow, meow meow meow-meow meow meow meow meow meow meow meow meow meow. "Meow'meow meow meow meow, meow meow!"

Meow meow meow meow meow meow meow meow meow meow meow meow meow meow. "Meow meow meow meow meow meow meow meow!"

"Meow, Meow, meow meow meow meow meow meow meow meow meow meow meow meow meow?"

"Meow meow meow meow meow meow meow meow meow meow, meow!"

"Meow meow, Meow'meow meow meow meow," Meow meow meow, meow meow meow meow meow, meow meow meow meow meow meow meow meow meow. "Meow meow meow meow meow Meow," meow meow meow meow meow—"meow meow meow, meow, meow meow meow meow meow, Meow meow meow meow Meow meow meow meow. Meow'meow meow meow meow meow meow. Meow meow, Meow meow meow! Meow'meow meow meow meow! Meow'meow meow!" meow meow meow meow meow meow, meow meow meow meow meow meow meow meow meow.

"Meow meow! Meow meow!" Meow meow meow. "Meow'meow meow, meow'meow meow!" "Meow meow! Meow meow meow meow meow meow meow meow meow meow meow meow meow!" "Meow'meow meow meow!"

"Meow'meow meow meow meow, meow, meow meow meow meow meow meow, meow meow!"

"Meow meow! Meow meow meow meow!"

Meow meow meow meow Meow'meow meow, meow meow meow meow. Meow meow meow meow meow meow meow meow meow meow meow. Meow meow meow meow meow, meow-meow meow. Meow meow meow meow meow meow, meow meow meow, meow meow meow meow meow meow; meow meow meow meow meow meow. Meow meow meow meow meow meow meow meow meow, meow meow meow meow meow? Meow meow meow meow meow meow meow meow meow meow meow meow meow meow! Meow meow meow meow meow meow meow meow meow meow meow meow meow Meow. Meow meow meow meow "meow," meow meow meow meow meow meow meow, meow meow meow meow, meow meow meow meow; meow meow meow meow meow, meow meow meow meow meow meow meow meow meow meow meow meow meow meow meow meow meow. Meow meow meow meow meow meow meow meow meow meow meow, meow Meow meow meow meow meow meow meow meow meow meow, meow meow meow meow meow meow meow meow.

"Meow meow meow meow, meow, meow," meow meow meow meow meow meow meow meow meow meow meow.

"Meow meow, meow meow meow," meow Meow, "meow meow meow meow meow. Meow'meow meow meow meow meow!" Meow meow meow meow meow meow meow meow, meow meow meow meow.

"Meow, meow," meow meow, "meow, meow meow meow meow? Meow, meow meow meow meow meow meow!"

"Meow meow, meow meow!" meow meow meow. "Meow meow meow meow meow, meow meow meow meow; meow meow, meow'meow meow!" meow meow meow meow meow meow meow, meow meow meow meow meow meow meow meow, meow, meow meow meow meow, meow meow meow meow. Meow meow meow meow meow meow meow meow. Meow meow meow, meow meow, meow meow meow meow meow meow.

"Meow meow meow meow," meow Meow, "meow'meow meow meow meow. Meow'meow meow meow meow!"

"Meow meow meow meow, meow meow meow Meow, meow meow?" meow meow meow meow meow meow meow.

"Meow meow meow meow meow meow? Meow meow meow meow meow meow meow meow meow," meow meow.

"Meow'meow meow meow," meow meow meow.

"Meow'meow meow! Meow'meow meow meow, Meow'meow meow meow Meow meow. Meow meow, meow meow meow! Meow meow, meow meow meow! Meow meow meow meow meow meow meow meow!..."

Meow meow meow meow meow meow meow meow meow meow meow: meow meow, meow meow meow meow meow meow, meow meow meow. Meow meow meow meow meow meow meow meow. Meow meow meow meow meow meow meow meow meow meow meow meow!

Meow meow meow meow meow meow meow meow meow meow meow meow meow meow meow meow meow meow meow. Meow meow meow meow.

"Meow meow meow meow meow, meow meow meow, meow meow meow," meow Meow.

"Meow meow meow meow, meow," meow meow meow meow meow meow meow meow meow meow meow meow meow meow meow, meow meow meow meow meow. Meow meow meow meow meow meow meow meow.

... Meow meow meow meow meow, meow meow meow meow meow, meow meow meow meow meow meow meow, meow meow meow meow! Meow meow meow, meow meow meow, meow meow meow meow. Meow meow meow meow meow meow meow meow meow meow meow meow meow meow, meow meow meow meow meow. Meow meow meow meow meow, meow meow meow meow meow meow-meow meow meow meow meow meow meow, meow meow meow meow meow meow meow. Meow meow meow meow meow meow meow meow meow meow meow meow meow, meow meow meow meow meow meow meow meow meow meow meow meow. Meow meow meow meow meow meow meow, meow meow meow meow meow.

"Meow'meow meow meow meow meow," Meow meow meow. Meow meow meow meow meow, meow meow meow meow meow meow meow meow meow meow meow meow meow, meow meow, meow meow meow meow meow meow meow meow meow meow meow meow meow meow meow meow meow meow meow.

"Meow'meow meow meow," meow meow meow meow. "Meow'meow meow meow!"

"Meow'meow meow meow," meow Meow meow meow meow meow meow meow meow meow meow. Meow meow meow meow meow meow meow.

"Meow meow, meow meow! Meow meow meow meow?" meow meow meow meow meow.

Meow Meow meow meow meow meow meow meow meow meow meow meow meow meow meow meow meow meow meow meow meow. Meow meow meow meow meow meow, meow meow meow meow meow meow

meow meow meow meow, meow meow meow meow meow meow meow meow meow meow, meow meow meow meow meow. Meow meow meow meow meow meow meow meow meow meow, meow meow meow meow meow meow meow meow meow meow meow meow meow, meow meow meow, meow meow meow meow. Meow meow meow meow meow meow meow meow meow meow meow meow meow meow.

"Meow'meow meow meow meow," meow meow meow meow meow.

"Meow'meow meow meow meow, meow, meow meow meow meow meow meow meow meow," meow meow meow meow meow meow.

"Meow meow meow meow meow! Meow meow meow," meow meow meow.

"Meow'meow meow meow! Meow meow," Meow meow meow; meow meow meow meow meow, meow meow meow meow meow meow meow meow meow meow meow.

"Meow meow," meow meow, meow meow meow meow meow meow meow meow meow meow meow meow meow meow. Meow meow meow; meow meow meow, meow meow, meow meow meow, meow meow meow meow meow meow meow meow meow meow meow meow meow meow meow meow meow meow meow meow meow.

"Meow meow meow," meow Meow meow meow meow meow meow, meow meow meow meow. Meow meow meow, meow meow meow meow, meow meow meow meow meow meow—meow, meow, meow, meow meow meow meow meow meow. Meow meow meow meow meow meow meow meow meow meow meow meow meow. Meow meow meow meow meow, meow meow meow meow meow meow.

"Meow meow meow," meow meow meow meow meow. "Meow meow'meow meow meow meow?"

"Meow meow!" meow Meow, meow meow meow, meow meow meow meow meow meow. Meow meow meow meow meow meow meow meow meow meow meow meow.

"Meow meow meow meow, meow meow meow meow Meow," meow meow meow meow meow meow meow.

Meow meow meow meow, meow meow, meow meow meow, meow, meow meow meow meow meow meow meow, meow meow meow meow meow meow meow meow meow meow meow, meow meow meow meow meow meow meow.... Meow meow meow meow meow meow meow meow meow meow meow meow meow meow meow Meow. Meow meow meow meow meow, meow meow meow meow meow meow, meow meow meow meow meow meow meow meow meow meow.

"Meow meow, meow! Meow meow meow meow," meow meow meow meow.

"Meow! Meow meow meow... meow... meow meow meow!" meow meow, meow meow meow meow meow meow meow meow meow meow meow meow meow meow.

"Meow meow meow.... Meow meow meow... meow'meow meow meow meow!" meow meow meow. Meow meow meow meow meow meow meow

meow meow meow meow, meow. Meow meow meow meow meow meow, meow meow meow—meow meow meow.

Meow meow meow, meow meow meow, meow meow meow meow meow, meow meow meow meow meow.

"Meow Meow, meow meow meow meow meow," meow meow, meow meow meow meow meow meow meow meow meow. "Meow meow meow meow? Meow meow meow meow meow meow? Meow meow meow meow!"

Meow meow meow meow: meow meow meow meow meow meow meow. Meow meow meow meow meow meow meow meow meow meow meow meow meow meow.

"Meow Meow!" meow meow, "meow meow meow, meow meow meow, meow Meow meow meow meow meow meow, meow Meow meow meow meow meow meow meow, meow meow meow meow... meow Meow meow meow meow meow meow meow meow, meow meow meow, meow meow meow; meow, meow meow meow meow meow... meow meow meow.... Meow Meow, meow meow meow?"

Meow meow meow meow meow meow meow meow meow meow.

"Meow meow meow Meow meow meow meow meow?" meow meow, meow meow meow, meow meow meow meow meow meow. "Meow meow meow Meow meow meow meow meow meow meow, meow meow meow Meow meow meow meow meow meow meow? Meow, meow, meow Meow meow meow meow meow... meow, meow Meow meow meow meow Meow meow meow meow meow meow meow.... Meow meow Meow meow meow meow meow, meow? Meow meow Meow meow? Meow Meow meow meow meow meow meow, Meow meow meow meow meow meow meow, meow, meow, meow... meow meow meow meow meow meow meow meow meow meow meow meow meow meow.

"Meow, Meow meow'meow meow meow, Meow meow'meow meow meow! Meow, meow meow meow meow meow meow meow meow meow meow, meow meow meow Meow meow meow meow meow meow meow meow meow meow, meow meow meow.... Meow Meow! Meow Meow meow'meow meow meow meow meow! Meow meow'meow meow meow, Meow meow'meow meow meow! Meow, meow meow meow Meow meow...?"

Meow meow meow meow meow, meow meow meow meow meow meow meow meow meow meow meow meow meow, meow meow meow meow meow. Meow meow meow, meow meow meow, meow meow meow meow meow meow, meow meow meow meow meow meow meow meow. Meow meow meow meow meow meow meow meow meow meow meow meow meow meow meow meow meow, meow meow meow meow meow meow meow meow meow meow meow meow meow meow meow meow meow. "Meow," meow meow, "meow meow meow meow—Meow meow meow meow... meow meow meow."

Meow meow meow, meow meow meow meow meow meow meow Meow, meow meow meow meow meow meow meow meow meow meow. Meow meow meow meow meow meow meow meow meow meow meow. Meow meow meow meow meow meow meow meow meow meow meow meow

meow meow meow meow meow meow meow meow. Meow, meow! Meow meow meow meow meow meow, meow meow, meow meow!

"Meow meow meow meow meow meow meow meow, Meow Meow," meow meow meow meow meow. "Meow meow meow-meow meow meow. Meow meow meow meow meow."

"Meow-meow?" meow Meow meow meow meow, meow meow meow meow meow meow meow meow.

"Meow meow meow, meow meow meow meow meow meow meow Meow Meow," meow meow meow'meow meow, meow meow meow meow. "Meow meow meow meow, meow meow meow meow meow meow. Meow meow meow meow meow meow meow meow—meow meow meow meow-meow meow meow meow meow meow meow meow meow!"

"Meow meow meow meow'meow meow meow meow meow Meow Meow," meow meow meow; "meow'meow meow meow, meow meow meow meow meow meow meow. Meow meow meow meow meow meow. Meow meow meow meow meow meow meow meow meow."

"Meow Meow meow meow?"

"Meow meow meow'meow meow-meow. Meow meow meow meow meow. Meow meow meow meow meow meow meow meow."

"Meow meow'meow meow meow meow meow meow," meow meow meow.

"Meow meow, Meow'meow meow," meow Meow, meow meow, meow meow meow meow meow meow.

Meow meow meow meow meow meow meow meow. Meow meow meow, meow, meow meow meow meow meow meow. Meow meow meow meow meow meow meow meow meow meow, meow meow meow meow meow meow meow. Meow meow meow, meow meow meow meow meow meow, meow meow meow meow meow meow meow'meow Meow, meow meow meow'meow meow meow meow meow, meow meow meow meow meow meow meow meow meow meow meow'meow meow meow meow meow meow meow meow meow.

Meow meow meow meow meow meow meow meow meow. Meow meow meow meow meow meow meow meow meow. Meow meow meow meow meow meow meow meow meow; meow meow meow meow meow meow meow meow meow meow meow meow meow meow meow meow, meow meow, meow meow meow meow meow meow meow meow.

Meow, meow meow meow meow meow meow meow meow meow meow meow, meow meow meow meow meow meow meow meow meow meow meow meow meow meow meow meow meow meow meow meow meow meow. Meow meow meow, meow meow meow meow meow meow meow meow meow meow meow meow, meow meow meow meow meow meow, meow meow meow meow meow meow, meow meow meow meow meow meow meow meow meow meow meow, meow meow meow meow meow meow meow, meow meow meow meow meow meow meow.

Meow meow meow meow meow meow, meow, meow meow meow meow, meow meow meow meow meow meow, meow meow meow meow. Meow meow meow meow meow meow meow meow meow meow meow meow

meow meow. Meow meow meow meow meow meow meow meow meow, meow meow meow meow meow meow meow meow meow meow meow. Meow meow meow meow meow meow meow meow meow meow meow meow meow meow meow meow meow meow meow, meow meow meow meow meow, meow meow meow meow, meow meow meow meow; meow, meow meow meow meow meow meow meow meow, meow meow meow meow meow meow meow meow meow.

Meow meow meow meow meow meow meow meow meow, meow meow meow meow meow meow meow meow meow meow meow, meow meow, meow meow meow meow meow-meow meow meow meow meow meow meow meow meow meow meow meow meow. Meow meow meow meow meow meow meow meow meow meow meow meow, meow meow meow, meow meow meow meow meow meow meow meow meow meow meow meow. Meow meow meow meow meow meow meow meow meow, meow meow meow meow meow meow meow meow meow meow meow meow. Meow meow meow meow meow meow meow, meow meow meow meow meow meow, meow meow meow, meow meow meow, meow meow meow meow. Meow meow meow meow, meow meow meow meow meow meow meow meow meow meow meow meow meow meow meow meow meow meow meow meow meow.

“Meow, meow meow meow meow meow, meow meow meow meow meow! Meow meow meow meow meow meow meow. Meow meow meow meow meow meow meow meow meow meow! Meow meow meow meow meow meow meow meow meow meow meow, meow Meow meow meow meow... (meow meow meow meow meow meow meow),” meow meow meow meow, meow meow meow meow meow meow meow meow meow. “Meow meow, meow, meow meow!” meow meow meow meow meow meow meow meow meow meow meow meow meow meow meow meow meow meow meow meow meow meow —”Meow meow, Meow meow meow meow meow meow meow meow meow meow; meow meow meow meow meow meow meow, meow meow meow meow meow meow meow meow. Meow Meow meow meow meow, meow meow meow, meow meow meow. Meow meow meow! Meow meow meow! ‘Meow meow meow!’ Meow meow, meow meow, meow meow.... Meow, meow meow meow meow meow meow meow meow; meow meow meow meow meow meow, meow meow meow, meow meow Meow meow meow meow meow?”

Meow meow meow meow meow meow meow meow.

“Meow,” meow meow meow meow meow meow meow meow meow meow, meow meow meow meow meow meow meow meow meow meow. “Meow, meow meow meow, Meow meow meow meow, meow meow meow meow meow! Meow meow meow meow meow meow meow, meow Meow Meow, meow meow, meow meow meow meow meow meow meow meow’meow meow. Meow, meow, Meow meow meow meow, meow meow meow meow meow meow meow meow meow, meow meow meow, meow meow meow. Meow meow... meow, meow meow meow meow meow meow! Meow meow, meow meow, meow meow meow meow meow meow meow meow meow meow meow meow meow meow meow meow! Meow Meow

Meow, meow meow meow meow, meow meow meow.... Meow meow, meow Meow meow meow meow meow meow meow meow meow meow meow meow meow meow meow—meow Meow meow meow meow meow, meow meow meow meow, meow meow," meow meow meow meow meow, meow meow meow meow—"meow, meow Meow, meow meow meow meow meow.... Meow meow, meow! Meow'meow meow meow meow meow meow'meow meow meow meow! Meow meow meow! Meow meow meow meow, meow meow meow meow meow meow meow meow meow meow meow meow meow meow meow... meow meow meow meow meow Meow meow meow meow meow meow!"

"Meow!" meow meow meow meow. Meow meow meow meow meow meow meow meow.

"Meow meow meow meow! Meow meow meow, meow, meow meow meow, Meow meow meow meow meow meow meow meow? Meow meow meow—meow meow meow meow meow meow meow meow meow meow meow, meow meow meow, meow meow Meow meow meow meow meow! Meow meow meow Meow meow meow meow, meow meow meow meow meow meow, meow meow meow, meow meow; meow meow meow meow meow meow meow meow meow meow meow meow meow meow meow meow meow meow meow meow meow meow. Meow meow meow meow meow meow Meow Meow meow meow meow meow meow meow meow; meow meow meow meow meow meow meow meow meow, meow meow'meow meow meow meow meow meow meow meow. Meow meow meow meow meow meow meow meow meow meow meow meow Meow meow meow! Meow meow meow Meow meow'meow meow meow? Meow meow meow Meow meow meow meow Meow meow meow. Meow'meow meow Meow meow meow. Meow meow meow meow meow meow meow meow meow.... Meow meow meow meow Meow meow meow meow meow meow!" Meow meow meow meow meow meow meow meow meow meow meow meow meow.

"Meow meow, meow," meow meow meow meow meow meow meow— "Meow meow, meow meow meow meow meow meow meow meow meow meow meow-meow meow—meow meow meow Meow Meow meow meow meow meow meow meow meow meow meow meow meow meow meow meow meow meow— meow meow meow meow Meow Meow meow meow meow meow meow meow meow meow, meow meow meow meow meow meow meow meow meow meow meow meow meow. Meow meow meow, Meow Meow meow meow meow meow meow (meow meow meow meow meow Meow Meow meow) meow Meow. Meow meow... meow.... Meow meow meow meow meow meow Meow Meow meow meow Meow'meow meow. Meow meow meow meow meow meow meow meow Meow meow meow meow meow meow meow meow meow meow meow meow meow: 'meow,' meow meow, 'meow meow meow meow meow meow meow meow meow meow meow meow meow meow meow meow meow?' Meow Meow Meow meow meow meow meow meow, meow meow meow meow meow... meow meow meow'meow meow meow meow. Meow Meow meow meow meow meow, meow meow meow; meow meow Meow Meow meow meow

meow meow meow meow.... Meow meow meow meow meow meow Meow' meow meow, meow meow meow meow; Meow meow meow meow meow meow meow meow meow meow meow meow meow meow meow meow meow meow meow. Meow meow meow, meow, meow meow meow meow. Meow meow meow meow meow meow, meow Meow meow meow meow, meow meow.... Meow... meow... meow meow meow meow meow meow meow meow... meow. Meow Meow meow meow meow meow meow, meow meow meow meow meow, meow meow meow meow meow meow meow meow meow meow meow meow Meow Meow. Meow meow Meow Meow, meow meow meow meow? Meow? Meow, meow, meow'meow meow meow meow Meow meow meow'meow meow. Meow meow meow... meow meow meow meow meow meow Meow; meow meow meow meow!... Meow meow meow meow meow meow meow meow meow. 'Meow, meow meow meow meow meow meow meow... Meow'meow meow meow meow meow meow meow meow meow'—meow'meow meow meow meow, 'meow,' meow meow, 'meow meow meow meow meow.' Meow meow meow meow meow meow meow—meow meow meow, meow meow meow meow meow meow meow meow meow meow meow meow, meow meow meow meow meow meow meow meow meow meow meow meow. Meow meow meow, meow meow Meow meow meow Meow'meow meow meow meow meow meow meow meow meow meow meow meow, meow, meow meow meow-meow meow meow!..."

Meow meow meow meow meow meow. Meow meow meow meow meow meow meow meow meow meow meow meow meow meow meow, meow meow meow meow meow meow meow meow meow meow meow meow meow meow meow meow meow meow meow "Meow Meow" meow meow meow meow meow. Meow meow meow meow meow meow. Meow meow-meow meow meow meow meow meow meow meow meow-meow. Meow meow meow meow meow meow meow meow meow meow meow. Meow meow meow meow meow meow meow meow, meow meow meow meow meow meow meow meow, meow meow meow meow meow meow. Meow meow meow meow meow meow meow meow meow meow meow meow meow meow, meow meow meow meow meow meow meow meow meow meow meow meow. Meow meow meow.

"Meow meow meow meow meow, meow. Meow.... Meow meow meow Meow Meow meow Meow meow meow meow, meow meow meow, meow meow meow meow Meow meow meow meow meow meow Meow. Meow meow meow meow: meow meow meow meow meow meow, meow meow meow. Meow meow meow meow meow meow, meow meow meow. 'Meow Meow meow meow meow meow meow meow meow meow, meow meow meow, meow!' Meow meow meow meow meow Meow meow meow meow meow meow meow meow meow! Meow meow meow meow meow meow meow meow, meow meow meow meow? Meow meow meow meow meow meow meow meow meow meow meow meow meow— meow meow, meow meow, Meow meow'meow meow. Meow, meow meow-meow—meow meow, meow meow, meow meow meow meow meow meow meow, meow meow meow meow meow meow. Meow meow meow Meow meow meow

meow meow meow Meow meow Meow Meow meow meow meow meow meow meow— meow meow meow meow meow meow meow—meow meow meow meow meow meow meow meow. Meow meow meow meow meow... meow meow meow, meow meow meow meow meow meow meow meow meow meow meow meow meow; meow meow meow meow'meow meow meow meow meow meow, meow meow meow meow meow meow meow meow, meow'meow meow meow meow meow, meow meow meow meow meow meow meow meow, meow, meow meow meow meow, meow meow meow meow, meow meow meow meow meow meow. Meow, meow meow meow, meow meow meow meow meow 'meow meow meow,' meow meow, 'meow meow'meow meow meow meow meow meow meow meow meow meow meow. Meow meow meow meow meow meow meow meow.' Meow meow meow, meow meow meow? Meow meow meow meow meow meow meow meow meow meow meow meow meow: meow Meow Meow meow meow meow meow meow meow meow meow meow Meow Meow meow meow meow meow, meow meow meow meow meow meow meow meow meow meow. Meow meow meow meow meow meow, meow meow. 'Meow Meow meow meow meow meow meow, meow, meow meow meow meow,' meow meow, 'meow meow meow meow meow meow meow meow meow meow meow meow meow meow meow, meow meow meow meow meow meow meow Meow Meow meow meow meow meow meow meow meow meow.' Meow meow meow, meow meow meow? 'Meow meow meow,' meow meow, 'Meow Meow, meow meow meow meow,' meow meow, 'meow meow meow meow meow meow meow meow meow meow, meow meow meow meow meow meow meow meow'meow meow meow meow meow meow,' (meow meow meow, meow meow meow;) 'meow meow,' meow meow, 'Meow meow meow meow meow meow meow meow meow.' Meow meow meow, meow meow meow meow, meow meow meow meow meow meow meow, meow meow meow meow meow meow, meow meow meow meow meow; meow, meow meow meow meow meow, meow meow meow meow meow meow meow, meow meow meow meow meow! Meow Meow meow'meow meow meow meow meow, meow, Meow meow'meow meow meow!... Meow meow meow meow Meow meow meow meow meow meow meow meow—meow- meow meow meow meow meow—meow meow meow meow meow: 'meow,' meow meow, 'meow meow meow.' Meow meow meow meow meow meow, meow meow? Meow meow meow meow meow meow meow, meow meow meow meow meow meow meow meow meow meow, meow meow?... Meow, meow meow meow meow, 'meow meow meow,' meow meow."

Meow meow meow, meow meow meow, meow meow meow meow meow meow meow. Meow meow meow meow. Meow meow, meow meow meow meow meow meow, meow meow meow meow meow meow meow, meow meow meow meow meow, meow meow meow meow meow meow meow meow meow meow meow meow meow. Meow meow meow meow meow meow meow meow. Meow meow meow meow meow meow meow meow.

"Meow meow, meow meow," meow Meow meow meow—"Meow, meow, meow meow meow meow meow meow meow meow meow, meow meow

meow meow meow, meow meow Meow meow meow meow meow meow meow meow meow meow meow meow meow meow meow meow meow, meow meow meow meow meow meow meow meow meow. Meow Meow meow meow meow meow.... Meow meow meow meow meow meow meow meow meow meow meow meow meow meow meow meow Meow meow meow meow meow meow meow Meow meow meow meow meow, meow meow Meow meow meow meow meow meow, meow meow Meow meow meow meow meow, meow meow Meow meow meow meow meow meow meow meow meow meow meow meow meow meow meow meow meow.... Meow meow meow meow meow.... Meow meow, meow. Meow, meow, meow" (Meow meow meow meow meow meow meow, meow meow meow meow meow meow meow meow meow) "meow, meow meow meow meow meow meow meow meow meow, meow meow meow meow, meow meow meow meow, meow meow meow, meow meow meow meow, meow meow meow meow meow meow, Meow meow meow Meow Meow meow meow meow meow meow, meow meow meow meow meow meow meow meow, meow meow meow meow Meow meow meow, meow meow meow meow meow, meow meow meow! Meow'meow meow meow meow meow Meow meow meow, meow meow meow meow meow meow meow meow meow'meow meow meow meow meow meow, meow meow meow meow meow meow meow meow meow meow Meow meow. Meow meow meow meow meow meow Meow meow meow... meow meow'meow meow meow meow meow!"

Meow meow meow meow meow meow meow, meow meow meow, meow meow meow meow meow meow meow meow meow meow meow meow. Meow meow meow meow meow meow meow meow meow meow meow meow meow meow meow meow meow meow, meow meow meow Meow, meow meow meow:

"Meow meow Meow meow meow meow Meow, Meow meow meow meow meow meow meow meow-meow-meow! Meow-meow-meow!"

"Meow meow'meow meow meow meow meow meow meow?" meow meow meow meow meow-meow; meow meow meow meow meow meow meow meow meow meow.

"Meow meow meow meow meow meow meow! Meow meow meow meow meow, meow meow meow meow meow-meow-meow-meow, meow-meow-meow meow," meow meow meow, meow meow meow meow meow meow meow meow meow meow meow meow meow meow meow meow. Meow meow meow meow meow meow meow meow, meow meow meow meow. Meow meow meow meow meow meow meow meow meow meow meow meow meow meow meow meow meow meow meow meow, meow meow meow meow. Meow meow meow meow meow meow meow meow.

"Meow'meow meow meow! meow'meow meow meow meow," meow meow meow meow meow meow—"meow meow meow meow meow! Meow meow meow meow, meow!"—meow meow meow meow meow meow meow meow meow. "Meow, meow meow! Meow meow, meow meow meow meow?"—meow meow meow meow meow meow Meow—"meow meow

meow! Meow meow meow meow meow meow? Meow meow meow meow meow meow, meow! Meow meow!"

Meow meow meow meow meow meow meow meow meow meow. Meow meow meow meow meow meow meow meow meow meow meow meow meow meow meow. Meow meow meow meow meow meow meow meow meow meow meow meow meow meow meow meow meow. Meow meow meow meow meow meow meow meow meow meow meow, meow meow meow meow meow, meow meow meow meow meow meow meow meow. Meow meow meow meow, meow Meow, meow meow meow meow meow, meow meow meow meow meow meow meow meow. Meow meow meow meow meow meow meow meow; meow meow meow meow meow meow meow meow: meow meow meow Meow Meow meow meow meow meow meow meow meow meow meow meow meow meow meow meow meow meow meow meow meow meow meow meow meow meow meow meow meow meow meow meow meow meow meow meow meow meow meow meow meow meow meow meow meow meow meow meow meow meow. Meow meow meow meow, Meow meow meow meow meow meow meow meow meow meow, meow meow meow meow meow meow meow meow meow meow meow meow meow meow meow meow meow meow meow meow meow meow meow meow meow meow meow. Meow meow meow meow, meow meow meow meow meow meow meow meow meow.

"Meow meow meow meow Meow'meow meow," meow meow meow meow, "meow meow Meow meow Meow meow meow meow." Meow meow meow meow meow meow meow meow meow meow meow meow meow meow meow meow meow meow meow meow meow meow meow, meow meow meow meow meow meow meow meow meow meow meow meow meow meow meow meow. "Meow meow meow meow," meow meow meow meow meow meow meow meow, meow meow meow meow—"meow meow meow meow.... Meow! Meow meow Meow meow meow meow meow meow-meow, meow meow meow meow meow meow, meow meow meow... meow meow meow... meow meow meow meow meow meow meow meow meow-meow meow meow meow meow. Meow meow Meow! Meow meow meow meow'meow meow meow! Meow meow'meow meow meow meow meow meow! Meow, meow meow meow meow meow meow meow! Meow'meow meow meow meow meow meow meow meow meow. Meow meow meow meow meow, meow meow!"

Meow meow meow meow.

"Meow meow meow Meow meow meow," meow meow meow meow meow meow'meow meow. "Meow meow meow meow meow meow meow meow, meow meow meow, Meow meow, meow meow meow meow meow—meow meow meow meow meow meow, meow meow meow meow meow meow meow meow meow meow'meow meow meow meow meow meow."

II

Meow meow meow meow meow meow. Meow meow meow meow meow meow meow meow meow, meow meow meow meow, meow meow meow, meow meow meow, meow meow meow meow meow meow meow. Meow meow meow meow meow meow meow meow meow meow! meow meow meow meow meow meow meow meow. Meow meow, meow meow meow meow meow meow meow meow meow meow meow meow. Meow meow meow meow meow meow meow—meow meow meow meow meow meow meow meow meow? Meow meow meow meow meow meow meow meow meow meow meow meow meow. Meow meow meow meow meow meow meow meow meow meow meow. Meow meow meow meow meow meow meow. Meow meow meow meow meow meow meow meow meow-meow meow? Meow meow? Meow Meow? Meow meow meow meow meow, meow meow meow meow meow meow meow? Meow meow meow meow meow meow meow Meow, meow meow meow meow meow meow meow meow meow meow meow. Meow meow meow meow meow meow meow meow meow meow meow meow meow meow: meow meow meow meow meow meow meow meow. Meow meow meow meow meow meow meow meow. Meow, meow meow meow meow meow meow meow meow meow meow meow meow! Meow meow meow meow meow meow, meow meow meow meow. Meow meow meow meow meow, meow meow meow meow meow meow meow meow meow meow meow meow, meow meow meow meow meow meow meow meow meow. Meow meow meow meow meow meow, Meow, meow meow meow, meow meow meow meow meow meow meow meow meow meow, meow meow meow meow meow meow meow "meow meow" meow meow meow, meow meow meow meow meow meow meow meow.

Meow meow meow meow meow meow meow, meow meow meow meow meow meow meow meow meow meow—meow meow meow meow meow meow meow. Meow meow meow meow meow meow meow meow meow meow meow meow meow meow meow meow meow meow meow-meow meow meow meow meow meow meow meow! Meow meow meow meow meow meow? Meow meow meow meow meow meow meow? Meow meow meow meow? Meow meow meow meow meow meow? Meow, meow meow meow meow meow meow meow meow meow meow meow meow meow meow meow meow meow meow, meow meow meow, meow meow meow meow. Meow meow meow meow meow meow meow meow meow; meow meow meow meow meow. Meow meow meow meow meow meow meow meow meow meow meow meow meow meow meow meow meow meow meow meow meow meow meow meow meow meow meow.

Meow meow meow meow meow meow meow meow meow—meow meow meow meow meow meow meow meow meow meow meow meow meow, meow meow, meow meow meow meow meow meow meow meow meow meow! Meow, meow meow meow meow meow meow meow! Meow meow meow meow meow meow meow meow meow. Meow meow meow meow meow meow meow meow.

Meow meow meow meow meow meow meow meow meow meow meow meow, meow meow meow meow meow meow meow meow meow meow meow meow meow meow. Meow meow meow meow, meow meow, meow meow meow meow meow meow meow meow meow meow meow meow meow meow meow meow meow meow meow meow meow meow meow meow meow meow meow meow.

"Meow meow meow," meow meow meow, "meow meow meow meow meow meow meow meow meow meow meow meow meow meow meow meow meow? Meow meow meow meow meow meow meow meow meow meow, meow, meow meow meow meow meow, meow meow meow meow meow meow meow meow meow... meow. Meow, meow meow meow meow, meow meow meow meow meow- meow!

"Meow meow meow meow meow meow meow meow meow?" meow meow meow meow. "Meow meow meow meow meow meow meow? Meow meow meow meow meow? Meow meow meow meow meow. Meow meow, meow meow meow meow meow, meow meow, meow meow meow meow meow meow meow meow meow meow meow. Meow, meow meow meow meow meow meow meow meow... meow meow'meow meow. Meow meow, meow meow meow meow meow meow meow meow meow meow meow meow meow meow meow meow meow meow meow meow meow meow meow meow meow meow meow. Meow meow meow meow meow meow meow meow, meow Meow meow'meow, meow meow Meow meow meow meow meow meow meow meow meow."

Meow meow meow meow meow meow meow meow meow meow, meow meow meow meow meow meow meow meow meow meow meow meow meow.

Meow meow meow meow meow meow: meow meow meow meow meow meow? Meow meow meow meow meow meow meow meow meow meow meow meow? Meow meow meow meow meow meow meow meow meow meow meow meow meow meow meow? Meow meow Meow meow meow, meow meow meow meow meow meow?

Meow meow meow meow meow meow meow, meow meow meow meow meow, meow meow meow meow meow meow meow meow meow meow meow meow, meow meow meow meow meow meow meow meow meow meow meow meow meow meow meow. Meow meow'meow meow meow meow meow meow meow meow meow meow meow meow meow, meow meow meow meow meow meow meow meow meow meow meow.

Meow meow meow meow meow meow meow meow meow meow meow meow meow meow meow meow meow, meow meow meow meow meow. Meow meow meow meow meow meow meow meow meow meow meow meow meow meow meow meow meow meow meow. Meow meow meow meow meow meow meow meow meow meow meow meow meow meow meow meow. Meow meow meow meow meow meow meow meow, meow meow meow meow, meow meow! Meow meow meow meow meow meow meow meow meow meow, meow meow meow meow, meow meow meow meow meow meow meow meow meow meow, meow meow meow meow meow meow meow, meow meow meow meow meow, meow meow meow

meow meow meow meow, meow meow meow meow meow meow meow meow meow meow meow meow meow meow? Meow meow meow meow meow meow meow meow meow meow.

Meow meow, meow meow, meow meow meow meow meow meow meow meow meow meow meow meow meow meow meow; meow meow meow meow meow meow meow meow. Meow meow meow meow meow meow meow meow meow. Meow meow meow meow meow meow meow meow meow meow meow meow meow, meow meow meow meow, meow meow meow meow meow meow meow meow meow. Meow meow meow meow meow meow meow meow meow meow meow meow meow meow meow meow meow meow. Meow meow meow meow meow meow meow, meow meow meow meow meow meow meow meow meow meow meow meow meow. Meow meow meow meow meow meow meow meow meow, meow meow meow meow meow meow meow meow meow meow meow meow meow meow meow meow. Meow meow meow Meow meow, meow meow, meow meow. Meow meow meow meow meow meow meow meow meow meow meow; meow Meow meow meow meow meow meow meow meow. Meow meow meow meow meow meow meow meow meow meow meow meow meow meow Meow. Meow meow meow Meow meow meow meow meow meow, meow meow meow meow meow meow. Meow meow meow meow meow meow. Meow meow meow meow meow meow meow; meow meow meow meow meow meow meow meow—meow, meow meow meow meow. Meow meow meow meow meow meow meow meow meow meow meow meow meow.

“Meow’meow meow meow,” meow meow meow meow. “Meow meow’meow meow meow meow meow meow; meow’meow meow meow meow’meow meow.”

Meow meow meow meow Meow, meow meow meow meow meow meow meow meow meow meow. Meow meow meow meow meow meow meow meow meow. Meow meow meow meow meow meow, meow meow meow meow meow. Meow meow meow meow meow meow meow meow meow.

“Meow’meow meow meow! Meow meow’meow meow meow Meow,” meow meow. “Meow meow meow meow meow.”

Meow meow meow meow meow meow meow Meow meow meow meow, meow meow meow meow meow meow meow meow meow. Meow meow meow. Meow meow meow meow meow meow meow meow meow meow meow. Meow meow meow meow meow meow; meow meow meow meow meow, meow meow meow meow meow. Meow meow meow meow meow meow meow meow meow meow, meow meow meow meow meow meow.

Meow meow meow meow meow meow meow meow: meow meow meow meow meow meow meow Meow? Meow meow meow meow meow meow meow meow; meow meow meow meow, meow meow meow meow meow meow meow meow meow meow meow meow. Meow meow meow meow meow, meow meow meow meow meow meow meow meow meow meow, meow meow meow meow meow meow. Meow meow meow meow meow, meow meow meow meow meow. Meow meow meow Meow meow meow meow meow meow meow meow meow meow. Meow meow meow meow

meow meow meow meow meow meow Meow. Meow meow meow meow meow meow meow meow meow meow meow. Meow meow meow meow meow meow meow meow, meow meow meow, meow meow Meow meow meow meow meow meow. Meow meow meow meow meow meow meow meow meow meow meow. Meow meow meow meow Meow meow meow, meow meow meow meow meow meow meow meow meow, meow meow meow meow meow meow meow meow. “Meow meow Meow Meow, meow meow meow meow, meow meow meow,” meow meow meow meow meow meow meow meow meow.

Meow meow meow meow meow meow meow meow meow meow meow meow meow meow. Meow meow meow meow meow meow meow meow meow meow meow meow; meow meow meow meow meow meow meow meow, meow, meow meow, meow meow meow meow meow meow meow meow meow. Meow meow meow meow meow meow meow meow meow meow.

Meow meow meow meow meow meow meow meow meow Meow meow meow Meow. Meow meow meow meow, meow meow meow meow meow meow meow meow meow meow meow meow meow. Meow meow meow meow meow meow meow meow meow meow meow meow meow meow meow meow meow meow meow Meow meow meow meow meow Meow. Meow meow meow meow meow meow meow meow meow meow. Meow meow meow meow meow meow meow meow meow meow meow, meow meow meow meow meow meow meow meow meow. Meow meow meow meow meow meow meow meow meow meow. Meow meow meow meow meow meow meow meow meow meow meow meow meow meow meow meow meow meow meow, meow meow meow meow meow meow, meow meow meow, meow meow meow meow meow. Meow meow, meow meow meow meow meow meow meow meow meow. Meow meow meow meow meow meow meow meow meow. Meow meow meow meow meow meow meow meow meow meow meow meow meow meow meow, meow meow meow meow meow, meow, meow meow meow meow. Meow meow meow meow meow meow meow meow meow meow meow meow meow meow meow meow meow meow meow; meow meow meow meow meow meow meow, meow meow meow. Meow meow meow meow meow meow meow meow meow meow. Meow meow meow meow meow meow meow meow, meow meow meow meow meow meow meow meow meow meow meow meow, meow meow meow meow meow meow meow meow meow meow meow meow meow, meow meow meow, meow meow meow meow meow. Meow meow meow meow meow meow meow meow meow meow meow; meow meow meow, meow meow meow meow meow meow meow meow meow meow meow meow meow. Meow meow meow meow meow meow, meow meow meow meow meow meow, meow meow meow, meow meow meow meow meow. Meow meow meow meow meow. Meow meow meow meow, meow meow meow, meow meow meow meow, meow meow meow meow meow meow meow meow meow meow meow meow meow. Meow meow meow meow, meow meow meow meow meow. Meow meow meow meow meow. Meow meow meow meow meow meow meow meow meow.

Meow meow meow meow meow meow meow meow. Meow meow meow meow meow meow meow meow meow meow meow. Meow meow meow meow meow meow, meow meow meow meow meow meow meow meow meow meow, meow meow meow meow meow meow, meow meow meow meow meow meow meow, meow meow meow meow meow meow meow meow meow.

Meow meow meow meow meow meow meow meow meow meow meow meow, meow meow meow meow meow meow meow meow meow. Meow meow meow meow Meow meow meow. Meow meow meow meow meow; meow meow meow meow meow meow meow meow meow meow meow meow meow meow. Meow meow meow meow meow meow meow meow meow meow meow meow; meow meow meow meow meow meow meow, meow meow meow meow. Meow meow meow meow meow meow meow meow meow meow, meow meow meow meow, meow meow meow meow meow meow meow meow meow meow meow meow meow meow.

Meow meow, meow meow meow meow meow meow, Meow meow meow. Meow meow meow meow meow meow meow meow meow meow, meow meow meow meow Meow meow meow meow meow meow meow meow. Meow meow meow meow meow meow meow. Meow meow meow meow meow meow meow meow meow. Meow meow meow meow meow meow meow. Meow meow Meow meow meow meow, meow meow meow meow; meow meow meow meow meow meow meow meow. Meow meow meow meow meow. Meow meow meow meow meow meow meow meow meow Meow Meow meow meow meow meow meow meow meow meow meow meow.

Meow meow meow meow meow meow meow meow meow meow; meow meow meow meow meow meow meow meow meow. Meow meow meow meow meow meow meow, Meow meow meow meow meow meow, meow meow meow meow meow meow meow, meow meow meow meow meow meow meow meow meow meow meow, meow meow meow meow meow meow meow meow meow. Meow meow meow meow meow meow meow meow.

Meow meow meow meow meow meow meow. Meow meow meow meow meow meow meow meow meow meow meow meow meow meow. Meow meow meow meow meow meow meow meow meow. Meow meow meow meow meow meow meow meow meow meow meow. Meow meow meow meow meow meow meow meow. Meow meow meow meow meow meow, meow meow meow meow meow meow meow meow meow. Meow meow meow meow meow meow meow meow meow meow meow meow meow meow meow meow meow meow meow meow....

Meow meow meow meow, meow meow meow; meow meow meow meow meow. Meow meow meow meow meow meow; meow meow meow meow meow meow meow meow meow meow meow meow meow meow, meow meow meow meow meow meow meow meow. Meow meow meow meow meow; meow meow meow meow meow meow meow meow meow meow meow meow meow meow meow.

Meow meow meow meow meow meow meow. Meow meow meow meow meow meow meow, meow meow meow meow meow meow meow meow meow! Meow meow meow meow meow meow meow meow meow meow meow meow meow meow meow meow, meow meow—meow meow meow meow meow meow.

Meow meow meow meow meow meow meow, meow meow meow meow meow, Meow meow meow meow meow meow meow meow meow meow. Meow meow meow meow meow meow meow meow meow meow meow meow meow meow meow meow meow meow meow; meow meow meow meow meow meow meow meow meow meow meow meow meow meow meow meow. Meow meow meow meow, meow meow meow meow meow meow meow meow. Meow'meow meow meow meow meow meow meow?

Meow meow meow meow. Meow meow meow meow meow meow meow meow meow meow meow meow. Meow meow meow meow meow meow meow. Meow meow meow meow meow meow meow; meow meow meow meow meow meow meow meow meow meow meow meow meow. Meow meow meow meow, meow meow meow meow meow meow! Meow, meow meow meow, meow meow meow meow, meow meow meow meow meow meow meow meow meow meow meow meow, meow meow meow meow meow meow meow meow. Meow meow meow meow meow meow meow meow meow meow meow meow, meow meow meow meow meow meow meow; meow meow meow meow. Meow meow meow meow meow meow meow meow meow meow meow meow meow meow meow meow meow meow meow.

Meow meow meow meow meow Meow Meow. Meow meow meow meow meow. Meow meow meow meow Meow; meow meow meow meow meow meow meow meow meow meow meow meow Meow meow meow. Meow meow meow meow meow meow meow meow meow meow meow meow, meow meow meow meow meow meow meow meow meow meow. Meow meow meow meow meow meow meow meow meow meow meow meow meow meow meow meow meow meow meow Meow. Meow meow meow meow meow meow meow meow meow meow meow meow meow meow meow meow meow meow meow meow meow. Meow meow meow meow meow meow meow.

Meow meow meow meow meow meow, meow meow meow meow meow meow meow: "Meow meow meow meow meow meow meow? Meow meow, meow meow meow meow...."

Meow meow meow meow meow meow meow meow, meow meow meow meow meow meow meow meow. Meow meow meow meow meow—meow meow meow meow—meow meow meow meow meow meow meow meow. Meow meow, meow meow meow! Meow meow meow meow meow meow meow meow meow meow meow meow meow meow meow meow meow meow meow meow meow meow meow meow meow meow. Meow meow meow meow meow meow meow meow meow meow meow meow meow meow, meow meow meow meow meow meow meow meow meow, meow meow meow meow meow meow meow, meow meow.

Meow meow meow meow meow meow meow meow meow—meow meow meow meow meow meow meow meow meow, meow meow meow meow meow meow, meow meow meow meow meow meow meow meow, meow meow meow meow meow meow meow meow. Meow meow meow meow meow meow meow meow meow, meow meow meow meow meow meow.

Meow meow meow meow Meow'meow meow, meow meow meow meow meow. Meow meow Meow meow meow meow meow meow meow meow meow. Meow meow meow meow meow meow. Meow meow meow meow meow meow meow, meow Meow meow meow Meow meow. Meow meow meow meow meow meow meow meow meow meow meow meow, meow meow meow meow meow. Meow meow meow meow meow meow meow meow meow, meow meow meow meow meow meow meow. Meow meow meow meow meow, Meow, meow meow meow meow; meow meow meow meow meow meow meow meow meow meow meow meow; meow meow meow meow meow meow meow meow meow meow. Meow meow meow meow, meow meow meow meow meow meow. Meow meow meow Meow meow meow meow meow meow meow meow meow meow meow meow. Meow meow meow meow meow meow meow meow. Meow meow meow, meow meow meow, meow meow meow meow meow Meow. Meow'meow meow meow meow meow meow meow meow meow meow meow meow meow meow meow meow meow meow Meow'meow meow meow meow meow meow meow meow meow meow meow meow meow meow meow meow.

Meow meow meow meow meow meow, meow Meow, meow meow meow meow'meow meow meow meow meow meow; meow meow meow meow meow meow meow meow meow. Meow meow meow meow, Meow meow meow meow meow meow meow meow meow meow meow meow, meow Meow meow meow meow. Meow meow meow meow meow meow meow meow meow meow meow meow meow meow meow, meow meow meow meow meow meow meow meow meow. Meow meow meow meow meow, meow meow meow meow meow. Meow meow meow Meow meow meow meow meow meow meow meow meow Meow meow meow meow—Meow meow... Meow meow meow meow meow, meow meow meow meow meow meow meow.

“Meow meow meow meow meow meow meow meow meow meow meow meow meow meow meow meow meow?” meow meow meow meow meow meow.

Meow meow meow meow meow. Meow meow meow meow meow, meow meow meow meow meow meow, meow meow meow meow meow meow meow meow meow meow meow meow meow meow meow meow. Meow meow meow meow meow meow meow meow meow meow meow—meow meow meow meow meow.

Meow meow meow meow meow meow, meow meow meow meow meow meow meow meow meow.

“Meow,” meow Meow, meow. “Meow meow meow meow meow meow, Meow. Meow meow meow meow meow meow meow meow meow meow-meow; meow meow meow meow meow meow meow meow'meow meow meow meow?"

Meow meow meow meow meow. Meow meow meow meow meow meow; meow meow meow meow meow meow, meow meow meow meow meow meow meow meow meow meow meow meow meow meow meow. Meow meow meow meow meow meow meow, meow meow meow meow meow meow meow.

"Meow meow, Meow, Meow'meow meow meow meow meow meow meow meow. Meow meow meow meow.... Meow meow'meow meow meow meow meow meow'meow meow meow meow meow meow. Meow meow meow meow meow meow meow? Meow meow meow meow meow meow meow meow meow meow meow meow meow meow meow, meow meow meow meow meow meow, meow Meow meow meow meow meow—meow'meow meow meow meow meow meow.... Meow! Meow meow Meow meow meow meow meow Meow, Meow meow meow meow meow. Meow'meow meow meow meow meow meow, meow Meow Meow; meow Meow meow meow meow, meow meow meow Meow meow meow! Meow Meow meow meow meow; Meow'meow meow meow meow meow meow. Meow meow Meow meow meow meow meow meow meow meow meow meow meow, meow meow meow meow meow meow meow meow meow meow. Meow'meow meow meow meow meow meow meow! Meow! meow meow Meow meow meow! Meow, meow meow meow meow?"

Meow meow meow meow meow meow meow meow meow. Meow meow meow meow meow meow meow meow meow meow meow; meow meow meow meow meow meow meow meow, meow meow meow, meow meow meow meow.

Meow meow meow Meow meow meow meow meow meow meow meow, meow meow meow meow meow meow meow meow. Meow meow meow meow meow meow meow meow meow meow meow meow, meow meow meow meow meow meow meow meow.

Meow meow meow meow meow; meow meow meow, meow meow meow meow meow. "Meow meow meow meow meow?" meow meow meow meow. "Meow meow Meow meow meow? Meow meow meow meow? Meow meow meow meow meow meow, meow meow meow meow Meow? Meow'meow meow meow meow."

"Meow meow, meow meow meow meow meow," Meow meow meow meow meow meow meow. "Meow meow, meow meow meow meow meow! Meow meow, Meow, meow...."

Meow meow meow meow meow meow meow meow.

Meow meow meow meow meow. Meow meow meow meow meow meow meow meow meow meow meow. Meow meow meow meow meow meow meow meow meow meow Meow meow meow, "meow meow meow." Meow meow meow meow meow meow meow, meow meow meow meow meow. Meow meow meow meow meow meow meow meow meow meow meow meow meow meow meow. Meow meow meow meow meow. Meow meow meow meow meow meow meow meow meow Meow meow meow meow meow meow.

"Meow meow meow meow? Meow meow meow meow? Meow meow, meow! Meow'meow meow meow," meow meow meow meow meow, meow meow meow, meow meow meow meow meow. "Meow'meow meow meow meow meow meow meow?" meow meow meow meow.

Meow meow meow meow meow meow meow meow meow. Meow meow meow meow meow meow-meow meow meow; meow meow meow meow. Meow meow meow meow meow meow meow meow meow.

"Meow meow meow, meow meow meow, meow meow?" meow meow meow meow meow meow meow meow meow. "Meow'meow meow meow meow meow meow meow... meow meow meow?"

Meow meow meow meow. Meow meow meow meow meow meow meow meow meow'meow meow meow meow. Meow meow meow meow meow meow meow meow meow meow meow meow meow meow-meow meow Meow, meow meow meow meow meow meow meow meow meow meow meow meow meow meow meow, meow meow meow meow meow meow meow meow meow meow, meow meow meow meow meow meow meow. Meow meow meow meow, meow meow meow meow meow, meow meow meow meow meow meow meow meow meow meow meow meow.

"Meow, meow meow meow meow Meow meow meow meow meow meow? Meow meow meow—meow meow; meow meow meow? Meow meow meow meow meow meow! Meow meow meow Meow meow meow; meow meow meow meow meow? Meow Meow meow meow? Meow, meow, Meow meow meow meow meow meow meow meow meow. Meow Meow meow meow meow? Meow, meow meow Meow'meow meow! Meow, Meow meow meow meow, Meow meow meow meow meow meow, meow meow meow meow meow meow! Meow meow meow meow meow meow meow meow, meow meow meow meow, meow meow meow meow meow! Meow Meow meow meow meow meow meow, meow meow meow meow Meow meow meow! Meow meow meow meow meow meow, meow!"

Meow meow meow meow meow meow, meow meow meow meow meow meow meow meow. Meow meow meow meow meow meow meow meow meow meow meow meow meow meow meow meow meow meow Meow Meow.

"Meow meow meow," meow meow meow meow meow meow meow.

Meow meow meow meow Meow Meow. Meow meow meow, meow meow meow meow meow meow meow, meow meow meow meow meow meow meow meow meow. Meow meow meow meow meow meow meow meow meow meow; meow meow meow meow meow meow meow meow meow meow meow meow meow meow. Meow meow meow meow meow meow meow meow meow meow; meow meow meow meow meow meow meow meow. Meow meow meow meow meow meow. Meow meow meow meow meow meow meow, meow meow meow meow meow meow meow meow meow meow meow meow meow meow meow. Meow meow meow meow meow meow meow meow meow meow meow meow, meow meow meow meow. Meow meow meow meow meow, meow meow meow meow meow; meow meow meow meow meow meow meow meow meow meow meow meow meow meow meow meow, meow meow meow meow meow.

Meow meow meow Meow'meow meow, "Meow meow meow meow-meow, meow meow meow meow meow, meow meow meow, meow meow meow meow meow meow meow, meow meow meow meow meow meow meow, 'Meow meow meow meow.'" Meow meow, meow meow. Meow meow meow meow meow meow meow meow meow meow, meow meow meow meow meow, meow meow meow meow meow meow meow meow meow meow meow meow meow meow meow meow meow, meow meow. Meow meow meow meow meow meow meow; meow meow meow meow meow meow meow meow meow meow meow meow meow meow meow. Meow meow meow meow meow meow meow meow meow meow meow meow meow. Meow meow meow meow meow meow meow meow....

Meow meow meow meow meow meow meow meow meow, meow meow meow meow meow, meow meow meow meow meow meow meow meow meow. Meow meow meow meow meow meow meow meow meow.

"Meow'meow meow," meow meow meow meow meow. Meow meow meow meow meow meow.

"Meow'meow meow meow Meow, meow, meow meow meow-meow meow meow meow meow meow meow. Meow'meow meow meow meow meow meow meow meow meow meow meow meow meow Meow. Meow meow meow meow," meow meow meow meow meow meow meow meow.

"Meow meow meow meow, meow!" meow meow meow.

"Meow meow meow," meow meow meow.

"Meow'meow meow meow meow'meow meow meow meow meow meow'meow meow."

Meow meow meow meow meow Meow, meow meow meow, "Meow meow meow meow," meow meow meow meow meow meow meow meow meow meow meow, meow meow. Meow meow meow meow meow, meow, meow, meow meow meow, meow meow meow meow meow meow meow meow meow meow. Meow meow meow meow meow meow meow meow meow meow meow meow meow meow; meow meow meow meow meow meow meow meow. Meow meow meow meow meow meow meow meow Meow Meow meow meow, meow meow meow meow, meow meow meow? Meow meow...."

Meow meow meow meow, meow meow meow meow meow meow meow meow meow, meow meow meow meow meow meow meow, meow meow meow meow meow meow meow meow meow meow meow meow meow. Meow meow meow meow meow meow meow meow. Meow meow meow meow meow meow meow meow meow, meow meow meow meow meow. Meow meow meow meow meow meow meow meow, meow meow meow, meow meow meow meow meow meow meow. "Meow meow? meow meow?" meow meow, meow. "Meow Meow meow meow meow meow meow meow meow meow meow? Meow meow meow meow meow." Meow meow meow meow meow meow meow meow meow "meow meow," Meow Meow. Meow meow meow meow meow meow? Meow'meow meow meow meow meow meow? Meow Meow Meow? Meow'meow meow meow meow meow meow meow meow Meow Meow'meow meow? Meow meow meow meow

meow meow meow meow.... Meow, meow! Meow meow "meow meow"! Meow meow meow meow meow, meow meow meow meow meow.

Meow meow meow meow meow, meow meow meow meow meow meow meow. Meow meow meow meow meow meow meow meow meow—meow meow meow meow meow meow meow. Meow meow meow meow meow meow meow meow meow meow meow. Meow meow meow meow meow meow. "Meow Meow meow meow meow meow," meow meow meow meow. Meow meow meow meow meow meow meow meow meow meow meow meow meow meow meow meow. Meow meow meow meow meow meow meow meow. Meow meow meow meow, meow, meow meow, Meow Meow.

"Meow meow meow?" Meow meow, meow meow meow meow meow meow. "Meow meow meow meow?"

"Meow-meow! Meow meow meow meow meow, meow meow meow meow meow, meow Meow meow meow Meow... meow meow meow meow meow meow meow meow meow... Meow'meow meow! 'Meow meow meow!'" meow meow meow meow meow.

Meow meow. Meow Meow Meow meow meow meow. Meow meow meow meow meow meow meow meow meow. "Meow meow meow meow meow meow," meow Meow. "Meow meow meow meow?"

"Meow'meow meow meow meow meow? Meow meow?" meow Meow Meow. Meow meow meow meow meow meow meow meow meow meow meow meow meow. "Meow meow'meow meow meow meow meow meow Meow'meow meow meow meow meow Meow meow meow... meow Meow'meow meow meow Meow meow. Meow meow meow, Meow... meow meow

"Meow."

"Meow meow, Meow. Meow meow'meow meow Meow'meow meow? Meow'meow meow Meow meow meow meow... Meow Meow, meow'meow meow, meow'meow meow?"

"Meow Meow."

"Meow, meow, meow meow, Meow Meow! Meow meow meow meow meow meow. Meow meow meow meow meow meow. Meow meow meow Meow'meow meow meow meow meow meow... meow Meow meow meow meow... meow meow meow meow meow meow meow meow meow meow meow meow... meow meow meow meow meow... meow meow meow meow meow meow meow... Meow meow meow! Meow meow meow meow meow meow meow meow meow meow meow meow meow! Meow meow meow Meow meow meow meow meow meow meow, meow meow meow meow'meow meow meow meow! Meow meow meow! Meow meow meow meow meow meow meow, meow meow meow meow meow meow meow meow, meow, meow meow, meow. Meow meow meow meow—meow, meow meow meow meow meow? Meow meow meow meow meow meow meow meow Meow meow meow meow; meow meow'meow meow meow meow, meow meow meow meow, Meow meow'meow meow meow! Meow meow meow meow meow meow meow meow meow meow, meow meow meow meow'meow... Meow Meow meow meow meow meow meow, meow meow meow meow meow meow? Meow meow meow meow meow meow?"

"Meow, meow meow meow meow."

"Meow'meow meow meow meow meow meow meow meow meow meow meow—meow meow meow meow meow meow. Meow meow Meow meow meow Meow meow meow meow meow meow. Meow meow meow! Meow meow meow meow meow meow meow meow meow meow—meow meow meow meow meow meow meow! Meow meow meow! Meow meow meow meow. Meow meow meow meow meow meow meow meow meow meow meow'meow meow?"

"Meow, Meow meow meow meow... Meow meow meow meow... Meow meow meow Meow meow meow Meow meow."

"Meow, meow! Meow meow, meow'meow meow meow, Meow meow. Meow, meow, Meow meow meow meow. Meow, meow'meow meow Meow. Meow'meow meow meow meow meow meow... meow meow meow meow meow meow... meow meow meow meow. Meow meow meow meow-meow meow, meow'meow meow; meow meow meow meow meow meow meow, meow meow, meow meow meow meow meow, meow meow meow meow. Meow meow meow meow meow meow meow meow, meow meow'meow meow meow meow meow meow meow meow, meow meow meow meow meow meow meow. Meow meow meow'meow meow meow meow meow meow meow meow Meow. Meow meow, meow meow. Meow meow meow meow meow meow meow meow meow'meow meow meow meow meow. Meow meow, meow meow meow, meow meow meow meow meow meow meow—meow meow meow meow, meow meow, meow meow!... Meow meow, meow meow meow meow meow, meow meow meow—meow'meow meow meow meow meow! Meow meow meow meow meow meow.... Meow meow meow Meow'meow Meow?"

Meow meow meow meow meow meow meow meow meow meow meow meow meow, meow meow meow meow meow meow meow meow meow meow meow meow meow meow meow meow meow meow "Meow Meow" meow meow meow meow meow. Meow meow meow meow meow meow. Meow meow-meow meow meow meow meow meow meow meow meow-meow. Meow meow meow meow meow meow meow meow meow meow meow. Meow meow meow meow meow meow meow meow, meow meow meow meow meow meow meow meow, meow meow meow meow meow meow. Meow meow meow meow meow meow meow meow meow meow meow meow meow meow, meow meow meow meow meow meow meow meow meow meow meow meow. Meow meow meow.

"Meow meow meow meow meow, meow. Meow.... Meow meow meow Meow Meow meow Meow meow meow meow, meow meow meow, meow meow meow meow Meow meow meow meow meow Meow. Meow meow meow meow: meow meow meow meow meow meow, meow meow meow. Meow meow meow meow meow meow, meow meow meow. 'Meow Meow meow meow meow meow meow meow meow, meow meow meow, meow!' Meow meow meow meow meow Meow meow meow meow meow meow meow meow meow! Meow meow meow meow meow meow meow meow, meow meow meow meow? Meow meow meow meow meow meow meow meow meow meow meow meow meow— meow meow, meow

meow, Meow meow'meow meow. Meow, meow meow-meow—meow meow, meow meow, meow meow meow meow meow meow meow, meow meow meow meow meow meow. Meow meow meow Meow meow meow meow meow meow Meow meow Meow Meow meow meow meow meow meow meow— meow meow meow meow meow meow meow—meow meow meow meow meow meow meow meow. Meow meow meow meow meow... meow meow meow, meow meow meow meow meow meow meow meow meow meow meow meow meow; meow meow meow meow'meow meow meow meow meow meow, meow meow meow meow meow meow meow meow, meow'meow meow meow meow meow, meow meow meow meow meow meow meow meow, meow, meow meow meow meow, meow meow meow meow, meow meow meow meow meow meow. Meow, meow meow meow, meow meow meow meow meow 'meow meow meow,' meow meow, 'meow meow'meow meow meow meow meow meow meow meow meow meow meow. Meow meow meow meow meow meow meow meow.' Meow meow meow, meow meow meow? Meow meow meow meow meow meow meow meow meow meow meow meow meow: meow Meow Meow meow meow meow meow meow meow meow meow meow Meow Meow meow meow meow meow, meow meow meow meow meow meow meow meow meow meow. Meow meow meow meow meow meow, meow meow. 'Meow Meow meow meow meow meow meow, meow, meow meow meow meow,' meow meow, 'meow meow meow meow meow meow meow meow meow meow meow meow meow meow meow, meow meow meow meow meow meow meow Meow Meow meow meow meow meow meow meow meow meow.' Meow meow meow, meow meow meow? 'Meow meow meow,' meow meow, 'Meow Meow, meow meow meow meow,' meow meow, 'meow meow meow meow meow meow meow meow meow meow, meow meow meow meow meow meow meow meow'meow meow meow meow meow meow,' (meow meow meow, meow meow meow;) 'meow meow,' meow meow, 'Meow meow meow meow meow meow meow meow meow.' Meow meow meow, meow meow meow meow, meow meow meow meow meow meow meow, meow meow meow meow meow meow, meow meow meow meow meow; meow, meow meow meow meow meow, meow meow meow meow meow meow meow, meow meow meow meow meow! Meow Meow meow'meow meow meow meow meow, meow, Meow meow'meow meow meow!... Meow meow meow meow Meow meow meow meow meow meow meow meow—meow- meow meow meow meow meow—meow meow meow meow meow: 'meow,' meow meow, 'meow meow meow.' Meow meow meow meow meow meow, meow meow? Meow meow meow meow meow meow meow, meow meow meow meow meow meow meow meow meow meow, meow meow?... Meow, meow meow meow meow, 'meow meow meow,' meow meow."

Meow meow meow meow meow meow, meow meow meow meow meow meow. Meow meow meow meow. "Meow meow meow meow meow meow meow?" meow meow meow-meow meow meow meow meow meow.

Meow meow meow meow meow meow meow. Meow meow meow meow meow meow meow meow meow meow meow meow meow meow

meow meow meow meow meow meow meow meow meow meow meow meow meow meow meow meow.

“Meow meow meow! Meow meow Meow meow meow meow?” Meow meow meow, meow meow meow meow meow meow, meow meow meow meow meow meow meow meow meow meow.

“Meow’meow meow meow!” “Meow meow meow!” “Meow meow meow meow meow!” Meow meow meow, meow meow meow.

“Meow meow meow, meow,” meow Meow meow meow meow, meow meow meow meow meow Meow— ”meow meow meow meow… Meow’meow meow, meow meow meow meow. Meow’meow meow meow Meow Meow—meow Meow meow.”

Meow meow meow meow meow meow meow meow meow meow meow meow meow meow meow meow. Meow meow meow meow meow meow meow meow meow meow meow meow meow meow meow meow meow meow. Meow meow meow meow meow meow meow meow meow. Meow meow meow meow meow meow meow meow meow meow meow meow meow meow meow meow meow meow.

Meow meow meow meow meow meow meow meow meow meow meow meow meow. Meow meow meow-meow meow meow meow meow meow meow meow meow meow meow meow-meow; meow meow meow meow meow meow meow meow meow. Meow meow meow meow meow, meow meow meow meow meow meow meow, meow meow’meow meow. Meow meow meow meow meow meow meow meow meow. Meow meow meow meow meow meow. Meow meow meow meow meow meow meow meow meow meow meow meow meow Meow meow, meow meow meow, meow meow meow meow meow meow meow-meow, meow meow meow. Meow meow meow meow meow meow meow meow meow meow-meow meow meow meow meow. Meow meow meow meow meow meow meow meow meow meow, meow meow meow meow meow, meow meow meow meow meow meow meow. Meow meow meow meow meow meow meow, meow meow meow, meow meow Meow Meow’meow meow meow meow meow meow meow, meow meow meow meow, meow meow meow meow. Meow meow meow meow meow meow meow meow meow meow. Meow meow meow meow meow meow meow meow meow meow meow meow meow.

Meow meow Meow Meow meow meow. Meow meow meow meow meow, meow meow meow meow, meow meow, meow meow meow meow meow meow meow meow meow meow meow meow meow. Meow meow meow meow meow meow meow meow meow meow, meow meow meow meow meow meow; meow meow meow meow meow meow meow meow meow meow meow meow. Meow meow meow meow meow meow meow meow meow meow meow meow meow meow. Meow meow meow meow meow meow meow meow meow meow meow meow meow meow-meow meow meow meow meow meow meow meow. Meow meow meow Meow meow meow meow meow meow meow meow meow meow meow meow Meow…. Meow meow meow meow meow meow meow meow meow meow meow meow. Meow meow meow meow meow meow meow meow meow, meow meow meow meow meow meow meow meow meow meow meow meow

meow meow. Meow meow meow meow meow meow meow meow meow meow meow meow, meow meow meow meow meow meow meow meow meow meow. Meow meow meow meow meow meow, meow meow meow meow meow meow meow meow meow meow meow meow meow meow meow meow meow meow meow meow meow meow meow meow meow.

"Meow!" meow meow meow meow meow meow, "meow meow meow meow! Meow meow! meow meow!... Meow meow meow meow meow? Meow'meow meow meow meow, meow meow! Meow meow meow meow meow meow! Meow meow meow meow? Meow meow meow meow! Meow!"

Meow meow meow meow meow meow. Meow meow meow meow meow meow meow meow meow meow meow meow. Meow meow meow meow meow.

"Meow meow meow meow?" meow meow—"Meow meow meow, meow meow meow meow meow meow? Meow meow meow meow meow meow meow meow meow!" meow meow meow meow meow meow meow meow meow meow meow meow meow meow meow meow. Meow meow meow meow meow meow meow meow meow meow meow.

"Meow meow meow meow meow meow meow! Meow meow meow meow meow, meow meow meow meow meow-meow-meow-meow, meow-meow-meow meow," meow meow meow, meow meow meow meow meow meow meow meow meow meow meow meow meow meow meow meow. Meow meow meow meow meow meow meow meow, meow meow meow meow. Meow meow meow meow meow meow meow meow meow meow meow meow meow meow meow meow meow meow meow meow, meow meow meow meow. Meow meow meow meow meow meow meow meow.

"Meow'meow meow meow! meow'meow meow meow meow," meow meow meow meow meow meow—"meow meow meow meow meow! Meow meow meow meow, meow!"—meow meow meow meow meow meow meow meow meow. "Meow, meow meow! Meow meow, meow meow meow meow?"—meow meow meow meow meow meow Meow—"meow meow meow! Meow meow meow meow meow meow? Meow meow meow meow meow meow, meow! Meow meow!"

Meow meow meow meow meow meow meow meow meow meow. Meow meow meow meow meow meow meow meow meow meow meow meow meow meow meow. Meow meow meow meow meow meow meow meow meow meow meow meow meow meow meow meow meow. Meow meow meow meow meow meow meow meow meow meow meow, meow meow meow meow meow, meow meow meow meow meow meow meow meow. Meow meow meow meow, meow Meow, meow meow meow meow meow, meow meow meow meow meow meow meow meow. Meow meow meow meow meow meow meow meow; meow meow meow meow meow meow meow meow: meow meow meow Meow Meow meow meow meow meow meow meow meow meow meow meow meow meow meow meow meow meow meow meow meow meow meow meow meow meow meow meow meow meow meow meow meow meow meow meow meow meow meow meow meow meow meow. Meow meow meow meow, Meow meow meow meow meow meow meow meow meow meow, meow meow meow meow meow meow

meow meow meow meow meow meow meow meow meow meow meow meow meow meow meow meow meow meow. Meow meow meow meow, meow meow meow meow meow meow meow meow meow.

"Meow meow meow meow Meow'meow meow," meow meow meow meow, "meow meow Meow meow Meow meow meow meow." Meow meow meow meow meow meow meow meow meow meow meow meow meow meow meow meow meow meow meow meow meow meow meow, meow meow meow meow meow meow meow meow meow meow meow meow meow meow meow meow. "Meow meow meow meow," meow meow meow meow meow meow meow meow, meow meow meow meow—"meow meow meow meow.... Meow! Meow meow Meow meow meow meow meow meow-meow, meow meow meow meow meow meow, meow meow meow... meow meow meow... meow meow meow meow meow meow meow meow meow-meow meow meow meow meow. Meow meow Meow! Meow meow meow meow'meow meow meow! Meow meow'meow meow meow meow meow meow! Meow, meow meow meow meow meow meow meow! Meow'meow meow meow meow meow meow meow meow meow. Meow meow meow meow meow, meow meow!"

Meow meow meow meow.

"Meow meow meow Meow meow meow," meow meow meow meow meow meow'meow meow. "Meow meow meow meow meow meow meow meow, meow meow meow, Meow meow, meow meow meow meow meow—meow meow meow meow meow meow, meow meow meow meow meow meow meow meow meow meow'meow meow meow meow meow meow."

Meow meow, meow meow meow meow meow meow, Meow meow meow. Meow meow meow meow meow meow meow meow meow meow, meow meow meow meow Meow meow meow meow meow meow meow meow. Meow meow meow meow meow meow. Meow meow meow meow meow meow meow meow meow. Meow meow meow meow meow meow meow meow. Meow meow Meow meow meow meow, meow meow meow meow; meow meow meow meow meow meow meow meow. Meow meow meow meow meow. Meow meow meow meow meow meow meow meow meow meow Meow Meow meow meow meow meow meow meow meow meow meow meow meow.

Meow meow meow meow meow meow meow meow meow meow; meow meow meow meow meow meow meow meow meow. Meow meow meow meow meow meow meow, Meow meow meow meow meow meow, meow meow meow meow meow meow meow, meow meow meow meow meow meow meow meow meow meow meow, meow meow meow meow meow meow meow meow meow. Meow meow meow meow meow meow meow.

Meow meow meow meow meow meow meow. Meow meow meow meow, meow meow meow'meow, meow meow meow meow meow meow meow meow meow, meow meow meow meow meow meow meow meow meow meow meow meow meow meow meow meow meow meow. Meow meow meow meow meow meow meow. Meow meow meow meow meow meow meow meow meow meow meow meow meow meow meow; meow meow

meow meow meow meow meow meow meow meow meow meow meow. Meow meow meow meow meow meow meow meow meow meow meow, meow meow meow meow meow meow meow meow meow meow meow meow meow meow meow meow meow meow. Meow meow meow meow meow meow meow meow meow meow, meow meow meow meow meow meow meow meow meow meow meow. Meow meow meow meow, meow meow meow, meow meow meow meow, meow meow meow, meow meow’ meow. Meow meow meow meow, meow meow meow meow meow, meow meow meow meow; meow meow meow meow meow meow meow, meow meow meow meow meow Meow meow meow meow meow meow meow. Meow meow meow, meow meow meow meow meow-meow, meow meow; meow meow meow meow, meow meow meow meow meow meow meow meow. Meow meow meow Meow meow meow; meow meow meow meow meow meow meow meow meow meow meow. Meow meow meow meow meow; meow meow meow meow meow meow. Meow meow meow meow meow meow meow meow meow meow; meow meow meow meow meow meow meow, meow meow meow meow meow. Meow meow meow meow meow meow meow meow, meow meow meow meow meow meow meow meow meow. Meow meow meow meow meow meow meow meow meow meow meow meow meow meow meow meow meow meow meow, meow meow meow meow meow meow meow. Meow meow meow meow meow meow meow meow meow, meow meow meow meow meow meow meow meow meow meow meow meow meow meow. Meow meow meow meow meow meow meow meow meow meow. Meow meow meow meow meow meow. Meow meow meow meow meow meow meow meow meow meow meow meow meow meow meow meow. Meow meow meow, meow meow meow meow meow. Meow meow meow meow meow meow meow meow.

Meow meow meow meow meow meow meow. Meow meow meow meow meow meow meow meow meow meow meow meow meow meow meow. Meow meow meow meow meow meow meow meow meow. Meow meow meow meow meow meow meow meow meow meow meow meow. Meow meow meow meow meow meow meow meow. Meow meow meow meow meow meow meow, meow meow meow meow meow meow meow meow meow meow. Meow meow meow meow meow meow meow meow meow meow meow meow meow meow meow meow meow meow meow meow....

Meow meow meow meow, meow meow meow; meow meow meow meow meow. Meow meow meow meow meow; meow meow meow meow meow meow meow meow meow meow meow meow meow, meow meow meow meow meow meow meow meow. Meow meow meow meow; meow meow meow meow meow meow meow meow meow meow meow meow meow meow meow.

Meow meow meow meow meow meow meow. Meow meow meow meow meow meow meow, meow meow meow meow meow meow meow meow meow meow! Meow meow meow meow meow meow meow meow meow meow meow meow meow meow meow meow, meow meow—meow meow meow meow meow meow.

Meow meow meow meow meow meow meow, meow meow meow meow meow, Meow meow meow meow meow meow meow meow meow meow. Meow meow meow meow meow meow meow meow meow meow meow meow meow meow meow meow meow meow meow; meow meow meow meow meow meow meow meow meow meow meow meow meow meow meow meow. Meow meow meow meow, meow meow meow meow meow meow meow meow. Meow'meow meow meow meow meow meow meow?

Meow meow meow meow. Meow meow meow meow meow meow meow meow meow meow meow meow. Meow meow meow meow meow meow meow. Meow meow meow meow meow meow meow; meow meow meow meow meow meow meow meow meow meow meow meow meow. Meow meow meow meow, meow meow meow meow meow meow! Meow, meow meow meow, meow meow meow meow, meow meow meow meow meow meow meow meow meow meow meow meow, meow meow meow meow meow meow meow meow. Meow meow meow meow meow meow meow meow meow meow meow, meow meow meow meow meow meow meow meow; meow meow meow meow. Meow meow meow meow meow meow meow meow meow meow meow meow meow meow meow meow meow meow.

Meow meow meow meow meow Meow Meow. Meow meow meow meow meow. Meow meow meow meow Meow; meow meow meow meow meow meow meow meow meow meow meow meow Meow meow meow. Meow meow meow meow meow meow meow meow meow meow meow meow, meow meow meow meow meow meow meow meow meow meow. Meow meow meow meow meow meow meow meow meow meow meow meow meow meow meow meow meow meow meow Meow. Meow meow meow meow meow meow meow meow meow meow meow meow meow meow meow meow meow meow meow meow meow. Meow meow meow meow meow meow meow.

Meow meow meow meow meow meow, meow meow meow meow meow meow meow: “Meow meow meow meow meow meow meow? Meow meow, meow meow meow meow....”

Meow meow meow meow meow meow meow meow, meow meow meow meow meow meow meow meow. Meow meow meow meow meow—meow meow meow meow—meow meow meow meow meow meow meow meow. Meow meow, meow meow meow! Meow meow meow meow meow meow meow meow meow meow meow meow meow meow meow meow meow meow meow meow meow meow meow meow meow meow. Meow meow meow meow meow meow meow meow meow meow meow meow meow meow meow, meow meow meow meow meow meow meow meow meow, meow meow meow meow meow meow meow, meow meow.

Meow meow meow meow meow meow meow meow meow—meow meow meow meow meow meow meow meow meow, meow meow meow meow meow meow, meow meow meow meow meow meow meow meow, meow meow meow meow meow meow meow meow. Meow meow meow meow meow meow meow meow meow, meow meow meow meow meow meow.